Cline & McHaffie

The People's Guide a Business, Political and Religious Directory of Marion Co.

Cline & McHaffie

The People's Guide a Business, Political and Religious Directory of Marion Co.

Reprint of the original, first published in 1874.

1st Edition 2024 | ISBN: 978-3-36884-605-3

Verlag (Publisher): Outlook Verlag GmbH, Zeilweg 44, 60439 Frankfurt, Deutschland
Vertretungsberechtigt (Authorized to represent): E. Roepke, Zeilweg 44, 60439 Frankfurt, Deutschland
Druck (Print): Books on Demand GmbH, In de Tarpen 42, 22848 Norderstedt, Deutschland

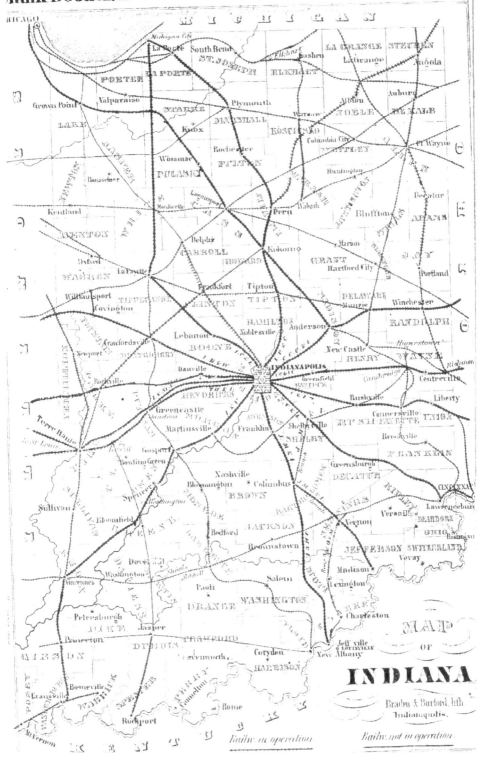

MAP OF

INDIANA

Braden & Burford, lith.
Indianapolis.

Railw. in operation   *Railw. not in operation*

THE

PEOPLE'S GUIDE

A BUSINESS, POLITICAL AND RELIGIOUS

Directory of Marion Co., Ind.

TOGETHER WITH A COLLECTION OF VERY IMPORTANT DOCUMENTS
AND STATISTICS CONNECTED WITH OUR MORAL,
POLITICAL AND SCIENTIFIC
HISTORY.

ALSO, A

Historical Sketch of Marion County,

AND A

BRIEF HISTORY OF EACH TOWNSHIP.

By CLINE & McHAFFIE.

INDIANAPOLIS:
INDIANAPOLIS PRINTING AND PUBLISHING HOUSE.
1874.

DECLARATION OF INDEPENDENCE.

IN CONGRESS, TUESDAY, JULY 4, 1776.

Agreeably to the order of the day, the Congress resolved itself into a committee of the whole, to take into their further consideration the Declaration; and, after some time, the President resumed the chair, and Mr. Harrison reported that the committee had agreed to a declaration, which they desired him to report. (The committee consisted of Jefferson, Franklin, John Adams, Sherman, and R. R. Livingston.)

The Declaration being read, was agreed to, as follows:

A DECLARATION

BY THE REPRESENTATIVES OF THE UNITED STATES OF AMERICA,
IN CONGRESS ASSEMBLED.

When, in the course of human events, it becomes necessary for one people to dissolve the political bands which have connected them with another, and to assume among the powers of the earth the separate and equal station to which the laws of nature and of nature's God entitle them, a decent respect for the opinions of mankind requires that they should declare the causes which impel them to the separation.

We hold these truths to be self-evident: that all men are created equal; that they are endowed by their Creator with certain inalienable rights; that among these are life, liberty, and the pursuit of happiness. That, to secure these rights, governments are instituted among men, deriving their just powers from the consent of the governed; that, whenever any form of government becomes destructive of these ends, it is the right of the people to alter or to abolish it, and to institute a new government, laying its foundation on such principles,

(3)

and organizing its powers in such form, as to them shall seem most likely to effect their safety and happiness. Prudence, indeed, will dictate that governments long established should not be changed for light and transient causes; and, accordingly, all experience hath shown that mankind are more disposed to suffer, while evils are sufferable, than to right themselves by abolishing the forms to which they are accustomed. But, when a long train of abuses and usurpations, pursuing invariably the same object, evinces a design to reduce them under absolute despotism, it is their right, it is their duty, to throw off such government, and to provide new guards for their future security. Such has been the patient sufferance of these colonies, and such is now the necessity which constrains them to alter their former systems of government. The history of the present King of Great Britain is a history of repeated injuries and usurpations, all having, in direct object, the establishment of an absolute tyranny over these States. To prove this, let facts be submitted to a candid world:

He has refused his assent to laws the most wholesome and necessary for the public good.

He has forbidden his Governors to pass laws of immediate and pressing importance, unless suspended in their operation till his assent should be obtained; and, when so suspended, he has utterly neglected to attend to them.

He has refused to pass other laws for the accommodation of large districts of people unless those people would relinquish the right of representation in the legislature—a right inestimable to them, and formidable to tyrants only.

He has called together legislative bodies at places unusual, uncomfortable, and distant from the depository of their public records, for the sole purpose of fatiguing them into compliance with his measures.

He has dissolved representative hou es repeatedly for opposing, with manly firmness, his invasions on the rights of the people.

He has refused, for a long time after such dissolutions, to cause others to be elected; whereby the legislative powers, incapable of annihilation, have returned to the people at large for their exercise, the State remaining, in the meantime, exposed to all the danger of invasion from without, and convulsions within.

He has endeavored to prevent the population of these States; for that purpose, obstructing the laws for naturalization of forei; ners; refusing to pass others to encourage their emigration hither, and raising the conditions of new appropriations of lands.

He has obstructed the administration of justice, by refusing his assent to laws for establishing judiciary powers.

He has made judges dependent on his will alone for the tenure of their offices and the amount and payment of their salaries.

He has erected a multitude of new offices, and sent hither swarms of officers to harass our people, and eat out their substances.

He has kept among us, in times of peace, standing armies, without the consent of our legislature.

He has affected to render the military independent of, and superior to, the civil power.

He has combined, with others, to subject us to a jurisdiction foreign to our constitution, and unacknowledged by our laws; giving his assent to their acts of pretended legislation:

For quartering large bodies of armed troops among us;

For protecting them, by mock trial, from punishment, for any murders which they should commit on the inhabitants of these States;

For cutting off our trade with all parts of the world;

For imposing taxes on us without our consent;

For depriving us, in many cases, of the benefits of trial by jury.

For transporting us beyond seas to be tried for pretended offenses.

For abolishing the free system of English laws in a neighboring province, establishing therein an arbitary government, and enlarging its boundaries, so as to render it at once an example and fit instrument for introducing the same absolute rule into these colonies;

For taking away our charters, abolishing our most valuable

laws, and altering, fundamentally, the powers of our government;

For suspending our own legislature, and declaring themselves invested with power to legislate for us in all cases whatsoever.

He has abdicated government here, by declaring us out of his protection, and waging war against us.

He has plundered our seas, ravaged our coast, burnt our towns, and destroyed the lives of our people.

He is, at this time, transporting large armies of foreign mercenaries to complete the works of death, desolation, and tyranny, already begun, with circumstances of cruelty and perfidy scarcely paralleled in the most barbarous ages, and totally unworthy the head of a civilized nation.

He has constrained our fellow-citizens, taken captive on the high seas, to bear arms against their country, to become the executioners of their friends and brethren, or to fall themselves by their hands.

He has excited domestic insurrections amongst us, and has endeavored to bring on the inhabitants of our frontiers, the merciless Indian savages, whose known rule of warfare is an undistinguished destruction, of all ages, sexes, and conditions.

In every stage of these oppressions, we have petitioned for redress, in the most humble terms; our repeated petitions have been answered only by repeated injury. A prince, whose character is thus marked by every act which may define a tyrant, is unfit to be the ruler of a free people.

Nor have we been wanting in attention to our British brethren. We have warned them, from time to time, of attempts made by their legislature to extend an unwarrantable jurisdiction over us. We have reminded them of the circumstances of our emigration and settlement here. We have appealed to their native justice and magnanimity, and we have conjured them, by the ties of our common kindred, to disavow these usurpations, which would inevitably interrupt our connections and correspondence. They, too, have been deaf to the voice of justice and consanguinity. We must, therefore, acquiesce in the necessity, which denounces our separation, and hold them, as we hold the rest of mankind, enemies in war—in peace, friends.

We, therefore, the representatives of the UNITED STATES OF AMERICA, in GENERAL CONGRESS assembled, appealing to the Supreme Judge of the World for the rectitude of our intentions, do, in the name, and by the authority of the good people of these colonies, solemnly publish and declare, That these United Colonies are, and of right ought to be, FREE AND INDEPENDENT STATES; that they are absolved from all allegiance to the British crown, and that all political connections between them and the State of Great Britain, is, and ought to be, totally dissolved; and that, as *FREE AND INDEPENDENT STATES*, they have full power to levy war, conclude peace, contract alliances, establish commerce, and to do all other acts and things which INDEPENDENT STATES may of right do. And for the support of this Declaration, with a firm reliance on the protection of DIVINE PROVIDENCE, we mutually pledge to each other, our lives, our fortunes, and our sacred honor.

The foregoing Declaration was, by order of Congress, engrossed, and signed by the following members:

JOHN HANCOCK.

New Hampshire.
JOSIAH BARTLETT.
WILLIAM WHIPPLE,
MATTHEW THORNTON.

Massachusetts Bay.
SAMUEL ADAMS,
JOHN ADAMS,
ROBERT TREAT PAYNE,
ELBRIDGE GERRY.

Connecticut.
ROGER SHERMAN,
SAMUEL HUNTINGTON,
WILLIAM WILLIAMS,
OLIVER WOLCOTT.

Rhode Island.
STEPHEN HOPKINS.
WILLIAM ELLERY,

New York.
WILLIAM FLOYD,
PHILIP LIVINGSTON,
FRANCIS LEWIS,
LEWIS MORRIS.

New Jersey.
RICHARD STOCKTON,
JOHN WITHERSPOON,
FRANCIS HOPKINSON,
JOHN HART,
ABRAHAM CLARK.

Pennsylvania.

ROBERT MORRIS,
BENJAMIN RUSH,
BENJAMIN FRANKLIN,
JOHN MORTON,
GEORGE CLYMER,
JAMES SMITH,
GEORGE TAYLOR,
JAMES WILSON,
GEORGE ROSS.

Delaware.

CÆSAR RODNEY,
GEORGE READ,
THOMAS M'KEEN.

Maryland.

SAMUEL CHASE,
WILLIAM PACA,
THOMAS STONE,
CHARLES CARROLL, of Car'n.

Georgia.

BUTTON GWINNETT,
LYMAN HALL,
GEORGE WALTON.

Virginia.

GEORGE WYTHE,
RICHARD HENRY LEE,
THOMAS JEFFERSON,
BENJAMIN HARRISON,
THOMAS NELSON, Jun.,
FRANCIS LIGHTFOOT LEE,
CARTER BRAXTON.

North Carolina.

WILLIAM HOOPER,
JOSEPH HEWES,
JOHN PENN.

South Carolina.

EDWARD RUTLEDGE,
THOMAS HAYWARD, Jun.,
THOMAS LYNCH, Jun.,
ARTHUR MIDDLETON.

CONSTITUTION

OF THE

UNITED STATES OF AMERICA.

——:o:——

We, the People of the United States, in order to form a more perfect
Union, establish justice, insure domestic tranquility, provide for the
common defense, promote the general welfare, and secure the blessings
of liberty to ourselves and our posterity, do ordain and establish this
Constitution for the United States of America.

ARTICLE I.

SECTION 1. All the legislative powers herein granted shall
be vested in a Congress of the United States, which shall consist of a Senate and House of Representatives.

SEC. 2. The House of Representatives shall be composed
of members chosen every second year by the people of the
several States; and the electors in each State shall have the
qualifications requisite for electors of the most numerous
branch of the State Legislature.

No person shall be a Representative who shall not have attained to the age of twenty-five years, and been seven years a
citizen of the United States, and who shall not, when elected,
be an inhabitant of that State in which he shall be chosen.

Representatives and direct taxes shall be apportioned among
the several States which may be included within this Union,
according to their respective numbers, which shall be determined by adding to the whole number of free persons, including those bound to service for a term of years, and excluding
Indians not taxed, three-fifths of all other persons. The actual
enumeration shall be made within three years after the first
meeting of the Congress of the United States, and within

(9)

every subsequent term of ten years, in such manner as they shall by law direct. The number of Representatives shall not exceed one for every thirty thousand, but each State shall have at least one Representative; and until such enumeration shall be made, the State of New Hampshire shall be entitled to choose three, Massachusetts eight, Rhode Island and Providence Plantations one, Connecticut five, New York six, New Jersey four, Pennsylvania eight, Delaware one, Maryland six, Virginia ten, North Carolina five, South Carolina five, and Georgia three.

When vacancies happen in the representation from any State, the Executive authority thereof shall issue Writs of Election to fill such vacancies.

The House of Representatives shall choose their Speaker and other officers; and shall have the sole power of impeachment.

SEC. 3. The Senate of the United States shall be composed of two Senators from each State, chosen by the Legislature thereof, for six years; and each Senator shall have one vote.

Immediately after they shall be assembled in consequence of the first election, they shall be divided as equally as may be into three classes. The seats of the Senators of the first class shall be vacated at the expiration of the second year, of the second class at the expiration of the fourth year, and of the third class at the expiration of the sixth year, so that one-third may be chosen every second year; and if vacancies happen by resignation, or otherwise, during the recess of the Legislature of any State, the Executive thereof may make temporary appointments until the next meeting of the Legislature, which shall then fill such vacancies.

No person shall be a Senator who shall not have attained to the age of thirty years, and been nine years a citizen of the United States, and who shall not, when elected, be an inhabitant of that State for which he shall be chosen.

The Vice President of the United States shall be President of the Senate, but shall have no vote, unless they be equally divided.

The Senate shall choose their other officers, and also a President *pro tempore*, in the absence of the Vice-President, or when he shall exercise the office of President of the United States.

The Senate shall have the sole power to try all impeachments. When sitting for that purpose, they shall be on oath or affirmation. When the President of the United States is being tried, the Chief Justice shall preside ; and no person shall be convicted without the concurrence of two-thirds of the members present.

Judgment in cases of impeachment shall not extend further than to removal from office, and disqualification to hold and enjoy any office of honor, trust or profit under the United States; but the party convicted shall nevertheless be liable and subject to indictment, trial, judgment and punishment, according to law.

Sec. 4. The times, places, and manner of holding elections for Senators and Representatives, shall be prescribed in each State by the Legislature thereof; but the Congress may, at any time, by law make or alter such regulations, except as the places of choosing Senators.

The Congress shall assemble at least once in every year, and such meeting shall be on the first Monday in December, unless they shall by law appoint a different day.

Sec. 5. Each House shall be the judge of the elections, returns, and qualifications of its own members, and a majority of each shall constitute a quorum to do business ; but a smaller number may adjourn from day to day, and may be authorized to compel the attendance of absent members, in such manner and under such penalties as each House may provide.

Each House may determine the Rules of its Proceedings, punish its members for disorderly behavior, and with the concurrence of two-thirds, expel a member.

Each House shall keep a Journal of its Proceedings, and from time to time publish the same, excepting such parts as may, in their judgment, require secrecy; and the yeas and nays of the members of either House on any question shall, at the desire of one-fifth of those present, be entered on the journal.

Neither House, during the session of Congress, shall, without the consent of the other, adjourn for more than three days, nor to any other place than that in which the two Houses shall be sitting.

Sec. 6. The Senators and Representatives shall receive a compensation for their services, to be ascertained by law and paid out of the treasury of the United States. They shall in all cases, except treason, felony, and breach of the peace, be privileged from arrest during their attendance at the session of their respective Houses, and in going to and returning from the same; and for any speech or debate in either House, they shall not be questioned in any other place.

No Senator or Representative shall, during the time for which he was elected, be appointed to any civil office under the authority of the United States, which shall have been created, or the emoluments whereof shall have been increased during such time, and no person holding any office under the United States shall be a member of either House during his continuance in office.

SEC. 7. All bills for raising revenue shall originate in the House of Representatives; but the Senate may propose or concur with amendments as on other bills.

Every bill which shall have passed the House of Representatives and the Senate, shall, before it becomes a law, be presented to the President of the United States: If he approve, he shall sign it; but if not, he shall return it, with his objections, to that House in which it shall have originated, who shall enter the objections at large on their Journal, and proceed to reconsider it. If, after such reconsideration, two-thirds of that House shall agree to pass the bill, it shall be sent, together with the objections, to the other House, by which it shall likewise be reconsidered, and if approved by two-thirds of that House, it shall become a law. But in all such cases the votes of both Houses shall be determined by yeas and nays, and the names of persons voting for and against the bill shall be entered on the Journal of each House respectively. If any bill shall not be returned by the President within ten days (Sundays excepted) after it shall have been presented to him, the same shall be a law, in like manner as if he had signed it, unless the Congress, by their adjournment, prevent its return, in which case it shall not be a law.

Every order, resolution, or vote to which the concurrence of the Senate and House of Representatives may be necessary (except on a question of adjournment) shall be presented to the President of the United States; and before the same shall take effect, shall be approved by him; or, being disapproved by him, shall be repassed by two-thirds of the Senate and

House of Representatives, according to the rules and limitations prescribed in the case of a bill.

Sec. 8. The Congress shall have power—

To lay and collect Taxes, Duties, Imposts and Excises, to pay the debts and provide for the common defense and general welfare of the United States: but all Duties, Imposts and Excises shall be uniform throughout the United States;

To borrow money on the credit of the United States;

To regulate commerce with foreign nations, and among the several States, and with the Indian tribes;

To establish an uniform rule of naturalization, and uniform laws on the subject of bankruptcies throughout the United States;

To coin money, regulate the value thereof and of foreign coin, and fix the standard of weights and measures;

To provide for the punishment of counterfeiting the securities and current coin of the United States;

To establish post-offices and post roads;

To promote the progress of science and useful arts, by securing for limited times to authors and inventors the exclusive right to their respective writings and discoveries;

To constitute tribunals inferior to the Supreme Court;

To define and punish piracies and felonies committed on the high seas, and offenses against the law of nations;

To declare war, grant letters of marque and reprisal, and make rules concerning captures on land and water;

To raise and support armies, but no appropriation of money to that use shall be for a longer term than two years;

To provide and maintain a navy;

To make rules for the government and regulation of the land and naval forces;

To provide for calling forth the militia to execute the laws of the Union, suppress insurrections, and repel invasions;

To provide for organizing, arming, and disciplining the militia, and for governing such part of them as may be employed in the service of the United States, reserving to the States respectively the appointment of the officers, and the authority of training the militia according to the discipline prescribed by Congress;

To exercise exclusive legislation, in all cases whatsoever, over such district (not exceeding ten miles square) as may, by cession of particular States, and the acceptance of Congress, become the Seat of the Government of the United States, and to exercise like authority over all places purchased by the consent of the Legislature of the State in which the same shall be, for the erection of forts, magazines, arsenals, dock-yards, and other needful buildings; and

To make all laws which shall be necessary and proper for carrying into execution the foregoing powers, and all other powers vested by this Constitution in the Government of the United States, or in any department or officer thereof.

SEC. 9. The migration or importation of such persons as any of the States now existing shall think proper to admit, shall not be prohibited by the Congress prior to the year one thousand eight hundred and eight, but a tax or duty may be imposed on such importation, not exceeding ten dollars for each person.

The privilege of the Writ of Habeas Corpus shall not be suspended, unless when, in cases of rebellion or invasion, the public safety may require it.

No bill of attainder or ex post facto law shall be passed.

No capitation, or other direct tax shall be laid, unless in proportion to the census or enumeration hereinbefore directed to be taken.

No tax or duty shall be laid on articles exported from any State.

No preference shall be given by any regulation of commerce or revenue to the ports of one State over those of another; nor shall vessels bound to or from one State, be obliged to enter, clear, or pay duties in another.

No money shall be drawn from the treasury but in consequence of appropriations made by law; and a regular statement and account of the receipts and expenditures of all public money shall be published from time to time.

No title of nobility shall be granted by the United States: And no person holding any office of profit or trust under them shall, without the consent of the Congress, accept of any present, emolument, office, or title, of any kind whatever, from any king, prince, or foreign State.

SEC. 10. No State shall enter into any treaty, alliance, or confederation: grant letters of marque or reprisal; coin money; emit bills of credit; make anything but gold and silver coin a tender in payment of debts; pass any bill of attainder, ex post facto law, or law impairing the obligation of contracts, or grant any title of nobility.

No State shall, without the consent of the Congress, lay any imposts or duties on imports or exports, except what may be absolutely necessary for executing its inspection laws; and the net produce of all duties and imposts, laid by any State on imports or exports, shall be for the use of the treasury of the United States; and all such laws shall be subject to the revision and control of the Congress.

No State shall, without the consent of Congress, lay any duty of tonnage, keep troops, or ships of war in time of peace, enter into any agreement or compact with another State, or with a foreign power, or engage in war, unless actually invaded, or in such imminent danger as will not admit of delay.

ARTICLE II.

SECTION 1. The Executive Power shall be vested in a President of the United States of America. He shall hold his office during the term of four years, and, together with the Vice-President, chosen for the same term, be elected as follows:

Each State shall appoint, in such manner as the Legislature thereof may direct, a number of electors equal to the number of Senators and Representatives to which the State may be entitled in the Congress; but no Senator or Representative, or person holding an office of trust or profit under the United States, shall be appointed an elector.

[The electors shall meet in their respective States, and vote by ballot for two persons—of one at least shall not be an inhabitant of the same State with themselves. And they shall make a list of all the persons voted for, and of the number of votes for each; which list they shall sign and certify, and transmit, sealed, to the seat of the Government of the United States, directed to the President of the Senate. The President of the Senate shall, in the presence of the Senate and House of Representatives, open all the certificates, and the votes shall then be counted. The person having the greatest number of votes shall be the President, if such number be a majority of the whole number of electors appointed; and if there be more than one who have such majority, and have an equal number of votes, then the House of Representatives shall immediately choose by ballot one of them for President;

and if no person have a majority, then from the five highest
on the list the said House shall, in like manner, choose the
President. But, in choosing the President, the votes shall be
taken by States, the representation from each State having
one vote. A quorum for this purpose shall consist of a member or members from two-thirds of the States, and a majority
of all the States shall be necessary to a choice. In every case,
after the choice of the President, the person having the greatest number of votes of the electors shall be the Vice-President.
But if there should remain two or more who have equal votes,
the Senate shall choose from them by ballot the Vice-President.*]

The Congress may determine the time of choosing the electors, and the day on which they shall give their votes; which
day shall be the same throughout the United States.

No person, except a natural born citizen, or a citizen of the
United States at the time of the adoption of this Constitution,
shall be eligible to the office of President; neither shall any
person be eligible to that office who shall not have attained
to the age of thirty-five years, and been fourteen years a resident within the United States.

In case of the removal of the President from office, or of his
death, resignation or inability to discharge the powers and
duties of the said office, the same shall devolve on the Vice
President; and the Congress may by law provide for the case
of removal, death, resignation, or inability, both of the President and Vice President, declaring what officer shall then act
as President; and such officer shall act accordingly until the
disability be removed, or a President shall be elected.

The President shall, at stated times, receive for his services
a compensation, which shall neither be increased nor diminished during the period for which he shall have been elected;
and he shall not receive within that period any other emolument from the United States, or any of them.

Before he enter on the execution of his office, he shall take
the following oath or affirmation:

' I do solemnly swear (or affirm) that I will faithfully execute the
office of President of the United States, and will, to the best of my abili-
ty, preserve, protect, and defend the Constitution of the United States."

Sec. 2   The President shall be Commander-in-Chief of the

---

* This clause has been repealed and annulled by the 12th amendment.

Army and Navy of the United States, and of the militia of the several States when called into the actual service of the United States; he may require the opinion, in writing, of the principal officer in each of the Executive Departments upon any subject relating to the duties of their respective offices; and he shall have power to grant reprieves and pardons for offenses against the United States, except in cases of impeachment.

He shall have power, by and with the advice and consent of the Senate, to make treaties, provided two-thirds of the Senate present concur; and he shall nominate, and by and with the advice and consent of the Senate, shall appoint Embassadors, other Public Ministers and Consuls, Judges of the Supreme Court, and all other officers of the United States whose appointments are not herein otherwise provided for, and which shall be established; but the Congress may by law vest the appointment of such inferior officers as they think proper in the President alone, in the Courts of Law, or in the Heads of Departments.

The President shall have power to fill up all vacancies that may happen during the recess of the Senate, by granting commissions, which shall expire at the end of their next session.

Sec. 3. He shall, from time to time, give to the Congress information of the state of the Union, and recommend to their consideration such measures as he shall judge necessary and expedient; he may, on extraordinary occasions, convene both Houses, or either of them; and, in case of disagreement between them with respect to the time of adjournment, he may adjourn them to such time as he shall think proper; he shall receive Embassadors and other public Ministers; he shall take care that the laws be faithfully executed, and shall commission all the officers of the United States.

Sec. 4. The President, Vice-President, and all Civil Officers of the United States, shall be removed from office on impeachment for, and conviction of, Treason, Bribery, or other high Crimes and Misdemeanors.

ARTICLE III.

Section 1. The judicial power of the United States shall be vested in one Supreme Court, and in such inferior Courts as

2

the Congress may from time to time ordain and establish. The Judges, both of the Supreme and inferior courts, shall hold their offices during good behavior, and shall, at stated times, receive for their services a compensation, which shall not be diminished during their continuance in office.

SEC. 2. The judicial power shall extend to all cases, in Law and Equity, arising under this Constitution, the Laws of the United States, and Treaties made, or which shall be made, under their authority; to all cases affecting Embassadors, other public Ministers and Consuls; to all cases of admiralty and maritime jurisdiction; to controversies to which the United States shall be a party; to controversies between two or more States; between a State and citizens of another State; between citizens of different States; between citizens of the same State claiming lands under grants of different States; and between a State, or the citizens thereof, and foreign States, citizens or subjects.

In all cases affecting Embassadors, other public Ministers and Consuls, and those in which a State shall be a party, the Supreme Court shall have original jurisdiction. In all the other cases before mentioned, the Supreme Court shall have appellate jurisdiction, both as to law and fact, with such exceptions and under such regulations as the Congress shall make.

The trial of all crimes, except in cases of Impeachment, shall be by jury; and such trial shall be held in the State where the said crimes shall have been committed; but when not committed within any State, the trial shall be at such place or places as the Congress may by law have directed.

SEC. 3. Treason against the United States shall consist only in levying war against them, or adhering to their enemies, giving them aid and comfort. No person shall be convicted of treason unless on the testimony of two witnesses to the same overt act, or on confession in open Court.

The Congress shall have power to declare the punishment of treason, but no Attainder of Treason shall work corruption of blood, or forfeiture, except during the life of the person attainted.

ARTICLE IV.

SECTION 1. Full faith and credit shall be given in each State to the public acts, records, and judicial proceedings of every other State. And the Congress may by general laws prescribe the manner in which such acts, records, and proceedings shall be proved, and the effect thereof.

SEC. 2. The citizens of each State shall be entitled to all privileges and immunities of citizens in the several States.

A person charged in any State with treason, felony, or other crime, who shall flee from justice, and be found in another State, shall, on demand of the executive authority of the State from which be fled, be delivered up, to be removed to the State having jurisdiction of the crime.

No person held to service or labor in one State, under the laws thereof, escaping into another, shall, in consequence of any law or regulation therein, be discharged from such service or labor, but shall be delivered up on claim of the party to whom such service or labor may be due.

SEC. 3. New States may be admitted by the Congress into this Union; but no new State shall be formed or erected within the jurisdiction of any other State ; nor any State be formed by the junction of two or more States or parts of States without the consent of the Legislatures of the States concerned, as well as of the Congress.

The Congress shall have power to dispose of and make all needful rules and regulations respecting the territory or other property belonging to the United States ; and nothing in this Constitution shall be so construed as to prejudice any claims of the United States, or any particular State.

SEC. 4. The United States shall guarantee to every State in this Union a republican form of Government, and shall protect each of them against invasion ; and on application of the Legislature, or of the Executive (when the Legislature can not be convened), against domestic violence.

ARTICLE V.

The Congress, whenever two-thirds of both Houses shall deem it necessary, shall propose amendments to the Constitution, or, on the application of the Legislatures of two-thirds of the several States, shall call a convention for proposing amendments, which, in either case, shall be valid to all intents and purposes, as part of this Constitution, when ratified by the Legislatures of three-fourths of the several States, or by conventions in three-fourths thereof, as the one or the other mode of ratification may be proposed by the Congress; *Provided*, That no amendment which may be made prior to the year one thousand eight hundred and eight shall in any manner affect the first and fourth classes in the ninth section of the first article; and that no State, without its consent, shall be deprived of its equal suffrage in the Senate.

ARTICLE VI.

All debts contracted and engagements entered into before the adoption of this Constitution, shall be as valid against the United States, under this Constitution, as under the Confederation.

This Constitution and the laws of the United States which shall be made in pursuance thereof; and all Treaties made, or which shall be made, under the authority of the United States, shall be the supreme law of the land; and the Judges in every State shall be bound thereby, anything in the Constitution or laws of any State to the contrary notwithstanding.

The Senators and Representatives before mentioned, and the members of the several State Legislatures, and all executive and judicial officers, both of the United States and of the several States, shall be bound by oath or affirmation to support this Constitution; but no religious test shall ever be required as a qualification to any office or public trust under the United States.

ARTICLE VII.

The ratification of the conventions of nine States shall be sufficient for the establishment of this Constitution between the States so ratifying the same.

DONE in convention, by the unanimous consent of the States present, the seventeenth day of September, in the year of our Lord one thousand seven hundred and eighty-seven, and of the Independence of the United States of America the twelfth. In Witness whereof, we have hereunto subscribed our names.

GEO. WASHINGTON,
Pres't and Deputy from Virginia.

New Hampshire.

JOHN LANGDON,   NICHOLAS GILMAN.

Massachusetts.

NATHANIEL GORHAM, RUFUS KING.

Connecticut.

WM. SAML. JOHNSON, ROGER SHERMAN.

New York.

ALEXANDER HAMILTON.

New Jersey.

WIL. LIVINGSTON, DAVID BREARLEY,
WM. PATERSON, JONA. DAYTON.

Pennsylvania.

B. FRANKLIN, THOMAS MIFFLIN,
ROBT. MORRIS, GEO CLYMER,
THO. FITZSIMONS, JARED INGERSOLL,
JAMES WILSON, GOUV. MORRIS.

Delaware.

GEO. READ, GUNNING BEDFORD, JR.
JOHN DICKINSON, RICHARD BASSETT.
JACO. BROOM,

Maryland.

JAMES M'HENRY, DAN. OF ST. THOS. JENIFER.
DANL. CARROLL,

Virginia.

JOHN BLAIR, JAMES MADISON, JR.

North Carolina.

WM. BLOUNT, RICH'D DOBBS SPAIGHT.
HU. WILLIAMSON,

South Carolina.

J. RUTLEDGE, CHARLES C. PINCKNEY.
CHARLES PINCKNEY, PIERCE BUTLER.

Georgia.

WILLIAM FEW, ABR. BALDWIN.

Attest: WILLIAM JACKSON, *Secretary.*

ARTICLES.

In addition to, and amendment of, the Constitution of the United States
of America, proposed by Congress, and ratified by the Legislatures of
the several States, pursuant to the fifth article of the original Constitution.

ARTICLE I.

Congress shall make no law respecting an establishment of
religion, or prohibiting the free exercise thereof; or abridging
the freedom of speech or of the press; or the right of the people peaceably to assemble, and to petition the Government
for a redress of grievances.

ARTICLE II.

A well-regulated Militia being necessary to the security of
a free State, the right of the people to keep and bear arms
shall not be infringed.

ARTICLE III.

No soldier shall, in time of peace, be quartered in any house,
without the consent of the owner, nor in time of war, but in a
manner to be prescribed by law.

ARTICLE IV.

The right of the people to be secure in their persons, houses,
papers, and effects, against unreasonable searches and seizures, shall not be violated, and no warrant shall issue but
upon probable cause, supported by oath or affirmation, and
particularly describing the place to be searched, and the persons or things to be seized.

ARTICLE V.

No person shall be held to answer for a capital, or otherwise
infamous crime, unless on a presentment or indictment of a
Grand Jury, except in cases arising in the land or naval forces,
or in the militia, when in actual service in time of war or public danger; nor shall any person be subject for the same
offense to be twice put in jeopardy of life or limb; nor shall
be compelled in any criminal case to be a witness against
himself, nor be deprived of life, liberty, or property, without

due process of law; nor shall private property be taken for public use without just compensation.

ARTICLE VI.

In all criminal prosecutions, the accused shall enjoy the right to a speedy and public trial, by an impartial jury of the State and district wherein the crime shall have been committed, which district shall have been previously ascertained by law, and to be informed of the nature and cause of the accusation to be confronted with the witnesses against him; to have compulsory process for obtaining witnesses in his favor, and to have the assistance of counsel for his defense.

ARTICLE VII.

In suits at common law, where the value in controversy shall exceed twenty dollars, the right of trial by jury shall be preserved, and no fact tried by a jury shall be otherwise re-examined in any Court of the United States, than according to the rules of the common law.

ARTICLE VIII.

Excessive bail shall not be required, nor excessive fines imposed, nor cruel and unusual punishments inflicted.

ARTICLE IX.

The enumeration in the Constitution of certain rights, shall not be construed to deny or disparage others retained by the people.

ARTICLE X.

The powers not delegated to the United States by the Constitution, nor prohibited by it to the States, are reserved to the States respectively, or to the people.

ARTICLE XI.

The judicial power of the United States shall not be construed to extend to any suit in law or equity, commenced or prosecuted against one of the United States by citizens of another State, or by citizens or subjects of any foreign State.

ARTICLE XII.

The Electors shall meet in their respective States, and vote by ballot for President and Vice-President, one of whom, at least, shall not be an inhabitant of the same State with themselves; they shall name in their ballot the person voted for as President, and in distinct ballots the person voted for as Vice-President, and they shall make distinct lists of all persons voted for as President, and all persons voted for as Vice-President, and of the number of votes for each, which lists they shall sign and certify, and transmit sealed to the seat of government of the United States, directed to the President of the Senate:—The President of the Senate shall, in presence of the Senate and House of Representatives, open all the certificates, and the votes shall then be counted; The person having the greatest number of votes for President shall be the President, if such number be a majority of the whole number of Electors appointed; and if no person have such majority, then from the persons having the highest numbers, not exceeding three, on the list of those voted for as President, the House of Representatives shall choose immediately by ballot the President. But in choosing the President, the votes shall be taken by States, the representation from each State having one; a quorum for this shall consist of a member or members from two-thirds of the States, and a majority of all the States shall be necessary to a choice. And if the House of Representatives shall not choose a President, whenever the right of choice shall devolve upon them, before the fourth day of March next following, then the Vice-President shall act as President, as in the case of the death or other constitutional disability of the President. The person having the greatest number of votes as Vice-President, shall be the Vice-President, if such number be a majority of the whole number of electors appointed; and if no person have a majority, then from the two highest numbers on the list, the Senate shall choose the Vice-President; a quorum for the purpose shall consist of two-thirds of the whole number of Senators, and a majority of the whole number shall be necessary to a choice. But no person constitutionally ineligible to the office of President, shall be eligible to that of Vice-President of the United States.

ARTICLE XIII.

"SECTION 1. Neither slavery nor involuntary servitude, except as a punishment for crime, whereof the party shall have been duly convicted, shall exist within the United States, or any place subject to their jurisdiction.

"SECTION 2. Congress shall have power to enforce this Article by appropriate legislation, approved February 1, 1863."

The Constitution was adopted on the 17th of September, 1787, by the convention appointed in pursuance of the Resolution of the Congress of the Confederation, of the 21st February, 1787, and ratified by the conventions of the several States, as follows:

By Convention of Delaware..................................7th December, 1787
" " Pennsylvania.............................12th December, 1787
" " New Jersey..............................18th December, 1787
" " Georgia.................................2d January, 1788
" " Connecticut................................9th January, 1788
" " Massachusetts.............................6th February, 1788
" " Maryland.....................................28th April, 1788
" " South Carolina................................28th May, 1788
" " New Hampshire...............................21st June, 1788
" " Virginia...26th June, 1788
" " New York.....................................26th July, 1788
" " North Carolina.........................21st November, 1789
" " Rhode Island................................29th May, 1790

The first ten of the Amendments were proposed on the 25th of September, 1789, and ratified by the constitutional number of States on the 15th December, 1791; the eleventh, on the 8th of January, 1798; and the twelfth, on the 25th September, 1804; and the thirteenth, on the ——, 186—.

CONSTITUTION

OF THE

STATE OF INDIANA.

——:o:——

PREAMBLE.

To THE END, that justice be established, public order maintained, and liberty perpetuated; WE the People of the State of Indiana, grateful to ALMIGHTY GOD for the free exercise of the right to choose our own form of government, do ordain this Constitution.

ARTICLE I.

BILL OF RIGHTS.

SECTION 1. WE DECLARE, That all men are created equal; that they are endowed by their Creator with certain unalienable rights; that among these are life, liberty, and the pursuit of happiness; that all power is inherent in the people; and that all free governments are, and of right ought to be, founded on their authority, and instituted for their peace, safety, and well being. For the advancement of these ends, the People have, at all times, an indefeasible right to alter and reform their government.

Sec. 2. All men shall be secured in their natural right to worship Almighty God, according to the dictates of their own consciences.

Sec. 3. No law shall, in any case whatever, control the free exercise and enjoyment of religious opinions, or interfere with the rights of conscience.

Sec. 4. No preference shall be given, by law, to any creed, religious society, or mode of worship; and no man shall be compelled to attend, erect, or support any place of worship, or to maintain any ministry, against his consent.

Sec. 5. No religious test shall be required, as a qualification for any office of trust or profit.

Sec. 6. No money shall be drawn from the treasury, for the benefit of any religious or theological institution.

Sec. 7. No person shall be rendered incompetent as a witness, in consequence of his opinions on matters of religion.

Sec. 8. The mode of administering an oath or affirmation, shall be such as may be most consistent with, and binding upon, the conscience of the person to whom such oath or affirmation may be administered.

Sec. 9. No law shall be passed, restraining the free interchange of thought and opinion, or restricting the right to speak, write, or print freely, on any subject whatever; but for the abuse of that right every person shall be responsible.

Sec. 10. In all prosecutions for libel, the truth of the matters alleged to be libelous may be given in justification.

Sec. 11. The right of the people to be secure in their persons, houses, papers, and effects, against unreasonable search or seizure, shall not be violated; and no warrant shall issue, but upon probable cause, supported by oath or affirmation, and particularly describing the place to be searched, and the person or thing to be seized.

Sec. 12. All courts shall be open; and every man, for injury done to him in his person, property or reputation, shall have remedy by due course of law. Justice shall be administered freely, and without purchase; completely, and without denial; speedily, and without delay.

Sec. 13. In all criminal prosecutions, the accused shall have the right to a public trial, by an impartial jury, in the county in which the offense shall have been committed; to be heard by himself and counsel; to demand the nature and cause of the accusation against him, and to have a copy thereof; to meet the witnesses face to face, and to have compulsory process for obtaining witnesses in his favor.

Sec. 14. No person shall be put in jeopardy twice for the same offense. No person, in any criminal prosecution, shall be compelled to testify against himself.

Sec. 15. No person arrested, or confined in jail, shall be treated with unnecessary rigor.

Sec. 16. Excessive bail shall not be required. Excessive fines shall not be imposed. Cruel and unusual punishment shall not be inflicted. All penalties shall be proportioned to the nature of the offense.

Sec. 17. Offenses, other than murder or treason, shall be bailable by sufficient sureties. Murder or treason shall not be bailable, when the proof is evident, or the presumption strong.

Sec. 18. The penal code shall be founded on the principles of reformation, and not of vindictive justice.

Sec. 19. In all criminal cases whatever, the jury shall have the right to determine the law and the facts.

Sec. 20. In all civil cases, the right of trial by jury shall remain inviolate.

Sec. 21. No man's particular services shall be demanded without just compensation. No man's property shall be taken by law, without just compensation; nor, except in case of the State, without such compensation first assessed and tendered.

Sce. 22. The privilege of the debtor to enjoy the necessary comforts of life, shall be recognized by wholesome laws, exempting a reasonable amount of property from seizure or sale for the payment of any debt or liability hereafter contracted; and there shall be no imprisonment for debt, except in case of fraud.

Sec. 23. The General Assembly shall not grant to any citizen, or class of citizens, privileges or immunities which, upon the same terms, shall not equally belong to all citizens.

Sec. 24. No *ex-post-facto* law, or law impairing the obligation of contracts, shall ever be passed.

Sec. 25. No law shall be passed, the taking effect of which shall be made to depend upon any authority, except as provided in this Constitution.

Sec. 26. The operation of the laws shall never be suspended, except by the authority of the General Assembly.

Sec. 27. The privilege of the writ of *habeas corpus* shall not be suspended, except in case of rebellion or invasion; and then, only if the public safety demand it.

Sec. 28. Treason against the State shall consist only in levying war against it, and in giving aid and comfort to its enemies.

Sec. 29. No person shall be convicted of treason, except on the testimony of two witnesses to the same overt act, or upon his confession in open court.

Sec. 30. No conviction shall work corruption of blood, or forfeiture of estate.

Sec. 31. No law shall restrain any of the inhabitants of the State from assembling together in a peaceable manner, to consult for their common good; nor from instructing their representatives; nor from applying to the General Assembly for redress of grievances.

Sec. 32. The people shall have a right to bear arms, for the defense of themselves and the State.

Sec. 33. The military shall be kept in strict subordination to the civil power.

Sec. 34. No soldier shall, in time of peace, be quartered in any house, without the consent of the owner; nor, in time of war, but in a manner to be prescribed by law.

Sec. 35. The General Assembly shall not grant any title of nobility, nor confer hereditary distinctions.

Sec. 36. Emigration from the State shall not be prohibited.

Sec. 37. There shall be neither slavery, nor involuntary servitude, within the State, otherwise than for the punishment of crimes, whereof the party shall have been duly convicted. No indenture of any Negro or Mulatto, made and executed out of the bounds of the State, shall be valid within the State.

ARTICLE II.

SUFFRAGE AND ELECTION.

Sec. 1. All elections shall be free and equal.

Sec. 2. In all elections, not otherwise provided for by this Constitution, every white male citizen of the United States, of the age of twenty-one years and upwards, who shall have resided in the State during the six months immediately preceding such election; and every white male, of foreign birth, of the age of twenty-one years and upwards, who shall have resided in the United States one year, and shall have resided in this State during the six months immediately preceding such election, and shall have declared his intention to become a citizen of the United States, conformably to the laws of the United States on the subject of naturalization, shall be entitled to vote in the township or precinct where he may reside.

Sec. 3. No soldier, seaman, or marine, in the army or navy of the United States, or of their allies, shall be deemed to have acquired a residence within the State, in consequence of having been stationed within the same; nor shall any such soldier, seaman, or marine have the right to vote.

Sec. 4. No person shall be deemed to have lost his residence in the State by reason of his absence, either on business of this State or of the United States.

Sec. 5. No Negro or Mulatto shall have the right of suffrage.

Sec. 6. Every person shall be disqualified from holding office during the term for which he may have been elected, who shall have given or offered a bribe, threat, or reward to procure his election.

Sec. 7. Every person who shall give or accept a challenge to fight a duel, or who shall knowingly carry to another person such challenge, or who shall agree to go out of the State to fight a duel, shall be ineligible to any office of trust or profit.

Sec. 8. The General Assembly shall have power to deprive of the right of suffrage, and to render ineligible, any person convicted of an infamous crime.

Sec. 9. No person holding a lucrative office or appointment under the United States, or under this State, shall be eligible to a seat in the General Assembly; nor shall any person hold more than one lucrative office at the same time, except as in this Constitution expressly permitted: *Provided*, that officers in the militia, to which there is attached no annual salary, and the office of Deputy Postmaster, where the compensation does not exceed ninety dollars per annum, shall not be deemed lucrative: *And provided, also*, that counties containing less than one thousand polls, may confer the office of Clerk, Recorder, and Auditor, or any two of said offices, upon the same person.

Sce. 10. No person who may hereafter be a collector or holder of public moneys, shall be eligible to any office of trust or profit, until he shall have accounted for, and paid over, according to law, all sums for which he may be liable.

Sec. 11. In all cases in which it is provided that an office shall not be filled by the same person more than a certain number of years continuously, an appointment *pro tempore*, shall not be reckoned a part of that term.

Sec. 12. In all cases, except treason, felony, and breach of the peace, electors shall be free from arrest, in going to elections, during their attendance there, and in returning from the same.

Sec. 13. All elections by the people shall be by ballot; and all elections by the General Assembly, or by either branch thereof, shall be *viva voce.*

Sec. 14. All general elections shall be held on the second Tuesday in October.

ARTICLE III.

DISTRIBUTION OF POWERS.

SECTION 1. The powers of the Government are divided into three separate departments; the Legislative, the Executive, including the Administrative, and the Judicial; and no person, charged with official duties under one of these departments, shall exercise any of the functions of another, except as in this Constitution expressly provided.

ARTICLE IV.

LEGISLATIVE.

SECTION 1. The Legislative authority of the State shall be vested in the General Assembly, which shall consist of a Senate and a House of Representatives. The style of every law shall be: "Be it enacted by the General Assembly oi the State of Indiana;" and no law shall be enacted except by bill.

Sec. 2. The Senate shall not exceed fifty, nor the House of Representatives one hundred members; and they shall be chosen by the electors of the respective counties or districts, into which the State may, from time to time, be divided.

Sec. 3. Senators shall be elected for the term of four years and Representatives for the term of two years, from the day next after their general election : *Provided, however,* that the Senators elect, at the second meeting of the General Assembly under this Constitution, shall be divided, by lot into two equal classes, as nearly as may be ; and the seats of Senators of the first class shall be vacated at the expiration of two years, and those of the second class at the expiration of four years; so that one-half as nearly as possible, shall be chosen biennially forever thereafter. And in case of increase in the number of Senators. they shall be annexed, by lot, to one or the other of the two classes, as to keep them as nearly equal as practicable.

Sec. 4. The General Assembly shall, at its second session after the adoption of this Constitution, and every six years thereafter, cause an enumeration to be made of all the white male inhabitants over the age of twenty-one years.

Sec. 5. The number of Senators and Representatives shall, at the session next following each period of making such enumeration, be fixed by law, and apportioned among the several counties, according to the number of white male inhabitants above twenty-one years of age in each: *Provided*, that the first and second election of members of the General Assembly under this Constitution shall be according to the apportionment last made by the General Assembly, before the adoption of this Constitution.

Sec. 6. A senatorial or representative district, where more than one county shall constitute a district, shall be composed of contiguous counties; and no county for senatorial apportionment shall ever be divided.

Sec. 7. No person shall be a senator or a representative who at the time of his election is not a citizen of the United States; nor any one who has not been, for two years next preceding his election, an inhabitant of this State, and, for one year next preceding his election, an inhabitant of the county or district whence he may be chosen. Senators shall be at least twenty-five, and Representatives at least twenty-one years of age.

Sec. 8. Senators and Representatives, in all cases except treason, felony, and breach of the peace, shall be privileged from arrest during the session of the General Assembly, and in going to and returning from the same, and shall not be subject to any civil process during the session of the General Assembly, nor during the fifteen days next before the commencement thereof. For any speech or debate in either house, a member shall not be questioned in any other place.

Sec. 9. The session of the General Assembly shall be held biennially at the capital of the State, commencing on the Thursday next after the first Monday of January, in the year one thousand eight hundred and fifty-three, and on the same day of every second year thereafter, unless a different day or place shall have been appointed by law. But if, in the opinion of the Governor, the public welfare shall require it, he may, at any time, by proclamation, call a special session.

Sec. 10. Each house when assembled shall choose its own officers (the President of the Senate excepted), judge of the elections, qualifications, and returns of its own members, determine its rules of proceeding, and sit upon its own adjournment. But neither house shall, without the consent of the other, adjourn for more than three days, nor to any place other than that in which it may be sitting.

Sec. 11. Two-thirds of each house shall constitute a quorum to do business, but a smaller number may meet, adjourn from day to day, and compel the attendance of absent members. A quorum being in attendance, if either house fail to effect an organization within the first five days thereafter, the members of the house so failing shall be entitled to no compensation from the end of the said five days, until an organization shall have been effected.

Sec. 12. Each house shall keep a journal of its proceedings, and publish the same. The yeas and nays, on any question, shall, at the request of any two members, be entered, together with the names of the members demanding the same, on the journal : *Provided*, that on a motion to adjourn, it shall reqiure one-tenth of the members present to order the yeas and nays.

Sec. 13. The doors of each house, and of committees of the whole, shall be kept open, except in such cases, as, in the opinion of either house, may require secrecy.

Sec. 14. Either house may punish its members for disorderly behavior, and may, with the concurrence of two-thirds, expel a member; but not a second time for the same cause.

Sec. 15. Either house, during its session, may punish by imprisonment, any person not a member, who shall have been guilty of disrespect to the house, by disorderly or contemptuous behavior in its presence; but such imprisonment shall not at any time exceed twenty-four hours.

Sec. 16. Each house shall have all powers necessary for a branch of the legislative department of a free and independent State.

Sec. 17. Bills may originate in either house, but may be amended or rejected in the other, except that bills for raising revenue shall originate in the House of Representatives.

Sec. 18. Every bill shall be read, by sections, on three several days, in each house; unless, in case of emergency, two-thirds of the house where such bill may be depending shall, by a vote of yeas and nays, deem it expedient to dispense with this rule; but the reading of a bill by sections, on its final passage, shall, in no case, be dispensed with; and the vote on the passage of every bill or joint resolution shall be taken by yeas and nays.

Sec. 19. Every act shall embrace but one subject and matters properly connected therewith; which subject shall be expressed in the title. But if any subject shall be embraced in an act which shall not be expressed in the title, such act shall be void only as to so much thereof as shall not be expressed in the title.

Sec. 20. Every act and joint resolution shall be plainly worded, avoiding, as far as practicable, the use of technical terms.

Sec. 21. No act shall ever be revised or amended by mere reference to its title; but the act revised, or section amended, shall be set forth and published at full length.

Sec. 22. The General Assembly shall not pass local or special laws, in any of the following enumerated cases, that is to say:

Regulating the jurisdiction and duties of justices of the peace and of constables;

For the punishment of crimes and misdemeanors;

Regulating the practice in courts of justice;

Providing for changing the venue in civil and criminal cases;

Granting divorces;

Changing the names of persons;

For laying out, opening and working on, highways, and for the election or appointment of supervisors;

Vacating roads, town plats, streets, alleys, and public squares;

Summoning and empanneling grand and petit juries, and providing for their compensation;

Regulating the election of county and township officers, and their compensation;

For the assessment and collection of taxes for State, county, township, or road purposes;

Providing for supporting common schools, and the preservation of school funds;

In relation to fees or salaries;

In relation to interest on money;

Providing for opening and conducting elections of State, county, or township officers, and designating the places of voting;

Providing for the sale of real estate belonging to minors or other persons laboring under legal disabilities, by executors, administrators, guardians, or trustees.

Sec. 23. In all the cases enumerated in the preceding section, and in all other cases where a general law can be made applicable, all laws shall be general, and of uniform operation throughout the State.

Sec. 24. Provisions may be made, by general law, for bringing suit against the State, as to all liabilities originating after the adoption of this Constitution; but no special act authorizing such suit to be brought, or making compensation to any person claiming damages against the State, shall ever be passed.

Sec. 25. A majority of all the members elected to each house, shall be necessary to pass every bill or joint resolution; and all bills and joint resolutions so passed, shall be signed by the presiding officers of the respective houses.

Sec. 26. Any member of either house shall have the right to protest, and to have his protest, with his reasons for dissent, entered on the journal.

Sec. 27. Every statute shall be a public law, unless otherwise declared in the statute itself.

Sec. 28. No act shall take effect, until the same shall have been published and circulated in the several counties of this State, by authority, except in case of emergency; which emergency shall be declared in the preamble, or in the body of the law.

Sec. 29. The members of the General Assembly shall receive for their services, a compensation, to be fixed by law; but no increase of compensation shall take effect during the session at which such increase may be made. No session of the General Assembly, except the first under this Constitution, shall extend beyond the term of sixty-one days, nor any special session beyond the term of forty days.

Sec. 30. No Senator or Representative shall, during the term for which he may have been elected, be eligible to any office, the election to which is vested in the General Assembly; nor shall he be appointed to any civil office of profit, which shall have been created, or the emoluments of which have been increased, during such term; but this latter provision shall not be construed to apply to any office elective by the people.

ARTICLE V

EXECUTIVE.

SECTION 1. The executive power of the State shall be vested in a Governor. He shall hold his office during four years, and shall not be eligible more than four years in any period of eight years.

Sec. 2. There shall be a Lieutenant-Governor, who shall hold his office during four years.

Sec. 3. The Governor and Lieutenant-Governor shall be elected at the times and places of choosing members of the General Assembly.

Sec. 4. In voting for Governor and Lieutenant-Governor the electors shall designate for whom they vote as Governor, and for whom as Lieutenant-Governor. The returns of every election for Governor and Lieutenant-Governor shall be sealed up and transmitted to the seat of Government, directed to the Speaker of the House of Representatives, who shall open and publish them in the presence of both Houses of the General Assembly.

Sec. 5. The person, respectively, having the highest number of votes for Governor and Lieutenant-Governor, shall be elected; but in case two or more persons shall have an equal, and the highest, number of votes for either office, the General Assembly shall, by joint vote, forthwith proceed to elect one of the said persons Governor or Lieutenant, as the case may be.

Sec. 6. Contested elections for Governor or Lieutenant-Governor, shall be determined by the General Assembly, in such manner as may be prescribed by law.

Sec. 7. No person shall be eligible to the office of Governor or Lieutenant-Governor, who shall not have been five years a citizen of the United States, and also a resident of the

State of Indiana during the five years next preceding his election, nor shall any person be eligible to either of the said offices, who shall not have attained the age of thirty years.

Sec. 8. No member of Congress, or person holding any office under the United States or under this State, shall fill the office of Governor or Lieutenant-Governor.

Sec. 9. The official term of the Governor and Lieutenant-Governor shall commence on the second Monday of January, in the year one thousand eight hundred and fifty-three; and on the same day every fourth year thereafter.

Sec. 10. In case of the removal of the Governor from office, or of his death, resignation, or inability to discharge the duties of the office, the same shall devolve on the Lieutenant-Governor; and the General Assembly shall, by law, provide for the case of removal from office, death, resignation, or inability, both of the Governor and Lieutenant-Governor, declaring what officer shall then act as Governor; and such officer shall act accordingly, until the disability be removed, or a Governor be elected.

Sec. 11. Whenever the Lieutenant-Governor shall act as Governor, or shall be unable to attend as President of the Senate, the Senate shall elect one of its own members as President for the occasion.

Sec. 12. The Governor shall be commander-in-chief of the military and naval forces, and may call out such forces to execute the laws, or to suppress insurrection or to repel invasion.

Sec. 13. He shall from time to time, give to the General Assembly information touching the condition of the State, and recommend such measures as he shall judge to be expedient.

Sec. 14. Every bill which shall have passed the General Assembly, shall be presented to the Governor; if he approve, he shall sign it; but if not, he shall return it, with his objections, to the house in which it shall have originated; which house shall enter the objections, at large, upon its journals, and proceed to reconsider the bill. If, after such reconsideration, a majority of all the members elected to that house, shall agree to pass the bill, it shall be sent, with the Governor's objections, to the other house, by which it shall likewise be reconsidered; and, if approved by a majority of all the members elected to that house, it shall be a law. If any bill shall not be returned by the Governor within three days, Sundays excepted, after it shall have been presented to him, it shall be a law, without his signature, unless the general adjournment shall prevent its return ; in which case it shall be a law, unless the Governor, within five days next after such adjournment, shall file such bill, with his objections thereto, in the office of Secretary of State; who shall lay the same before the General Assembly, at its next session, in like manner as if it had been returned by the Governor. But no bill shall be presented to the Governor, within two days next previous to the final adjournment of the General Assembly.

Sec. 15. The Governor shall transact all necessary business with the officers of the government, and may require information, in writing, from the officers of the administrative department, upon any subject relating to the duties of their respective offices.

Sec. 16. He shall take care that the laws be faithfully executed.

Sec. 17. He shall have the power to grant reprieves, commutations, and pardons, after conviction, for all offenses, except treason and cases of impeachment, subject to such regulations as may be provided by law. Upon conviction for treason, he shall have power to suspend the execution of the sentence, until the case shall be reported to the General Assembly, at its next meeting; when the General Assembly shall either grant a pardon, commute the sentence, direct the execution of a sentence, or grant a further reprieve. He shall have power to remit fines and forfeitures, under such regulations as may be prescribed by law; and shall report to the General Assembly, at its next meeting, each case of reprieve, commutation, or pardon granted, and also the names of all persons in whose favor remission of fines and forfeitures shall have been made, and the several amounts remitted: *Provided, however,* that the General Assembly may, by law, constitute a council, to be composed of officers of State, without whose advice and consent the Governor shall not have power to grant pardons, in any case, except such as may, by law, be left to his sole power.

Sec. 18. When, during a recess of the General Assembly, a vacancy shall happen in any office, the appointment to which is vested in the General Assembly; or when, at any time, a vacancy shall have occurred in any other State office, or in the office of judge of any court; the Governor shall fill such vacancy by appointment, which shall expire when a successor shall have been elected and qualified.

Sec. 19. He shall issue writs of election, to fill such vacancies as may have occurred in the General Assembly.

Sec. 20. Should the seat of government become dangerous from disease, or a common enemy, he may convene the General Assembly at any other place.

Sec. 21. The Lieutenant Governor shall, by virtue of his office, be President of the Senate; have a right, when in committee of the whole, to join in debate, and to vote on all subjects; and, whenever the Senate shall be equally divided, he shall give the casting vote.

Sec. 22. The Governor shall, at stated times, receive for his services a compensation, which shall neither be increased nor diminished during the term for which he shall have been elected.

Sec. 23. The Lieutenant Governor, while he shall act as President of the Senate, shall receive for his services the same compensation as the Speaker of the House of Representatives; and any person acting as Governor, shall receive the compensation attached to the office of Governor.

Sec. 24. Neither the Governor nor the Lieutenant Governor shall be eligible to any other office, during the term for which he shall have been elected.

ARTICLE VI.

ADMINISTRATIVE.

Section 1. There shall be elected by the voters of the State an Auditor, a Treasurer of State, who shall, severally, hold their offices for two years. They shall perform such duties, as may be enjoined by law; and no person shall be eligible to either of said offices, more than four years in any period of six years.

Sec. 2. There shall be elected, in each county, by the voters thereof, at the time of holding general elections, a clerk of the circuit court, auditor, recorder, treasurer, sheriff, coroner, and surveyor. The clerk, auditor, and recorder shall continue in office four years; and no person shall be eligible to the office of clerk, recorder, or auditor, more than eight years, in any period of twelve years. The treasurer, sheirff, coroner, and surveyor, shall continue in office two years; and no person shall be eligible to the office of treasurer or sheriff more than four years in any period of six years.

Sec. 3. Such other county and township officers as may be necessary, shall be elected, or appointed, in such manner as may be prescribed by law.

Sec. 4. No person shall be elected, or appointed as a county officer, who shall not be an elector of the county; nor any one who shall not have been an inhabitant thereof during one year next preceding his appointment, if the county shall have been so long organized, but if the county shall not have been so long organized, then within the limits of the county or counties, out of which the same shall have been taken.

Sec. 5. The Governor, and the Secretary, Auditor, and Treasurer of State shall, severally, reside and keep the public records, books and papers, in any manner relating to their respective offices, at the seat of government.

Sec. 6. All county, township, and town officers shall reside within their respective counties, townships, and towns; and shall keep their respective offices at such places therein, and perform such duties, as may be directed by law.

Sec. 7. All State officers shall, for crime, incapacity, or negligence, be liable to be removed from office, either by impeachment by the House of Representatives, to be tried by the Senate, or by a joint resolution of the General Assembly; two-thirds of the members elected to each branch voting, in either case, therefor.

Sec. 8. All State, county, township, and town officers, may be impeached, or removed from office, in such manner as may be prescribed by law.

Sec. 9. Vacancies in county, township, and town offices shall be filled in such manner as may be prescribed by law.

Sec. 10. The General Assembly may confer upon the boards doing county business in the several counties, powers of a local administrative character.

ARTICLE VII.

JUDICIAL

SECTION 1. The Judicial power of the State shall be vested in a Supreme Court, in Circuit Courts, and in such inferior Courts as the General Assembly may establish.

Sec. 2. The Supreme Court shall consist of not less than three, nor more than five Judges; a majority of whom shall form a quorum. They shall hold their offices for six years, if they so long behave well.

Sec. 3. The State shall be divided into as many districts as there are judges of the Supreme Court; and such districts shall be formed of contiguous territory, as nearly equal in population, as, without dividing a county, the same can be made. One of said judges shall be elected from each district, and reside therein; but said judge shall be elected by the electors of the State at large.

Sec. 4. The Supreme Court shall have jurisdiction, co-extensive with the limits of the State, in appeals and writs of error, under such regulations and restrictions as may be prescribed by law. It shall also have such original jurisdiction as the General Assembly may confer.

Sec. 5. The Supreme Court shall, upon the decision of every case, give a statement in writing of each question arising in the record of such case, and the dicision of the court thereon.

Sec. 6. The General Assembly shall provide, by law, for the speedy publication of the decisions of the Supreme Court, made under this Constitution; but no judge shall be allowed to report such decisions.

Sec. 7. There shall be elected by the voters of the State, a Clerk of the Supreme Court, who shall hold his office four years, and whose duties shall be prescribed by law.

Sec. 8. The circuit courts shall each consist of one judge, and shall have such civil and criminal jurisdiction as may be prescribed by law.

Sec. 9. The State shall from time to time. be divided into judicial circuits; and a judge for each circuit shall be elected by the voters thereof. He shall reside within the circuit, and shall hold his office for the term of six years, if he so long behave well.

Sec. 10. The General Assembly may provide by law, that the judge of one circuit may hold the courts of another circuit, in cases of necessity or convenience; and in case of temporary inability of any judge, from sickness or other cause, to hold the courts in his circuit, provision may be made, by law, for holding such courts.

Sec. 11. There shall be elected in each judicial circuit, by the voters thereof, a prosecuting attorney, who shall hold his office for two years.

Sec. 12. Any judge or prosecuting attorney, who shall have been convicted of corruption or other high crime, may, on information in the name of the State, be removed from office by the Supreme Court, or in such other manner as may be prescribed by law.

Sec. 13. The judges of the Supreme Court and circuit courts shall, at stated times, receive a compensation, which shall not be diminished during their continuance in office.

Sec. 14. A conpetent number of justices of the peace shall be elected, by the voters in each township in the several counties. They shall continue in office four years, and their powers and duties shall be prescribed by law.

Sec. 15. All judicial officers shall be conservators of the peace in their respective jurisdictions.

Sec. 16. No person elected to any judicial office, shall, during the term for which he shall have been elected, be eligible to any office of trust or profit, under the State, other than a judicial office.

Sec. 17. The General Assembly may modify, or abolish, the grand jury system.

Sec. 18. All criminal prosecutions shall be carried on in the name, and by the authority of the State; and the style of all process shall be: "The State of Indiana."

Sec. 19. Tribunals of conciliation may be established, with such powers and duties as shall be prescribed by law; or the powers and duties of the same may be conferred upon other courts of justice; but such tribunals or other courts, when sitting as such, shall have no power to render judgment to be obligatory on the parties, unless they voluntarily submit their matters of difference, and agree to abide the judgment of such tribunal or court.

Sec. 20. The General Assembly, at its first session after the adoption of this Constitution, shall provide for the appointment of three commissioners, whose duty it shall be to revise, simplify, and abridge the rules, practice, pleadings, and forms of the courts of justice. And they shall provide for abolishing the distinct forms of action at law, now in use, and that justice shall be administered in a uniform mode of pleading, without distinction between law and equity. And the General Assembly may, also, make it the duty of said commissioners to reduce into a systematic code, the general statute law of the State; and said commissioners shall report the result of their labors to the General Assembly, with such recommendations and suggestions, as to abridgment and amendment, as to said commissioners, may seem necessary or proper. Provision shall be made, by law, for filling vacancies, regulating the tenure of office and the compensation of said commissioners.

Sec. 21. Every person of good moral character, being a voter, shall be entitled to admission to practice law in all courts of justice.

ARTICLE VIII.

EDUCATION.

SECTION 1. Knowledge and learning, generally diffused throughout a community, being essential to the preservation of a free government, it shall be the duty of the General Assembly to encourage, by all suitable means, moral intellectual, scientific, and agricultural improvement; to provide, by law, for a general and uniform system of common schools, wherein tuition shall be without charge, and equally open to all.

Sec. 2. The common school fund shall consist of the congressional township fund, and the lands belonging thereto;

The surplus revenue fund;

The saline fund and the lands belonging thereto;

The bank tax fund, and the funds arising from the one hundred and fourteenth section of the charter of the State Bank of Indiana;

The fund to be derived from the sale of county seminaries, and the moneys and property heretofore held for such seminaries; from the fines assessed for breaches of the penal laws of the State; and from all forfeitures which may accrue;

All lands and other estate which shall escheat to the State, for want of heirs or kindred entitled to the inheritance;

All lands that have been, or may hereafter be, granted to the State, where no special purpose is expressed in the grant, and the proceeds of the sales thereof; including the proceeds of the sales of the Swamp Lands, granted to the State of Indiana by the act of Congress of the 28th of September, 1850, after deducting the expenses of selecting and draining the same;

Taxes on the property of corporations, that may be assessed by the General Assembly for common school purposes.

Sec. 3. The principal of the common school fund shall remain a perpetual fund, which may be increased, but shall never be diminished; and the income thereof shall be inviolably appropriated to the support of common schools, and to no other purpose whatever.

Sec. 4. The General Assembly shall invest, in some safe and profitable manner, all such portions of the common school fund as have not heretofore been entrusted to the several counties; and shall make provision, by law, for the distribution among the several counties of the interest thereof.

Sec. 5. If any county shall fail to demand its proportion of such interest for common school purposes, the same shall be reinvested for the benefit of such county.

Sec. 6. The several counties shall be held liable for the preservation of so much of the said fund as may be intrusted to them, and for the payment of the annual interest thereon.

Sec. 7. All trust funds held by the State shall remain inviolate, and be faithfully, and exclusively applied to the purpose for which the trust was created.

Sec. 8. The General Assembly shall provide for the election, by the voters of the State, of a State Superintendent of Public Instruction, who shall hold his office for two years, and whose duties and compensation shall be prescribed by law.

ARTICLE IX.

STATE INSTITUTIONS.

SECTION 1. It shall be the duty of the General Assembly to provide by law for the support of Institututions for the education of the Deaf and Dumb, and of the Blind; and also for the treatment of the Insane.

Sec. 2. The General Assembly shall provide Houses of Refuge for the correction and reformation of juvenile offenders.

Sec. 3. The county boards shall have power to provide farms, as an asylum for those persons who, by reason of age, infirmity or other misfortune, have claims upon the sympathies and aid of society.

ARTICLE X.

FINANCE.

Section 1. The General Assembly shall provide by law for a uniform and equal rate of assessment and taxation; and shall prescribe such regulations as shall secure a just valuation for taxation of all property, both real and personal, excepting such only for municipal, educational, literary, scientific, religious or charitable purposes, as may be specially exempted by law.

Sec. 2. All the revenues derived from the sale of any of the public works belonging to the State, and from the net annual income thereof, and any surplus that may at any time remain in the treasury, derived from taxation for general State purposes, after the payment of the ordinary expenses of the government, and of the interest on bonds of the State, other than bank bonds, shall be annually applied, under the direction of the General Assembly, to the payment of the principal of the public debt.

Sec. 3. No money shall be drawn from the treasury but in pursuance of appropriations made by law.

Sec. 4. An accurate statement of the receipts and expenditures of the public money, shall be published with the laws of each regular session of the General Assembly.

Sec. 5. No law shall authorize any debt to be contracted, on behalf of the State, except in the following cases: To meet casual deficits in the revenue; to pay the interest on the State Debt; to repel invasion, suppress insurrection, or if hostilities be threatened, provide for the public defense.

Sec. 6. No county shall subscribe for stock in any incorporated company, unless the same be paid for at the time of such subscription; nor shall any county loan its credit to any incorporated company, nor borrow money for the purpose of taking stock in any such company; nor shall the General Assembly ever, on behalf of the State, assume the debts of

any county, city, town, or township, nor of any corporation
whatever.

ARTICLE XI.

CORPORATIONS.

SECTION 1. The General Assembly shall not have power to
establish, or incorporate, any bank or banking company, or
moneyed institution, for the porpose of issuing bills of credit,
or bills payable to order or bearer, except under the conditions prescribed in this Constitution.

Sec. 2. No banks shall be established otherwise than under
a general banking law, except as provided in the fourth section of this article.

Sec. 3. If the General Assembly shall enact a general
banking law, such law shall provide for the registry and
countersigning, by an officer of State, of all paper credit designed to be circulated as money; and ample collateral security, readily convertible into specie, for the redemption of
the same in gold or silver, shall be required; which collateral
security shall be under the control of the proper officer or
officers of State.

Sec. 4. The General Assembly may also charter a bank
with branches, without collateral security, as required in the
preceding section.

Sec. 5. If the General Assembly shall establish a bank
with branches, the branches shall be mutually responsible
for each other's liabilities, upon all paper credit issued as
money.

Sec. 6. The stockholders in every bank, or banking company, shall be individually responsible to an amount over and
above their stock, equal to their respective shares of stock,
for all debts or liabilities of said bank or banking company.

Sec. 7. All bills or notes issued as money, shall be, at all
times, redeemable in gold or silver; and no law shall be
passed, sanctioning, directly or indirectly, the suspension, by
any bank or banking company, of specie payments.

Sec. 8. Holders of bank notes shall be entitled, in case of
insolvency, to preference of payment over all other creditors.

Sec. 9. No bank shall receive, directly or indirectly, a
greater rate of interest than shall be allowed, by law, to individuals loaning money.

Sec. 10. Every bank or banking company shall be required to cease all banking operations within twenty years from the time of its organization, and promptly thereafter to close its business.

Sec. 11. The General Assembly is not prohibited from investing the Trust Funds in a bank with branches; but in case of such investment, the safety of the same shall be guaranteed by unquestionable security.

Sec. 12. The State shall not be a stockholder in any bank after the expiration of the present bank charter; nor shall the credit of the State ever be given, or loaned, in aid of any person, association or corporation; nor shall the State hereafter become a stockholder in any corporation or association.

Sec. 13. Corporations, other than banking, shall not be created by special act, but may be formed under general laws.

Sec. 14. Dues from corporations, other than banking, shall be secured by such individual liability of the corporators, or other means, as may be prescribed by law.

ARTICLE XII.

MILITIA.

SECTION 1. The militia shall consist of all able-bodied white male persons, between the ages of eighteen and forty-five years, except such as may be exempted by the laws of the United States, or of this State; and shall be organized, officered, armed, equipped, and trained, in such manner as may be provided by law.

Sec. 2. The Governor shall appoint the Adjutant, Quartermaster and Commissary Generals.

Sec. 3. All militia officers shall be commissioned by the Governor, and shall hold their offices not longer than six years.

Sec. 4. The General Assembly shall determine the method of dividing the militia into divisions, brigades, regiments, batalions and companies, and fix the rank of all staff officers.

Sec. 5. The militia may be divided into classes of sedentary and active militia, in such manner as shall be prescribed by law.

Sec. 6. No person conscientiously opposed to bearing arms shall be compelled to do militia duty; but such person shall pay an equivalent for exemption; the amount to be prescribed by law.

ARTICLE XIII.

NEGROES AND MULATTOES.

Sec. 1. No Negro or Mulatto shall come into, or settle in, the State, after the adoption of this Constitution.

Sec. 2. All contracts made with any Negro or Mulatto coming into the State, contrary to the provisions of the foregoing section, shall be void; and any person who shall employ such Negro or Mulatto, or otherwise encourage him to remain in the State, shall be fined in any sum not less than ten dollars, nor more than five hundred dollars.

Sec. 3. All fines which may be collected for a violation of the provisions of this article, or of any law which may hereafter be passed for the purpose of carrying the same into execution, shall be set apart and appropriated for the colonization of such Negroes and Mulattoes, and their descendants, as may be in the State at the adoption of this Constitution, and may be willing to emigrate.

Sec. 4. The General Assembly shall pass laws to carry out the provisions of this article.

ARTICLE XIV.

BOUNDARIES

Section 1. In order that the boundaries of the State may be known and established, it is hereby ordained and declared, that the State of Indiana is bounded, on the east, by the meridian line which forms the western boundary of the State of Ohio; on the south, by the Ohio River, from the mouth of the Great Miami River to the mouth of the Wabash River; on the west, by a line drawn along the middle of the Wabash River, from its mouth to a point where a due north line, drawn from the town of Vincennes, would last touch the north-western shore of said Wabash River; and, thence, by a due north line, until the same shall intersect an east and west line, drawn through a point ten miles north of the southern extreme of Lake Michigan; on the north, by said east and west line, until the same shall intersect the first mentioned meridian line, which forms the western boundary of the State of Ohio.

Sec. 2. The State of Indiana shall possess jurisdiction and sovereignty co extensive with the boundaries declared in the preceding section; and shall have concurrent jurisdiction, in civil and criminal cases, with the State of Kentucky on the Ohio River, and with the State of Illinois on the Wabash River, so far as said rivers form the common boundary between this State and said States respectively.

ARTICLE XV.

MISCELLANEOUS.

SECTION 1. All officers whose appointment is not otherwise provided for in this Constitution, shall be chosen in such manner as now is, or hereafter may be, prescribed by law.

Sec. 2. When the duration of any office is not provided for by this Constitution, it may be declared by law ; and, if not so declored, such office shall be held during the pleasure of the authority making the appointment. But the General Assembly shall not create any office, the tenure of which shall be longer than four years.

Sec. 3. Whenever it is provided in this Constitution, or in any law which may be hereafter passed, that any officer other than a member of the General Assembly, shall hold his office for any given term, the same shall be construed to mean, that such officer shall hold his office for such term, and until his successor shall have been elected and qualified.

Sec. 4 Every person elected or appointed to any office under this Constitution shall, before entering on the duties thereof, take an oath or affirmation, to support the Constitution of this State, and of the United States, and also an oath of office.

Sec. 5. There shall be a seal of State kept by the Governor for official purposes, which shall be called the seal of the State of Indiana.

Sec. 6. All commissions shall issue in the name of the State, shall be signed by the Governor, sealed with the State seal, and attested by the Secretary of State.

Sec. 7. No county shall be reduced to an area less than four hundred square miles ; nor shall any county under that area be further reduced.

Sec. 8. No lottery shall be authorized ; nor shall the sale of lottery tickets be allowed.

Sec. 9. The following grounds, owned by the State in Indianapolis, namely : the State House Square, the Governor's

4

Circle, and so much of out-lot numbered one hundred and forty-seven, as lies north of the arm of the Central Canal, shall not be sold or leased.

Sec. 10. It shall be the duty of the General Assembly to provide for the permanent enclosure and preservation of the Tippecanoe Battle Ground.

ARTICLE XVI.

AMENDMENTS.

SECTION 1. Any amendment or amendments to this Constitution may be proposed in either branch of the General Assembly, and if the same shall be agreed to by a majority of the members elected to each of the two houses, such proposed amendment or amendments, shall with the yeas and nays thereon, be entered on their journals, and referred to the General Assembly to be chosen at the next general election; and if in the General Assembly so next chosen, such proposed amendment or amendments shall be agreed to by a majority of all the members elected to each house, then it shall be the duty of the General Assembly to submit such amendment or amendments to the electors of the State; and if a majority of said electors shall ratify the same, such amendment or amendments shall become a part of this Constitution.

Sec. 2. If two or more amendments shall be submitted at the same time, they shall be submitted in such manner that the electors shall vote for or against each of such amendments separately; and while an amendment or amendments which shall have been agreed upon by one General Assembly shall be awaiting the action of a succeeding General Assembly, or of the electors, no additional amendment or amendments shall be proposed.

SCHEDULE.

This Constitution, if adopted, shall take effect on the first day of November, in the year one thousand eight hundred and fifty-one, and shall supersede the Constitution adopted in the year one thousand eight hundred and sixteen. That no inconvenience may arise from the change in the government, it is hereby ordained as follows:—

First. All laws now in force, and not inconsistent with this

Constitution, shall remain in force, until they shall expire or be repealed.

Second. All indictments, prosecutions, suits, pleas, plaints, and other proceedings, pending in any of the Courts, shall be prosecuted to final judgment and execution; and all appeals, writs of error, certiorari, and injunctions, shall be carried on in the several Courts, in the same manner as is now provided by law.

Third. All fines, penalties, and forfeitures, due or accruing to the State, or to any county therein, shall inure to the State, or to such county, in the manner prescribed by law. All bonds executed to the State, or to any officer, in his official capacity, shall remain in force and inure to the use of those concerned.

Fourth. All acts of incorporation for municipal purposes shall continue in force under this Constitution, until such time as the General Assembly shall, in its discretion, modify or repeal the same.

Fifth. The Governor, at the expiration of the present official term, shall continue to act until his successor shall have been sworn into office.

Sixth. There shall be a session of the General Assembly, commencing on the first Monday of December, in the year one thousand eight hundred and fifty-one.

Seventh. Senators now in office and holding over, under the existing Constitution, and such as may be elected at the next general election, and the Representatives then elected, shall continue in office until the first general election under this Constitution.

Eighth. The first general election under this Constitution, shall be held in the year one thousand eight hundred and fifty-two.

Ninth. The first election for Governor, Lieutenant Governor, Judges of the Supreme Courts and Circuit Courts, Clerk of the Supreme Court, Prosecuting Attorney, Secretary, Auditor, and Treasurer of State, and State Superintendent of Public Instruction, under this Constitution, shall be held at the general election in the year one thousand eight hundred and fifty-two; and such of said officers as may be in office, when this Constitution shall go into effect, shall continue in their respective offices, until their successors shall have been elected and qualified.

Tenth. Every person elected by popular vote, and now in any office which is continued by this Constitution, and every person who shall be so elected to any such office before the taking effect of this Constitution, (except as in this Constitution otherwise provided,) shall continue in office until the term for which such person has been, or may be, elected, shall expire: *Provided*, That no such person shall continue in office after the taking effect of this Constitution, for a longer period than the term of such office in this Constitution prescribed.

Eleventh. On the taking effect of this Constitution, all officers thereby continued in office, shall, before proceeding in the further discharge of their duties, take an oath, or affirmation, to support this Constitution.

Twelfth. All vacancies that may occur in existing offices, prior to the first general election under this Constitution, shall be filled in the manner now prescribed by law.

Thirteenth. At the time of submitting this Constitution to the electors for their approval or disapproval, the article numbered thirteen, in relation to Negroes and Mulattoes, shall be submitted as a distinct proposition, in the following form: "Exclusion and Colonization of Negroes and Mulattoes," "Aye" or "No." And if a majority of the votes cast shall be in favor of said article, then the same shall form a part of this Constitution; otherwise, it shall be void. and form no part thereof.

Fourteenth. No Article or Section of this Constitution shall be submitted, as a distinct proposition, to a vote of the electors, otherwise than as herein provided.

Fifteenth. Whenever a portion of the citizens of the counties of Perry and Spencer shall deem it expedient to form, of the contiguous territory of said counties, a new county, it shall be the duty of those interested in the organization of such new county, to lay off the same by proper metes and bounds, of equal portions as nearly as practicable, not to exceed one-third of the territory of each of said counties. The proposal to create such new county shall be submitted to the voters of said counties, at a general election, in such manner as shall be prescribed by law. And if a majority of all the votes given at said election shall be in favor of the organization of said new county, it shall be the duty of the General Assembly to organize the same out of the territory thus designated.

Sixteenth. The General Assembly may alter or amend the charter of Clarksville, and make such regulations as may be necessary for carrying into effect the objects contemplated in granting the same; and the funds belonging to said town shall be applied according to the intention of the grantor.

Done in Convention, at Indianapolis, the tenth day of February, in the year of our Lord one thousand eight hundred and fifty-one ; and of the Independence of the United State, the seventy-fifth.

GEORGE WHITFIELD CARR,

President, and Delegate from the County of Lawrence.

Attest: Wm. H. English,

Principal Secretary.

George L. Sites,
Herman G. Barkwell,   } *Assistant Secretaries.*
Robert M. Evans,

EMANCIPATION PROCLAMATION.

————:o:————

Whereas, On the twenty-second day of September, in the year of our Lord, one thousand eight hundred and sixty-two, a proclamation was issued by the President of the United States, containing among other things the following, to-wit:

That, on the first day of January, in the year of our Lord, one thousand eight hundred and sixty-three, all persons held as slaves within any State, or designated part of a State, the people whereof shall then be in rebellion against the United States, shall be then, henceforth and forever free, and the Executive Government of the United States, including the military and naval authorities thereof, will recognize and maintain the freedom of such persons, or any of them, in any efforts they may make for their actual freedom.

That the Executive will, on the first day of January aforesaid, by proclamation, designate the States and parts of States, if any, in which the people therein respectively shall then be in rebellion against the United States, and the fact that any State, or the people thereof, shall on that day be in good faith represented in the Congress of the United States by members chosen thereto, at elections wherein a majority of the qualified voters of such States shall have participated, shall, in the absence of strong countervailing testimony, be deemed conclusive that such State and the people thereof are not then in rebellion against the United States.

Now, therefore, I, Abraham Lincoln, President of the United States, by virtue of the power in me vested as Commander-in-Chief of the Army and Navy of the United States, in time of actual armed rebellion against the authority and Government of the United States, and as a fit necessary war measure for suppressing said rebellion, do, on this first day of January, in the year of our Lord, one thousand eight hundred and sixty-three, and in accordance with my purpose so to do, publicly proclaimed for the full period of one hundred days

(54)

from the day of the first above mentioned order, and designate, as the States and parts of States wherein the people thereof respectively are this day in rebellion againt the United States, the following to wit: Arkansas, Texas, Louisiana, except the parishes of St. Bernard, Plaquemines, Jefferson, St. John, St. Charles, St. James, Ascension, Assumption, Terre Bonne, Lafourche, St. Mary, St. Martin and Orleans, including the city of New Orleans. Mississippi, Alabama, Florida, Georgia, South Carolina, North Carolina, and Virginia, except the forty-eight counties designated as West Virginia, and also the counties of Berkeley, Accomac, Northampton. Elizabeth City, York, Princess Ann, and Norfolk, including the cities of Norfolk and Portsmouth, and which excepted parts are, for the present, left precisely as if this proclamation were not issued.

And by virtue of the power, and for the purpose aforesaid, I do order and declare that all persons held as slaves within said designated States and parts of States are, and henceforward, shall be free; and that the Executive Government of the United States, including the military and naval authorities thereof, will recognize and maintain the freedom of said persons.

And I hereby enjoin upon the people so declared to be free to abstain from all violence, unless in necessary self-defense ; and I recommend to them that, in all cases, when allowed, they labor faithfully for reasonable wages.

And I further declare and make known that such persons of suitable condition will be received into the armed service of the United States, to garrison forts, positions, stations, and other places, and to man vessels of all sorts in said service.

And upon this, sincerely believed to be an act of justice, warranted by the Constitution upon military necessity, I invoke the considerate judgment of mankind and the gracious favor of Almighty God.

In witness whereof I have hereunto set my hand and caused the seal of the United States to be affixed.

Done at the City of Washington, this first day of January, in the year of our Lord one thousand eight hundred {SEAL} and sixty-three, and of the Independence of the United States of America the eighty-seventh.

By the President: ABRAHAM LINCOLN.

WILLIAM H. SEWARD, *Secretary of State.*

POLITICAL PLATFORMS.

————:o:————

PLATFORM OF THE BRECKINRIDGE PARTY OF 1860.

Resolved, That the platform adopted by the Democratic party at Cincinnati be affirmed, with the following explanatory resolutions:

1. That the government of a territory organized by an act of Congress is provisional and temporary, and during its existence all citizens of the United States have an equal right to settle with their property in the territory, without their rights, either in person or property, being destroyed by congressional or territorial legislation.

2. That it is the duty of the Federal Government, in all its departments, to protect the rights of persons and property in the territories, and wherever else its constitutional authority extends.

3. That when the settlers in a territory, having an adequate population, form a State Constitution, the right of sovereignty commences, and being consummated by their admission into the Union, they stand on an equality with the people of other States, and a State thus organized ought to be admitted into the Federal Union, whether its constitution prohibits or recognizes the institution of slavery.

4. That the Democratic party are in favor of the acquisition of Cuba, on such terms as shall be honorable to ourselves and just to Spain, at the earliest practicable moment.

5. That the enactments of State Legislatures to defeat the faithful execution of the Fugitive Slave Law are hostile in character, subversive of the Constitution, and revolutionary in their effect.

6. That the Democracy of the United States recognize it as an imperative duty of the government to protect the natural-

ized citizen in all his rights, whether in home or in foreign lands, to the same extent as its native born citizens.

WHEREAS, One of the greatest necessities of the age, in a political, commercial, postal, and military point of view, is a speedy communication between the Pacific and Atlantic coasts; therefore, be it resolved,

7. That the National Democratic party do hereby pledge themselves to use every means in their power to secure the passage of some bill, to the extent of the Constitutional authority by Congress, for the construction of a railroad to the Pacific Ocean at the earliest practicable moment.

PLATFORM OF THE DOUGLAS PARTY OF 1860.

Resolved, That we, the Democracy of the Union in Convention assembled, hereby declare our affirmation of the resolutions unanimously adopted and declared as a platform of principles by the Democratic Convention at Cincinnati, in the year 1856, believing that Democratic principles are unchangable in their nature when applied to the same subject matter, and we recommend as our only further resolutions the following:

That inasmuch as differences of opinion exist in the Democratic party as to the nature and extent of the powers of a Territorial Legislature, and as to the powers and duties of Congress, under the Constitution of the United States, over the institution of slavery in the territories;

Resolved, That the Democratic party will abide by the decision of the Supreme Court of the United States over the institution of slavery in the territories.

Resolved, That it is the duty of the United States to afford ample and complete protection to all its citizens, at home or abroad, and whether native or foreign born.

Resolved, That one of the necessities of the age, in a military, commercial, and postal point of view, is a speedy communication between the Atlantic and Pacific States, and the Democratic party pledge such constitutional enactment as will insure the construction of a railroad to the Pacific coast at the earliest practical period.

Resolved, That the Democratic party are in favor of the acquisition of the Island of Cuba, on such terms as shall be honorable to ourselves and just to Spain.

Resolved, That the enactments of State Legislatures to defeat the faithful execution of the Fugitive Slave Law are hostile in character, subversive to the Constitution, and revolutionary in their effect.

Resolved, That it is in accordance with the Cincinnati Platform, that during the existence of Territorial Governments, the measure of restriction, whatever it may be, imposed by the Federal Constitution on the power of the Territorial Legislature over the subject of the domestic relations, as the same has been or shall hereafter be decided by the Supreme Court of the United States, should be respected by all good citizens, and enforced with promptness and fidelity by every branch of the General Government.

THE REPUBLICAN PLATFORM OF 1860.

Resolved, That we, the delegated representatives of the Republican electors of the United States, in Convention assembled, in the discharge of the duty we owe to our constituents and our country, unite in the following resolutions:

1. That the history of the nation during the last four years has fully established the propriety and necessity of the organization and perpetuation of the Republican party, and that the causes which called it into existence are permanent in their nature, and now, more than ever, demand its peaceful and constitutional triumph.

2. That the maintenance of the principles promulgated in the Declaration of Independence, and embodied in the Federal Constitution, that "all men are created equal; that they are endowed by their Creator with certain inalienable rights, among which are those of life, liberty and the pursuit of happiness, and that Governments are instituted among men to secure the enjoyment of these rights, deriving their just power from the consent of the governed"—are essential to the preservation of our republican institutions, and that the Federal Constitution, the rights of the States, and the union of the States, must and shall be preserved.

3. That to the union of the States this nation owes its unpre-cedented increase in population, its surprising developments of material resources; its rapid augmentation of wealth; its happiness at home and its honor abroad; and we hold in abhorrence all schemes for disunion, come from whatever source they may; and we congratulate the country that no Republican member of Congress has uttered or countenanced the threats of disunion as often made by the Democratic mem-bers of Congress, without rebuke and with applause from their political associates; and we denounce those threats of disunion in case of a popular overthrow of their ascendency, as denying the vital principles of a free Government, and as an avowal of contemplated treason which it is the imperative duty of an indignant people sternly to rebuke and forever silence.

4. That the maintenance inviolate, of the rights of the States, and especially of each State, to order and control its own domestic institutions according to its own judgment ex-clusively, is essential to that balance of power on which the perfection and endurance of our political fabric depends; and we denounce the lawless invasion by armed force of the soil of any State or Territory, no matter under what pretext, as one of the gravest of crimes.

5. That the present Democratic Administration has far ex-ceeded our worst apprehensions in the measureless subserviency to the exactions of a sectional interest, as especially evinced in its desperate exertions to force the infamous Lecompton Constitution upon the protesting people of Kansas, construing the relation between master and servant to involve an unqual-ified property in persons; in its attempted enforcement every where, on land and sea, through the intervention of Congress and of the Federal Courts, of the extreme pretensions of a purely local interest; and in its general and unvarying abuse of the power entrusted to it by a confiding people.

6. That the people justly view with alarm the reckless ex-travagance which pervades every department of the Federal Government. That a return to right economy and accounta-bility is indispensible to arrest the plunder of the public treasury by favored partisans, while the recent startling devel-opments of frauds and corruption at the Federal metropolis show that an entire change of administration is imperatively demanded.

7. That the new dogma that the Constitution of its own force carries slavery into any or all the Territories of the United States, is a dangerous political heresy, at variance with the explicit provisions of that instrument itself, with cotemporaneous exposition, and with legislative and judicial precedents, that it is revolutionary in its tendency and subversive of the peace and harmony of the country.

8. That the nominal condition of all the territory of the United States is that of freedom; that as our Republican fathers, when they had abolished slavery in all our national territory, ordained that no person should be deprived of life, liberty or property without due process of law, it becomes our duty by legislation, whenever such legislation is necessary, to maintain this provision of the Constitution against all attempts to violate it; and we deny the authority of Congress, or a Territorial Legislature, or of any individual, to give legal existence to slavery in any Territory of the United States.

9. That we brand the recent re-opening of the African Slave Trade, under the cover of our national flag, aided by perversions of judicial power, as a crime against humanity, and a burning shame to our country and age; and we call upon Congress to take prompt and efficient measures for the total and final suppression of that exercrable traffic.

10. That in the recent vetoes by their Federal Governors of the acts of the Legislatures of Kansas and Nebraska, prohibiting slavery in these Territories, we find a practical illustration of the boasted Democratic principles of non-intervention and Popular Sovereignty, embodied in the Kansas-Nebraska bill, and a demonstration of the deception and fraud involved therein.

11. That Kansas should, of right, be immediately admitted as a State under the Constitution recently formed and adopted by her people, and accepted by the House of Representatives.

12. That while providing revenue for the support of the General Government, by duties upon imports, sound policy requires such an adjustment of these imports as to encourage the development of the industrial interests of the whole country, and we commend that policy of National Exchange which secures to the working men liberal wages, agriculture remunerative prices, to merchants and manufacturers an ade-

quate reward for their skill, labor and enterprise, and to the nation commercial prosperity and independence.

13. That we protest against any sale or alienation to others of the public lands held by actual settlers, and against any view of the free homestead policy, which regards the settlers as paupers or suppliants for public bounty, and we demand the passage by Congress of the complete and satisfactory homestead measure which has already passed the House.

14. That the National Republican party is opposed to any change in our naturalization laws, or any State Legislation, by which the rights of citizenship hitherto accorded to immigrants from foreign lands shall be abridged or impaired, and in favor of giving a full and efficient protection to the rights of all classes of citizens, whether native or naturalized, both at home and abroad.

15. That appropriations by Congress for river and harbor improvements of a national character, is required for the accommodation and security of an existing commerce, or authorized by the Constitution and justified by the obligation of the Government to protect the lives and property of its citizens.

16. That a railroad to the Pacific ocean is imperatively demanded by the interests of the whole country; and that the Federal Government ought to render immediate and efficient aid in its construction, and that preliminary thereto, a daily overland mail should be promptly established.

17. Finally, having thus set forth our distinctive principles and views, we invite the co-operation of all citizens, however differing in other questions, who substantially agree with us, in their affirmance and support.

PLATFORM OF THE NATIONAL CONSTITUTIONAL PARTY OF 1860.

The Union, the Constitution and the Laws.

UNION PLATFORM, ADOPTED AT BALTIMORE, JUNE 8, 1864.

Resolved, That it is the highest duty of every American citizen to maintain against all its enemies, the integrity of the Union, and the paramount authority of the Constitution and laws of the United States, and that, laying all political opinions aside, we pledge ourselves, as Union men, animated by a common sentiment, and aiming at a common object, to do everything in our power to aid the Government in quelling, by force of arms, the rebellion now raging against its authority, and bringing to the punishment due to their crimes, the rebels and traitors arrayed against it.

Resolved, That we approve the determination of the Government of the United States not to compromise with rebels or to offer any terms of peace, except such as may be based upon an unconditional surrender of their hostility, &c., and a return to their just allegiance to the Constitution and laws of the United States, and that we call upon the Government to maintain this position, and to prosecute the war with the utmost possible vigor to the complete suppression of the rebellion, in full reliance upon the self-sacrifices, the patriotism, the heroic valor, and the undying devotion of the American people to their country and its free institutions.

Resolved, That slavery was the cause, and now constitutes the strength of the rebellion. and that as it must be always and everywhere hostile to the principles of Republican Governments, justice and the national safety demand its utter and complete extirpation from the soil of the Republic, and that we uphold and maintain the acts and proclamations by which the Government, in its own defence, has aimed a death blow at this gigantic evil. We are in favor, furthermore, of such an amendment to the Constitution, to be made by the people in conformity with its provisions, as shall terminate and forever prohibit the existence of slavery within the limits of the jurisdiction of the United States.

Resolved, That the thanks of the American people are due to the soldiers and sailors of the army and navy, who have periled their lives in defence of their country, and in vindication of the honor of the flag; that the nation owes them some permanent recognition of their patriotism and their valor, and ample and permanent provision for those of their survivors who have received disabling and honorable wounds in the service of their country, and that the memories of those who have fallen in its defense, shall be held in grateful and everlasting remembrance.

Resolved, That we approve and applaud the political wisdom, the unselfish patriotism and unswerving fidelity to the Constitution and the principles of American liberty with which Abraham Lincoln has discharged, under circumstances of unparalelled difficuly, the great duties and responsibilities of the Presidential office; that we approve and endorse, as demanded by the emergency and essential to the preservation of the nation, and as within the Constitution, the measures and acts which he has adopted to defend the nation against its open and secret foes; especially the Proclamation of Emancipation, and the employment, as Union soldiers, of men heretofore held in slavery, and that we have full confidence in his determination to carry these and all other Constitutional measures, essential to the salvation of the country, into full and complete effect.

Resolved, That we deem it essential to the general welfare, that harmony should prevail in the national councils, and we regard as worthy of public confidence and official trust those only who cordially endorse the principles proclaimed in these resolutions, and which should characterize the administration of the Government.

Resolved, That the Government owes to all men employed in its armies, without distinction of color, the full protection of the laws of war, and any violation of these laws and of the usages of civilized nations in the time of war, by the rebels now in arms, should be made the subject of full and prompt redress.

Resolved, That the foreign immigration, which in the past has added so much to the wealth and development of resources and increase of power to this nation, the asylum of the oppressed of all nations, should be fostered and encouraged by a liberal and just policy.

Resolved, That we are in favor of the speedy construction of the railroad to the Pacific.

Resolved, That the national faith is pledged for the redemption of the public debt and must be kept inviolate; and that for this purpose we recommend economy and rigid responsibilities in the public expenditures, and a vigorous and just system of taxation; that it is the duty of every loyal State to sustain the use of the national currency.

Resolved, That we approve the position taken by the Government, that the people of the United States can never regard with indifference the attempt of European power to overthrow by force, or to supplant by fraud, the institutions of any Republican government on the Western Continent, and that they will view with extreme jealousy, as menacing to the peace and independence of this our country, the efforts of any such power to obtain new footholds for monarchial governments sustained by a foreign military force in near proximity to the United States.

FREMONT PLATFORM, ADOPTED AT CLEVELAND, MAY 31, 1864.

1. That the Federal Union must be preserved.

2. That the Constitution and laws of the United States must be observed and obeyed.

3. That the rebellion must be suppressed by the force of arms, and without compromise.

4. That the rights of Free Speech, Free Press, and the Habeas Corpus must be held inviolate, save in districts where martial law has been proclaimed.

5. That the rebellion has destroyed slavery, and the Federal Constitution should be amended to prohibit its re-establishment.

6. That the right for asylum, except for crime, and subject to law, is a recognized principle—a principle of American liberty; that any violation of it must not be overlooked, and must not go unrebuked.

7. That the National policy known as the Monroe doctrine has become a recognized principle, and that the establishment of an anti-republican form of government on this continent by a foreign power can not be tolerated.

8. That the gratitude and support of the nation is due to the faithful soldiers, and the earnest leaders of the Union army and navy, for their heroic achievements and valor in defense of our imperiled country and of civil liberty.

9. That the one term policy for the Presidency adopted by

the people is strengthened by the existing crisis, and shall be maintained by constitutional amendments.

10. That the Constitution shall be so amended that the President and Vice President shall be elected by a direct vote of the people.

11. That the reconstruction of the rebellious States belongs to the people through their representatives in Congress, and not to the Executive.

12. That the confiscation of the lands of the rebels and their distribution among the soldiers and actual settlers is a measure of justice ; that integrity and economy are demanded at all times in the measures of the government, and that now the want of this is criminal.

NATIONAL DEMOCRATIC PLATFORM OF 1864.

Resolved, That in the future, as in the past, we will adhere with unswerving fidelity to the Union under the Constitution as the only solid foundation of our strength, security and happiness as a people, and as a framework of government equally conducive to the welfare and prosperity of all the States, both Northern and Southern.

Resolved, That this Convention does explicitly declare, as the sense of the American people, that after four years of failure to restore the Union by experiment of war, during which, under the pretence of military necessity or war power higher than the Constitution, the Constitution itself has been disregarded in every part, and public liberty and private right alike trodden down, and the material prosperity of the country essentially impaired, justice, humanity, liberty and the public welfare demand that immediate efforts be made for a cessation of hostilities with a view to an ultimate convention of the States, or other peaceable means, to the end that at the earliest practical moment peace may be restored on the basis of the Federal Union of the States.

Resolved, That the direct interference of the military authorities of the United States in the recent elections held in Kentucky, Maryland, Missouri and Delaware was a shameful

5

violation of the Constitution, and a repetition of such acts in the approaching election will be held as revolutionary, and resisted with all the means and power under our control.

Resolved, That the aim and object of the Democratic party is to preserve the Federal Union and the rights of the States unimpaired, and they hereby declare that they consider that the administrative usurpation of extraordinary and dangerous powers not granted by the Constitution, the subversion of the civil by military law in States not in insurrection, the arbitrary military arrest, imprisonment, trial and sentence of American citizens in States where the civil law exists in full force, the suppression of freedom of speech and of the press, the denial of the right of asylum, the open and avowed right of disregard of State rights, the employment of unusual test oaths, and the interference with, and denial of the right of the people to bear arms in their defense, is calculated to prevent a restoration of the Union and a perpetuation of the Government deriving its just powers from the consent of the governed.

Resolved, That the shameful disregard of the Administration to its duty in respect to our fellow-citizens who now are, and long have been, prisoners of war in a suffering condition, deserves the severest reprobation on the score alike of public policy and common humanity.

Resolved, That the sympathy of the Democratic party is heartily and earnestly extended to the soldiery of our army and sailors of our navy who are and have been in the field and on the sea, under the flag of their country, and in the event of its attaining power, they will receive all the care, protection and regard that the brave soldiers and sailors of the Republic have so nobly earned.

THE CHICAGO PLATFORM, 1868.

The following is the platform as adopted:

The National Republican Party of the United States, assembled in National Convention, in the city of Chicago, on the 20th day of May, 1868, make the following declaration of principles:

1. We congratulate the country on the assured success of

the reconstruction policy of Congress, as evinced by the adoption, in the majority of the States lately in rebellion, of constitutions securing equal civil and political rights to all; and it is the duty of the Government to sustain those constitutions and to prevent the people of such States from being remitted to a state of anarchy.

2. The guarantee by Congress of equal suffrage to all loyal men at the South was demanded by every consideration of public safety, of gratitude, and of justice, and must be maintained, while the question of suffrage in all the loyal States properly belongs to the people of those States.

3. We denounce all forms of repudiation as a national crime, and the national honor requires the payment of the public indebtedness in the utmost good faith to all creditors at home and abroad, not only according to the letter but the spirit of the laws under which it was contracted.

4. It is due to the labor of the nation that taxation should be equalized and reduced as rapidly as the national faith will permit.

5. The national debt, contracted as it has been for the preservation of the Union for all time to come, should be extended over a fair period for redemption; and it is the duty of Congress to reduce the rate of interest thereon whenever it can be honestly done.

6. That the best policy to diminish our burden of debt is to so improve our credit that capitalists will seek to loan us money at lower rates of interest than we now pay, and must continue to pay, so long as repudiation, partial or total, open or covert, is threatened or suspected.

7. The Government of the United States should be administered with the strictest economy, and the corruptions which have been so shamefully nursed and fostered by ANDREW JOHNSON call loudly for radical reform.

8. We professedly deplore the untimely and tragic death of ABRAHAM LINCOLN, and regret the accession of ANDREW JOHNSON to the Presidency, who has acted treacherously to the people who elected him, and the cause he was pledged to support—who has usurped high legislative and judicial functions—who has refused to execute the laws—who has used his high office to induce other officers to ignore and violate the laws—who has employed his executive powers to render inse-

cure the property, the peace, liberty, and life of the citizen—who has abused the pardoning power—who has denounced the National Legislature as unconstitutional—persistently and corruptly resisted, by every measure in his power, every proper attempt at the reconstruction of the States lately in rebellion—who has perverted the public patronage into an engine of wholesale corruption, and who has been justly impeached for high crimes and misdemeanors, and properly pronounced guilty thereof by the vote of thirty-five Senators.

9. The doctrine of Great Britain and other European Powers, that because a man is once a subject he is always so, must be resisted at every hazard by the United States as a relic of the feudal times, not authorized by the law of nations, and at war with our national honor and independence. Naturalized citizens are entitled to be protected in all their rights of citizenship as though they were native born; and no citizen of the United States, native or naturalized, must be liable to arrest and imprisonment by any foreign power for acts done or words spoken in this country; and if so arrested and imprisoned it is the duty of the Government to interfere in his behalf.

10. Of all who were faithful in the trials of the late war there were none entitled to more especial honor than the brave soldiers and seamen who endured the hardships of campaign and cruise, and imperiled their lives in the service of the country. The bounties and pensions provided by the laws for these brave defenders of the nation are obligations never to be forgotten. The widows and orphans of the gallant dead are the wards of the people, a sacred legacy bequeathed to the nation's protecting care.

11. Foreign emigration, which in the past has added so much to the wealth, development, and resources and increase of power to this nation, the asylum of the oppressed of all nations, should be fostered and encouraged by a liberal and just policy.

12. This Convention declares itself in sympathy with all the oppressed people which are struggling for their rights.

The following resolutions were also adopted unanimously, and are added to the declaration of principles:

Resolved, That we highly commend the spirit of magnanimity and forgiveness with which the men who have served in the rebellion, but now frankly and honestly co-operate with us in restoring the peace of the country and reconstructing the Southern State governments upon the basis of impartial justice and equal rights, are received back into the communion of the loyal people. And we favor the removal of the disqualifications and restrictions placed upon the late rebels in the same measure as the spirit of loyalty will direct, and as may be consistent with the safety of the loyal people.

Resolved, That we recognize the great principles laid down in the immortal Declaration of Independence as the true foundation of Democratic government; and we hail with gladness every effort toward making these principles a living reality on every inch of American soil.

DEMOCRATIC PLATFORM OF 1868.

The Democratic party, in National Convention assembled, reposing its trust in the intelligence, patriotism, and discriminating justice of the people, standing upon the Constitution as the foundation and limitation of the powers of the Government and the guarantee of the liberties of the citizen, and recognizing the questions of slavery and secession as having been settled for all time to come by the war or the voluntary action of the Southern States in Constitutional Conventions assembled, and never to be revived or re-agitated, do, with the return of peace, demand:

1. The immediate restoration of all the States to their rights in the Union under the Constitution of the civil Government and in the American people.

2. Amnesty for all past political offenses; the regulation of the elective franchise in the States by their citizens.

3. Payment of the public debt of the United States as rapidly as practicable, all money drawn from the people by taxation, except so much as is requisite for the necessities of the Government economically administered being honestly applied to such payment, and where the obligations of the Government do not expressly state upon their face or the law under which they were issued does not provide that they shall be paid in coin they ought, in right and justice, be paid in the lawful money of the United States.

4. Equal taxation of every species of property according to the value; reducing Government bonds and other public securities.

5. One currency for the Government and the people, the laborer and the office-holder, pensioner and the soldier, the producer and the bondholder.

6. Economy in the administration of the Government; the reduction of the standing army and navy; the abolition of the Freedmen's Bureau, and all political instrumentalities designed to secure negro supremacy; simplification of the system and discontinuance of inquisitorial modes of assessing and collecting internal revenue, that the burden of taxation may be equalized and lessened, and the credit of the Government and the currency made good; the repeal of all enactments for enrolling the State militia into a national force in time of peace; and a tariff for revenue upon foreign imports and such equal taxation under the internal revenue laws as will afford incidental protection to domestic manufactures as well, without impairing the revenue, impose the least burden upon and best promote and encourage the great industrial interests of the country.

7. Reform of abuses in the Administration; the expulsion of corrupt men from office; the abrogation of useless offices; the restoration of the rightful authority to and the independence of the Executive and Judicial Departments of the Government; the subordination of the military to the civil power, to the end that the usurpation of Congress and the despotism of the sword may cease.

8. Equal rights and protection for naturalized and native born citizens at home and abroad; the assertion of American nationality, which will command the respect of foreign powers furnish an example and encouragement to people struggling for national integrity, constitutional liberty, and individual rights; and the maintenance of the rights of naturalized citizens against the absolute doctrine of immutable allegiance and the claims of foreign powers to punish them for alleged crimes committed beyond their jurisdiction. In demanding these measures and reforms, we arraign the radical party for its disregard of right and the unparalleled oppression and tyranny which have marked its career, after the most solemn and unanimous pledge of both houses of Congress to prose-

cute the war exclusively for the maintenance of the Government and the preservation of the Union under the Constitution. It has repeatedly violated that most sacred pledge under which was rallied that noble volunteer army which carried our flag to victory. Instead of restoring the Union it has, so far as it is in its power, dissolved it, and subjected ten States in time of peace to military despotism and negro supremacy. It has nullified there the right of trial by jury ; it has abolished the writ of habeas corpus, that most sacred writ of liberty ; it has overthrown the freedom of speech and of the press ; it has substituted arbitrary seizures and arrests, military trials, secret star chambers, and inquisitions for constitutional tribunals; it has disregarded, in time of peace, the right of the people to be free from search and seizure ; it has entered the post-office and telegraph office, and even the private rooms of individuals and seized there their private papers and letters, without any specification or notice of affidavit, as required by the organic law. It has converted the American Capitol into a bastile; it has established a system of spies and official espionage to which the constitutional monarchies of Europe never dare to resort. It has abolished the right of appeal on important constitutional questions to the supreme judicial tribunals, and threatens to curtail or destroy its original jurisdiction, which is irrevocably vested by the Constitution : while the learned Chief Justice has been subjected to the most atrocious calumnies merely because he would not prostitute his high office to the support of the false and partisan charges against the President. Its corruption and extravagance have exceeded anything known in history, and by its frauds and monopolies it has nearly doubled the burden of the debt created during the war. It has stripped the President of his Constitutional power of appointment even of his own Cabinet. Under its repeated assaults the pillars of the Government are rocking to their base; and should it succeed in November next, and inaugurate its President, we will meet as a subjected and conquered people amid the ruins of liberty and the scattered fragments of the Constitution; and we do declare and resolve that ever since the people of the United States threw off all subjection to the British crown, the privilege and trust of suffrage have belonged to the several States, and have been granted, regulated, and controlled exclusively by the political power of each State respectively, and any attempt by Congress, on any pretext whatever, to deprive any State of this right, or interfere with this exercise, is a flagrant usurpation of power which can find no warrant in the Constitution, and if sanctioned by the people will subvert our form of Government, and can only end in a single, centralized and consolidated Government, in which the separate existence of the States will be entirely absorbed, and an unqualified despotism then be established in place of a Federal Union of coequal States, and that we regard the reconstruction acts so called of Congress such usurpations and unconstitutional, revolutionary and void; that our soldiers and sailors who carried the flag of our country to victory against a most gallant and determined foe must ever be gratefully remembered, and all the guarantees given in their favor must be faithfully carried into execution; that the public lands should be distributed widely among the people and should be disposed of either under the pre-emption of the homestead lands and sold in reasonable quantities, and to none but actual occupants, at the price established by the Government. When the grants of the public lands may be allowed necessary for the encouragement of important public improvements, the proceeds of the sale of such lands, and not the lands themselves, should be so applied; that the President of the United States, Andrew Johnson, exercising the power of his high office in resisting the aggressions of Congress on the constitutional rights of the States and the people, is entitled to the gratitude of the whole American people, and on behalf of the Democratic party, we tender him our thanks for his patriotic efforts in that regard.

Upon this platform the Democratic party appeal to every patriot, including all the conservative element, and all who desire to support the Constitution and restore the Union, forgetting all past differences of opinion, to unite with us in the present great struggle for the liberties of the people; and that to all such, to whatever party they may have heretofore belonged, we extend the right hand of fellowship, and hail all such co-operating with us as friends and brothers.

REPUBLICAN PLATFORM, 1872.

The Republican party of the United States, assembled in national convention in the city of Philadelphia on the 5th and 6th days of June, 1872, again declares its faith, appeals to its history, and announces its position upon the questions before the country:

1. During eleven years of supremacy it has accepted with grand courage the solemn duties of the time. It suppressed a gigantic rebellion, emancipated four millions of slaves, decreed the equal citizenship of all, and established universal suffrage. Exhibiting unparalelled magnanimity, it criminally punished no man for political offenses, and warmly welcomed all who proved loyalty by obeying the laws and dealing justly with their neighbors. It has steadily decreased with firm hand the resultant disorders of a great war, and initiated a wise and humane policy toward the Indians. The Pacific railroad and similar vast enterprises have been generously aided and successfully conducted, the public lands freely given to actual settlers, immigration protected and encouraged, and a full acknowledgement of the naturalized citizen's rights secured from European Powers. A uniform national currency has been provided, repudiation frowned down, the national credit sustained under the most extraordinary burdens, and new bonds negotiated at lower rates. The revenues have been carefully collected and honestly applied. Despite annual large reductions of the rates of taxation, the public debt has been reduced during General Grant's Presidency at the rate of a hundred millions a year, great financial crises have been avoided, and peace and plenty prevail throughout the land. Menacing foreign difficulties have been peacefully and honorably composed, and the honor and power of the nation kept in high respect throughout the world. This glorious record of the past is the party's best pledge for the future. We believe the people will not intrust the Government to any party or combination of men composed chiefly of those who have resisted every step of this benificent progress.

2. The recent amendments to the national Constitution should be cordially sustained because they are right, not

merely tolerated because they are law, and should be carried
out according to their spirit by appropriate legislation, the
enforcement of which can safely be intrusted only to the
party that secured those amendments.

3.   Complete liberty and exact equality in the enjoyment
of all civil, political and public rights should be established
and effectually maintained throughout the Union by efficient
and appropriate State and Federal legislation.   Neither the
law nor its administration should admit any discrimination in
respect of citizens by reason of race, creed, color, or previous
condition of servitude.

4.   The national Government should seek to maintain honorable peace with all nation, protecting its citizens everywhere and sympathizing with all peoples who strive for greater
liberty.

5.   Any system of the civil service under which the subor-
dinate positions of the government are considered rewards for
mere party zeal is fatally demoralizing, and we therefore favor
a reform of the system by laws which shall abolish the evils
of patronage and make honesty, efficiency, and fidelity the
essential qualifications for public positions, without creating a
life tenure of office.

6.   We are opposed to further grants of the public lands to
corporations and monopolies, and demand that the national
domain be set apart for free homes for the people.

7.   The annual revenue, after paying current expenditures,
pensions, and the interest on the public debt, should furnish
a moderate balance for the reduction of the principal, and
that revenue, except so much as may be derived from a tax
upon tobacco and liquors, should be raised by duties upon im-
portations, the details of which should be so adjusted as to
aid in securing remunerative wages to labor, and promote the
industries, prosperity, and growth of the whole country.

8.   We hold in undying honor the soldiers and sailors whose
valor saved the Union.   Their pensions are a sacred debt of
the nation, and the widows and orphans of those who died for
their country are entitled to the care of a generous and grateful people.   We favor such additional legislation as will extend the bounty of the Government to all our soldiers and

sailors who were honorably discharged, and who in the line of duty became disabled, without regard to the length of service or the cause of such discharge.

9. The doctrine of Great Britain and other European Powers concerning allegiance—"once a subject always a subject"—having at last through the efforts of the Republican party been abandoned, and the American idea of the individual's right to transfer allegiance having been accepted by European nations, it is the duty of our Government to guard with jealous care the rights of adopted citizens against the assumption of unauthorized claims by their former Governments, and we urge continued careful encouragement and protection of voluntary immigration.

10. The franking privilege ought to be abolished, and the way prepared for a speedy reduction in the rates of postage.

11 Among the questions which press for attention is that which concerns the relations of capital and labor, and the Republican party recognizes the duty of so shaping legislation as to secure full protection and the amplest field for capital, and for labor, the creator of capital, the largest opportunities and a just share of the mutual profits of these two great servants of civilization.

12. We hold that Congress and the President have only fulfilled an imperative duty in their measures for the suppression of violent and treasonable organizations in certain lately rebellious regions, and for the protection of the ballot-box; and therefore they are entitled to the thanks of the nation.

13. We denounce repudiation of the public debt, in any form or disguise as a national crime. We witness with pride the reduction of the principal of the debt, and the rates of interest upon the balance, and confidently expect that our excellent national currency will be perfected by a speedy resumption of specie payment.

14. The Republican party is mindful of its obligations to the loyal women of America for their noble devotion to the cause of freedom. Their admission to wider fields of usefulness is viewed with satisfaction; and the honest demand of

any class of citizens for additional rights should be treated with respectful consideration.

15. We heartily approve the action of Congress in extending amnesty to those lately in rebellion, and rejoice in the growth of peace and fraternal feeling throughout the land.

16. The Republican party proposes to respect the rights reserved by the people to themselves as carefully as the powers delegated by them to the State and to the Federal Government. It disapproves of the resort to unconstitutional laws for the purpose of removing evils, by interference with rights not surrendered by the people to either the State or national Government.

17. It is the duty of the General Government to adopt such measures as may tend to encourage and restore American commerce and ship-building.

18. We believe that the modest patriotism, the earnest purpose, the sound judgment, the practical wisdom, the incorruptible integrity, and the illustrious services of Ulysses S. Grant have commended him to the heart of the American people, and with him at our head we start to day upon a new march to victory.

19. Henry Wilson, nominated for the Vice-Presidency, known to the whole land from the early days of the great struggle for liberty as an indefatigable laborer in all campaigns, an incorruptible legislator and representative man of American institutions, is worthy to associate with our great leader and share the honors which we pledge our best efforts to bestow upon them.

NATIONAL LIBERAL REPUBLICAN CONVENTION, 1872.

ADDRESS TO THE PEOPLE OF THE UNITED STATES.

The Administration now in power has rendered itself guilty of wanton disregard of the laws of the land, and of usurping powers not granted by the Constitution; it has acted as if the laws had binding force only for those who are governed, and not for those who govern. It has thus struck a blow at the fundamental principles of constitutional government and the liberties of the citizen.

The President of the United States has openly used the powers and opportunities of his high office for the promotion of personal ends.

He has kept notoriously corrupt and unworthy men in places of power and responsibility, to the detriment of the public interest.

He has used the public service of the Government as a machinery of corruption and personal influence, and has inter-fered with tyrannical arrogance in the political affairs of States and municipalities.

He has rewarded with influential and lucrative offices men who had acquired his favor by valuable presents, thus stimu lating the demoralization of our political life by his conspicu-ous example.

He has shown himself deplorably unequal to the task im-posed upon him by the necessities of the country, and culpa-bly careless of the responsibilities of his high office. .

The partizans of the Administration, assuming to be the Republican party and controlling its organization, have at-tempted to justify such wrongs and palliate such abuses to the end of maintaining partisan ascendency.

They have stood in the way of necessary investigations and indispensable reforms, pretending that no serious fault could be found with the present administration of public affairs, thus seeking to blind the eyes of the people.

They have kept alive the passions and resentment of the late civil war, to use them for their own advantage , they have resorted to arbitrary measures in direct conflict with the organic law, instead of appealing to the better instincts and latent patriotism of the Southern people by restoring to them these rights, the enjoyment of which is indispensable to a successful administration of their local affairs, and would tend to revive a patriotic and hopeful national feeling.

They have degraded themselves and the name of their party, once justly entitled to the confidence of the nation, by a base sycophancy to the dispenser of executive power and patron-age, unworthy of republican freemen; they have sought to silence the voice of just criticism, and stifle the moral sense of the people, and to subjugate public opinion by tyrannical party discipline.

They are striving to maintain themselves in authority for

selfish ends by an unscrupulous use of the power which right-fully belongs to the people, and should be employed only in the service of the country.

Believing that an organization thus led and controlled can no longer be of service to the best interests of the Republic, we have resolved to make an independent appeal to the sober judgment, conscience, and patriotism of the American people.

RESOLUTIONS.

We, the Liberal Republicans of the United States, in National Convention assembled at Cincinnati, proclaim the following principles as essential to just government:

1. We recognize the equality of all men before the law, and hold that it is the duty of government, in its dealings with the people, to mete out equal and exact justice to all, of whatever nativity, race, color, or persuasion, religious or political.

2. We pledge ourselves to maintain the Union of these States, emancipation and enfranchisement, and to oppose any re-opening of the questions settled by the thirteenth, four-teenth, and fifteenth amendments of the Constitution.

3. We demand the immediate and absolute removal of all disabilities imposed on account of the rebellion, which was finally subdued seven years ago, believing that universal am-nesty will result in complete pacification in all sections of the country.

4. Local self-government, with impartial suffrage, will guard the rights of all citizens more securely than any centralized power. The public welfare requires the supremacy of the civil over the military authority, and the freedom of person under the protection of the *habeas corpus*. We demand for the indi-vidual the largest liberty consistent with public order, for the State self-government, and for the nation a return to the methods of peace and the constitutional limitations of power.

5. The civil service of the Government has become a mere instrument of partisan tyranny and personal ambition, and an object of selfish greed. It is a scandal and reproach upon free institutions, and breeds a demoralization dangerous to the perpetuity of republican government. We therefore regard a thorough reform of the civil service as one of the most press-ing necessities of the hour; that honesty, capacity, and fidelity

constitute the only valid claims to public employment; that the offices of the Government cease to be a matter of arbitrary favoritism and patronage, and that public station shall become again a post of honor. To this end it is imperatively required that no President shall be a candidate for re election.

6. We demand a system of Federal taxation which shall not unnecessarily interfere with the industry of the people, and which shall provide the means necessary to pay the expenses of the Government, economically administered, the pensions, the interest on the public debt, and a moderate reduction annually of the principal thereof; and recognizing that there are in our midst honest but irreconcilable differences of opinion with regard to the respective systems of protection and free trade, we remit the discussion of the subject to the people in their congressional districts and the decision of Congress thereon, wholly free from executive interference or dictation.

7. The public credit must be sacredly maintained, and we denounce repudiation in every form and guise.

8. A speedy return to specie payments is demanded alike by the highest considerations of commercial morality and honest government.

9. We remember with gratitude the heroism and sacrifices of the soldiers and sailors of the Republic, and no act of ours shall ever detract from their justly earned fame or the full rewards of their patriotism.

10. We are opposed to all further grants of lands to railroads or other corporations. The public domain should be held sacred to actual settlers.

11. We hold that is the duty of the Government in its intercourse with foreign nations to cultivate the friendships of peace by treating with all on fair and equal terms, regarding it alike dishonorable either to demand what is not right or submit to what is wrong.

12. For the promotion and success of these vital principles and the support of the candidates nominated by this convention we invite and cordially welcome the co-operation of all patriotic citizens, without regard to previous political affiliations.

NATIONAL DEMOCRATIC CONVENTION, 1872.

We, the Democratic electors of the United States in Convention assembled, do present the following principles, already adopted at Cincinnati, as essential to just government.

1. We recognize the equality of all men before the law, and hold that it is the duty of Government in its dealings with the people to mete out equal and exact justice to all, of whatever nativity, race, color, or persuasion, religious or political.

2. We pledge ourselves to maintain the union of these States, emancipation, and enfranchisement, and to oppose any re-opening of the questions settled by the thirteenth, fourteenth and fifteenth amendments to the Constitution.

3. We demand the immediate and absolute removal of all disabilities imposed on account of the rebellion, which was finally subdued seven years ago, believing that universal amnesty will result in complete pacification in all sections of the country.

4. Local self-government, with impartial suffrage, will guard the rights of all citizens more securely than any centralized power. The public welfare requires the supremacy of the civil over the military authority, and freedom of person under the protection of the *habeas corpus*. We demand for the individual the largest liberty consistent with public order; for the State self-government, and for the nation a return to the methods of peace and the constitutional limitations of power.

5. The civil service of the Government has become a mere instrument of partisan tyranny and personal ambition, and an object of selfish greed. It is a scandal and reproach upon free institutions and breeds a demoralization dangerous to the perpetuity of republican government. We therefore regard a thorough reform of the civil service as one of the most pressing necessities of the hour; that honesty, capacity, and fidelity constitute the only valid claim to public employment; that the offices of the government cease to be a matter of arbitrary favoritism and patronage, and that public station become again a post of honor. To this end it is imperatively required that no President shall be a candidate for re-election.

6. We demand a system of Federal taxation which shall not unnecessarily interfere with the industry of the people, and which shall provide the means necessary to pay the expenses of the Government, economically administered, the pensions, the interest on the public debt, and a moderate reduction annually of the principal thereof; and recognizing that there are in our midst honest but irreconcilable differences of opinion with regard to the respective systems of protection and free trade, we remit the discussion of the subject to the people in their Congressional districts, and to the decision of the Congress thereon, wholly free from executive interference or dictation.

7. The public credit must be sacredly maintained, and we denounce repudiation in every form and guise.

8. A speedy return to specie payment is demanded alike by the highest considerations of commercial morality and honest government.

9. We remember with gratitude the heroism and sacrifices of the soldiers and sailors of the Republic, and no act of ours shall ever detract from their justly earned fame for the full reward of their patriotism.

10. We are opposed to all further grants of lands to railroads or other corporations. The public domain should be held sacred to actual settlers.

11. We hold that it is the duty of the Government in its intercourse with foreign nations to cultivate the friendships of peace, by treating with all on fair and equal terms, regarding it alike dishonorable either to demand what is not right or to submit to what is wrong.

12. For the promotion and success of these vital principles, and the support of the candidates nominated by this convention, we invite and cordially welcome the co-operation of all patriotic citizens, without regard to previous political affiliations.

NATIONAL LABOR REFORM CONVENTION, 1872.

We hold that all political power is inherent in the people, and free government founded on their authority and established for their benefit; that all citizens are equal in political rights, entitled to the largest religious and political liberty compatible with the good order of society, as also the use and enjoyment of the fruits of their labor and talents ; and no man or set of men is entitled to exclusive separable endowments and privileges, or immunities from the Government, but in consideration of public services; and any laws destructive of these fundamental principles are without moral binding force, and should be repealed. And believing that all the evils resulting from unjust legislation now affecting the industrial classes can be removed by the adoption of the principle contained in the following declaration : Therefore,

Resolved, That it is the duty of the Government to establish a just standard of distribution of capital and labor by providing a purely national circulating medium, based on the faith and resources of the nation, issued directly to the people without the intervention of any system of banking corporations, which money shall be legal tender in the payment of all debts, public and private, and interchangeable at the option of the holder for Government bonds bearing a rate of interest not to exceed 3-65 per cent., subject to future legislation by Congress.

2. That the national debt should be paid in good faith, according to the original contract, at the earliest option of the Government, without mortgaging the property of the people or the future exigencies of labor to enrich a few capitalists at home and abroad.

3. That justice demands that the burden of Government should be so adjusted as to bear equally on all classes, and that the exemption from taxation of Government bonds bearing extravagant rates of interest is a violation of all just principles of revenue laws.

4. That the public lands of the United States belong to the people and should not be sold to individuals nor granted to corporations, but should be held as a sacred trust for the benefit of the people, and should be granted to landless settlers only, in amounts not exceeding one hundred and sixty acres of land.

5. That Congress should modify the tariff so as to admit free such articles of common use as we can neither produce nor grow, and lay duties for revenue mainly upon articles of luxury and upon such articles of manufacture as will, we hav-

ing the raw materials, assist in further developing the resources of the country.

6. That the presence in our country of Chinese laborers, imported by capitalists in large numbers for servile use, is an evil, entailing want and its attendant train of misery and crime on all classes of the American people, and should be prohibited by legislation.

7. That we ask for the enactment of a law by which all mechanics and day-laborers employed by or on behalf of the Government, whether directly or indirectly, through persons, firms, or corporations, contracting with the State, shall conform to the reduced standard of eight hours a day, recently adopted by Congress for national employes, and also for an amendment to the acts of incorporation for cities and towns by which all laborers and mechanics employed at their expense shall conform to the same number of hours.

8. That the enlightened spirit of the age demands the abolition of the system of contract labor in our prisons and other reformatory institutions.

9. That the protection of life, liberty, and property are the three cardinal principles of Government, and the first two are more sacred than the latter; therefore money needed for prosecuting wars should, as it is required, be assessed and collected from the wealthy of the country, and not entailed as a burden on posterity.

10. That it is the duty of the Government to exercise its power over railroads and telegraph corporations, that they shall not in any case be privileged to exact such rates of freight, transportation, or charges, by whatever name, as may bear unduly or unequally upon the producer or consumer.

11. That there should be such a reform in the civil service of the national Government as will remove it beyond all partisan influence, and place it in the charge and under the direction of intelligent and competent business men.

12. That as both history and experience teaches us that power ever seeks to perpetuate itself by every and all means, and that its prolonged possession in the hands of one person is always dangerous to the interests of a free people, and believing that the spirit of our organic laws and the stability and safety of our free institutions are best obeyed on the one

hand, and secured on the other, by a regular constitutional change in the chief of the country at each election : therefore, we are in favor of limiting the occupancy of the presidential chair to one term.

13. That we are in favor of granting general amnesty and restoring the Union at once on the basis of equality of rights and privileges to all, the impartial administration of justice being the only true bond of union to bind the States together and restore the Government of the people.

14. That we demand the subjection of the military to the civil authorities, and the confinement of its operations to national purposes alone.

15. That we deem it expedient for Congress to supervise the patent laws, so as to give labor more fully the benefit of its own ideas and inventions.

16. That fitness, and not political or personal considerations, should be the only recommendation to public office, either appointive or elective, and any and all laws looking to the establishment of this principle are heartily approved.

THE BAXTER LIQUOR LAW.

AN ACT to regulate the sale of intoxicating liquors; to provide against
evils resulting from any sale thereof; to furnish remedies for damages
suffered by any person in consequence of such sale; prescribing penal
ties; to repeal all laws contravening the provisions of this act, and
declaring an emergency.

[APPROVED FEBRUARY 27, 1873.]

SECTION 1. *Be it enacted by the General Assembly of the
State of Indiana,* That it shall be unlawful for any person or
persons, by himself or agent, to sell, barter, or give away for
any purpose of gain, to any person whomsoever, any intoxicating liquors to be drunk in, upon, or about the building or
premises where the liquor is sold, bartered, or given away, or
in any room, building, or premises adjoining to or connected
with the place where the liquor is sold, bartered, or given
away for the purpose of gain, until such person or persons
shall have obtained a permit therefor from the board of commissioners of the county where he resides, as hereinafter
provided.

Sec. 2. Any person desiring a permit to sell intoxicating
liquors to be drunk on the premises, shall file in the office of
the auditor of the proper county, not less than twenty days
before the first day of the term of any regular session of the
board of commissioners of such county, a petition in writing,
stating therein the building or number, street, ward or township wherein the permission is asked to be granted, praying
for such permit, and certifying that the applicant is a resident
voter of such county, and a citizen of the State of Indiana, and
that he is a proper person to have and receive such permit;
which petition shall be signed by the applicant, and also by a
majority of the legal voters resident in the ward, if it be in a

(85)

city or town, if it be in an incorporated town, or township
wherein the applicant proposes to sell intoxicating liquors;
such petition shall be kept on file by the auditor until the
next ensuing regular session of the board of commissioners,
when it shall be presented to the board for their action. The
board shall examine such petition, and if satisfied the same is
in proper form, and that it has been signed as hereinbefore
required, shall direct a permit to be issued under the hand
and seal of said auditor, and delivered to the person named in
such permit, upon his complying with the provisions of this
act and paying the costs of filing and recording said petition
and costs of issuing said permit.

Sec. 3. Before the granting of a permit by the board of
commissioners, the applicant shall cause to be executed and
properly acknowledged before an officer authorized to take
acknowledgment of deeds, a bond payable to the State of
Indiana, in the sum of three thousand dollars, with good free-
hold security thereon of not less than two persons, to be approved by the board of commissioners, and conditioned for the
payment of any and all fines, penalties and forfeitures incurred
by reason of the violation of any of the provisions of this act;
and conditioned further, that the principal and sureties therein
named shall be jointly and severally liable, and shall pay to
any person or persons, any and all damages which shall in any
manner be suffered by or inflicted upon any such person or
persons, either in person or property, or means of support, by
reason of any sale or sales of intoxicating liquors to any person,
by the person receiving such permit or by any of his agents
or employees. Separate suits may be brought on said bond
by the person or persons injured, but the aggregate amount
recovered thereon shall not exceed the said sum of three
thousand dollars, and in case the amount of said bond shall be
exhausted by recoveries thereon, a new bond in the same pen-
alty and with like sureties shall be filed within ten days, and
in default thereof said permit shall be deemed to be revoked.
Such bond, after its approval by the board of commissioners,
shall be filed in the office of the auditor of the county, and
shall be recorded by such auditor forthwith in a book prepared
for that purpose, and shall there remain for the use of the

State of Indiana, and for the use of any person or persons suffering any damage as hereinbefore set forth. Such bond may be sued and recovered upon in any court having civil jurisdiction in the county (except justices' courts) by or for the use of any person or persons, or their legal representatives, who may be injured or damaged by reason of any sale or sales of intoxicating liquors by the person receiving the permit or by any of his agents or employees. The record of the bond or a copy thereof, duly certified by such auditor, shall be admissible in evidence in any suit on such bond, and shall have the same force and effect as the original bond would have if offered in evidence.

Sec. 4. The whole number of votes cast for candidates for Congress at the last preceding Congressional election in the township, and the whole number of votes cast for councilman or trustee in any ward or town, at the last preceding municipal election in any city or town in which the applicant for permit desires to sell said intoxicating liquors, shall be deemed to be the whole number of legal voters of such ward, town or township, a majority of whose names shall be signed to the petition of such applicant; and it is further provided, that any person not a legal voter in said ward, town or township. who shall sign said petition, or any person who signs the name of any person other than himself, without the permission previously obtained of said person to so sign his name, shall be fined not less than fifty nor more than one hundred dollars for each signature so made.

Sec. 5. No permit, as herein provided for, shall be granted for a longer or shorter time than one year. It shall be the duty of the Auditor of the county to furnish the person to whom such permit is granted, a copy of the order of the Commissioners granting the permit, which copy shall show in conspicuous letters the date of the commencement of such permit, and of its expiration; *and it is further provided*, That such copy of the order of the Commissioners, certified by the Auditor, shall be hung up in a conspicuous place in the room where said liquor is sold, where the same may at all times be seen and read by any person desiring so to do. Should any person holding a permit be convicted of a violation of any of the provisions of this act, such conviction shall work a forfeiture of his permit, and of all rights thereunder; and no permit shall thereafter be granted to such person before the expiration of five years from the date of such conviction.

Sec. 6. It shall be unlawful for any person, by himself, or agent, to sell, barter, or give intoxicating liquors to any minor, or to any person intoxicated, or to any person who is in the habit of getting intoxicated.

Sec. 7. All places where intoxicating liquor is sold in violation of this act, shall be taken, held. and declared to be common nuisances; all rooms, taverns, eating-houses, bazaars, restaurants, drug stores, groceries, coffee-houses, cellars, or other places of public resort, where intoxicating liquors are sold in violation of this act, shall be shut up and abated as public nuisances, upon conviction of the keeper thereof, who shall be punished as hereinafter provided.

Sec. 8. Any person or persons who shall by the sale of intoxicating liquor, with or without permit, cause the intoxication, in whole or in part, of any other person, shall be liable for and be compelled to pay a reasonable compensation to any person who may take charge of and provide for such intoxicated person, for every day he or she is so cared for, which sum may be recovered in an action of debt before any court having competent jurisdiction.

Sec. 9. It shall be unlawful for any person to get intoxicated. A person found in a state of intoxication shall upon conviction thereof, be fined in the sum of five dollars. Any person convicted of intoxication shall be required upon the trial to designate the person or persons from whom the liquor in whole or in part was obtained. In default of so designating such person, he or she shall in addition to the fine above mentioned, and as a part of his or her punishment for the offense, be imprisoned in the county jail not less than one day nor more than ten days, at the discretion of the court.

Sec. 10. A permit granted under this act shall not authorize the person so receiving it to sell intoxicating liquors on Sunday, nor upon the day of any State, county, township, or municipal election, in the township, town or city where the same may be held; nor upon Christmas day, nor upon the Fourth of July, nor upon any Thanksgiving day, nor upon any public holiday, nor between nine o clock P. M. and six o'clock

A. M.; and any and all sales made on any such day, or after nine o'clock on any evening, are hereby declared to be unlawful, and upon conviction thereof, the person so selling shall be fined not less than five dollars nor more than twenty-five dollars for each sale made in violation of this section.

Sec. 11. The bartering or giving away of intoxicating liquors, or other shift or device to evade the provisions of this act, by any person or persons keeping liquors for sale, or by his agent or employee, at the place where the same are kept for sale, shall be deemed and held to be an unlawful selling or giving away for the purpose of gain within the provisions of this act.

Sec. 12. In addition to the remedy and right of action provided for in section eight of this act, every husband, wife, child, parent, guardian, employer, or other person who shall be injured in person or property, or means of support, by any intoxicated person, or in consequence of the intoxication, habitual or otherwise, of any person, shall have a right of action in his or her name, severally or jointly, against any person or persons who shall, by selling, bartering, or giving away intoxicating liquors have caused the intoxication, in whole or in part, of such person, and any person or persons owning, renting, leasing or permitting the occupation of any building or premises, and having knowledge that intoxicating liquor is to be sold therein, or having leased the same for other purposes, shall knowingly permit therein the sale of intoxicating liquor, or who having been informed that intoxicating liquor is sold therein that has caused, in whole or in part, the intoxication of any person, who shall not immediately, after being so informed, take legal steps in good faith to dispossess said tenant or lessee, shall be liable jointly with the person selling, bartering or giving away intoxicating liquor as aforesaid, to any person or persons injured, for all damages, and for exemplary damages; *Provided*, however, that execution on any such judgment shall first be levied on the property of the person selling, bartering or giving away such liquor, and in the event of a failure or insufficiency of such property to satisfy the judgment, then of the property of the other defendants. A married woman shall have the same right to bring suit and to control the same, and the ammount recovered as a *femme sole*, and all damages recovered by a minor under this act shall be paid either to such minor or to his or her parent, guardian or next friend, as the court shall direct. The unlawful sale or giving away of intoxicating liquor shall work a forfeiture of all rights of the lessee or tenant under any lease or contract of rent, upon the premises where such unlawful sale, bartering or giving away shall take place. All suits for damages under this act may be by any appropriate action in any of the courts in this State having competent jurisdiction. All judgments recovered under the provisions of this act may be enforced without any relief or benefit from the valuation or appraisement laws.

Sec. 13. In all cases where husband, wife, parent, child or guardian shall have a right of action as provided in section twelve of this act, and shall fail or refuse to prosecute the same, and in all cases where such intoxicated person has neither husband, wife, parent, child or guardian, the township trustee or other officer having charge of the poor of the township where such intoxicated person resides, shall have a right of action as provided in said section twelve, and it is hereby made the duty of such officer to prosecute all such actions in the name of such township. All money collected upon such judgments, after deducting therefrom all costs and charges against such township occasioned thereby, shall be paid by the township trustee, or other officer, into the treasury of the county for the benefit of the poor of such county; provided that the name of any husband, wife, parent, child or guardian, upon proper petition therefore before final judgment, may be substituted for the name of the township, but such person so substituted shall have no power to dismiss such action, or compromise the same in any manner, except by permission of the court.

Sec. 14. For every violation of the provisions of the first and sixth sections of this act, the person so offending shall forfeit and pay a fine of not less than ten dollars nor more than fifty dollars, or be imprisoned in the jail of the county not less than ten nor more than thirty days. For every violation of the provisions of the seventh section of this act, any person convicted as the keeper of any of the places therein declared to be nuisances, shall forfeit and pay a fine of not less than twenty nor more than fifty dollars, and such place or places, so kept by such person so convicted, shall be shut up and abated as a common nuisance by the order of the court before which such conviction may be had as a further punishment, and such order shall be a part of the judgment of conviction.

Sec. 15. For the payment of all fines, costs and damages assessed or adjudged against any person or persons in consequence of the sale of intoxicating liquors as provided for in this act, the real estate and personal property of such person or persons, of every kind, shall be liable, and such fines, costs and damages shall be a lien upon such real estate until paid.

Sec. 16. The penalties and provisions made in the fourteenth section of this act may be enforced by indictment in any court of record having criminal jurisdiction; and all pecuniary fines or penalties provided for in any of the sections of this act, except the eighth and twelfth, may be enforced and prosecuted for before any justice of the peace of the proper county, in an action of debt, in the name of the State of Indiana as plaintiff; and in case of conviction, the offender shall stand committed to the jail of the county until judgment and costs are fully paid, and the magistrate or court in which the conviction is had, shall issue a writ of *capias ad satisfaciendum* therefor. Justices of the peace shall have jurisdiction of all actions arising under the eighth and twelfth sections of this act, when the amount in controversy does not exceed two hundred dollars, such actions to be prosecuted in the name of the party injured or entitled to the debt or damages provided for in said eighth and twelfth sections.

Sec. 17. It shall be unlawful for any person to buy for or furnish to any person who is at the time intoxicated, or in the habit of getting intoxicated, or to buy for or furnish to any minor, to be drunk by such minor, any intoxicating liquor. Any person or persons violating this section shall be fined not less than five dollars nor more than fifty dollars.

Sec. 18. In all prosecutions under this act, by indictment or otherwise, it shall not be necessary to state the kind of liquor sold, or to describe the place where sold, and it shall not be necessary to state the name of the person to whom sold. In all cases, the person or persons to whom intoxicating liquors shall be sold in violation of this act, shall be competent witnesses to prove such facts or any others tending thereto.

Sec. 19. The following form of complaint shall be sufficient in criminal proceedings before justices of the peace or mayors, under this act when applicable, but may be varied to suit the nature of the case, namely :

STATE OF INDIANA,   COUNTY, ss. Before me, A. B., a justice of the peace of said county, (or mayor of, &c., as the case may be), personally came C. D., who, being duly sworn according to law, deposeth and saith that on or about the   day of   , in the year   , at the county aforesaid, E. F. did sell intoxicating liquors to one G. H. to be drunk in the place where sold, (or to G. H., a minor, &c.,) or to a person intoxicated, or in the habit of getting intoxicated, as the case may be, where intoxicating liquors are sold in violation of law, and further saith not.

(Signed)   C. D.
Sworn to and subscribed before me this   day of A. D.,

Sec. 20. All laws and parts of laws conflicting with this act, or with any of the provisions of this act, be and the same are hereby repealed; but nothing in this act shall be so construed as to prohibit the common councils of cities and the boards of trustees of incorporated towns, from demanding and enforcing a fee for permit, from all keepers of coffee houses, saloons, or other places where intoxicating liquor is sold and drunk within the limits of their respective corporations.

Sec. 21. It is hereby declared that an emergeny exists for the immediate taking effect of this act, it shall, therefore, be in force from and after its passage, except in so far as relates to those who hold a license under the existing laws of the State. This act shall apply to such as now have license immediately after the expiration thereof.

GEOLOGICAL ITEMS.

——:o:——

"It is not easy to give an accurate and comprehensive defi-
nition of the science of geology. It is, indeed, not so much
one science, as the application of all the physical sciences to
the examination of the structure of the earth, the investigation of the processes concerned in the production of that
structure, and the history of their action. That this large
view of geology is not only a true but a necessary one, is
shown by the fact, that it was not until considerable advances
had been made in all the physical sciences which relate directly to the earth, that geology could begin to exist in any
worthy form. It was not until the chemist was able to explain
the nature of the mineral substances of which rocks are composed; not till the geographer and meteorologist had explored
the surface of the earth, and taught us the extent of land and
water, and the powers of winds, currents, rains, glaciers, earthquakes and volcanoes; not until the naturalist had classified,
named, and described the greater part of existing animals and
plants, and explained their anatomical structure, and the laws
of their distribution in space;—that the geologist could, with
any chance of arriving at sure and definite results, commence
his researches into the structure and composition of rocks and
the causes which produced them, or utilize his discoveries of
the remains of animals and plants that are inclosed in them.
He could not until then discriminate with certainty batween
igneous and aqueous rocks, between living and extinct animals, and was, therefore, unable to lay down any one of the foun-
dations on which his own science was to rest."--*Encyclopedia
Britannica, 8th edition, vol. xv.*

If there is any one fact which the study of geology teaches
more unmistakably than another, it is, that the matter composing the crust of the earth, from the time when it was first
called into existence by the *fiat* of the Creator to the present,
has been subjected to an endless cycle of mutations. There

(93)

may have been periods of comparative rest and quiescen_e, but none of perfect stagnation and stability; so that the present condition and configuration of the earth's surface may be considered as the last result of a series of cosmical changes, which commenced with the dawn of creation, and are continuing on into the future.

"Had the exterior crust of the earth been subjected to no modifying causes, the world would have presented the same appearance now as at the time of its creation. The distribution of land and sea would have remained the same; there would have been the same surface arrangement of hill, valley and plain, and the same unvarying aspects of animal and vegetable existence. Under such circumstances, geology, instead of striving to present a consecutive history of change and progress, would have been limited to a mere description of permanently enduring appearances. The case. however, is widely different." There is no part of the present land-surface of the globe which has not at some time been covered by the ocean, while much of the present sea bottom has been in turn dry land. Many of the loftiest and most extensive ranges of mountains upon the globe—the Alps, the Andes, and the Himalayas—are of comparatively recent elevation (recent as compared with the White Mountains of New England, or the Appallachian chain of the Atlantic States); while the commencement of the existence of every animal and vegetable species at present found upon the earth was long subsequent to the existence of the myriad organisms, whose remains are now found fossil beneath its surface.

The agencies which have produced, and are still tending to produce, changes in the constitution and structure of our planet, may be classified as follows : 1. Igneous agencies, or such as manifest themselves in connection with some deep-seated source of heat in the interior of the globe. 2. Aqueous, or those arising from the action of the water. 3. Atmospheric, or those operating through the medium of the atmosphere. 4. Organic, or those depending on animal and vegetable growth. 5. Chemical, or those resulting from the chemical action of substances on each other.— *Wells' Illustrated Geology.*

THE TEMPERATURE OF THE EARTH.

The following are some of the observations made most recently on this subject: In England, observations have been made in the vertical shafts of two very deep coal mines, viz., at Monkwearmouth, which is 1800 feet deep, and Dunkinfield, which is upwards of 2000 feet deep, and in both cases the observations were made while the workmen were sinking the shafts, and with every precaution against the influence of any extraneous causes. The former gave an increase of 1 deg. of Fahrenheit for every sixty feet of depth, and the latter 1 deg. for about every seventy feet. The artesian well of Grenelle (Paris), is 1800 feet deep; observations made by Arago, during the boring, showed that the average increase of temperature in this was 1 deg. for sixty feet. At Mordorff, Luxemburg, the depth of the artesian well is 2400 feet, and the increase in temperature 1 deg. for every fifty-seven feet. At the artesian well of New Seltzwork, in Westphalia, the depth is 2100 feet, and the increase 1 deg. for every fifty-five feet. At Louisville, Ky., the depth of an artesian well, finished in 1859, is 2086 feet deep, and the average increase is 1 deg. for every sixty-seven feet below the first ninety feet from the surface. In the silver mine of Guanaxato, Mexico, 1713 feet deep, the increase is 1 deg. for every forty-five feet. In the coal mines of Eastern Virginia, the increase is about 1 deg. for every sixty feet.

VOLCANIC ERUPTIONS.

One or two remarkable instances of volcanic eruptions may be briefly noticed. First, for duration and force we may refer to that which took place in the island of Sumbawa (one of the Sunda Islands lying east of Java), in the year 1815. It commenced on the 5th of April, and did not entirely cease until July. Its influence (i. e. shocks, and the noise of the explosions) was perceptible over an area 1,800 miles in diameter, while within the range of its more immediate vicinity, embracing a space of 400 miles, its effects were most terrific. In Java, 300 miles distant, it seemed to be awfully present. The sky was overcast at noon-day with clouds of ashes, which the light of the sun was unable to penetrate, and fields, streets, and houses were covered with ashes to the depth of several inches. At Sumbawa itself, immense columns of flame appeared to burst forth from the top of the volcano, Tombora, and in a short time the whole mountain appeared like a mass of liquid fire, which gradually extended in every direction. As the eruption continued, a darkness supervened, so profound as to obscure even the light of the flames; showers of stones and ashes fell continuously over the whole island; the sea rose twelve feet higher than it had ever been known to do before; and finally a whirlwind ensued, which tore up the largest trees, and carried them into the air, together with men, horses, cattle, and whatever else came within its influence. Of 12,000 inhabitants in the vicinity only six are believed to have escaped, and of some entire villages not even a vestige remained.

In 1772, the Papandayang, one of the loftiest volcanic mountains in Java, after a short but severe eruption, suddenly fell in and disappeared in the earth, carrying with it about ninety square miles of territory. Forty villages were engulfed, or covered with ejected matter, at the same time, and nearly 3,000 persons perished.— *Wells' Illustrated Geology.*

DESCRIPTIONS OF AN EARTHQUAKE.

" A powerful eathquake," says Mr. Darwin, "at once destroys the oldest associations; the world, the very emblem of all that is solid, has moved beneath our feet like a crust over a fluid; one second of time has conveyed to the mind a strange idea of insecurity, which hours of reflection would never have created."

" To man," says Humbolt, " the earthquake conveys an idea of some universal and unlimited danger. We may flee from the crater of a volcano in active eruption, or from a locality threatened by the approach of a lava stream; but in an earthquake, direct our flight whithersoever we will, we still feel as though we trod upon the very focus of destruction. Every sound—the faintest motion in the air—arrests our attention, and we no longer trust the ground on which we stand. Animals, especially dogs and swine, participate in the same anxious disquietude; and even crocodiles, in the rivers of South America, which at other times are dumb, have been observed to quit the water and run, with loud cries, into the adjacent forests."

AQUEOUS AND ATMOSPHERIC AGENCIES.

The aqueous and atmospheric agencies most prominently concerned in producing geological changes, are *rains, and the gasses and moisture of the atmosphere, winds, ice, and snow, springs, rivers, waves, tides, and oceanic currents.*

The operation of water, acting mechanically, is, under all circumstances, to wear down the higher portions of the earth's crust, and transport the materials to lower localities—an action which obviously tends to reduce the whole surface to a smooth and uniform level. On the other hand, the operations of igneous agents—volcanoes, earthquakes, etc.—by breaking up and elevating the crust of the earth, tend to counteract the equalizing action of water and to produce that diversity of surface which is indispensable to variety in both the vegetable and animal kingdoms. These two forces, therefore—the aqueous and the igneous—may be considered as antagonistic to each other, and to them may be ascribed the principal modifications which have taken place, and are still taking place, in the crust of the globe.— *Well's Illustrated Geology.*

CORAL REEFS.

"The ocean," says Mr. Darwin, "throwing its breakers on the outer shore, appears an invincible enemy, yet we see it resisted, and even conquered, by means which at first seem weak and inefficient. No periods of repose are granted, and the heavy swell caused by the steady action of the trade wind never ceases. The breakers exceed in violence those of our temperate regions; and it is impossible to behold them without feeling a conviction that rocks of granite or quartz would ultimately be demolished by such irresistable forces. Yet these low coral islands stand and are victorious, for here another power, antagonistic to the former, takes part in the contest. The organic forces separate the atoms of carbonate of lime, one by one, from the foaming breakers, and unite them into a symmetrical structure; myriads of architects are at work day and night, month after month, and we see their soft and gelatinous bodies, through the agency of the vital laws, conquering the great mechanical power of the waves of the ocean, which neither the art of man nor the mechanical works of nature could successfully resist." The animals which produce coral are very simple, and resemble plants both in their figures and colors.

7

THE FIRST FORMED STRATIFIED ROCKS.

The adoption of the theory, that our earth was once in a state of entire molten fluidity, involves the existence of a subsequent period, when its primeval crust had sufficiently cooled down to allow of the condensation of watery vapor and of the existence of a sea upon its surface. Whenever this happened, the eroding and destructive action of water must have immediately manifested itself, while the particles of the consolidated igneous crust, worn off by the action of waves, tides, and currents, and deposited as sediments, would naturally produce stratified formations.

The internal heat of the earth at that period, however, must have continued to act with great intensity near the surface, and the strata first deposited, consequently, were, in all probability, soon greatly metamorphosed, i. e., remelted down to form igneous rocks, or converted into hard crystalline semiigneous rocks, that retained, in part, their original lines of stratification.

Whether any of these first formed stratified rocks are in existence, and open to our inspection, it is impossible to affirm. Some geologists incline to the opinion that they were entirely remelted, and are now represented by the older or fundamental granites, which, in some instances, appear to have an obscurely stratified structure.

Be this as it may, it is, however, a matter of fact, that the oldest rocks of which we have any knowledge, which exhibit evidence of a sedimentary origin, appear to have been formed under conditions analogous to those above supposed. Thus, they are all more or less crystalline and indurated ; their lines of stratification are indistinct, and often altogether obliterated ; and their whole aspect is very different from what is usually ascribed to rocks deposited in water.— *Wells' Illustrated Geology.*

FORMATION OF COAL.

It is now universally admitted by geologists, that coal is a mass of compressed, altered, and mineralized vegetation, just as sandstone is consolidated sand, and the slate and shale consolidated clay or mud.

The evidence upon which the belief is founded may be briefly stated, as follows :

1st. The enormous profusion of fossil plants, in the form of impressions of leaves, trunks, branches, and barks of trees, found in immediate connection with coal seams. 2d. Coal is composed of carbon, hydrogen, and oxygen, the same elements (though differing in proportion) which enter into the composition of plants. 3d. The substance of coal, when examined under the microscope, affords unmistakable evidence of a vegetable (cellular) structure. 4th. All the stages of gradation between perfect wood and perfect coal may be traced with the greatest certainty.

But granting the vegetable origin of coal, the question immediately suggests itself: Under what circumstances could so great an amount of vegetable matter have ever accumulated?—the magnitude of which may be realized in a degree, from the asserted fact "that all the forests of the United States, if gathered into one heap, would fail to furnish the materials of a single coal seam equal to that of Pittsburg, Penn."

Furthermore, coal is found stratified, laminated, and extended, in horizontal beds, which often cover very large areas, with a nearly constant thickness—the great Pittsburg coal seam, above referred to for example, having a nearly uniform thickness of from eight to twelve feet, and is estimated to have once covered a surface of 90,000 square miles. Coal, moreover, is ordinarily encased between beds of shale or sandstone, which bear evident proof of having been slowly deposited in quiet waters. In some coal fields, as many as seventy seams of coal, varying in thickness from a few inches to four, six, eight, ten, twelve, and twenty feet, occur thus interstratified with shales and sandstones; and yet, notwithstanding these frequent alternations of material, the purity of the coal is such, that it rarely contains any considerable admixture of mud, sand, or other foreign mineral substances.

In explanation of these phenomena, various hypotheses have been suggested, but the general opinion of the best geologists of the present day is, that the vegetable matter constituting coal, must, in the main, have grown and accumulated in immense jungles and peat mosses for many years; that the land must have then sunk, and become the basin of a lake or estuary, into which rivers carried mud and sand; these, covering the vegetable matter, gradually consolidated into shales and sandstones, while the vegetable matter itself underwent the process of mineralization, and was converted into

coal. This being done, it is supposed that the area of deposit
was again elevated, so as to become once more the scene of
luxuriant vegetation; then again submerged, and overlaid by
new depc   of sandstone and shale; then once more elevated
and cov   with plants, and again submerged; and these al-
ternat'   of submergence and elevations are presumed to
have   en place as often as there are beds of coal in any particular coal field.—*Well's Illustrated Geology.*

CLIMATIC CONDITIONS OF THE CARBONIFEROUS ERA.

There is one circumstance in connection with the formation
of coal which has given rise to a vast amount of ingenious
speculation and hypotheses, viz: the apparent sameness of
external conditions over such extensive areas of the earth as
are now occupied by our known coal fields. Thus, the same
gigantic ferns and club-mosses are found alike in the coal
fields of America, Europe, Melville Island, Greenland, and
Australia—regions widely separated, and at once tropical,
temperate, and frigid. To account for this luxuriance and
homogeneity of vegetable growth various causes have been
suggested, as the earth's central heat, a change in the earth's
axis, a larger percentage of carbonic acid in the atmosphere,
the planetary system moving through warmer regions of space,
and the like; but thus far geologists have arrived at no definite
conclusions on the subject.

Deposits of carbonaceous matter have occurred at almost
every period of the earth's history, as is evidenced by the fact
that thin seams of coal are found in almost all the geological
systems; but the coal beds which admit of economical working are almost exclusively confined to the carboniferous system. The only exceptions are a few coal fields belonging to
the Oolitic or Jurassic system, which, in Virginia and some
other localities, admit of profitable mining. It seems, therefore, certain, that whatever may have been the conditions
which allowed of so abundant a terrestrial vegetation at this
particular epoch of the earth's history, those conditions ceased
about the time when the era of the Carboniferous system ter-
minated. A high temperature was evidently not one of these
conditions, for there are evidences of it afterwards; and some
authorities incline to the belief that the superabundance of
carbonic acid gas, which is supposed to have existed during

this era, was expended before its close. "There can be no doubt that the infusion of a large amount of this gas into the atmosphere at the present day would be attended by precisely the same circumstances as in the time of the coal epoch. The higher forms of animal life would not have a place on earth. Vegetation would be enormous; and coal strata would be formed from the vast accumulations of woody matter, which would gather in every favorable locality."

DISTRIBUTION OF COAL.

Coal is very widely distributed over the world, although some countries are more highly favored than others. Available coal fields occur in Great Britain ; in Spain, France, Belgium and Middle Europe; in India, China and Japan ; in the islands of the Indian Archipelago ; in Australia and New Zealand ; in South America, Chili and Peru ; in Greenland, Melville Island and in British America. But nowhere is the coal formation more extensively displayed than in the United States, and nowhere are its beds of greater thickness, more convenient for working, or of more valuable quality.

The eastern half of the continent of North America exhibits five great coal fields, extending from Newfoundland to Arkansas: 1. The *first*, or most eastern, is that of the British Provinces, Newfoundland, Nova Scotia, and New Brunswick. Its area is probably about 9,000 square miles, though only one tenth of this surface appears to be underlaid by productive coal seams. 2. The *second*, or Great Appalachian coal field, extends from Pennsylvania and Ohio to near Tuscaloosa, in the interior of Alabama. It is about 875 miles long, and is estimated to contain 70,000 square miles. 3. A *third*, and smaller coal field, occupies the center of the State of Michigan; it covers an area of about 15,000 square miles, but is not very productive. 4. A *fourth* great coal field is situated in the States of Kentucky, Indiana and Illionois. Its area is estimated at 50,000 square miles. 5. The *fifth*, and most western, occurs in Iowa, Missouri and Arkansas, and occupies an area of about 57,000 square miles. Besides these great deposits, coal is also found in New England, Kansas, Nebraska, and Texas.

The aggregate space underlaid by the coal fields of North America amounts to at least 200,000 square miles, or to more than twenty times the area which includes all the known coal deposits of Europe.— *Wells' Geology.*

MISCELLANEOUS.

The number of species of animals that now inhabit the globe is about 250,000. The number of fossil species of animals and plants cannot be reliably estimated, but it is safe to say that the number of the different extinct species that have been found in fossil state exceeds many times the number of all the different species now living.

Geologists claim four distinct periods or ages of the earth's history. Beginning at the oldest, they are called or named, First, the Azoic period, or period deficient of the evidence of life; Second, Paleozoic, or period of ancient life; Third, the Mesozoic, or period of middle life; Fourth, or last period, called Cainozoic. This period includes the Post Tertiary, or recent system of rocks or period of recent life.

A picture of the Azoic period has thus been imagined by Hugh Miller. "During the early part of the Azoic period we may imagine," he says, "a dark atmosphere of steam and vapor, which, for age after age conceals the face of the sun, and through which the moon or stars never penetrates; oceans of thermal waters, heated in a thousand centers to the boiling point; low, half molten islands, dim through the fog and scarce more fixed than waves themselves, that heave and tremble under the impulsions of the igneous agencies; roaring geysers that ever and anon throw up their intermittent jets of boiling fluid, vapor and thick steam, from these tremulous lands; and in the dim outskirts of the scene, the red gleam of fire shot forth from yawning cracks and deep chasms. Such would be the probable state of things among the times of the earlier gneiss and mica-chist deposits—times buried deep in that chaotic night which must have continued to exist for, may hap, many ages after that beginning of things in which God created the heavens and the earth."

At length, however, as the earth's surface gradually cooled down and the enveloping waters sunk to a lower temperature, let us suppose during the latter times of the mica schist and the earlier times of the clay slate, the steam atmosphere would become less dense and thick, and finally the rays of the sun would struggle through it; at first doubtful and diffused, forming a faint twilight, but gradually strengthening, as the later ages of the slate formation passed away, until at the close of the great primary period day and night—the one still dim and grey, the other wrapped in the pall of darkness—would succeed each other as now, as the earth revolved on its axis.

The number of active volcanoes on our globe are about 275 Humboldt suggests the idea that volcanoes are merely vents located above some far extended subterranean crack or fissure in the crust of the earth, through which the molten matter of the interior escapes to the surface.

The falls of Niagara are 150 feet in height, and the average amount of water passing over each minute is estimated at 670,000 tons. This water, by its abrading power, has undoubtedly excavated for itself the gorge or channel—seven miles long, 200 feet deep, and 1,200 to 2,000 feet wide—which now intervenes between the falls and Lake Ontario. The minimum time required to wear through this space has been estimated by Sir Charles Lyell, at 35,000 years.— *Well's Illustrated Geol.*

STRATIFIED ROCKS.

The stratified rocks of Great Britain have been studied more than any other of the earth, and as the result of these investigations it has been found that the extinct mammalia, found in fossiliferous rocks, is more numerous by half than all the species now existing; and of molluscs, the fossil species nine times as numerous as the living species; the fossil fish five times, the reptiles ten times, and the radiate fourteen times.

The geologist finds no trace of that golden age of the world of which the poets delighted to sing, when all creatures lived together in peace, and wars and bloodshed were unknown. Ever since animal life began on our planet, there existed, in all departments of being, carniverous classes, who could not live but by the death of their neighbors; and who were armed, in consequence, for their destruction, like the butcher with his axe and knife, and the angler with his hook and spear.

In Europe, the caverns or caves that have been discovered, have contained the remains or skeletons of a great many of the different species of animals that now inhabit the earth, and of others that are now extinct. For instance, the bones and skeletons of the mammoth are found in great numbers; also of the mastadon, the epoch of the mastadon, in a geological sense, is very recent. Some think that the mammoths and mastadons did not become entirely extinct in this country until after the advent of man. Sir Charles Lyell is of the opinion that the period of the extinction of the mastadon, although recent, must have been many thousand years ago.

PHILOSOPHY.

—:o:—

No two particles of matter can occupy the same space at the same time.

All bodies weigh heaviest at the earth's surface. A body that weighs 10 pounds at the earth's surface will weigh but $2\frac{1}{2}$ pounds 4,000 miles high.

Take two cog-wheels of the same size; let one stand still put the cogs together and put the other in motion, and when it has made one-half revolution around the standing wheel it will have made a full revolution on its own center, notwithstanding only one-half of the cogs of its own surface has touched the standing wheel.

The atmosphere is the lightest in wet, rainy weather; yet we find people very often who think different. The medium pressure of the atmosphere is about fifteen pounds to the square inch, but this is not always the case. The pressure will vary in the same locality, and sometimes be greater or less. The medium hight that atmospheric pressure will raise water is about 33 feet; but this calculation only holds good at the level of the sea, because as we ascend from the sea level the pressure becomes less; hence, our calculations for raising water by atmospheric pressure must be governed by the pressure that atmosphere has at the hight of the position above the sea level. Illustration: At sea level atmospheric pressure fifteen pounds to the square inch; one mile above sea level, about $12\frac{1}{4}$ pounds; two miles above, 10 pounds; three miles, $7\frac{1}{2}$ pounds; consequently, on an elevation three miles high, water cannot be raised but about $16\frac{1}{2}$ feet by the weight of the air.

The top or upper part of a wagon wheel passes through a greater amount of space in a given time when running than the bottom; or, in other words, runs the fastest.

The piston rod of a steam engine makes two complete stops at every revolution of the crank attached to the end of the pitman.

Horse Power.—The average power of a horse is sufficient to raise a weight of about 23,000 pounds one foot per minute, but when calculating the horse power of a steam engine it is estimated at 33,000 pounds. It then follows that a ten horse powers team engine is, in fact, about equal to fourteen average horses.

Power of Steam.—One cubic foot of water converted into steam will raise the enormous weight of three and a half million pounds one foot, or seven hundred pounds one mile high.

All bodies or particles of matter fall to the eath by the attraction of gravity, and their speed is in proportion to their density; but take away the resisting force of the atmosphere, then a cork or feather will fall as fast as a bullet.

Resultant motion may be illustrated by holding a ball or weight in your hand and dropping it from the top of your head while running, you will find that you cannot run fast enough to overtake the ball before it strikes the ground.

A ball may be shot from a cannon from the top of a tower on a horizontal plain, and another dropped from the mouth of the cannon at the same time, and they will both strike the earth at the same time, provided the surface be horizontal with the cannon.

Lever power is almost indispensable, or in other words, without it we could scarcely do anything; yet to take in consideration distance and speed, there is not a particle of power gained by a lever. Illustration: Suppose a lever 20 feet long, the fulcrum 2 feet from one end of the lever, 10 pounds on the long end of the lever is equal to 100 pounds on the short end; but to raise the 100 pounds one foot the ten pounds passes through 10 feet of space, consequently it travels ten times as fast as the 100 pounds, so all that is gained in power is lost in speed and distance; because if both ends of the lever was of the same length while one end of the lever was passing through ten feet of space the other end would pass through the same ten feet; and ten pounds would raise ten pounds ten feet high, or ten times as high as the ten pounds on the long end of the lever would raise the 100 pounds on the short end.

SKETCHES OF ASTRONOMY.

———:o:———

ORIGIN OF THE SOLAR SYSTEM.

Many theories have been propounded at different periods of the history of astronomy, respecting the original formation of our Solar System, as well as all other suns and systems, which it has pleased the GREAT CREATOR OF ALL THINGS to call into existence, but no one has gained so great favor or excited so violent opposition, as the theory first proposed by Sir William Herschel, and afterwards more especially applied by the celebrated La Place to the formation of the solar system.

This theory may be thus stated :—In the beginning all the matter composing the sun, planets, and satellites was diffused through space, in a state of exceedingly minute division, the ultimate particles being held asunder by the repulsion of heat. In process of time, under the action of gravitation, the mass assumed a round or globular shape, and the particles tending to the centre of gravity, a motion of rotation on an axis would commence. The great mass, now gradually cooling and condensing, must increase its rotary motion, thereby increasing the centrifugal force at the equator of the revolving mass, until, finally, a ring of matter is actually detached from the equator, and is left revolving in space by the shrinking away from it, of the interior mass. If now we follow this isolated ring of matter, we find every reason to believe that its particles will gradually coalesce into a globular form, and in turn form satellites, as it was itself formed. It is unnecessary to pursue the reasoning further, for the same laws which produce one planet from the equator of the central revolving mass, may produce many—until finally, the process is ended by a partial solidification of the central mass, so great, that gravity aided by the attraction of cohesion, is more than sufficient to resist the action of the centrifugal force, and no further change occurs.

It has been urged in favor of this theory, that it accounts for the striking peculiarities which are found in the organization of the solar system. That the rings of Saturn are positive proofs of the truth of the theory, they having cooled and condensed without breaking. That the individuals constituting a system thus produced, must revolve and rotate as do the planets and satellites, and in orbits of the precise figure and position, as those occupied by the planets. It accounts for the rotation of the sun on its axis, and presents a solution of the strange appearance connected with the sun called the Zodiacal Light. It goes further and accounts for the formation of single, double, and multiple suns and stars—and by the remains of chaotic matter in the interstics between the stars, and which are finally drawn to some particular sun, whose influence in the end preponderates, accounts for the comets which enter our system from every region in space.

In support of this theory it has been urged that the comets, in their organization, presents us with specimens of this finely divided nebulous or chaotic matter—and that the telescope reveals cloudy patches of light of indefinite extent, scattered throughout space, which give evidence of being yet unformed and chaotic. That many stars are found in which the bright nucleus or centre is surrounded by a halo or haze of nebulous light, and that round nebulous bodies are seen with the telescope, of an extent vastly greater than would fill the entire space encircled by the enormous orbit of the planet La Verrier, or having a diameter greater than 7,000 millions of miles.

Such are a few of the arguments in support of this most extraordinary theory. We now present the objections which have been most strongly insisted on. The retrograde motions of the satellites of Herschel, and their great inclination to the plane of the ecliptic can not be accounted for by this theory. That computation shows that no atmosphere of condensed nebulous matter can extend to so great a distance from the sun, as does the matter composing the Zodiacal Light, and, finally, that the nebulous matter in the heavens will ultimately be resolved into immense congeries and clusters of stars, whose great distance has hitherto defied the power of the best instruments.

In reply to the first objection, the friends of the theory doubt the facts with reference to the satellites of Herschel. They reply that the matter composing the Zodiacal Light being in the nature of cometary matter, is thrown to a greater distance from the sun than gravity would warrant, by that power residing in the sun which is able on the approach of comets to project those enormous trains of light, which sometimes render them so wonderful. As to the last objection, it is urged that although many nebulæ will doubtless be resolved into stars, by using more powerful telescopes, yet that these same telescopes will reveal more new nebulæ which cannot be resolved, than they will resolve—and as to the existence of nebulous matter, it is perfectly demonstrated by the physical organization of comets, and the existence of nebulous stars.

Such was the state of the Astronomical argument, when Lord Rosse's Great Reflector was first applied to the exploration of the distant regions of space. In a religious point of view, this theory had excited no small amount of discussion, in consequence of its supposed Atheistical tendencies. The friends of the theory contend that it was no more Atheistical to admit the formation of the universe by law, than to acknowledge that it is now sustained by laws. Indeed since we must go to the first great cause for matter in its chaotic state, as well as for the laws which govern matter, that this theory gave to us a grander view of the omniscience and omnipotence of God than could be obtained from any other source. In fine, that it harmonized with the declaration of scripture, which tells us that "In the beginning God created the heavens and the earth, and the earth was *without form and void.*" If the earth came into existence in its present condition, then it had *form* and was *not void.* Hence, this first grand declaration of the inspired writer must refer to the formation of the matter of which the heavens and earth were afterwards formed. Some went so far as to trace out dimly a full account of this theory in the order of creation, as laid down in Gensis.

Let us now proceed to the discoveries of Lord Rosse, and their influence on this greatly disputed theory. The space penetrating power of his six feet reflector is much greater than that of Sir William Herschel's great telescope, and it was anticipated that many nebulæ which were unresolved into clusters of stars by Hershel, would yield under the greater power and light of Lord Rosse's telescope. This has proved to be the fact. Very many nebulæ have been removed from their old places, and must hereafter figure among the clusters, while we are informed that many yet remain, even of the old nebulæ, which defy the power of the monster telescope.

The most remarkable object which has been resolved by Lord Rosse, is the great nebula in Orion, one of the most extraordinary objects in the heavens. Its size is enormous, and its figure very extraordinary. In certain parts adjoining the nebula the heavens are *jet black*, either from contrast or by the vacuity of these regions. Two immense spurs of light are seen to project from the principal mass of the nebula, and to extend to a most extraordinary distance. This will be better understood, by remembering that at the distance at which this nebula is removed from us, the entire diameter of the earth's orbit, 190 millions of miles, is an invisable point, less than one second, while this nebula extends to many thousands of times this distance, and more probably to many millions of times.

Several stars have been found, and are visible on the nebula, but have hitherto been regarded as being between the eye of the observer and this remote object. Sir William Herschel was unable to resolve this mysterious body, and yet the nebula gave indications of being of the resolvable kind by its irregular and curdled appearance under high powers. Several years since Dr. J. Lamont, of Munich, after a rigid scrutiny, of this nebula with his great Refractor, pronounced a portion of it to be composed of minute *stellar points*, and predicted its final perfect resolution into stars by greater power. This prediction has been fully verified, for Lord Rosse's great Reflector has solved the mystery, and filled this extraordinary object with the "jewelry of stars."

But the question recurs, what have the defenders of the nebular theory lost, or its enemies gained by this interesting discovery? We are all liable to reach conclusions too hastily, and to join issue on false points. If the nebular theory depended for its existance upon the irresolvability of the nebula in Orion, then indeed has the theory been entirely exploded. But this is not the fact. No one has asserted that the great nebula in Orion was *nebulous matter*, and if it were not, then none existed. Such an issue would have been a false one, had it been made.

The theory has neither lost nor gained by the discoveries

thus far made; what time may develope it is impossible to
say. In case certain data can be obtained, which appear to be
accessible, then indeed may we demonstrate its truth or false-
hood, by mathematical investigation. Until then, the safer
plan is neither to adopt nor reject, but investigate until absolute truth shall reward our long continued labor, and reveal
the mystery of the organization of that stupendous system, or
which our humble planet forms an insignificant part.—*Smith's
Astronomy.*

The sun is the center of the solar system, around which all
other planets belonging to our universe revolve. The names
of all the primary planets that have been discovered that constitute the solar system, are the Sun, Mercury, Venus, the
Earth, Mars, Jupiter, Saturn, Herschel, Uranus, Neptune, and
twenty-three asteroids, or small planets. The approximate
distance each of the large planets travel in making one revolution around the sun is about as follows:

Mercury, number of miles				220,000,000
Venus,	"	"	"	408,000,000
Earth,	"	"	"	570,000,000
Mars,	"	"	"	852,000,000
Jupiter,	"	"	"	2,910,000,000
Saturn,	"	"	"	5,340,000.000
Herschel,	"	"	"	10,800,000,000
La Verrier	"	"	"	17,100,000,000

COMETS.

Very little is known of the physical nature of comets.
They are thought by some astronomers to be about as dense
as smoke. They are bodies that revolve around the sun in
very elongated orbits, and some astronomers think that the
greater number visit our system but once, and then fly off in
nearly straight lines, and go to revolve around other suns in
the far-off distant heavens. The length of the tail of a comet,
as measured by astronomers, seem almost incredible.

Comet of 1680, length of the tail			123,000,000	miles.
Do.	1744,	"	"	35,000,000	"
Do.	1769,	"	"	48,000,000	"
Do.	1811,	"	"	130,000 000	"
Do.	1843,	"	"	130,000,000	"

The sun is 1,384,472 times as large as the earth; Jupiter is
1,280 times larger than the earth, and Saturn 1,000 times.

DIRECTIONS FOR FINDING THE NORTH STAR, AT ANY TIME.

Every pupil should be instructed in the manner of pointing out the North Star at any time of the night. If they are enabled to do this at any time, it will assist them in making other important observations, as well as being of use on many occasions which occur in the life of every man. Many persons have been lost in a *prairie* or other unfrequented places, when if they had been able to have told the points of the compass they could have extricated themselves from their lost situation. This may be done in a very easy manner. There is hardly a child of ten years of age who cannot at any time of night point out the stars in the Great Bear which form what is called the *Great Dipper.* Now if an imaginary line be drawn through the two stars which form the front edge of the Dipper, from the bottom towards the top, and continued about 20 degrees, it will pass very near the North Star—so near that it cannot be mistaken, there being no other stars of that magnitude near it. It should be borne in mind that this rule holds good in whatever position the Dipper may be at the time.— *Smith's Illustrated Astronomy.*

ECLIPSES.

Eclipses are among the most interesting phenomena presented to us by the heavenly bodies. In all ages, when an eclipse has taken place, it has excited the profound attention of the learned, and the fears and superstitions of the ignorant. The causes of eclipses before the seventeenth century were known only to a few, and they generally took advantage of this knowledge to impose upon the credulity of the ignorant by pretending that they were inspired by the Gods. Among the ancient nations, the Chaldeans were the foremost in their observations of the phenomena of the heavens; perhaps this was owing in some measure to their occupation; they being shepherds were obliged to watch their flocks by night to protect them from the wild beasts which were at that time numerous. Men under such circumstances would naturally be led to watch closely the movements of the heavenly bodies, and more especially so, for in the earlier periods of the world they had no correct mode of reckoning time in order to determine the seasons or the proper seed time and harvest.

Eclipses attracted the particular attention of the Chaldeans, and by a series of observations extended through several centuries, they discovered a very important fact relating to eclipses, although they did not understand the cause.

By comparing the records which had been made for a great length of time, they found that a certain period of time elapsed between eclipses of the same kind and magnitude; that is, if 18 years, 11 days, 7 hours and 43 minutes, were added to the time of the happening of any eclipse, it would show the time of the return of the same eclipse; the only differences would be that it would not happen at the same time in the day and it would be a little greater or less than the previous eclipse—thus they were able to predict eclipses with sufficient accuracy to answer their designs upon the ignorant without understanding the laws by which these periodical returns were produced.

To explain this briefly, it must be remembered that the moon's orbit makes an angle with the plane of the earth's orbit of 5¼ deg.; these two points where the moon's orbit cuts the plane of the earth's orbit, are called nodes. Now we will suppose that on any day at noon it is new moon, and the moon is just 16 deg. from her descending node, the shadow of the moon would just *touch* the earth at the north pole; in 223 lunations, or 18 years, 11 days, 7 hours, 43 minutes thereafter, the moon would come nearly to the same position as it was at the beginning, consequently there would be another small eclipse of the sun, and at the expiration af every 223 lunations it would return, and at each return the moon's shadow would pass across the earth a little more to the south until the eclipse had appeared about 77 times, when it would pass off at the south pole, occupying a period of 1,388 years: The same period would not commence again until the expiration of 12,-492 years. Each eclipse which takes place during any year, belongs to a separate and similar period. Those periods of eclipses which come in at the moon's ascending node, first come on to the earth at the south pole, and at each return the moon's shadow passes across the earth more to the north, and after appearing about 77 times, they finally leave the earth at the north pole.—*Smith's Astronomy.*

IMMENSITY OF SPACE.

Great is the immensity of space. Light travels at the rate of one hundred and ninety-two thousand miles per second, and yet at this great speed it would take it over thirty million years to come from some of the far off nebulas to the earth. Some ideas of the immensity of space may be gathered by the calculation of the distance that light would travel in thirty millions of years, and then supposing that the distance ascertained by the calculation, was to the remaining distance as one drop of water is to the ocean. In all probability the most powerful telescope has only brought to view a small portion of creation.

The nearest fixed stars, according to the best astronomical calculation, 20,000,000,000,000 of miles from the earth. To assist the mind of the reader to get some idea of the immensity of this distance, I have taken the pains to make the following calculation: Suppose that when the Lord past sentence upon Cain for killing his brother, that he had banished him to the nearest fixed star, and had caused a whirlwind or some other power to have taken him at the rate of one thousand miles an hour day and night from that time till now, counting the time past six thousand years, at 360 days travel to the year, he would have traveled at the end of the six thousand years only one 3.80th part of the distance, and at the same rate of speed at the end of two million years from this time he would not reach his destination, but would yet be one trillion three hundred and eighty-two billion four hundred million miles from his future home, or place of banishment. So you see that after two million and six thousand years travel at the enormous speed of one thousand miles an hour, leaves a distance yet untraveled equal to about fifty-five million times the distance of Cook's voyage around the earth.

PAY OF GOVERNMENT OFFICERS.

President of the United States	per annum,	$50,000 00
Vice-President	" "	8,000 00
Cabinet Officers each	" "	8,000 00
Speaker of the House of Representatives	" "	8,000 00
Members of Congress	" "	5,000 00
Chief Justice of the United States	" "	6,500 00
Associate Justices	" "	6,000 00

MINISTERS TO FOREIGN COUNTIES.

In Great Britain or France	per annum	17,500 00
In Russia, Spain, Prussia, Austria, Italy, China, Mexico or Brazil	" "	12,000 00
In Chili or Peru	" "	10,000 00
In Nicaragua	" "	7,000 00
In Portugal, Belgium, Netherlands, Denmark, Sweden, Switzerland, Hawaiian Islands, Ecuador, Argentine Confederation, Venezuela and all other foreign countries	" "	7,500 00

WAR DEPARTMENT.

Lieutenant-General	per month	720 00
Major-General	" "	445 00
Brigadier-General	" "	299 50
Adjutant General	" annum	3,950 00
Surgeon-General	" "	3,594 00
Paymaster-General	" "	2,740 00
Commissary-General	" "	2,552 00
Surgeon-General	" month	299 50

OFFICERS OF INFANTRY AND ARTILLERY.

Colonel	per month	194 00
Lieutenant-Colonel	" "	170 00
Major	" "	151 00
Captain	" "	118 50
First Lieutenant	" "	108 50
Second Lieutenant	" "	103 50
Brevet Second Lieutenant	" "	103 50

ORDNANCE AND TOPOGRAPHICAL DEPARTMENT.

Chief of Ordnance	per month	407 50
Colonel	" "	221 00
Lieutenant-Colonel	" "	211 00
Major	" "	187 00
Captain	" "	129 00
First Lieutenant	" "	112 83
Second Lieut	" "	112 83
Brevet Second Lieutenant	" "	112 83

(114)

RELIGIOUS.

The number of Protestants of the world, according to the statistics of all nations, is about as follows:

United States	83,000,000
Great Britain and Ireland	25,000,000
Asia and Armenia	5,000,000
British America and West Indies	4,000,000
France, Belgium and Holland	5,000,000
South America	1,500,000
Sweden, Norway and Denmark	7,600,000
The German Empire	25,000,000
Throughout the rest of the world	13,000,000
Total	121,000,000

Or about one in every fourteen of the inhabitants of the world are Protestants. Of this number there is about one in every four identified with or members of the different Protestant churches of the world. It then follows that the entire membership of all the Protestant churches of the world amounts to one in fifty-six of the inhabitants.

The number of Roman Catholics (approximately correct) is as follows:

United States	3,500,000
Great Britain and Ireland	6,000,000
Russia	7,200,000
South America	21,000,000
France	36,000,000
Austria and Venetia	28,000,000
Spain	17,000,000
Other parts of the world	60,000,000
Total	200,900,000

Pagans, or those who worshipped idols, or created things or beings, they number near three-fourths of the entire inhabitants of the earth. They number at present about 1,000,000,000. This includes the Mohammedans, the Buddhists and the Mormons, or Latter Day Saints. Of this number there is to be found in the United States, of Mormons, 75,000. And strange as it may seem, we have about 60,000 Heathen idol worship-

(115)

pers, who have began erecting their temples on American soil. There is one in San Francisco, California, and I understand one is being erected at Denver City, Colorado.

The number of church edifices and value of church property of the principal religious organizations in the United States, are as follows:

NAME.	CHURCHES.	VALUE.
Baptist (regular)	12,857	$39,220,221
Baptist (other)	1,105	2,378,977
Christian	2,822	6,425,137
Congregational	2,715	25,069,698
Episcopal	2,601	36,514,549
Evangelical Association	641	2,301,650
Friends	662	3,939,560
Jews	152	5,155,234
Lutheran	2,776	14,917,747
Methodist	21,337	69,854,121
Moravian	67	709,100
Mormon	171	656,750
Swedenborgian	61	869,700
Presbyterian (regular)	5,683	47,828,732
Presbyterian (other)	1,388	5,436,524
Dutch Reform	468	10,359,255
Late German Reform	1,145	5,775,215
Roman Catholic	3,806	60,985,566
Second Advent	140	306,240
Shakers	18	86,900
Spiritualist	22	100,150
Unitarian	310	6,282,675
United Brethren	937	1,819,810
Universalist	602	5,692,325
Unknown (union)	552	965,295
Unknown Local Missions	27	687,800
Total	63,082	$354,483,581

STATISTICAL.

Alabama	996,992	Missouri	1,721,295
Arkansas	484,471	Nebraska	122,993
California	560,247	Nevada	42,491
Connecticut	537,454	New Hampshire	318,300
Delaware	125,015	New Jersey	906,095
Florida	187,748	New York	4,382,759
Georgia	1,184,109	North Carolina	1,071,361
Illinois	2,539,891	Ohio	2,665,260
Indiana	1,680,637	Oregon	90,923
Iowa	1,194,020	Pennsylvania	3,521,951
Kansas	364,399	Rhode Island	217,353
Kentucky	1,321,011	South Carolina	705,606
Louisiana	726,915	Tennessee	1,258,520
Maine	626,915	Texas	818,579
Maryland	780,894	Vermont	330,551
Massachusetts	1,457,351	Virginia	1,225,163
Michigan	1,184,059	West Virginia	442,014
Minnesota	459,706	Wisconsin	1,054,670
Mississippi	827,922		
		Total	38,115,641

POPULATION OF THE TERRITORIES.

Arizona	9,658	New Mexico	91,874
Colorado	39,864	Utah	86,786
Dakota	14,181	Washington	29,955
District of Columbia	131,700	Wyoming	9,118
Idaho	14,999		
Montana	20,595	Total	442,730

POPULATION OF THE PRINCIPAL CITIES.

New York, N. Y.	942,292	Charleston, S. C.	48,956
Philadelphia, Pa.	674,022	Indianapolis, Ind.	80,244
Brooklyn, N. Y.	396,099	Troy, N. Y.	40,465
St. Louis, Mo.	310,864	Syracuse, N. Y.	43,051

POPULATION OF THE PRINCIPAL CITIES—CONTINUED:

Chicago, Ill.	298,977	Worcester, Mass.	41,105
Baltimore, Md.	267,354	Lowell, Mass.	40,928
Boston, Mass.	250,526	Memphis, Tenn.	40,226
Cincinnati, Ohio	216,239	Cambridge, Mass.	39,634
New Orleans, La.	191,418	Hartford, Conn.	37,180
San Francisco, Cal.	149,473	Scranton, Pa.	35,092
Buffalo, N. Y.	117,714	Reading, Pa.	33,630
Washington, D. C.	109,199	Patterson, N. J.	33,579
Newark, N. J.	105,059	Kansas City, Mo.	32,260
Louisville, Ky.	100,753	Mobile, Ala.	32,034
Cleveland, Ohio	92,829	Toledo, Ohio	31,584
Pittsburgh, Pa.	86,076	Portland, Me.	31,413
Jersey City, N. J.	82,546	Columbus, Ohio	31,274
Detroit, Mich.	79,577	Wilmington, Del.	30,841
Milwaukee, Wis.	71,440	Dayton, Ohio	30,473
Albany, N. Y.	69,422	Lawrence, Mass.	28,921
Providence, R. I.	68,904	Utica, N. Y.	28,804
Rochester, N. Y.	62,386	Charlestown, Mass.	28,323
Allegheny, Pa.	53,180	Savannah, Ga.	28,235
Richmond, Va.	51,038	Lynn, Mass.	28,233
New Haven, Conn.	50,840	Fall River, Mass.	26,766

THE NUMBER of all the male citizens over the age of twenty-one years in the United States and Territories, as shown by the statistics of the last Census:

Alabama	202,046	Missouri	380,235
Arizona	3,397	Montana	11,523
Arkansas	100,043	Nebraska	36,169
California	145,802	Nevada	18,652
Colorado	15,515	New Hampshire	83,361
Connecticut	127,499	New Jersey	194,109
Dakota	5,234	New Mexico	22,442
Delaware	28,207	New York	981,587
District of Columbia	31,622	North Carolina	214,224
Florida	38,854	Ohio	592,350
Georgia	234,919	Oregon	24,608
Idaho	5,557	Pennsylvania	776,345
Illinois	542,843	Rhode Island	43,996
Indiana	376,780	South Carolina	146,614
Iowa	255,802	Tennessee	259,016
Kansas	99,065	Texas	169,215
Kentucky	282,305	Utah	10,147
Louisiana	159,201	Vermont	74,867
Maine	153,160	Virginia	266,680
Maryland	169,845	Washington	7,902

NUMBER MALE CITIZENS, etc.—COTINUED:

Massachusetts	312,770	West Virginia	93,435
Michigan	274,459	Wisconsin	203,077
Minnesota	75,274	Wyoming	5,297
Mississippi	169,737		
		Total,	8,425,941

By the above the full amount of the vote of each State is shown, and as the vote for President in 1872 was not a strict party vote, we will give the vote for President in 1868, as polled for Grant and Seymour, as we think this more satisfactory.

VOTE OF EACH STATE OF THE UNION.

	Rep.	Dem.
Alabama	76,366	72,086
Arkansas	22,152	19,078
California	54,592	54,078
Connecticut	50,996	47,951
Delaware	7,623	10,980
Florida (By Legislature.)		
Georgia	57,134	102,822
Illinois	250,293	199,143
Indiana	176,552	166,980
Iowa	120,399	74,040
Kansas	31,046	14,019
Kentucky	39,569	115,889
Louisiana	33,263	80,225
Maine	70,426	42,396
Maryland	30,438	62,357
Massachusetts	136,437	59,408
Michigan	128,550	97,069
Minnesota	43,542	28,072
Mississippi (No vote.)		
Missouri	85,671	59,878
Nebraska	9,729	5,439
Nevada	6,480	5,218
New Hampshire	38,191	31,224
New Jersey	80,121	83,001
New York	419,883	429,883
North Carolina	96,226	84,090
Ohio	280,828	238,700
Oregon	10,961	11,125
Pennsylvania	342,280	313,382
Rhode Island	12,903	6,548
South Carolina	62,301	45,237
Tennessee	56,757	26,313
Texas (No vote.)		

Vermont..	44,167	12,045
Virginia (No vote.)		
West Virginia..	29,025	20,306
Wisconsin...	108,857	84,710
Total..	3,012,188	2,703,590

POPULATION OF INDIANA BY COUNTIES, 1870.

Adams............................	11,382	Madison..........................	22,770
Allen	43,494	Marion............................	71,939
Bartholomew....................	21,131	Marshal	20,211
Benton	5,615	Martin............................	11,103
Blackford	6,272	Miami.............................	21,052
Boone	22,593	Monroe	14,168
Brown	8,681	Montgomery....................	23,765
Carroll...........................	16,152	Morgan...........................	17,528
Cass	24,193	Newton	5,829
Clarke	24,770	Noble..............................	20,389
Clay...............................	19,084	Ohio	5,837
Clinton............................	17,330	Orange............................	13,497
Crawford..........................	9,851	Owen	16,137
Daviess	16,747	Park	18,166
Dearborn.........................	24,116	Perry	14,801
Decatur	19,053	Pike................................	13,779
DeKalb............................	17,167	Porter	13,942
Delaware.........................	19,030	Posey..............................	19,185
Dubois............................	12,597	Pulaski	7,801
Elkhart............................	26,026	Putnam............................	21,514
Fayette	10,476	Randolph	22,862
Floyd..............................	23,300	Ripley	20,977
Fountain	16,389	Rush	17,626
Franklin..........................	20,223	Scott...............................	7,823
Fulton.............................	12,726	Shelby	21,892
Gibson	17,371	Spencer	17,998
Grant	18,487	Starke.............................	3,888
Greene............................	19,514	Steuben...........................	12,854
Hamilton	20,882	St. Joseph.......................	25,322
Hancock	15,123	Sullivan	18,453
Harrison	19,913	Switzerland......................	12,134
Hendricks	20,277	Tippecanoe......................	33,515
Henry.............................	22,986	Tipton.............................	11,953
Howard...........................	15,847	Union..............................	6,341
Huntington	12,036	Vanderburg	33,145
Jackson	18,974	Vermillion........................	10,840
Jasper.............................	6,354	Vigo	33,549

POPULATION CF INDIANA BY COUNTIES—CONTINUED.

Jay	15,000	Wabash	21,305
Jefferson	29,741	Warren	10,204
Jennings	16,218	Warrick	17,653
Johnson	18,366	Washington	18,495
Knox	21,562	Wayne	34,048
Kosciusko	23,531	Wells	13,585
LaGrange	14,148	White	10,554
Lake	12,339	Whitley	14,399
LaPorte	27,062		
Lawrence	14,628	Total	1,680,637

INDIANA TOWNS THAT HAVE 500, OR OVER, INHABITANTS.

Decatur, Adams county	858
New Haven, Allen county	912
Ft. Wayne, Allen county	17,718
Monroeville, Allen county	630
Columbus, Bartholomew county	3,359
Hope, Bartholomew county	765
Oxford, Benton county	519
Hartford, Blackford county	878
Lebanon, Boone county	1,572
Zionsville, Boone county	956
Jamestown, Boone county	603
Thorntown, Boone county	1,526
Delphi, Carroll county	1,614
Browntown, Cass county	903
Logansport, Cass county	8,950
West Logan, Cass county	978
Charleston, Clarke county	2,204
Jeffersonville, Clarke county	7,254
Brazil, Clay county	2,186
Staunton, Clay county	587
Knightsville, Clay county	1,071
Harmony, Clay county	597
Bowling Green, Clay county	606
Frankfort, Clinton county	1,300
Leavenworth, Crawford county	567
Washington, Daviess county	2,901
Aurora, Dearborn county	3,304
Cochran, Dearborn county	675
Lawrenceburg, Dearborn county	3,159
Moore's Hill, Dearborn county	617
Waterloo, DeKalb county	1,259
Auburn, DeKalb county	677
Muncie, Delaware county	2,992

Jasper, Dubois county	547
Elkhart, Elkhart county	3,265
Goshen, Elkhart county	3,133
Bristol, Elkhart county	681
Connersville, Fayette county	2,496
New Albany, Floyd county	15,396
Attica, Fountain county	2,273
Covington, Fountain county	1,888
Laurel, Franklin county	741
Rochester, Fulton county	1,528
Owensville, Gibson county	522
Princeton, Gibson county	1,847
Patoka, Gibson county	844
Marion, Grant county	1,658
Jonesboro, Grant county	581
Bloomfield, Green county	656
Westfield, Hamilton county	608
Noblesville, Hamilton county	1,435
Greenfield, Hancock county	1,203
Corydon, Harrison county	747
Danville, Hendricks county	1,080
Plainfield, Hendricks county	795
Brownsburg, Hendricks county	551
Middletown, Henry county	711
Knightstown, Henry county	1,528
Kokomo, Howard county	2,177
Roanoke, Huntington county	627
Brownstown, Jackson county	572
Seymour, Jackson county	2,372
Rensselaer, Jasper county	617
Hanover, Jefferson county	564
North Madison, Jefferson county	1,007
Madison, Jefferson county	10,709
North Vernon, Jennings county	1,758
Vernon, Jennings county	673
Edinburg, Johnson county	1,799
Franklin City	2,707
Vincennes, Knox county	5,440
Pierceton, Kosciusko county	1,063
LaGrange, LaGrange county	1,038
LaPorte, LaPorte county	6,581
Michigan City, LaPorte county	3,985
Westville City, LaPorte county	640
Mitchell, Lawrence county	1,087

INDIANA TOWNS, ETC.—CONTINUED.

Anderson, Madison county	3,126
Pendleton, Madison county	675
Bourborn, Marshall county	874
Plymouth, Marshall county	2,482
Shoals, Martin county	512
Loogootee, Martin county	748
Peru, Miami county	3,617
Bloomington, Monroe county	1,030
Ladoga, Montgomery county	878
Crawfordsville, Montgomery county	3,701
Mooresville, Morgan county	1,229
Martinsville, Morgan county	1,131
Kentland, Newton county	802
Kendallville, Noble county	2,164
Ligonier, Noble county	1,514
Rising Sun, Ohio county	1,760
Orleans, Orange county	905
Paoli, Orange county	628
Spencer, Owen county	971
Gosport, Owen county	860
Rockville, Park county	1,187
Montezuma, Park, county	624
Cannelton, Perry county	2,481
Tell City, Perry county	1,660
Petersburg, Pike county	923
Valparaiso, Porter county	2,765
Mount Vernon, Posey county	2,880
New Harmony, Posey county	836
Winnamack, Pulaski county	906
Greencastle, Putnam county	3,227
Ridgeville, Randolph county	716
Farmland, Randolph county	532
Union City, Randolph county	1,439
Winchester, Randolph county	1,456
Versails, Ripley county	500
Rushville, Rush county	1,696
Shelbyville, Shelby county	2,731
Rockport, Spencer county	1,720
Angola, Steuben county	1,072
Mishawaka, St. Joseph county	2,617
South Bend, St. Joseph county	7,206
Sullivan, Sullivan county	1,396
Lafayette, Tippecanoe county	13,516
Tipton, Tipton county	892

INDIANA TOWNS, ETC.—CONTINUED.

Liberty, Union county	700
Evansville, Vanderburgh county	21,830
Clinton, Vermillion county	564
Perrysville, Vermillion county	690
Terre Haute, Vigo county	16,103
Lagro, Wabash county	519
Wabash City, Wabash county	2,881
Williamsport, Warren county	988
Booneville, Warrick county	1,039
Newburg, Warrick county	1,464
Salem, Washington county	1,294
Centreville, Wayne county	1,077
East Germantown, Wayne county	536
Hagerstown, Wayne county	833
Richmond, Wayne county	9,445
Milton, Wayne county	823
Blufftown, Wells county	1,138
Monticello, White county	887
Columbia, Whitley county	1,633

SABBATH SCHOOLS.

—————:o:—————

The first Sabbath School that we have been able to find a record of, was established in the year 1769 in the town of Wycumbe, England, by a young Methodist lady by the name of Hannah Ball. A few years after this another young lady who afterwards became the wife of Samuel Bradburn, suggested the idea of Sabbath Schools to Robert Rakes. He being a man of quick perception and great energy saw at once the advantages to be gained by schools of this kind. He immediately set to work and organized a school in the city of Gloucester, England, and through his labors and influence other cities of that country were induced to establish Sabbath Schools and work for the Sunday School interest.

The first Sabbath School established in the United States was organized by Bishop Asbury, in the year 1786, in Hanover County, Va., at the house of Mr. Thomas Cranshaw. The progress of Sabbath Schools in the United States until about the year 1830, was rather slow, as but few of the Christian denominations up to that time had become interested in the Sunday School cause. But one by one, the different organizations of Christians have gradually adopted the institution of Sabbath Schools, till now, the popular method of all churches for the religious training of the young is the Sunday School. Now, in every land and nation, where Christian people reside, the Sabbath School cause is advancing.

> The organization of Sabbath Schools,
>   Remember one and all,
> Was first established in Wycumbe,
>   By Miss Hannah Ball.

> After this Miss Bradburn
>   Suggested to Robert Rakes
> To organize a Sabbath School,
>   And helped him set the stakes.

(125)

They organized in Gloucester,
  The banner they unfurled,
The fame and name of which has spread,
  Almost throughout the world.

The honor due to Robert Rakes,
  Miss Bradburn and Miss Ball.
Should not be given to Robert Rakes,
  But given to them all.

For the institution of Sabbath Schools,
  The honor is due Miss Ball.
To her for lighting up the lamp,
  We give the honor all.

Miss Bradburn she is worthy of
  Our honor, love, and praise,
For her suggestions, and her work,
  In keeping up the blaze.

And to Robert Rakes is due
  The honor of school extension,
For adding fuel to the light,
  And widening its dimension.

VALUABLE RECIPES.

—:o:—

For Cleaning Silverware, and for Silvering Copper.—One-fourth ounce crystal nitrate of silver, one-half ounce cream of tartar, one-fourth ounce of common salt; pulverize all to a fine powder together, bottle it up and it is ready for use. Apply with a woolen rag, wetting the rag so as the powder will stick to it.

For Distemper in Horses.—Ground ginger, two ounces; flour of sulphur, two ounces; copperas, two ounces; Spanish brown, two ounces; saltpeter, one-half ounce; mix thoroughly. Give a tablespoonful once a day in bran mash. Keep the animal warm and dry, with light exercise.

Whitewash for Out Doors.—Take good white unslacked lime, one peck; salt, one quart; two pounds Spanish whiting; one gallon good flour paste; first slack the lime in hot water; be sure to put enough on to keep the lime from burning; then add while warm the salt and Spanish white, and then the paste; let stand over night. It is better to have it warm while applying it.

For Removing Paint From Glass.—Baking soda and warm water.

Antidote for Poison.—Give sweet oil in large doses.

For Worms in Children.—Santenine, nine grains; calomel, six grains; white sugar, eighteen grains; mix well; make in six powders for a child two years old, and give one before each meal for two days; work off with oil.

For Removing Grease Spots From Cloth.—Soda, two drachms; borax, one drachm; dissolve it together in one ounce of hot water, then add one ounce of alcohol. Shake it well and apply with woolen rag or brush, rubbing briskly.

(127)

To Get Rid of Little Ants.—Use salt and water freely where they infest.

Washing Fluid.—Borax, one pound; soda, one pound; dissolve in two gallons of hot water. Put the clothes in the tub, cover them with water containing a half gallon of the fluid, and let stand over night.

For Toothache, Headache, Neuralgia, and Rheumatic Pains.—Make a liniment of the following preparations: One ounce of tincture of Amonia, one ounce tincture of camphor, one ounce oil of organum, one-half ounce oil of cedar, one ounce oil of hemlock, and one quart linseed oil; mix all together, put it in a bottle and shake well. Directions for using. Apply the liniment freely to the affected parts, and rub and bathe it as often as three or four times daily. For the toothaehe, put a little on a piece of cotton, and put it in the tooth, and rub it on the jaw of the patient. I have found this to be one of the best liniments in use.

For Cuts and Bruises on Man or Beast.—Take two ounces tincture of camphor, two ounces linseed oil, one ounce of turpentine; mix all together, and apply to the affected parts.

For Pickling Beef.—To 100 pounds of beef take one gallon of salt, three-fourths of a pound of sugar, three ounces black pepper ground; add together, put all in a kettle containing three gallons of water; boil slowly, and skim occasionally. Pack the beef in tight tubs, and cover with the brine.

Book Binding.   Blank Books.

BOOK AND JOB

PRINTING

IN ALL ITS VARIETIES,

NEATLY EXECUTED,

AT THE

Printing and Publishing House,

J. M. TILFORD,

PRESIDENT.

OFFICE:

S. E. Corner Circle and Meridian,

INDIANAPOLIS.

Newspapers.   Magazines.

DIRECTORY

OF

MARION COUNTY

FOR 1874.

PREFACE.

In presenting this work to the citizens of Marion county, we
will say that we have made an effort to compile a complete
directory of the business of Marion county, and have used
every means to have it void of mistakes. We have invariably
instructed our agents to have each individual spell his own
name, so that it might be correct. There is no rule for spelling
individual names; therefore the same name is often spelled in
different ways. Yet, with all our pains, it is possible we may
have made more or less mistakes, as it is almost impossible to
make a directory without them; still, we hope that our patrons
may find this work in the main correct as a guide to the business of the county.

In making our canvass for the directory we have gathered a
few facts and statistics relative to the past and present which
we, in our plain and unvarnished manner, herein record. Although it is not presumable that we can give all the facts of
interest appertaining to the county's history in a work of this
kind, yet we feel assured that we can give enough to be of some
interest to the reader, and that it will help to preserve the names
and memory of some of the old pioneer settlers who have toiled
to heap blessings on this people, and that the statistics of the
past and present will give the reader some idea of the growth
and present wealth of the county.

For the facts and items of information that we have obtained we are indebted to a number of the old settlers with whom it has been our privilege to converse, and to each we return our thanks, and especially to Jacob Bruce, J. H. B. Nowland, John H. Martin, Obadiah Harris, are we indebted for early reminiscences and information in regard to the first settlers.

Hoping that this work may be found worthy of the patronage bestowed upon it, and that our patrons may find it equal to the promises made to them by our canvassers, we now present it to our subscribers.

HISTORICAL SKETCH

OF

MARION COUNTY.

MARION COUNTY was named in honor of General Francis
Marion. It is located in the center of the State of Indiana,
and is bounded as follows: On the north by Boone and Hamilton counties, on the east by Hancock and Shelby, on the south
by Johnson and Morgan, and on the west by Hendricks county.
The surface is generally level or slightly rolling, except a part
of the north and a small portion of the southwest, which is
more diversified. Rolling fields, low bottom land and bluffs or
hills all present themselves to the eye of the passer by in one
view, making those parts of the county to appear very pictur-
esque and beautiful. There is near one half of this county
which might be termed first and second bottom. The soil of
the greater part of the county is a rich black loam, and very
productive, especially the White River bottoms, which are not
surpassed in the yield of Indian corn, wheat, rye and vegetables
by any other part of the State. Fruit of all kinds usually
grown in this climate does well here, especially the small varieties, which are here grown to perfection. The rolling and bro-
ken hill land of the county is not so rich, but produces well
and is more profitable for grazing, being better adapted to blue-
grass, which seems to be a spontaneous growth of those parts
of the county.

The timber of the county, as found by the early settlers, was very heavy and fine, and consisted principally of sugar-tree, walnut, burr oak, ash, white oak, beech, sycamore, hickory and poplar. At the present time the timber near the city of Indianapolis is scarce, but in the more rural districts or out-townships there is yet a good supply for all present purposes, and if taken care of it will supply the demand for many years to come.

The gravel and sand beds of the county are almost inexhaustible; in fact, the greater part of the county is based on gravel or sand beds, which are generally from three to five feet below the surface.

The county is watered by White River, Fall Creek, Sugar Creek, Eagle Creek, Buck Creek, and other smaller streams. White River runs through the county near the center in rather a southwest direction. This is the second river of importance in the State. Fall Creek enters the county in the extreme northeast corner, runs in a southwest direction, and empties into White River at Indianapolis. The citizens of the county are making a change in the mouth of this creek, so that it will empty into White River about one and one-fourth miles above its present mouth. Eagle Creek takes its rise near Zionsville, in Boone county, and enters Marion county near the northwest corner, and meanders along the western border of the county in a due south direction until it passes through Pike township and enters Wayne, when its course is southeast to where it empties its crystal waters into White River. The southeast part of the county is watered by Sugar Creek, Buck Creek and spring branches.

The natural advantages of this county are many, among which are, its geographical location, its numerous streams of never-failing stock-water, its fine, rich bottom-lands, its bountiful supply of sand and gravel, etc. Deprive this county of the benefits it has received by the location of the State capital, and it would still be one of the wealthiest and best-improved counties in the State.

INTRODUCTION TO THE PAST HISTORY OF THE COUNTY.

Prior to the year 1800 Indiana composed a part of what was then called the Northwestern Territory. Said Territory included all of Illinois, Minnesota, Wisconsin, and near all of Michigan and Indiana. In the year 1800 the Territory was divided, or in other words the boundaries of a new Territory were marked out and established by law, and named Indiana Territory. The seat of government for the time being was at Vincennes, in Knox county, and the legal business of the Territory was transacted there for thirteen years. In the year 1813 the seat of government was removed to Corydon. On the eleventh day of December, 1816, by a joint resolution of Congress, Indiana was admitted to the sisterhood of States, at which time the Congress of the United States donated four sections of unsold government land to the State for the purpose of a location for a permanent capital, said land to be selected by the State Legislature. All of Central Indiana at that time was in possession of the Indians, and, as it was thought prudent by the Legislature that the seat of government should be located near the center, they therefore postponed making a selection until a treaty could be made with the Indians and the central part of the State relinquished by them. In the year 1818 the government of the United States appointed Governor Cass, Governor Jennings, and Judge Parke as commissioners on the part of the United States to meet in council with the Indian tribes and purchase their claims to the said lands. The council met at St. Mary's the same year, and a treaty was negotiated, whereby the Indians gave up all claim on Central Indiana except a few small reservations, and agreed to move off and give full possession within three years. They also agreed that the settlement of the territory by the whites might commence at any time after said treaty. From that time all of Central Indiana except the few reservations that were still held by our dusky neighbors was consid-

ered accessible to settlement by the whites, and the settlement
of this county began soon after.

FIRST SETTLERS.

Prior to the year 1819 no white man had ever settled or made
a home in Marion county. No marks of civilization could here
be found; no vestige of a dwelling to shelter the weary, way-
worn traveler from the bleak winds or pelting rains, save now
and then an Indian wigwam. The county then was inhabited
by the savage Indian, wild beasts and serpents; the tall old forest and thick woods were untouched by the hand of civilization.
The wa-oo of the owl, the croak of the bullfrog, the howl of the
wolf, and the yell of the savage made chin music for all of central Indiana, which was a doleful, desolate wilderness.

In this condition the daring pioneers and brave settlers found
Marion county in the year 1819. According to the best information that we have been able to obtain, the settlement of the
county began in that year. During that fall and winter a few
settlements were made in the county, which acted as a stimulus
to the State Legislature men to hurry up the selection of a location whereon to build the State capitol. The Legislature
which convened that winter saw proper to appoint commissioners to make said selection. They therefore appointed Joseph
Bartholomew, John Conner, John Tipton, Thomas Emerson,
William Prince, Stephen Ludlow, John Gillaland, George Hunt,
Frederick Rapp and Jesse B. Durham. After said commissioners had visited several settlements and locations on White River,
near the center of the State, and made a thorough examination
of each, they wisely concluded to locate the capital at Indianapolis, as they considered this point possessed of more advantages than any other. This spot was selected and agreed upon
by the commissioners on the 7th of June, 1820. At that time
there were less than a half-dozen families in the place, but the
rejoicing that was experienced by that little band of rusty pio-

neers over the selection almost beggars description. They now began to look forward to a better day, when their lands and homes would be valuable; when the savage Indian would take his wandering beat to the distant west; to the time when civilized and intelligent citizens should possess the land and a city be built. Yet it is not presumable they ever thought that it would acquire such grand dimensions in so short a space of time as is now to be seen.

The location of the capital being established emigration began to flow into the county from the settled parts of this State and other States of the Union, and the increase of population was very rapid, although the State offices were not removed from Corydon to this place until the fall of 1824, and the Legislature not till January, 1825. Prior to their removal, the county had been organized and the legal machinery of the county put in motion. The increase of her population from the fall of 1819 to the spring of 1822, had swelled her numbers to a sufficiency for self-government, or in other words, to elect their own county officers. Governor Jonathan Jennings, the first governor of the State after its admittance into the Union, appointed W. W. Wick Presiding Judge of the Fifth Judicial District, and Harvey Bates Sheriff of Marion county, with the power of calling an election to be held on the 5th of October, 1822, for the purpose of electing the necessary county officers. At said election James M. Ray was elected Clerk of Marion county, and Harvey Bates was elected Sheriff.

Some of the first settlers of the county that should be held in remembrance by the rising generation, and who withstood the hardships and privations which are incident to pioneer life, were,

John McCormick,	Dr. Samuel G. Mitchell.
Isaac Willson,	Thomas Chinn,
The Harding Brothers,	Christopher Harrison,
The Widow Harding,	Alex. Ralston,

Jeremiah Johnston,
George Pogue,
Matthias R. Nowland,
Billy Townsen,
Robert Wilmott,
George Buckner,
Maxwell Cowans,
Daniel Shafer,
Dr. Livingston Dunlap,
John Givan,
James Givan,
Alexander W. Russel,
Dr. Isaac Coe,
James Blake,
Wm. Reagan,
Obadiah Harris,
James Paxton,
Thos. Anderson,
Calvin Fletcher,
Daniel Yandes,
S. Morrows,
John Foudry,
John Johnson,
Reason Reagan,
Thomas O'Neal,
Hugh O'Neal,
Jacob Bruce,

James McCoy,
Harvey Bates,
J. H. B. Nowland,
Matt. T. Nowland,
J. P. Duvall,
Lismond Basye,
Simon Yandes,
Henry Bradley,
Andrew Willson,
Caleb Scudder,
Samuel S. Rooker,
James Kettleman,
James M. Ray,
George Smith,
Isaac Kinder,
John C. Hume,
Wm. H. McCormick,
Samuel Johnson,
Nicholas McCarty,
George Norwood,
George Bush,
The Crumbaugh Family,
The Barnhill Family,
The Gladdens,
The Walpoles,
The Collups,
The Whetzels.

We would be pleased to have the space and information to give the names of all the early settlers of the county, but as we have not, and as the names of all those who are still living will be shown up in the directory part of this book, giving the name, age, and date of settlement of each, we consider the above sufficient in this connection.

The oldest settler now living in the county is, according to our best information, the wife of Jacob Bruce. Mrs. Bruce is the daughter of William Reagan, and was born in the year 1811. She came to this county with her father in the fall or winter of 1819. She was joined in marriage to Jacob Bruce when quite young in the house they now occupy, and have lived on the same farm ever since. Their residence is about a quarter of a mile north of the Exposition grounds, and was the first brick house built in the county. It was built by Mr. Reagan, Mrs. Bruce's father.

The first merchant in the county was Daniel Shafer, a Pennsylvania Dutchman, who located at Indianapolis some time in the winter of 1820–21. His storehouse and dwelling was a log cabin, located near the south end of Meridian street.

John Givan located at Indianapolis in the spring of 1821, and engaged in selling goods, continuing the business for many years. It is asserted by some that Mr. Givan sold the first dry goods in the county.

The first wedding celebrated in the county was that of Jerry Johnson and Miss Rachel Reagan. At the time of Jerry's courtship and marriage there was no Clerk of Marion county to issue a license. The legal business of the county was done at Connersville, and Jerry being destitute of a horse he walked from Indianapolis to Connersville, barefoot, for his license, a distance of about sixty miles. When he had procured his license he found that there was no justice of the peace or minister in the county to tie the knot; so poor Jerry had to wait about six weeks for a minister to come along before he could claim Rachel as his own.

Mordecai Harding, the son of Robert Harding, was the first white child born in the county.

The first church built in the county was the Old School Baptist Church at Indianapolis.

The first postmaster in the county was Samuel Henderson,

who held the office for many years. He was removed by Gen. Jackson, and John Cane was appointed to fill the vacancy. The postoffice was at Indianapolis.

The first Sabbath-school was organized at Indianapolis in the year 1823. It was held in Mr. Caleb Scudder's cabinet shop, near where the State House now stands.

Caleb Scudder was the first cabinet-maker in the county.

The first wagon-maker that located in the county was George Norwood, who came to Indianapolis in 1822.

The first watchmaker that located in Marion county was Humphrey Griffith. He began business in Indianapolis in the year 1825.

The first man that manufactured hats in the county was John Shunk. His hat shop was located near where Kingan's pork house stands.

Andrew Byrne was the first tailor that settled in the county. He began business in Indianapolis in the spring of 1821.

The first mill built in the county was built by Isaac Willson, near Indianapolis

The first lawyer that settled and began the practice of law, was Calvin Fletcher. He was also the first Prosecuting Attorney for the 5th Judicial Circuit. He located at Indianapolis in the year 1821, and followed the profession for many years. He was a successful lawyer as well as a practical joker.

The first physician that settled in the county was Dr. Samuel Mitchel. He came to the county in the year 1821. Dr. Isaac Coe, Dr. Livingston Dunlap and Dr. Jonathan Cool all settled here the same year, not long after Dr. Mitchel came.

The first newspaper published in the county was the *Indianapolis Gazette*. The office was owned and the paper edited by George Smith and Nathaniel Bolton. The first number of said paper was issued in January, 1822.

The first blacksmith in the county was John Van Blaricum. He located at Indianapolis in 1821.

The first keel-boat ever run up White River to Indianapolis was landed there in 1821. The cargo belonged to Mr. Noland and a Kentucky gentleman, and the boat was in charge of Mr. Alexander W. Russel.

The State capital, or seat of government, had been fixed by law to remain at Corydon, until the year 1825, but the speedy increase of the population of Indianapolis, and the completion of her new court house, together with the high prices charged for board by the citizens of Corydon, induced the members of the Legislature to make an effort for its removal one year sooner. They introduced a resolution for the change, and in order to affect it they altered the time of convening the Legislature. Prior to that time they had met on the first Monday in December of each year, but this resolution, which was adopted in the winter of 1823–24, fixed the time to assemble on the first Monday in January, which was one month later in the winter; so that the Legislature could meet on the first month in the year of 1825 instead of the last month in the year of 1824. In the fall of 1824 the State offices were removed to Indianapolis, and on the first Monday in January 1825 the Legislature convened at the new court house of Marion county.

At that time the accommodations for entertainment in Indianapolis were limited, the guest or boarders generally occupying the same room with the family, or if they happened to be so lucky as to find a cabin with a spare room it was considered sufficient accommodation for at least a half-dozen boarders, yet, their tables would groan with the good things and fat of the land, which consisted chiefly of a good supply of corn bread, sassafras tea, wild meats, sweet milk, pumpkin sauce, and what we now term Granger pie. The price of board was two dollars, and of keeping a horse fifty cents, per week.

The roads of that day were few, and in very bad condition. In order to make a road they would blaze the timber on the

line they wished to run it, and the traveler was guided by the
white spots made on the trees. The travel was generally done
on foot or on horseback; wagons were seldom brought into use.

They had but little use for a market, except such as was furnished by the fur trader, who provided them with a few neces-
saries, as whiskey and tobacco, and took their furs and skins in
exchange, or if any one was so fortunate as to have a surplus
load of produce, they found a market for it by hauling it to
Cincinnati or Lawrenceburg.

Their mails were carried on horseback, and they were very
lucky if they received them twice a month. Very often they
were detained by high water, as there were no bridges over the
streams. The floods of water that fell would make them im-
passable; yet the faithful carrier delayed as little time as possible,
and very often urged his trusty steed to swim them.

Their mills, or corn crackers, were run by water or horse
power, but most generally they were horse mills, and the cus-
tomer who furnished the grist would also furnish the horse to
propel the mill.

The agricultural products of the county were in proportion
to the number of acres of improved land and the facilities for
cultivating the same; therefore when there were but few cleared
fields in the county, when the heavens were almost obscured
by the intervening forest foliage, when the land was covered
with ponds and marshes, when the forest stood proud in its
natural state, it was impossible for the pioneer settler to depend
on the agricultural proceeds of the county for support, but had
to resort to his rifle and trap to procure the meat for his table
and for skins to exchange for clothing. Then the chief products were Indian corn and vegetables, or, as one of the old
settlers informed us, the chief products of the county were
water snakes, lizards, oposums, wild turkeys, raccoons and
ginseng root.

The domestic animals of the county consisted of a very limited supply of poor horses and thin cattle, and the pioneer's trusty dogs.

Churches were few and far between; their meetings were generally held at the settlers' cabins. Their school houses were rude structures built of round logs, clapboard roofs and spring seats, that is the boy or girl would spring from the soft side of a split puncheon when struck by the ox gad of the teacher, which was frequently brought into use and was considered an indispensable article for keeping good order.

It is quite amusing to hear some of the old settlers tell of their hunts, their sports, their hardships and pleasures, but more especially of their school boy days, in the first settling of this county; but the scene is changed and that day is passed. Fifty years have wrought a mighty change in the land, a change that beggars description.

Our dusky neighbor, the red man of the forest, has long since taken up his line of march, and now wanders in the distant prairie. His savage yell and scalping-knife are no more to be feared by this people. The wild beasts of the forest have fled to parts unknown—to a land more congenial to their safety. The scream of the panther and howl of the wolf are no more to be heard, and the serpent has hunted his hole. The 'coon dog and fox hound, that were considered of so much importance by the pioneer settler, are seldom needed for that purpose. Ginseng diggers have had to resort to a more lucrative profession, and the huntsman has unslung his rifle. The heavy forests have been felled by the ax of the settlers; farms have been cleared, ponds ditched, the land tilled, and wonderful improvements have been made. Her rail pens that were used for the sheltering of stock, are things of the past, and fine barns have taken their places; the wigwam and cabin have been superseded by fine dwellings and beautiful mansions; the old log school-houses

that were few in number have vanished, and now at almost
every cross-road in the county there is a beautiful building for
that purpose.   Fine churches and temples of worship dot the
land in every quarter ; gravel-roads and railroads have been built,
telegraphs erected, towns and villages have sprung up, and a
city reared with her hundred steeples, which is the pride of the
State and a wonder to the early settler.   We no longer hear the
blast of the long tin horn which was carried by the post-boy ; it
has long since sounded its last note to greet the ear of the wait-
ing people who rejoiced at its coming, while the steed of the
rider has been superseded by the iron-horse and the telegraph ;
our mails are received twice a day, and we communicate with
all parts of the civilized world at lightning speed.   The hum of
the mill, the buzz of the saw, the clatter of power-looms, the
hammering of machine-shops, and the noise of the steam-whis-
tle are heard in every direction.

The increase of the population of the county has been as follows :

POPULATION OF COUNTY.

1820,	less than 100
1830,	7,192
1840,	16,080
1850,	24,103
1860,	39,855
1870,	72,000
and to-day,	over 100,000

While the wealth of the county has more than kept pace with
her increase of population.

There are now nine civil townships with the following population and vote, approximately correct :

	Population.	Vote.
Center,	85,000	16,868
Decatur,	1,700	333

							Population.	Vote.
Franklin,	.	.	.	.	.	.	2,500	485
Lawrence,	.	.	.	.	.	.	2,500	470
Perry,	.	.	.	.	.	.	2,700	495
Pike,	.	.	.	.	.	.	2,400	377
Warren,	:	.	.	.	.	.	2,400	540
Washington,		.	.	.	.	.	2,600	428
Wayne,	.	:	.	.	.	.	4,000	671

She has now 138,900 acres of improved land valued at over twenty millions of dollars, and produces annually near 400,000 bushels of winter wheat, 60,000 bushels of rye, 200,000 bushels of Indian corn, 50,000 bushels of oats, 15,000 bushels of barley, 40,000 pounds of wool, 90,000 bushels of Irish potatoes, 245,000 pounds of butter and 14,000 tons of hay, and thousands of dollars worth of vegetables. She has 10,000 head of horses and mules, over 20,000 head of cattle, 15,000 head of sheep, and 30,000 head of swine. The total estimated value of all live stock in the county is near two million of dollars.

She has over one thousand manufacturing establishments, consisting of foundries, machine shops, flouring mills, sawmills, planing mills, sewing machine factory, stave factories, piano factories, furniture manufactories, blacksmith shops, carriage and wagon shops, and many other things too tedious to mention. Said establishments give employment to near 10,000 hands, and use over one million dollars worth of raw material annually, and manufacture over two million of dollars worth of manufactured articles.

The assessed value of all the taxable property in the county, real and personal, is near one hundred million of dollars, and yet said estimate does not give the true value by about one half. The true value will reach at least $200,000,000.

10

CENTER TOWNSHIP.

This township is located in the center of the county, and is bounded on the east by Warren township, on the south by Perry, on the west by Wayne and on the north by Washington, and contains forty-two square miles. The surface is level or slightly rolling, with the exception of a few small bluffs or breaks on White River and Fall Creek. The soil is very rich, composed of a black loam mixed with sand.

In this township is to be found about nine-tenths of the entire wealth of the county. Indianapolis is located near its center. This city contains about 80,000 inhabitants, and is the greatest railroad center in the United States, and perhaps the greatest in the world, while its manufacturing interest is second to no city in the west. Its advantages are many, among which are its geographical location, its numerous railroads which center here and branch out in all directions, by which we can reach the shores of Maine and the Pacific Ocean, the northern Lakes and Gulf of Mexico. Its inexhaustable supply of pure water, its easy access to cheap coal, cheap iron and cheap timber; its beautiful academies and institutions of learning; its clean streets and pure atmosphere; its enterprising business men and cheap rents; its many temples of worship and beautiful surroundings, all tend to invite the capitalist and laborer, the business man and the manufacturer, to settle within her limits, which ere long will make this one of the foremost manufacturing cities in the world.

VOTE OF CENTER TOWNSHIP FOR SECRETARY OF STATE.

	Neff.	Curry.	Stout.
First Ward,	464	588	
Second Ward,	511	808	
Third Ward,	483	820	
Fourth Ward,	826	1155	
Fifth Ward,	1111	448	1
Sixth Ward,	932	431	
Seventh Ward,	783	401	
Eighth Ward,	703	438	
Ninth Ward,	715	692	
Tenth Ward,	254	738	3
Eleventh Ward,	223	593	
Twelfth Ward,	678	193	
Thirteenth Ward,	674	424	
Center Township South,	212	212	
Center Township North,	175	182	

CHURCHES.

A. M. E. Church, known as Allen Chapel; Broadway, near Christian avenue; Rev. W. K. Revels, pastor; membership, 300; average attendance Sabbath school, 150; value of church property, $5000.

Ames M. E. Church, corner Madison avenue and Union St.; Rev. F. A. Hutcheson, pastor; membership, 253; average attendance Sabbath school, 280; probable value church property, $9000.

Asbury M. E. Church, corner South street and Virginia avenue; Rev. Geo. L. Curtiss, pastor; membership, 283; average attendance Sabbath school, 200; value of church property, $35,-000.

Bethel A. M. E. Church, West Vermont street, near the canal; Rev. D. P. Seaton, pastor; membership, 550; average attendance Sunday school, 200; M. Harris, superintendent; value of church property, including parsonage, $35,000.

Blackford Street M. E. Church, corner Blackford and Market streets; Rev. H. N. King, pastor; membership, 215; average attendance Sabbath school, 120; value of church property, $7000.

California Street M. E. Church, corner California and North streets; Rev. J. E. Brant, pastor; membership, 242; average attendance Sabbath school, 203; value of church property, $25,000.

First German M. E. Church, corner New Jersey and New York streets; Rev. H. G. Lich, pastor; membership, 250; average attendance Sabbath school, 190; C. A. J. Schramm, superintendent; value of church property, $31,500.

Grace M. E. Church, corner East and Market streets; Rev. A. B. Lathrop, pastor; membership, 306; average attendance Sabbath school, 225; value of church property, $25,000.

German M. E. Church, corner New York and New Jersey streets; Rev. G. Nachtrieb, pastor.

Massachusetts Avenue M. E. Church, Oak street, north of Massachusetts avenue; Rev. T. H. Lynch, pastor; membership, 277; average attendance Sabbath school, 175; value of church property, $5000.

Meridian Street M. E. Church, cor. Meridian and New York streets; Rev. H. R. Naylor, pastor; membership, 579; average attendance Sabbath school, 418; value of church property, $140,000.

Patterson M. E. Church, Yandes street, north of Seventh; Rev. A. Hanway, pastor; membership, 65; average attendance Sabbath school, 75; value of church property, $4000.

Roberts Park M. E. Church, corner Delaware and Vermont streets; Rev. J. H. Bayliss, pastor; membership, 668; average attendance Sabbath school, 250; value of church property, $130,000.

Riverside M. E. Church, corner West and McCarty streets; Rev. H. N. King, pastor; membership, 129; average attendance Sabbath school, 96.

Second German M. E. Church, corner Prospect and Laurel streets; Rev. Michael Koehl, pastor; average attendance Sabbath school, 35; pastor, superintendent; value of church property, $3500.

Trinity M. E. Church, corner Alabama and North streets; Rev. E. B. Snyder, pastor; membership, 236; average attendance Sabbath school, 230; value of church property, $20,000.

Third Street M. E. Church, Third street, west of Illinois; Rev. S. T. Gillett, pastor; membership, 155; average attendance Sabbath school, 152; value of church property, $8000.

Woodlawn M. E. Church, corner Prospect and Laurel streets; Rev. W. H. Kendrick, pastor.

First Baptist Church, northeast corner Pennsylvania and New York streets; Rev. Henry Day, pastor; membership, 503; Sabbath school superintendent, George B. Loomis; average attendance of scholars, 372; value of church property, $50,000.

Second Baptist Church (colored), Michigan street, between West and Canal; Rev. M. Broyles, pastor; membership, 600; average attendance Sabbath school, 250; superintendent, Anderson Lewis; value of church property, $25,000.

Garden Baptist Church, west side Bright, north of New York street; Rev. S. Cornelius, pastor; membership, 105; average attendance Sabbath school, 150; superintendent, H. Knippenberg; value of church property, $5000.

German Baptist Church, southwest corner North and Davidson streets; Rev. G. Koopman, pastor; membership, 16; average attendance Sabbath school, 115; superintendent, G. Koopman; value of church property, $7000.

Judson Baptist Church, west side Fletcher Avenue; Rev. Henry Smith, pastor; membership, 55; average attendance Sabbath school, 133; superintendent, A. D. Templeton; value of church property, $2000.

North Baptist Church, corner Cherry and Broadway streets; Rev. J. B. Shaff, pastor; membership, 91; average attendance Sabbath school, 189; C. P. Jacobs, superintendent; value of church property, $7000.

North Indianapolis Mission Church, under control of the Indianapolis Baptist Union; value of Church property, $3000.

South Street Baptist Church, corner South and Noble streets; Rev. J. S. Gillespie, pastor; membership, 115; average attendance Sabbath school, 290; superintendent, H. C. Adams; value of church property, $12,000.

Zion's Baptist Church (colored), corner Second street and I., C. and L. R. R.; Rev. William Singleton, pastor; membership, 145; average attendance Sabbath school, 50; superintendent, Conrad Burley; value of church property, $1000.

Lick Creek Baptist Church, (vacant lot,) worship in school house; Rev. Anderson Simmons, pastor; membership, 30; value of lot, $800.

Christian Chapel, corner Ohio and Delaware streets; Elder W. F. Black, pastor; membership, 800; average attendance Sabbath school, 250; superintendent, Howard Cale; value of church property, $40,000.

Second Christian Church (colored); First street, near I., C. and L. R. R.; Elder R. Conrad, pastor; membership, 75; average attendance Sabbath school, 100; value of church property, $2,000.

Third Christian Church, Home avenue, between College avenue and Ash street; Elder John C. Miller, pastor; membership, 375; average attendance Sabbath school, 200; value of church property, $10,000.

Fourth Christian Church, Fayette, between North aud Walnut streets; Elder O. A. Burgess, pastor; membership, 200; average attendance Sabbath school, 150; value of church property, $7000.

Salem Chapel, Christian Church; Fifth and North Illinois streets; no regular pastor; average attendance Sabbath school, 125; value of church property, $7000.

Olive Branch Christian Church; South Meridian, near McCarty street; Elder L. H. Jameson, pastor; membership, 100; average attendance Sabbath school, 200; value of church property, $10,000.

Ovid Butler Mission, near corner Prospect street and Virginia avenue; supplied by Elder W. F. Black; membership, 75; average attendance Sabbath school, 100; church not completed.

Plymouth Congregational Church, corner Circle and Meridian streets; Rev. Oliver S. Dean, pastor; membership, 175; average attendance Sabbath school, 100; value of church property, $50,000.

Mayflower Congregational Church, St. Clair street, near East; Rev. N. A. Hyde, pastor; membership, 70; average attendance Sabbath school, 125; value of church property, $8000.

First Presbyterian Church, corner of Pennsylvania and New York streets; Rev. J. P. E. Kumler, pastor; membership, 411; Sabbath school, 225; value of church property, $150,000.

Second Presbyterian Church, corner Pennsylvania and Vermont streets; Rev. John L. Withrow, D. D., pastor; membership, 460; Sunday school, 360; value of church property, $150,000.

Third Presbyterian Church, corner of Illinois and Ohio streets; Rev. George W. F. Birch, pastor; membership, 436; Sunday school, 289; value of church property, $75,000.

Fourth Presbyterian Church; Rev. Edward B. Mason, pastor;

membership, 188; Sunday school, 95 ; value of church property, $100,000.

Fifth Presbyterian Church ; Rev. Joshua R. Mitchell, pastor ; membership, 158; Sunday school, 250; value of church property, when completed, $15,000.

Olivet Presbyterian Church, corner of Union and McCarty streets; Rev. John B. Brandt, pastor; membership, 139; Sunday school, 200; value of church property, $12,000.

Seventh Presbyterian Church, Elm street, north of Cedar; Rev. Charles H. Raymond, pastor; membership, 301 ; average attendance Sabbath school, 450; value of church property, $12,000.

Eighth Presbyterian Church, Indianola; Walnut street, west of White River; Rev. John R. Sutherland, pastor; membership, 100; average attendance Sabbath school, 145; value of church property, $8000.

Ninth Presbyterian Church, corner North street and railroad, in east part of city; no pastor; membership, 45; average attendance Sabbath school, 250; value of church property, $9000.

Tenth Presbyterian Church (Memorial), corner Christian avenue and Bellefontaine street; Rev. Hanford A. Edson, D. D., pastor; membership, 167; average attendance Sabbath school, 300; value of church property, $125,000.

German Christian Aid Society; membership, 40; capital, $800; meets monthly in German M. E. Church, corner New York and New Jersey streets; charter dated June 5, 1874.

First German Reform Church, 39 North Alabama street; Rev. Herman Helming, pastor ; membership, including children, 368 ; Sabbath School, 120; value of church property, including parsonage, $35,000.

Second German Reform Church, south of Washington on East street; Rev. M. G. I. Stern, pastor; membership, including children, 169; Sabbath school, 100.

First Salem Church of the Evangelical Association, corner of New Jersey and Wabash streets; Rev. H. L. Fisher, pastor; membership, 126; Sabbath school, 110; value of church property, $12,000.

Second Church of the Evangelical Association, corner of Peru street and Christian avenue; Rev. M. Klaiber, pastor; membership, 45; Sunday school, 60; value of church property, $7000.

Christ Church (Episcopal); corner Circle and Meridian streets; Rev. E. A. Bradley, rector; membership, 250; average attendance Sabbath School, 250; value of church property, $85,000.

St. Paul's Church, Episcopal; corner New York and Illinois streets; rectorship vacant; membership; 200; average attendance Sabbath school, 150; value of church property, $70,000.

Grace Church, Episcopal; corner Pennsylvania and St. Joseph streets; Rev. —— Judd; rector; membership, 85; average attendance Sabbath school, 100; value church property, $10,000.

Holy Innocents Church, Episcopal; Fletcher avenue; Rev. George B. Engle, rector; membership, 80; average attendance Sabbath school, 300; value of church property, $7,000.

St. James Mission Chapel, Episcopal; corner West and Walnut streets; Rev. Thos. W. McLean, deacon; membership, 25; average attendance Sabbath school, 75; value of church property, $5,000.

Friends' Meeting House; corner Delaware and St. Clair streets; Enos G. Pray, Calvin W. Prichard, Wm. G. Johnson, Wm. S. Wooton, Sarah J. Smith and Jane Trueblood, ministers; membership, 250; average attendance Sabbath school, 100; value of church property, $15,000.

Indianapolis Hebrew Congregation; temple on Market street, near East; Rev. M. Messing, rabbi; membership, 60; average attendance Sabbath school, 63; conducted by the rabbi; value of church property, $35,000.

Orthodox Hebrew Synagogue, Delaware street, south of South street; at present no rabbi; membership, 50; no Sabbath school; value of church property, $3000.

Zion's Church, Evangelical Lutheran, Ohio between Meridian and Illinois streets; Rev. Herman Quinius, pastor; membership, including children, 600; Sabbath school, 200; value of church property, $50,000.

First English Evangelical· Church, present location corner New York and Alabama streets; new church to be built in 1875 on the corner of Walnut and Pennsylvania streets; Rev. M. H. Richards, pastor; membership, 150; Sabbath school, 100; value of church property, $30,000.

St. Paul's Evangelical Lutheran Church, corner East and Georgia streets; Rev. Christian Hochstetter, pastor; membership, including children, 1500; Christian doctrine at 2 o'clock every Sabbath; value of Church property, $85,000.

Danish Lutheran Church, corner Beaty and McCarty streets; Rev. E. P. Jenson, pastor; membership, including children, 200; value of church property, $8,000.

Danish Lutheran Church, New Jersey near McCarty street; Rev. O. L. Kergeberg, pastor; membership, including children, 100; value of church property, $7,000.

Unity Unitarian Church, near Tennessee on Michigan street; no regular pastor; membership, 80; Sabbath school attendance, 65; value of church property, $15,000.

St. John's Cathedral (Catholic), Tennessee street, between Maryland and Georgia; Very Rev. Aug. Bessonies, pastor; Rev. Edw. Spelmann and Rev. Dennis O'Donohue, assistants; membership, children included, about 5000; average attendance Sunday school, about 500; the boys' Sunday school is kept by the Brothers of the Sacred Heart, the girls' by the Sisters of Providence; value of church property, about $200,000.

St. Mary's Church (German Catholic), Maryland street, between Pennsylvania and Delaware; Rev. A. Scheideler, pastor; membership, 4000; average attendance Sunday school, 400; kept by the Sisters of St. Francis and the pastor; value of church property, $85,000.

St. Patrick's Church (Catholic), southwest corner Dougherty and Short streets; Rev. P. R. Fitzpatrick, pastor; membership, 2500; average attendance Sunday school, 150; kept by the pastor; value of church property, $60,000.

St. Joseph's Church (Catholic), Vermont street, between East and Liberty; Rev. H. Alerding, pastor; membership, 1500; value of church property, $50,000.

Swedenborgian Church; 333 North Alabama street; membership, 75.

Young Men's Christian Association; 35 North Illinois street. Free reading-room open from 8 A. M. to 9 P. M. Strangers are welcome.

SECRET SOCIETIES.

Capital City Lodge, No. 312, F. and A. M.; meets in Grand Masonic Hall, corner Tennessee and Washington streets; membership, 136; resources, $1,000.

Ancient Landmarks Lodge, No. 319, F. and A. M.; meets in Condit's Block, South Meridian street; membership, 175; date of charter, June, 1864; resources, $3,000.

Center Lodge, No. 23, F. and A. M.; meets in Condit's Block; membership, 320; date of charter, Dec. 17, 1835; resources, $3,000.

Marion Lodge, No. 35, F. and A. M.; meets in Ætna Building; membership, 221.

Mystic Tie Lodge, No. 398, F. and A. M.; meets in Condit's Block, South Meridian street; membership, 165; charter dated May 25, 1869; resources, $2,500.

Oriental Lodge, U. D., F. and A. M.; meets in Buschman's Block, corner Ft. Wayne avenue and St. Mary street; membership, 30.

Indianapolis Chapter, No. 5; meets in Masonic Hall; membership, 159.

Keystone Chapter, No. 6, R. A. M.; membership, 70; resources, $500.

Indianapolis Council, No. 2; meets in Masonic Hall; membership, 138.

Raper Commandery, No. 1; meets in Masonic Hall; membership, 128.

Central Lodge, No. 1, A. Y. M.; meets in Judah's Building, East Washington street, opp. Court House; membership, 140; resources, $500.

Alpha Chapter, No. 1, A. Y. M.; meets in hall opp. Court House; membership, 40.

Indianapolis Lodge, No. 465, I. O. O. F.; meets Tuesday evenings in Mankedick's Hall, at terminus of Virginia avenue; membership, 40; resources, $500.

Germania Lodge, No. 129, I. O. O. F.; meets Thursday evenings in Grand Lodge Hall; membership, 290; resources, $11,000.

Teutonia Encampment, No. 57, I. O. O. F.; meets on second and fourth Friday nights in each month; membership, 135; resources, $2000.

Center Lodge, No. 18, I. O. O. F.; meets Tuesday evenings at Grand Lodge Hall; membership, 200; resources, $16,000.

Olive Branch Lodge, No. —, I. O. O. F.; meets on second Saturday in each month.

Philoxenian Lodge, No. 44, I. O O. F., meets in Grand Lodge Hall every Wednesday evening; membership, 275; resources, $20,000.

Metropolitan Encampment, No. 5, I. O. O. F., meets in Grand Encampment Hall on the first and third Monday evenings of each month; membership, 170; resources, $2,000.

Capital Lodge, No. 124, I. O. O. F., meets in Grand Lodge Hall every Friday evening; membership, 225; resources, $10,000.

Marion Encampment, No. 35, I. O. O. F., meets in Grand Lodge Hall on the second and fourth Monday evenings of each month; membership, 80; resources, $7,000.

Lincoln Union Lodge, No. 1486, Grand United Order of Odd Fellows; meets in Wright's Hall, Washington street, near corner of Pennsylvania; membership, 100; value of property, $3000.

Marion Lodge, No. 1, K of P.; meets every Wednesday evening, in Knights of Pythias Hall, corner Pennsylvania and Market streets; membership, 181; total resources, $2244.40.

Olive Branch Lodge, No. 2, K. of P.; meets every Saturday evening, in Knights of Pythias Hall; membership, 175; resources, $2706.62.

Koerner Lodge, No. 6, K. of P. (German); meets every Monday evening, in Knights of Pythias Hall; membership, 107; resources, $1282.

Star Lodge, No. 7, K. of P.; meets every Tuesday evening, in Knights of Pythias Hall; membership, 171; resources, $4414.70.

Excelsior Lodge, No. 25, K. of P.; meets every Friday evening, in Knights of Pythias Hall; membership, 89; resources, $892.03.

Palmetto Tribe, No. 17, I. O. R. M.; meets in Griffith's Block, every Monday evening.

Red Cloud Tribe, No. 18, I. O. R. M.; meets every Wednesday evening.

Tioga Lodge, No. 81, I. O. R. M.; meets every Tuesday evening.

Minewa Tribe, No. 31, I. O. R. M.; meets every Thursday evening.

Schiller Lodge, No. 1, Black Knights; hall 14 and 16 South Delaware street.

Woden Lodge, No. 42, Harrigarri; meets in hall, 14 and 16 South Delaware street, every first and third Friday of each month.

Frega Lodge, No. 63, Harrigarri; meets on Tuesday evenings.

Abraham Lodge, No. —, I. O. B. B.; meets Sunday evenings at Hall, 14 and 16 South Delaware street.

Union Lodge, No. 6, A. O. U. W.; meets Thursday evening at Griffith's Block.

Eagle Lodge, No. 11, A. O. U. W.; meets Thursday evenings at hall in Griffiths Block.

Lodge No. 1, A. O. H.; meets Wednesday evenings at Hall, southwest corner of South and Delaware streets.

Lodge No. 2, A. O. H.; meets Monday evenings at St. John's school-house hall.

Octavia Grove, No. 3, U. A. O. D.; meets every Monday evening; hall, southeast corner Illinois and Georgia streets.

Humbold Grove, No. 8, U. A. O. D.; meets every Wednesday evening.

Stonehenge Grove, No. 11, U. A. O. D.; meets every Thursday evening.

Washington Supreme Arch Chapter, No. 3, U. A. O. D.; meets second and last Friday of each month; Herman Gruenert, L. H.; Carl Wilhelm, Secretary.

High School, corner of Pennsylvania and Michigan streets.

The public schools range from 1 to 20 in Indianapolis. The township schools outside of the city are 15 in number.

Value of all school property of city, . . . 750,000

Value of township school property, . . . 40,500

Total of township and city, ... $790,500

Township Trustee, M. Doherty.

Superintendent of City Schools, G. W. Brown.

County Superintendent, Walter S. Smith.

Northwestern Christian University will move to Irvington in the fall of 1875; endowment, $400,000; value of building and grounds, 100,000.

DIRECTORY OF CENTER TOWNSHIP.

ADAMS & HATCH; dry goods, dress goods and merchant tailoring, 66 East Washington street, Indianapolis.

AYRES, L. S.; proprietor of Trade Palace dry goods store, 26 and 28 West Washington street, Indianapolis; bds Occidental Hotel. Born in N. Y. 1824; settled in M. C. 1872.

ABROMET, ADOLPHUS; general insurance agent; office in Ætna Building, Indianapolis; res 126 West Maryland St. Born in Prussia 1830; settled in M. C. 1861.

Aughenbaugh & Williams; druggists; 99 South Illinois street, Indianapolis.

Aughenbaugh, Wm.; res 248 South East street, Indianapolis. Born in Md. 1852; settled in M. C. 1865.

Anderson, D.; Palace Saloon; 23 North Illinois street, Indianapolis.

Atkinson, C. W.; plumbing and gas fitting; 251 North Illinois street, Indianapolis; res same. Born in Ind. 1848; settled in M. C. 1873.

Adams, J. H.; proprietor Adams House; 130 South Illinois street, Indianapolis. Born in N. Y. 1827; settled in M. C. 1863. Dem.

ATKINS, E. C. & CO.; diamond cross-cut saw factory; Illinois street, south of Union Depot, Indianapolis.

ATKINS, E. C.; res 348 North Tennessee street, Indianapolis. Born in Conn. 1833; settled in M. C. 1857.

ALDAG, CHARLES; manufacturer and dealer in boots and shoes; 175 East Washington street, Indianapolis. Born in Germany 1826; settled in M. C. 1848.

Aldag, Frank; with Chas. Aldag. Born in Ind. 1856.

Alexander & Craig; confectioners; 14 East Washington street, Indianapolis.

ANDERSON, W. C.; examines titles and furnishes abstracts of real estate in Marion county; office, 10 East Washington street, Indianapolis. Born in Germany 1839; settled in M. C. 1869.

Adams, J. W.; boots and shoes; 49 and 53 West Washington street, Indianapolis; res corner Fourth and Illinois streets. Born in Va. 1834; settled in M. C. 1860.

Andress, J.; Capital House, West Washington street, Indianapolis. Born in Pa. 1831; settled in M. C. 1872.

ARTIS, W. H.; proprietor barber shop; 197½ West Washington street, Indianapolis; res North West street, near corner West and Ohio. Born in N. C. 1827; settled in M. C. 1847.

Albershardt, H. F.; boots and shoes; 139 East Washington street, Indianapolis; res 85 North Noble street. Born in Hanover 1835; settled in M. C. 1868. Dem.

ALGEO, S.; assistant city engineer; res 159 Winston street, Indianapolis. Born in Ireland 1829; settled in M. C. 1863.

Alexander, D. S.; journalist; 135 North Illinois street, Indianapolis. Born in Maine 1845; settled in M. C. 1874.

ADAMS, K. T.; res 104 College avenue, Indianapolis. Born in N. Y. about 1828; settled in M. C. 1872.

Admire, O. R.; physician; 72 East Washington street, Indianapolis; res 84 Christian avenue. Born in Ky. 1828; settled in M. C. 1871. Rep.

Atkinson, E.; grocer; 99 Virginia avenue, Indianapolis; res 309 East South street. Born in Ill. 1853; settled in M. C. 1872.

Abbett, Dr.; res and office 35 Virginia avenue, Indianapolis. Born in Ind. 1838; settled in M. C. 1850.

Abbet, F. M.; physician; 33 Virginia avenue, Indianapolis; res 41 Huron street. Born in Ky. 1840; settled in M. C. 1865.

Althouse, J.; edge tool manufacturer; 191 South Meridian St., Indianapolis; res 200 Huron street. Born in Pa. 1820; settled in M. C. 1874.

Amos & Stokely; plumbers and gas fitters; 21 and 23 Massachusetts avenue, Indianapolis.

Amos, Isaac; res 78 Columbia avenue, Indianapolis. Born in Ind. 1842; settled in M. C. 184-.

Arnold, John; res 222 North Illinois street, Indianapolis.

ADKINSON, ELIZABETH; farmer; 2¾ m n Indianapolis. Born in Pa. 1824.

ALLEN, H. R.; firm of Allen & Johnson, National Surgical Institute; res 392 North Meridian street.

ALLEN & JOHNSON; proprietors National Surgical Institute, corner Illinois and Georgia streets.

Arnholter, Henry & Bro.; manufacturers of and dealers in saddlery goods; 213 East Washington street, Indianapolis.

Alley, E. L.; firm of Neal & Alley, res 383 East Washington street, Indianapolis. Born in Ohio 1820; settled in M. C. 1872.

Adams, Henry C.; principal deputy sheriff of Marion county; office, court house, Indianapolis.

Adams, G. F.; res 125 East New York street, Indianapolis. Born in Mass.

II

ADAMS, G. F. & CO.; dealers in furnaces, ranges, stoves and house furnishing goods; 39 South Meridian street, Indianapolis.

Adams, Wm. L.; res Pennsylvania street.

ANDERSON, SAMUEL S.; attorney at law; office 5 and 7 Hubbard's Block, Indianapolis; res 279 East South street. Born in M. C. 1853.

AMERICAN FIRE INSURANCE CO. of Philadelphia; office for the State of Indiana, 18 South Meridian street, Indianapolis.

AIKMAN, J. B.; fire insurance; Indianapolis; bds Sherman House. Born in Ind.

Anderson, L. N.; res 444 North Tennessee street, Indianapolis. Born in Ohio 1827; settled in M. C. 1853.

ANKANBROCK, HENRY; dealer in fancy groceries, provisions, also wines and liquors; 355 South Delaware street, Indianapolis; res same. Born in Prussia 1820; settled in M. C. 1850.

AUGINBAUGH, W.; druggist; 150 Virginia avenue, Indianapolis. Born in Md.; settled in M. C. 1865.

Abraham, Simon; dealer in cigars; 490 Virginia avenue, Indianapolis.

Anderson, Hattie; cigars and candy; 31 Kentucky avenue, Indianapolis.

ADKINSON, W. P.; attorney at law; 83 East Washington street, Indianapolis; res 263 East Washington street. Born in Ind. 1848; settled in M. C. 1873. Rep. Liberal.

Alcon, Albert; firm of Forbs & Alcon; res 422 Virginia avenue, Indianapolis. Born in Ohio 1839; settled in M. C. 1866.

ALCOTT, A. G.; firm of J. B. Cleaveland & Co.; res North Alabama street, south of St. Mary, Indianapolis.

ARDEN, J. & CO.; real estate brokers; 36 North Delaware street, opposite Court House, Indianapolis.

ARDEN, J.; res 233 North Liberty street, Indianapolis. Born in N. Y. 1834; settled in M. C. 1867.

Amos, A. S.; life insurance; res 326 North Meridian street, Indianapolis. Born in N. Y. 1813; settled in M. C. 1857.

Alexander, G. W. & Co.; real estate brokers; office, 25 West Washington street, Indianapolis.

Anderson, G. W.; res 39 Christian avenue, Indianapolis. Born in Ind. 1838; settled in M. C. 1863.

Andrews, L. N.; of Mothershead, Morris & Co.; res North Tennessee street, Indianapolis.

ANDERSON, BULLOCK & SCHOFIELD; importers and wholesale dealers in hardware; 62 South Meridian street, Indianapolis.

ANDERSON, JAMES T.; res northeast corner Sixth and Delaware streets, Indianapolis. Born in Scotland 1821; settled in M. C. 1865.

Andrew; John B.; restaurant and eating house; 26 West Louisiana street, Indianapolis.

Arthur, R. C.; grocer; 301 and 303 South West street, Indianapolis. Born in Ireland 1849; settled in M. C. 1869.

Adams, Samuel & Bro.; brick manufacturers; 1 mile southeast of corporation line.

Atlas Works, car manufacturing establishment; located near Exposition Building, Indianapolis.

ADAMS, GEO. F. & CO.; planing and saw mill; terminus of Massachusetts avenue, Indianapolis.

ADAMS, GEO. F. & CO.; stoves, house furnishing goods, etc.; 39 South Meridian street, Indianapolis.

Aufderhide, G.; dealer in cigars and tobacco; 137 Ft. Wayne avenue, Indianapolis.

ALLEN, HENRY; livery and sale stable; 27 and 29 East Pearl street, Indianapolis; res 132 West Vermont street. Born in Europe 1824; settled in M. C. 1853. Horses kept by the day, week or month, at reasonable rates.

ADAMS, MANSUR & CO.; carpets and wall paper; 47 and 49 South Meridian street.

Athon, James S.; physician; rooms 5 and 7, over 24½ Kentucky avenue, Indianapolis; res 529 North Meridian street. Born in Va. 1811; settled in M. C. 1853.

Arnold, John; res 222 North Illinois street, Indianapolis.

Adams, Henry C.; deputy sheriff Marion county.

Anderson, Geo. P.; firm of Anderson & Morris; notary public and real estate dealer; 49 South Pennsylvania street, Indianapolis. Born in Ohio 1824; settled in M. C. 1836. Rep.

ARMSTRONG, HENRY, SEN. & CO.; State agents for the University Medicines of New York; 17 Indiana avenue, Indianapolis; res 431 North Tennessee street. Born in Ky. 1808; settled in M. C. 1872. Christian.

ARMSTRONG, HENRY, JR.; firm of Henry Armstrong, sen. & Co.; dealer in coal; 17 Indiana avenue, Indianapolis; res 431 North Tennessee street. Born in Ind. 1850; settled in M. C. 1872. Christian.

Anderson, David G.; carpenter; 70 Indiana avenue, Indianapolis. Born in Pa. 1815; settled in M. C. 1831. Dem. Prot.

ALBERT, E.; dealer in staple and fancy groceries; 256 Indiana avenue, Indianapolis; res 382 Blake street. Born in Pa. 1833; settled in M. C. 1866. Rep. English Lutheran.

ABBETT, WM. A.; dealer in stoves and all kinds of tinware; builders' jobbing a specialty; 173 Indiana avenue, Indianapolis. Born in Ind. 1850; settled in M .C. 1873. Rep. Prot.

ANDRA, JOHN; manufacturer and dealer in saddles, harness, collars and whips; repairing neatly done on short notice; 178 East Washington street, Indianapolis. Born in Hanover, Germany, 1821; settled in M. C. 1851. Protestant.

ADAMS, D. O.; photographer; 39½ East Washington street. All work neatly executed on short notice.

Austin, Geo. T.; Weed sewing machine adjuster; 42 North Pennsylvania street, Indianapolis; res 136 East St. Clair street. Born in Ohio 1837; settled in M. C. 1866.

Adams, I. B.; lumber manufacturer; North Indianapolis. Born in Ind. 1832.

Altland, Hiram; constable; 45 East Washington street, Indianapolis; res 92 Columbia Avenue. Born in Pa. 1840; settled in M. C. 1853. Rep. Methodist.

Arbuckle, Matthew; real estate broker; 1 Glenn's Block, Indianapolis; res 712 North Delaware street. Born in Ind. 1839; settled in M. C. 1864. Rep. Orthodox.

Ayers, Levi; farmer; res on Michigan Road, 3 miles southeast Indianapolis. Born in N. J. 1808; settled in M. C. 1858. Dem. Presbyterian.

Annan, Chas.; firm of J. W. Copeland & Co., Indianapolis; bds Sherman House. Born in N. Y. 1847; settled in M. C. 1863.

ARMSTRONG, JOHN; farmer; opp Crown Hill, North Indianapolis. Born in Ohio 1813; settled in M. C. 1848.

ARMSTRONG, E. J.; farmer; opp Crown Hill, North Indianapolis. Born in Ohio 1845; settled in M. C. 1848.

Armstrong, J. W.; farmer; opp Crown Hill, North Indianapolis. Born in Ohio 1838; settled in M. C. 1848.

Archibold, B. J.; grocery and saloon; corner Seventh street and Michigan avenue, Indianapolis. Born in Ireland 1839; settled in M. C. 1865.

Burgess, C. C.; life insurance agent; office 13 East Washington street, Indianapolis; res 23 East Michigan street. Born in Vt. 1823; settled in M. C. 1862. Rep. Presbyterian.

BRANT, REV. J. E.; pastor California Street M. E. Church, cor North and California streets. Born in 1837; settled in M. C. 1873.

Ballard, Millicent; proprietress of boarding house; 60 West Market street, Indianapolis.

BOYD, FRANK A.; dealer in railway machine oil, varnish, white lead, mineral paints, etc.; 29 West Pearl street, Indianapolis; res 733 North Meridian street. Born in Indiana 1838; settled in M. C. 1862.

BUDD, J. R. & CO.; dealers and shippers of eggs, butter, poultry and game; 25 West Pearl street, Indianapolis.

BUDD, J. R.; res 114 Bellefontaine street, Indianapolis. Born in N. J. 1831; settled in M. C. 1852.

Bond, A. V.; firm of Mull & Bond; res 273 North Tennessee street. Born in Ind. 1832; settled in M. C. 1853.

BALL, J. M.; dentist; office 19 West Maryland street, Indianapolis. Born in Ohio 1837; settled in M. C. 1864.

Black, Washington; proprietor of grist mill; corner of Clifford and Archer avenues, Indianapolis.

BRYAN, JAMES W.; dairy; 3 m n e Indianapolis. Born in M. C. 1844. Rep. Protestant.

BLALOCK, MATTIE; dress maker; 9 Massachusetts avenue, Indianapolis.

Budd, Mrs. A. A.; dress maker; 13 Massachusetts avenue, Indianapolis; res 72 East Ohio street.

Bigger, R. H.; physician; office 19½ Virginia avenue, Indianapolis; res 161 Buchanan street. Born in Canada 1837; settled in M. C. 1874.

Bunnagel, Fred.; bakery and res 524 South East street; Indianapolis. Born in Germany 1842; settled in M. C. 1857.

Bossert, John; bakery and res 412 South Meridian street, Indianapolis. Born in Germany 1827; settled in M. C. 1854.

Boaher, Henry; meat market and res 422 South Meridian street, Indianapolis. Born in Germany 1821; settled in M. C. 1852.

BRYCE, P. F.; steam baker and manufacturer of butter crackers and steam baked-bread, which is kept by all first-class grocers; a fresh supply always on hand, at Bryce's steam bakery, 14 and 16 East South street.

Bryce, P. F.; res 13 e South street. Born in Scotland 1826; settled in M. C. 1870.

BUEHRIG, WM.; saloon and res corner of South and Pennsylvania streets, Indianapolis. The best brands of liquors always on hand. Born in Ind. 1844; settled in M. C. 1845.

BUEHRIG, HENRY; with Wm. Buehrig, saloon; res corner South and Pennsylvania streets, Indianapolis. Born in New Orleans 1841; settled in M. C. 1845.

Berg, Gus; pipeman of engine company; res Dougherty street, Indianapolis. Born in M. C. 1852.

BRANSON, D. A.; of David Branson & Co.; res corner Park avenue and St. Clair street, Indianapolis.

BERGUNDTHAL, D. C.; res 59 West Maryland street, Indianapolis. Born in Ohio.

Byrkit Bros.; manufacturers of doors, blinds, etc.; corner Tennessee and Georgia streets, Indianapolis.

Boyd & Lippincott; oils, paints and varnish; 25 East Georgia street, Indianapolis.

BYRAM, CORNELIUS & CO.; wholesale dry goods and notions; 101, 103 and 105 South Meridian street, Indianapolis.

BROUSE, J. A.; proprietor Brouse Block and capitalist, Indianapolis; superannuated minister of Southeast Indiana Conference M. E. Church; res Chicago. Born in Ohio 1808; settled in M. C. 1832; moved to Chicago 1870.

BROUSE, CAPTAIN C. W.; real estate dealer and capitalist; office Thorpe's Block, Indianapolis; res 150 College avenue. Born in 1839; settled in M. C. 1854.

BROOKS, C. W.; stencil cutter; 22 and 23 Talbott's Block, North Pennsylvania street, Indianapolis; bds 223 Vermont street. Born in Mich. 1850; settled in M. C. 1874.

Baggs, Frederick; internal revenue collector; room 15, post office building, North Pennsylvania street, Indianapolis; res 100 North Alabama street. Born in Maryland 1824; settled in M. C. 1846. Rep.

BRUBAKER, HENRY W.; physician and surgeon; room 2, McOuat's Block, Kentucky avenue, Indianapolis; res 65 West Michigan street. Born in Pa. 1826; settled in M. C. 1854.

Browning, E.; register U. S. Land Office; res 224 West New York street, Indianapolis. Born in Va.; settled in M. C. 1836.

BALLARD, G. M.; register U. S. Land Office, and dealer in western lands, Indianapolis; res 275 North Meridian street. Born in Ky. 1833; settled in M. C. 1851.

Bingham, Joseph; reporter Evening News; room Martindale's Block, Indianapolis. Born in Ind. 1849; settled in M. C. 1857.

BROWN, JAMES G.; tailor; room 27, 3d floor Martindale's Block, North Pennsylvania street, Indianapolis. Born in Ky. 1813; settled in M. C. 1825.

Baker, Conrad; ex-governor of Indiana; attorney at law; 23 South Pennsylvania street, Indianapolis; res 81 North Tennessee street. Born in Pa. 1817; settled in M. C. 1867. Rep.

BELLIS, WM.; superintendent Western Machine Works, Sinker, Davis & Co., South Pennsylvania street, Indianapolis; res 302 South Pennsylvania street. Born in England 1821; settled in M. C. 1870.

BARTHOLOMEW & DUMONT; real estate brokers; 82 East Market street, Indianapolis.

BARTHOLOMEW, C. G.; res Irvington. Born in Ohio 1830; settled in M. C. 1872.

Bohn, Gustavus; draftsman; 92 East Market street, Indianapolis; res 175 Madison avenue. Born in Germany 1827; settled in M. C. 1865.

BEHYMER, LEWIS; firm of Wm. Love & Co.

Brouse, Anderson; retired carpenter; res 130 East New York street, Indianapolis. Born in Va. 1801; settled in M. C. 1835. Rep. Methodist.

BATTY, NOLAN & TARKINGTON; real estate agents; 46 North Delaware street, Indianapolis.

BATTY, JOHN H.; res Woodlawn Avenue, Indianapolis. Born in England 1825; settled in M. C. 1846. Call on him for abstract of titles.

BERNHAMER, WILL. F. A.; German attorney, notary public; 46 North Delaware street, Indianapolis; res 119 Dougherty street. Abstracts of titles furnished. Born in Indianapolis 1849.

Blue, B. F.; clerk for J. H. Batty, abstract office, 46 North Delaware street, Indianapolis. Born in M. C. 1850.

Bell, Wm. E.; real estate and fire insurance agent; 40 North Delaware street, Indianapolis.

Burns, D. V.; attorney at law; 25 and 26 Baldwin's Block, Indianapolis; res 109 Central Avenue. Born in Ind. 1841; settled in M. C. 1866.

Bull, H. K. Jr. & Co.; railway supplies; 26 Virginia avenue, Indianapolis; res 205 East Ohio street.

Baggerly, C. W.; cigar manufacturer; 32 Virginia avenue, Indianapolis.

Benson, D. S.; new and second hand furniture ; 85 East Washington street, Indianapolis; res 69 North East street.

BULLARD, WILLIAM ; physician and surgeon ; North Alabama street, Indianapolis.

BARNARD, JOHNSON & CO.; loan brokers and real estate agents; 75 and 77 East Market street, Indianapolis.

Barnard, M. R.; res 35 Cherry street, Indianapolis. Born in Mass. 1824; settled in M. C. 1867.

Barnard, E. E.; res 35 Cherry street, Indianapolis. Born in N. Y. 1847; settled in M. C. 1867.

BROSSEL, H.; boot and shoe manufacturer; 79 East Market street, Indianapolis; res same; boots and shoes made to order. Born in Germany 1830; settled in M. C. 1873.

Bixby & Norton; attorneys at law; rooms 7 and 8 Baldwin's Block, corner Delaware and Market streets, Indianapolis.

Baker, James P.; law office, 3 and 4 Baldwin's Block, Indianap_olis; res 359 North Pennsylvania street. Born in Ind. 1844; settled in M. C. 1868.

BORTS, FREDRICK; butcher and meat dealer; 106 South Illinois street, Indianapolis; res 76 North Kansas street. Born in Germany 1835; settled in M. C. 1854.

Bigelow, J. K.; physician; firm of Todd, Bro. & Bigelow; res 547 North Illinois street, Indianapolis. Born in Ohio 1833; settled in M. C. 1865.

Barbour, O. P.; physician and surgeon; office 6 Shiveley's Block, Massachusetts avenue, Indianapolis. Born in Ky. 1827; settled in M. C. 1874.

Bunger, M. E.; firm of Elder, Bunger & Co.; res 290, corner of Lincoln avenue, Indianapolis.

BELL, M.; druggist and dealer in fancy articles, pure medicines, wines, liquors and dye stuffs; 261 Massachusetts avenue, Indianapolis; res 484 North East street. Born in Va. 1831; settled in M. C. 1856.

Bailey, Mrs. M. J.; dealer in notions and fancy Goods; 187 Massachusetts avenue; res same.

BARNHILL & BROTHERS; dealers in fancy groceries, produce and provisions; 99 Massachusetts avenue, Indianapolis.

Barnhill, C.; res 478 North Pennsylvania street, Indianapolis. Born in Ind. 1853. Rep. Protestant.

Barnhill, D. C.; res 478 Pennsylvania street, Indianapolis. Born in M. C. 1850. Rep. Christian.

BOYD, J. T.; physician and surgeon; 27 Massachusetts avenue, Indianapolis; res 117 Massachusetts avenue. Born in N. Y. 1823; settled in M. C. 1859. Rep. Presbyterian.

BIBB, WILLIAM A.; firm of Outland & Bibb; res 15 Cincinnati street, Indianapolis. Born in Ky. 1845; settled in M. C. 1866.

BELL, A. R.; editor Daily Evening Union; office, room No. 1, over 21 North Meridian street, Indianapolis; res 385 South East street. Born in Va. 1843; settled in M. C. 1863. Dem. Protestant.

BROUGH, JOHN W.; city editor Daily Evening Union; office, room No. 1, over 21 North Meridian street, Indianapolis; res 333 South Alabama street. Born in Ohio 1836; settled in M. C. 1854.

• BURLEY, JOSHUA; carpenter and contractor; res corner of Washington and Meridian streets. Born in Ohio 1820; settled in M. C. 1871.

Beck, S. T.; jeweler; 63 East Washington street, Indianapolis. Born in Ind. 1844.

BARNITZ, CHARLES; real estate agent; 83 East Washington street, Indianapolis; res 177 South Noble street. Born in Pa. 1802; settled in M. C. 1856. Rep. Protestant.

Becker & Huber; merchant tailors; 77 East Washington street, Indianapolis.

Becker, Jacob; firm of Becker & Huber; res 180 North New Jersey street, Indianapolis. Born in Germany 1826; settled in M. C. 1856.

Becker, Chas.; tailor; 77 East Washington street, Indianapolis; res 180 North New Jersey street. Born in Ind. 1858.

Biddle, Stephen; pump manufacturer; 6 Virginia avenue, Indianapolis; res 173 Woodlawn avenue. Born in Ky. 1828; settled in M. C. 1871.

BASS, LOVEL; restaurant; Indianapolis. Born in N. C. 1816; settled in M. C. 1840.

BROWN, AUSTIN H.; firm of Caldwell & Brown; general insurance; Indianapolis; res 290 South Meridian street. Born in Ind. 1827; settled in M. C. 1837.

Butler, C. C.; res 106 Cherry street, Indianapolis. Born in Ohio 1844; settled in M. C. 1852.

BELT RAILWAY; office 33 South Meridian street, Indianapolis; H. C. Lord, Pres't; Wm. Wiley Smith, Vice Pres't; J. F. Richardson, Sup't; Rob't F. Read, Chief Engineer.

BOND & ROGERS; real estate brokers; room 15, Hubbard's Block, Indianapolis.

BOND, PLEASANT; res College avenue, corner Lincoln St. Born in Ind. 1835; settled in M. C. 1840.

BROWN, W. H.; architect; rooms 25 and 27 Hubbard's Block, 3d floor, Indianapolis; res 141 West New York street. Born in Ind. 1840; settled in M. C. 1854.

BLUE, E. N.; firm of White & Blue; Indianapolis; res 261 West Washington street. Born in Ala. 1852; settled in M. C. 1871.

Brown, A. M.; book-keeper for McGilliard, Carpenter & Co.; Indianapolis; res 124 North Tennessee street. Born in Ohio 1853; settled in M. C. 1870.

BAUGHER, F. W.; dealer in hides, wool and fur; 30 South Meridian street, Indianapolis; res 392 North Alabama St. Born in Pa. 1846; settled in M. C. 1869.

Burns, H.; attorney at law; 25 and 26 Baldwin's Block, Indianapolis. Born in Ind. 1836; settled in M. C. 1874.

Bogert, James; wholesale and retail dealer in trunks; room 2 North Meridian street, under Bee Hive, Indianapolis; res 364 North Mississippi street. Born in N. J. 1819; settled in M. C. 1867.

BULLOCK, JAMES B.; firm of Anderson, Bullock & Schofield; res northeast corner Tinker and Meridian streets, Indianapolis. Born in Pa. 1825; settled in M. C. 1865.

Beardsley & Moore; general insurance agents; 30 and 32 South Illinois street, Indianapolis.

BRUSON, J. A.; with Benson & Burkhart; 281 and 283 West Washington street, Indianapolis; res 391 West Washington street. Born in Ky. 1828; settled in M. C. 1853.

BENSON & BURKHART; blacksmiths; 281 and 283 West Washington street, Indianapolis.

BURKHART, JOHN; with Benson & Burkhart; 281 and 283 West Washington street, Indianapolis; res West Vermont street. Born in Kentucky 1845; settled in M. C. 1848.

Baxter & Davis; grocers; 250 West Washington street, Indianapolis.

Baxter, Peter; res 250 West Washington street, Indianapolis. Born in Ohio 1817; settled in M. C. 1864.

Besi, W. K.; fancy grocer; 284 West Washington street, Indianapolis; res same. Born in Ind. 1841; settled in M. C. 1867.

BUEHLER, JOHN; saloon; 367 South Delaware street, Indianapolis; res same. Born in Germany 1846; settled in M. C. 1866.

BLOOMINGTON HOUSE; West Washington street, Indianapolis. Boarding by the week, day or meal, reasonable.

BUTSCH & DICKSON; dealers in coal, coke and lime; office 13 Virginia avenue, Indianapolis.

Bonsieur, J. P.; physician; 45 Virginia avenue, Indianapolis; res 666 North Tennessee street. Born in England 1842; settled in M. C. 1869.

Blackmore, D. & Co.; commission merchants; 72 and 74 South Delaware street, Indianapolis.

Bradley, G. S.; res 23 Woodlawn avenue, Indianapolis. Born in New York 1840; settled in M. C. 1870.

Booth, Wm.; manufacturer of stockings, shirts and drawers; 145 North Delaware street, Indianapolis. Born in England 1808; settled in M. C. 1871.

Black, John N.; barber; 10 South Pennsylvania street, Indianapolis. Born in Ind. 1850; settled in M. C. 1870. Rep. Protestant.

Briggs, Alfred; farmer; 2½ m s of Governor's Circle, on Three-Notch Road. Born in Ind. 1816; settled in M. C. 1862.

Budd, Wm.; brick manufacturer; 2½ m s of Circle. Born in Ind. 1849; settled in M. C. 1874.

Borgman, F.; firm of Borgman & Klassing; brick manufacturer; ½ m s e new corporation line, on New Bethel gravel road.

Bridges, William; blacksmith; Brightwood. Born in England 1840; settled in M. C. 1871. Rep. Protestant.

Bunnell, J. C.; farmer and gardener; 1¼ m n e Indianapolis. Born in Ky. 1833; settled in M. C. 1862. Dem. Prot.

BROWN, DAVID W.; retired farmer; 1¼ m n e corporation line, Indianapolis. Born in M. C. 1828. Rep. Lutheran.

BAILEY, I. C. & SON; photographers; enlarging pictures a specialty; room No. 17, third floor, Vinton's Block, North Pennsylvania street, Indianapolis.

BAILEY, I. C. Born in N. H. 1821; settled in M. C. 1873.

BAILEY, S. I. Born in N. H. 1854; settled in M. C. 1873.

Becker & Schwinge; grocers; 31 North Pennsylvania street, Indianapolis.

BEAL, R. H.; attorney at law; office No. 11 Talbott's Block, North Pennsylvania street, Indianapolis; bds 590 North Illinois street. Born in Ind. 1852; settled in M. C. 1874. Rep. Protestant.

BISHOP, J. M.; attorney at law; office Nos. 4 and 5 Talbott's Block, Indianapolis; res 25 School street. Born in Ind. 1848; settled in M. C. 1873. Rep. Protestant.

Bryan, J. M.; druggist; Virginia avenue, Indianapolis. Born in Ky. 1849; settled in M. C. 1864.

Bessel, J. B.; confectioner; 312 Virginia avenue, Indianapolis. Born in Md. 1854; settled in M. C. 1871.

Besener, J. F. & Son; grocers; 179 North East street, Indianapolis.

BECKER, JACOB; manufacturer of cigars; 27 South New Jersey street, Indianapolis. Born in N. Y. 1846; settled in M. C. 1865.

Brankman, John F.; farmer and retired carpenter; 3½ m n e Indianapolis. Born in Germany 1823; settled in M. C. 1853. Dem. Lutheran.

Berkhofer, Mrs.; dealer in confectionery, cigars and tobacco; 42 Kentucky avenue, Indianapolis.

BURCHMANN, C. P.; custom tailor; 30 Kentucky avenue, Indianapolis. Suits guaranteed to fit, and all work warranted.

Ballweg, A.; guns, pistols and fishing tackle; 129 West Washington street, Indianapolis; res 171 Madison avenue.

Bowers, Riley; grocer; 282 North Noble street, Indianapolis.

BEHRNZ, B. M.; cheap groceries; 13 North Davidson street, Indianapolis.

Beck, Samuel & Son; gunsmiths; 63 East Washington street, Indianapolis.

Beck, Samuel; firm of Samuel Beck & Son; res 152 North Mississippi street, Indianapolis. Born in Pa. 1809; settled in M. C. 1833. Dem. Methodist.

BILLING, A.; model maker and dealer in mathematical and philosophical instruments; 96 South Delaware street, Indianapolis; res 92 Bradshaw street. Born in Pa. 1828; settled in M. C. 1866.

BOTT, G.; bakery; 377 South Delaware street, Indianapolis; res same. Born in Germany 1838; settled in M. C. 1864.

BROCHHOUSEN, PETER; proprietor of grist mill on Madison avenue, Indianapolis; res 104 Coburn street. Born in Prussia 1832; settled in M. C. 1862.

Brown, Albert; saloon keeper and grocer; 387 South Delaware street, Indianapolis; res same. Born in Germany 1827; settled in M. C. 1854.

Barlow, T. J.; proprietor California wine room; 22 North Delaware street, Indianapolis; res 229 West Washington street. Born in Ireland 1845; settled in M. C. 1856.

Brown, J. H. F.; copper and sheet iron works; 143 North Delaware street, Indianapolis.

Browning, Wood; druggist; south end of Virginia avenue, Indianapolis. Born in Ind. 1845; settled in M. C. 1862.

BOYCE, JOHN; confectioner; 142 Virginia avenue, Indianapolis; a pure supply always on hand. Born in Ind. 1852; settled in M. C. 1871. Rep. Protestant.

BALL, W. W.; carriage manufactory; corner of College ave. and Tinker street, Indianapolis; res 266 Lincoln avenue. Has manufactured over one million dollars worth of carriages and buggies. Born in Ohio 1838; settled in M. C. 1872.

BRUCE, GEORGE; farmer; 80 rods north of corporation line. Born in Ohio 1802; settled in M. C. 1827. Was one of the first settlers of Marion county. (See history of county.)

BRUCE, JAMES A.; farmer and dairyman; 1½ m n Exposition Building. Born in M. C.

Bramer & Bro.; brick manufacturers; 1 m e corporation.

Bramer, Fred. Born in Germany 1849; settled in M. C. 1868.

Bramer, H. Born in Germany 1844; settled in M. C. 1868.

BUTLER, O. D.; Deputy County Clerk; res 227 Home avenue, Indianapolis. Born in Indianapolis 1837. Rep.

BLACK, GEO. W.; firm of G. W. Black & Co., wholesale dealers in fancy notions, toys, etc.; 24 West Washington street, Indianapolis; res 75 West Ohio street. Born in Ohio 1843; settled in M. C. 1864. Rep. Methodist.

Back, Clemens; manufacturer of cigars and wholesale and retail tobacconist; 209 East Washington street, Indianapolis; res 94 South Noble street.

Brundage, E. C.; livery and feed stable; 223 East Washington street, Indianapolis; res 339 East Market street. Born in N. Y. 1836; settled in M. C. 1856.

Burns, H.; saloon; 52 South Illinois street, Indianapolis. Born in Ireland; settled in M. C. 1863.

Bradbury, C. E.; real estate agent; 15 Virginia avenue, Indianapolis. Born in Ind. 1847; settled in M. C. 1873. Rep.

Bradbury, W. K.; real estate agent; 15 Virginia avenue, Indianapolis. Born in Ind. 1849; settled in M. C. 1873. Rep.

BARTHOLOMEW & CO.; dealers in groceries and provisions, flour and feed; 302 Massachusetts avenue, Indianapolis.

BARTHOLOMEW, V. G.; res 302 Massachusetts avenue, Indianapolis. Born in Ohio 1856; settled in M. C. 1872.

BARTHOLOMEW, C. G.; Christian minister; Irvington. Born in Ohio 1830; settled in M. C. 1872. Rep.

Bodine & Walton; groceries and provisions; 211 Christian avenue, Indianapolis.

Bodine, W. A.; res 47 Christian avenue, Indianapolis. Born in Ind. 1835; settled in M. C. 1873.

Buschmann, Wm.; wholesale and retail grocer; corner Fort Wayne avenue and St. Mary street, Indianapolis.

BROWN, WALTER S.; dealer in pure drugs and medicines, and fancy articles; corner Ft. Wayne avenue and St. Clair street, Indianapolis. Born in Ind. 1840; settled in M. C., 1861.

Beck & Sullivan; lawyers; 24 East Washington street, Indianapolis.

Breckenridge, J. W.; 16 East Washington street, Indianapolis. Born in Ky. 1848; settled in M. C. 1871. Rep. Presby.

BINGHAM, W. P. & CO.; watch makers and dealers in watch material and tools, both wholesale and retail; 50 East Washington street, Indianapolis.

Barnes, A. A.; commission merchant; 69 West Washington street, Indianapolis; res 782 North Illinois street. Born in Vt. 1839; settled in M. C. 1864. Rep. M. Baptist.

BINGHAM, W. P.; res 182 North California street, Indianapolis. Born in N. Y. 1833; settled in M. C. 1854.

Bowel, E.; confectioner; 147 West Washington street, Indianapolis.

BROWN, F. M.; wholesale and retail grocery house; 59 West Washington street, Indianapolis; res 223 West New York street. Born in Pa. 1834; settled in M. C. 1862. Rep. Methodist.

Blatz, Katharina; dealer in groceries, produce and provisions; 140 South Illinois street, Indianapolis. Born in Germany 1839; settled in M. C. 1864.

12

BAMBERGER, H.; hats, caps and furs; 16 East Washington street, Indianapolis; res 1 Fort Wayne avenue. Born in Germany 1837; settled in M. C. 1855.

BAKER, T.; proprietor MASON HOUSE; 75 South Illinois street, Indianapolis. Born in Ohio 1822; settled in M. C. 1874. Rep.

Ballard, A.; res 28 Circle street, Indianapolis. Born in Va. 1820; settled in M. C. 1844.

BALLARD & CO.; general commission merchants, dealers in flour, grain, feed and produce; 81 North Illinois street, Indianapolis.

BALLARD, W. F.; res 403 West New York street, Indianapolis. Born in Ind. 1840; settled in M. C. 1873.

Blake, J. W.; hackman; 67 North Illinois street, second floor, Indianapolis. Born in Va. 1825; settled in M. C. 1867. M. Baptist.

BUTTERFIELD, G. K.; wholesale and retail commission merchant, dealer in staple and fancy groceries, also all kinds of fruit; 69 North Illinois street, Indianapolis; res 196 West Ohio street. Born in M. C. 1841. Rep. Methodist.

Brooks, G. C.; clerk; 515 North Mississippi street, Indianapolis; Born in Ohio 1844.

BRADEN, WM.; firm of BRADEN & BURFORD; 21 West Washington street, Indianapolis; res 94 North Meridian street.

BOWEN, STEWART & CO.; wholesale and retail dealers in books and stationery; 18 West Washington street, Indianapolis.

BOWEN, SILAS T.; res 82 West Vermont street, Indianapolis. Born in N. Y. 1819; settled in M. C. 1853. Dem. Presb.

Breedlove & McClelland; real estate agents; 31 West Washington street, Indianapolis.

Bryan, T. N.; physician; 24½ Kentucky avenue, Indianapolis; res 346 East South street. Born in M. C. 1833. M. Baptist.

Bigelow, J. K.; physician; 24½ Kentucky avenue, Indianapolis; res 547 North Illinois street. Born in Ohio 1833; settled in M. C. 1865. Rep.

Breunninger, A.; grocer; 113 West Washington street, Indianapolis. Born in Germany 1824; settled in M. C. 1851.

Burnett, J. C.; deputy Auditor of State; res 276 North Mississippi street, Indianapolis. Born in N. J. 1833; settled in M. C. 1861. Rep.

Buck, R. H.; real estate broker; 72½ East Washington street, Indianapolis; res 324 College avenue. Born in Ohio 1820; settled in M. C. 1870. Rep. Methodist.

Baird, J. E.; surveyor and civil engineer; 72½ East Washington street, Indianapolis; res 165 Massachusetts avenue. Born in Ohio 1829; settled in M. C. 1872. Rep.

BRINDLE, MARY ANN; hosiery factory; 90 East Washington street, Indianapolis. Born in England 1827; settled in M. C. 1869.

BOHN, A.; book-keeper for Robertson & Schnider; res 175 Madison avenue, Indianapolis. Born in Ohio 1855; settled in M. C. 1867.

Bartholomew, H. & Son; boot and shoe merchants; 98 East Washington street, Indianapolis.

Bartholomew, H.; res 183 East Ohio street, Indianapolis. Born in Mass. 1813; settled in M. C. 1871. Rep.

Bartholomew, H. M.; res 183 East Ohio street, Indianapolis.

BRADSHAW, W. A. & SON; 44 and 46 East Washington street, Indianapolis; dealers in all kinds of musical merchandize.

BRADSHAW, W. A.; investing agent; 44 and 46 East Washington street, Indianapolis; res 384 North New Jersey street. Born in Va. 1823; settled in M. C. 1836. Rep. Presbyterian.

Bloomer, I. L.; lawyer; 32½ East Washington street, Indianapolis.

Beck, A. T.; res corner Tennessee and Ohio streets, Indianapolis. Episcopalian.

Benham & Stedman; dealers in pianos, stools and covers; 36 East Washington street, Indianapolis.

Benham, Henry L.; dealer in organs, band instruments and publisher of Benham's Musical Review; 36 East Washington street, Indianapolis; res 33 West Iowa street. Born in N. Y. 1848; settled in M. C. 1863. Rep. Presbyterian.

Bieler, T. L.; res 218 East McCarty street, Indianapolis. Born in Germany 1839; settled in M. C. 1861.

Brown, T. B.; railroad agent; res 27 East North street, Indianapolis. Born in Ohio 1836; settled in M. C. 1857.

BURROWS, ASA W.; book-keeper for Security Life Ins. Co.; office 95 East Washington street, Indianapolis; res. 35 Virginia avenue. Born in Ohio 1853; settled in M. C. 1860.

Brush, John C.; lawyer; over 95 East Washington street, Indianapolis.

BROWN, EDGAR A.; attorney at law; 95 East Washington street, Indianapolis; res 363 North Alabama street. Born in Ohio; settled in M. C. 1872.

Bradbury, D. M.; lawyer; 95 East Washington street, Indianapolis; res 363 North Alabama street. Born in Ind. 1834; settled in M. C. 1871.

Bunting, G. W.; architect; Indianapolis. Born in Pa. 1829; settled in M. C. 1873.

BOHLEN, D. A.; architect; office over 95 East Washington street, 3d floor, Indianapolis; res 71 North Noble street. Born in Germany 1827; settled in M. C. 1853.

Birch, L; groceries; 119 and 121 South Illinois street, Indianapolis; res 35 West Georgia street. Born in Ky. 1840; settled in M. C. 1861.

Bourgonne & Hartman; cigars and tobacco; 186 South Illinois street, Indianapolis.

Bourgonne, ———; res 140 Union street, Indianapolis. Born in France 1836; settled in M. C. 1853.

BURKERT, ED. A.; dealer in notions, trimmings, and a general assortment of ladies' furnishing; 60 North Illinois street, Indianapolis; res 128 West Pratt street. Born in Pa. 1842; settled in M. C. 1868. Rep. Presbyterian.

Boyd, L. A.; firm of Harrington & Boyd, carriage manufacturers; res 119 North New Jersey street. Born in Ind. 1850; settled in M. C. 1874.

Blucher, J.; boot and shoemaker; 208 South Illinois street, Indianapolis. Born in Germany 1837; settled in M. C. 1871.

BIGHAM, H. S.; councilman 9th ward, and general agent Buffalo Scale Co.; 153 East Washington street, Indianapolis; res 510 East Washington street. Born in Pa. 1842; settled in M. C. 1866.

Bevan, J.; groceries; 523 North Illinois street, corner First; res 25 West First street. Born in Ohio 1829; settled in M. C. 1872. Dem.

Balz, P. H.; butcher; 427 North Illinois street, Indianapolis.

Bombarger, David; res 287 Indiana avenue, Indianapolis. Born in Pa. 1817; settled in M. C. 1849.

Burgess, E. T.; foreman No. 1 Fire Engine Co.; 147 Indiana avenue, Indianapolis. Born in Mass. 1837; settled in M. C. 1867. Indpt.

Bishop, George M.; engineer No. 1 Fire Engine Co.; 147 Indiana avenue, Indianapolis. Born in Va. 1840.

Bishop, James L.; No. 1 Engine House, Indianapolis. Born in Va. 1846.

Boyle, James J.; firm of A. Reed & Co.; soda water manufacturers. Born in Mo. 1843; settled in M. C. 1868. Dem. Catholic.

BARTMASS, WM. J., M. D. and jeweler; 166 Indiana avenue, Indianapolis. Born in Ill. 1834; settled in M. C. 1873. Dem. Christian.

Biedenmeister, C. A.; fire insurance agent; 151 East Washington street, Indianapolis; res 149 North East street.

Brown, Ellwood E., dealer in new and second hand furniture; 178 Indiana avenue, Indianapolis. Born in Pa. 1845; settled in M. C. 1872.

BOLSER, GEO. W.; sign and carriage painter; 178 Indiana avenue, Indianapolis; res 284 Blake street. Born in Ohio 1843; settled in M. C. 1862. Rep. Protestant.

Burns, William; retail liquor; 251 Indiana avenue, Indianapolis; res 255 Indiana avenue. Born in Ireland 1841; settled in M. C. 1864. Indpt. R. Catholic.

Bœtticher, Julius; editor and publisher of the Indiana Volksblatt; 164 East Washington street, Indianapolis. Born in Nardhousen, Prussia; 1813; settled in M.C. 1848.

BURR, N. B.; firm of Burr & Miller, real estate agents; 45 East Washington street, up stairs, Indianapolis; res 295 North East street. Born in N. Y. 1822; settled in M. C. 1868. Rep. Liberal.

Billingsley & Williams; wholesale fruit and produce merchants; 76 West Washington street, Indianapolis.

BRENT, F. J.; firm of Brent & Elder, photographers; 210 and 212 East Washington street, Indianapolis. All work neatly done at low prices. Born in England 1841; settled in M. C. 1867.

BROWN JOHN; barber and hair dresser; 218 East Washington street, Indianapolis. Born in Ky. 1839; settled in M. C. 1870. Rep. Protestant.

Bollinger, James; firm of Dreher & Bollinger, dealers in notions; 250 East Washington street, Indianapolis; res 244 North East street. Born in Pa.; settled in M. C. 1860. Rep. Methodist.

Baldus, John; boarding house, saloon and beer garden; 252 East Washington street. Indianapolis. Born in Nassau, Germany, 1823; settled in M. C. 1869.

Buell, C. H.; manufacturer of medicines; 334 East Washington street, Indianapolis. Born in N. Y. 1831; settled in M. C. 1854.

BUENNAGEL, JOSEPH; firm of Fred Stitz & Co., manufacturers and wholesale and retail dealers in cigars and tobacco;
328 East Washington street, Indianapolis; res 128 North
Liberty street. Born in Bavaria, Germany, 1853; settled
in M. C. 1857.

BUTLER, T. H.; firm of A. C. Remy & Co., wholesale and retail dealers in flour, grain and produce, general brokers and
commission merchants; 308 East Washington street, Indianapolis; res cor Third and Illinois streets. Born in Ind.
1833; settled in M. C. 1870.

BROWN, C. W.; firm of A. C. Remy & Co., commission merchants; 308 East Washington street, Indianapolis. Born
in Ind. 1840; settled in M. C. 1870.

Boyd, I. J.; dealer in new and second-hand wagons and buggies;
480 East Washington street, Indianapolis. Born in M. C.
1850.

Burd, W.; firm of Burd & Duncan; room 38 Martindale's
Block, Indianapolis. Born in Ohio 1845; settled in M. C.
1874.

Boley, S. Monroe; druggist; 412 West North street, Indianapolis. Born in Ind. 1851; settled in M. C. 1870.

Burton, Daniel; manufacturer of flour barrels; 419 West New
York street, Indianapolis. Born in Va. 1832; settled in M.
C. 1863.

BRACKIN & THOMPSON; dealers in lumber, lath and shingles, also dressed flooring and siding; yard, No. 180 West
Market street, Indianapolis.

BRACKIN, THOMAS E.; firm of Brackin & Thompson; res
269 North California street, Indianapolis. Born in Pa. 1819;
settled in M. C. 1855.

Berner, Chas. F.; grocer; 256 North Blake street, Indianapolis.
Born in Germany 1831; settled in M. C. 1854.

Broyles, Moses; minister Second Baptist Church; res 260 North
Blake street, Indianapolis. Born in Md. 1820; settled in
M. C. 1857.

Beam, David; firm of Emerson & Beam; dealers and manufacturers of doors, sash, blinds, and all kinds of lumber; 225 and 229 West Market street, Indianapolis; res 187 South Tennessee street. Born in Pa. 1815; settled in M. C. 1839.

Blake, John G.; president Manhattan Marble Works; res 308 North Tennessee street, Indianapolis.

Blake, Wm. M.; secretary Manhattan Marble Works; res 308 North Tennessee street, Indianapolis.

Brown, Fred. A.; bds southeast corner New York and Meridian streets, Indianapolis.

Bryan, J. W.; dealer in drugs and medicines; 48 West Louisiana street, Indianapolis; res 748 North Illinois street. Born in Ky. 1836; settled in M. C. 1863.

Burton, John C. & Co.; wholesale dealers in boots and shoes; 114 South Meridian street, Indianapolis.

Bretz, Adam; grocer; 42 West Louisiana street, Indianapolis; res 118 South Illinois street. Born in Germany 1829; settled in M. C. 1854.

Bach, John; restaurant; 32 West Louisiana street, Indianapolis. Born in Germany 1832; settled in M. C. 1857.

Bombarger, Jacob E.; grocery and feed store; 46 and 48 Indiana avenue, Indianapolis; res 46 Camp street. Born in M. C. 1849.

BURFORD, WM.; firm of Braden & Burford, lithographers, printers and blank book manufacturers; 21 West Washington street, Indianapolis; res 82 West Market street. Born in Mo. 1846; settled in M. C. 1867. Presbyterian.

Boyles, M. W.; real estate agent; 64½ East Washington street, Indianapolis. Born in Pa. 1834; settled in M. C. 1855. Methodist.

Boyce, Augustin; 209 North Pennsylvania street, Indianapolis. Born in Ohio 1842; settled in M. C. 1870. Rep. Presb.

Cooper, J. J.; farmer and trader; res Home avenue, Indianapolis. Born in Ind. 1830; settled in M. C. 1863.

Clark, D. L.; photographer; 33 West Washington street, Indianapolis; res 21 Stephen street. Born in Ohio 1849; settled in M. C. 1866.

Cowen, R. B.; clerk Masonic Mutual Benefit Society; 24 Kentucky avenue, Indianapolis; res 416 North Pennsylvania street. Born in N. Y. 1844; settled in M. C. 1865.

CURRY, HON. W. W.; Secretary of State; Indianapolis. Born in Ky. 1824; settled in M. C. 1873. Rep. Universalist minister.

Claflin, C. C.; tailor; second floor, 42 West Washington street, Indianapolis; res 437 North Tennessee street. Born in Mass. 1834; settled in M. C. 1861. Rep. Congregationalist.

Culloden, F.; real estate agent; res 77 West Second street, Indianapolis. Born in Ireland 1834; settled in M. C. 1870. Rep. Episcopalian.

COOK, C. H. & CO.; dealers in and repairers of all kinds of sewing machines; keep needles and attachments on hand at all times; 36 West Washington street, Indianapolis.

Cannon, L. G.; railroad secretary; 101½ East Washington street, Indianapolis; res 24 Ft. Wayne avenue. Born in Ind. 1847; settled in M. C. 1866.

CRAFT, HIRAM J.; deputy city treasurer, Indianapolis; office 181 City Hall; res 221 North New Jersey street. Born in Ohio 1836; settled in M. C. 1859.

Council, J. F.; res 120 Park avenue, Indianapolis. Born in M. C. 1834. Dem. Christian.

Carr, R. S. & Son; hat store; 45 West Washington street, Indianapolis.

Cobb, E. A.; druggist; 48 West Washington street, Indianapolis; res 248 North Illinois street. Born in Ind. 1836; settled in M. C. 1865. Rep. Presbyterian.

Clarke, A. D.; salesman at Bowen & Stewart's; res 121 North Mississippi street, Indianapolis.

CLAPP, THOMAS H.; watchmaker and jeweler; 13 North Meridian street, Indianapolis; res 176 East Walnut street. Born in Mass. 1837; settled in M. C. 1873. Congregationalist.

Conner, Thos.; boot and shoemaker; Indianapolis. Born in Ireland 1823; settled in M. C. 1860.

COOK, C. H.; res. 124 North Tennessee street, Indianapolis. Born in Pa. 1843; settled in M. C. 1871.

Cooper, J. W.; Indianapolis. Born in Ind. 1844; settled in M. C. 1872. Rep.

CAMPBELL, GEORGE H.; attorney at law; rooms 5 and 6, 82 East Washington street, Indianapolis; res 350 North Illinois street. Born in M. C. 1847. Dem.

Carter, G.; lawyer; 96 East Washington street, Indianapolis; res 544 North Tennessee street. Born in Ind. 1836; settled in M. C. 1858. Rep. Presbyterian.

COLDEN & JOHNSTON; real estate brokers; office No. 94½ East Washington street, Indianapolis.

COLDEN, J. E.; of Colden & Johnston; res southwest corner Dearborn and Morris streets, Indianapolis. Born in Ind. 1834; settled in M. C. 1853.

Carle, H. M.; jeweler; 44 and 46 East Washington street, Indianapolis; res 176 Walnut street. Born in Md. 1851; settled in M. C. 1873. Dem. Episcopalian.

Chapman, Hammond & H.; 30 East Washington street, Indianapolis.

CHURCHMAN, F. M.; doing business with S. A. Fletcher & Co., FLETCHER'S BANK, Indianapolis; res Franklin township.

Cox, Wm. C.; druggist; 18 East Washington street, Indianapolis. Born in M. C. 1834.

Carmichael, J. D.; books and stationery; 60 East Washington street, Indianapolis; res 456 North Meridian street. Born in Ohio 1817; settled in M. C. 1855. Presbyterian.

Condit, J. D., No. 1 Blackford's Block, Indianapolis; res 722 North Meridian street. Born in N. J. 1825; settled in M. C. 1862.

Case & Marsh, harness and leather dealers; 79 West Washington street, Indianapolis.

Case, E. E.; res 94 North Mississippi street, Indianapolis. Born in Vt. 1822; settled in M. C. 1862. Rep.

Campbell, John; druggist; 149 West Washington street, Indianapolis; res 115 North Illinois street. Born in Ind. 1846; settled in M. C. 1865. Methodist.

Citizens' Mutual Benefit Association, 123½ East Washington street, Indianapolis.

CUMMINGS & SELLERS; wholesale and retail dealers in all kinds of tin, glass and wooden ware ; 302 and 304 North Illinois street, Indianapolis.

Cummings, M. M.; res 409 North Pennsylvania street, Indianapolis. Born in N. J. 1839; settled in M. C. 1871. Rep. Methodist.

CATHCART & CLELAND; BOOKSELLERS; 26 East Washington street, Indianapolis.

Cathcart, R. W.; res 258 South New Jersey street, Indianapolis. Born in Ohio 1843; settled in M. C. 1850. Presbyterian.

Cleland, Jno. E.; firm of Cathcart & Cleland ; Indianapolis. Born in M. C. 1840.

Continental Life Insurance agency; Fletcher's Bank Building, Indianapolis.

Copeland & Co.; millinery goods; 8 East Washington street, Indianapolis.

Copeland, J. W.; res 372 North Meridian street, Indianapolis. Born in Mass. 1829; settled in M. C. 1851.

Chambers, J. G.; Fancy Bazaar; 6 East Washington street, Indianapolis; res 44 North East street. Born in Ind. 1831; settled in M. C. 1850.

Cady, E.; res 353 North Illinois street, Indianapolis. Born in Ohio 1840; settled in M. C. 1864. Rep.

Cadwallader, J.; artist; corner Washington and Illinois streets, third floor, Indianapolis; res 50 Circle street. Born in Pa. 1826; settled in M. C. 1872. Rep. Unitarian.

Carey, Wm.; boot and shoemaker; 34 North Illinois street, Indianapolis; res 428 West New York street. Born in Ireland 1839; settled in M. C. 1868. Catholic.

Curry, William; cigars and tobacco; 97 ½ North Illinois street, Indianapolis. Born in New York 1856; settled in M. C. 1872. Rep.

CONTI, A.; keeps a variety of fruits and confectionery goods; corner Washington and Illinois streets, Indianapolis. Born in Italy 1844; settled in M. C. 1867.

Carroll & Phipps; saloon; 110 South Illinois street, Indianapolis.

CROSBY, MICHAEL; saloon; 139 South Illinois street, Indianapolis. Born in Ireland 1841; settled in M. C. 1863.

CORNELIUS, REV. S.; pastor Garden Baptist Church; north of New York on Bright street, Indianapolis; res 146 North Blackford street. Born in Va. 1825; settled in M. C. 1870.

Cohn, F.; clothing; 133 South Illinois street, Indianapolis. Born in Germany 1848; settled in M. C. 1872. Dem.

Crawford, C. C.; 360 East Market street, Indianapolis. Born in Ohio 1844; settled in M. C. 1869. Rep. Methodist.

Collins, J. E.; news agent; 138 South Illinois street, Indianapolis.

COTTRELL, THOMAS G. & CO.; 177 East Washington St., Indianapolis; dealers in tin plate, tinners' tools, and all necessary materials to supply the trade.

Cottrell, John; res 285 North Delaware street, Indianapolis. Born in M. C. 1854.

Cottrell, Thos. G.; res 285 North Delaware street, Indianapolis. Born in Indianapolis 1852.

Cottrell, T.; res 285 North Delaware street, Indianapolis. Born in Wales about 1828; settled in M. C. 1848.

Cohen & Son; brokers; 31 South Illnois street, Indianapolis.

CLINTON, JOHN R.; city clerk; Indianapolis; office in City Hall; res 41 Bradshaw street. Born in Scotland 1848; settled in M. C. 1871. Catholic.

Cohen, H.; res 81 West Georgia street, Indianapolis. Born in England 1840; settled in M. C. 1867.

Conroy, J.; tailor; over 87 South Illinois street, Indianapolis. Born in Ohio 1852; settled in M. C. 1859.

- Conlen, P.; pawnbroker; 66 North Illinois street, Indianapolis. Born in Ireland 1838; settled in M. C. 1863.

Cady Bros.; boots and shoes; 58 North Illinois street, Indianapolis.

Cady, D.; res 353 North Illinois street, Indianapolis. Born in Ohio 1833; settled in M. C. 1859. Rep. Episcopalian.

Clark, Wm.; physician; 69 North Illinois street, Indianapolis; res 180 West Ohio street. Born in Md. 1801; settled in M. C. 1864. Dem. Christian.

Campbell, I. S.; cigars and tobacco; 41 North Illinois street, Indianapolis. Born in Del. 1811; settled in M. C. 1869. Rep. Methodist.

Cordray, J. F.; jeweler; room 9, Claypool's Block, corner Illinois and Washington streets, Indianapolis. Born in Ohio 1852; settled in M. C. 1874.

Chambers, P. L.; tobacco; 73 North Illinois street, Indianapolis. Born in N. Y. 1851; settled in M. C. 1873.

CLARK, W. H.; res 180 West Ohio street, Indianapolis. Born in Md. 1830; settled in M. C. 1864. Dem. Christian.

Clawson, J. C.; proprietor Galt House; 127 South Illinois street, Indianapolis. Born in Ohio 1831; settled in M. C. 1869.

Claypool, Newton; life insurance agent; Claypool's Block, corner Washington and Illinois streets, Indianapolis.

CARLISLE, WILLIAM; grocer; Greenwood. Born in Ind. 1845; settled in Johnson county, 1874. Dem.

CARPENTER, J. S.; firm of McGilliard, Carpenter & Co.; res on Ash street, Indianapolis.

COX, CHAS. H.; seal engraver and manufacturer of stencils; 26 South Meridian street, Indianapolis; res 268 West Vermont street. Born in M. C. 1844.

CAMPBELL, STOCK; reporter of *Daily Evening Union;* room 1, over 21 North Meridian street, Indianapolis; res 333 South Alabama street. Born in Ohio 1841; settled in M. C. 1872.

CHILD, JOHN A.; Sec'y of Franklin Fire Insurance Co.; office in Co's building, Indianapolis; res 250 East Vermont street. Born in England 1836; settled in M. C. 1871.

Child, John A., jr.; supply department of Franklin Fire Insurance Co.; Indianapolis. Born in Ind. 1857; settled in M. C. 1871.

Compton, J. A.; physician; 80 East Market street, Indianapolis, res 110 North Delaware street. Born in N. Y. 1839; settled in M. C. 1873.

Cruse, J. S.; tobacconist; 46 North Delaware street, Indianapolis. Born in Ind. 1858; settled in M. C. 1862.

CLEAVELAND, J. B. & CO.; real estate brokers and agents; 42 North Delaware street, Indianapolis.

CLEAVELAND, J. B.; res 600 North Alabama street, Indianapolis. Born in Canada 1826; settled in M. C. 1863.

CLEAVELAND, CHAS. F.; Born in Canada 1855; settled in M. C. 1863.

Capital City Planing Mill Co.; dealers in lumber, lath, shingles, siding, flooring; stair building a specialty; R. Cosby, president; B. W. Cole, secretary; Robert Jones, foreman of store department; Massachusetts avenue, Indianapolis.

Custer & Whippo; dealers in fancy groceries and provisions of all kinds; 399 North New Jersey street, Indianapolis.

CHAMNESS, E. & E. B.; dealers in stoves and tinware; general job work done to order; corner Fort Wayne avenue and New Jersey street, Indianapolis.

CHAMNESS, E. B.; res at Anderson. Born in Ind. 1836; settled in M. C. 1874.

CHAMNESS, ELI; bds at 84 Christian avenue, Indianapolis. Born in Ind. 1834; settled in M. C. 1873.

COLLINGS, O. P.; physician and surgeon; room over 24½ Kentucky avenue, Indianapolis. Born in Ind. 1852; settled in M. C. 1872.

COVENDER, H. J.; proprietor Central House; 31 West Ohio street, Indianapolis. Born in Ind. 1838; settled in M. C. 1873.

COX, FOSTER & CO.; dealers in lumber; office and yard at 155 West First street, Indianapolis.

Cox, Geo. W.; res 339 North Pennsylvania street, Indianapolis.

Custer, S. F.; res Wayne county. Born in Ohio 1819.

CAVITT, M.; confectioner; 64 Virginia avenue, Indianapolis. Born in Ind. 1842; settled in M. C. 1861. Dem. Christ.

CABINET MAKERS' UNION manufactures all kinds of furniture, chairs, etc.; corner of Market and Winston streets, Indianapolis.

Cook & Bro.; grocers; 207 Davidson street, Indianapolis.

COBURN & JONES; dealers in all kinds of dressed and rough lumber; two squares West of Union Depot, Indianapolis.

Chair Manufacturing Company; warerooms 184, 186 and 190 West New York street, Indianapolis.

Christman & Co.; tobacconists; corner Mississippi and Pearl streets, Indianapolis.

Crossland & Sawyer; wholesale confectioneries, canned goods and nuts; 80 South Meridian street, Indianapolis.

CAREY, HARVEY G.; firm of Layman, Carey & Co.; res 284 North Meridian street, Indianapolis. Born in Ohio; settled in M. C. 1863.

CAREY, S. B.; firm of Layman, Carey & Co.; res 325 North Pennsylvania street, Indianapolis.

C. C. & I. Railway office, 145 South Meridian street, Indianapolis. Superintendent, C. C. Gale.

Cole, J. C.; tenant farmer; 1 m e corporation line. Born in Va. 1822; settled in M. C. 1840.

Close & Mason; Bee Hive Store; dry goods and notions; corner Washington and Meridian streets, Indianapolis.

CAPITO, G. H.; dealer in new and second hand furniture, stoves, carpets, etc.; 237 East Washington street, Indianapolis; res same. Born in Ind. 1836; settled in M. C. 1873.

Cook, Wm. & Co.; dealers in dry goods, groceries, etc.; 247 East Washington street, Indianapolis.

Cook, Wm.; firm of Wm. Cook & Co.; res 83 South East street, Indianapolis. Born in Germany 1817; settled in M.C. 1838.

Craft, R. P.; Deputy Sheriff; res 496 North Tennessee street, Indianapolis. Born in Ky. 1842; settled in M. C. 1845.

Costigan, T. J.; railroader; res 86 North Illinois street, Indianapolis. Born in Ind. 1845.

CALDWELL, BROWN & CO.; general insurance and loan agents, stock and bond brokers; 11 North Meridian street, Indianapolis.

CIRCLE HOUSE; 15 North Meridian street, Indianapolis. Good accomodations at reasonable rates.

Coe, O. K.; pitch, gravel and tin roofing; office 41 Hubbard's Block, Indianapolis. Born in N. Y. 1815; settled in M. C. 1873.

Cooper & Powell; managers of Protection Life Insurance Company; office 22 Hubbard's Block, Indianapolis.

Cooper, J. O.; Indianapolis. Born in Canada 1839; settled in M. C. 1874.

COE, CHAS. B.; collecting agent of North Western Mutual Life Insurance Co.; office, room 16 Hubbard's Block, Indianapolis. Born in Wis. 1842; settled in M. C. 1869.

Cooper, W. C.; physician and surgeon; Indianapolis. Born in Ohio 1835; settled in M. C. 1871.

Cress, J. B.; physician; office, room 3, Franklin Life Insurance Building, Indianapolis. Born in Ind. 1847; settled in M. C. 1850. Rep.

CHAPPELL, AARON; harness shop; 262 West Washington street, Indianapolis; bds 261 West Washington street. Born in Ind. 1849; settled in M. C. 1874.

Chappell, W.; with A. Chappell, 262 West Washington street, Indianapolis; bds 261 West Washington street. Born in Ind. 1845; settled in M. C. 1874.

COTTRELL, THOS,; Peddlers' Exchange; 276 West Washington street, Indianapolis; importers of tin plate, metals, tinners' stock, etc.

CHAPMAN & MILLIGAN; wagon manufactory; wagons made to order and warranted.

CROSIER, WM.; firm of Laughlin & Crosier; res 226 South Alabama street, Indianapolis. Born in Ind. 1845; settled in M. C. 1873.

Campbell, A. C.; grocer; 665 Virginia avenue, Indianapolis. Born in Pa. 1845; settled in M. C. 1874.

CHAMBERLAND, J. V. & CO.; pork packers and dealers; 43 South Delaware street, Indianapolis.

Crane, S. D.; watchmaker and jeweler; 67 Virginia avenue, Indianapolis. Born in M. C. 1852.

Connely, Robert & Co.; coal, coke, and lime; res 134 North Meridian street, Indianapolis.

Colter, R. S.; grocer; 302 South East street, Indianapolis; res same. Born in Ireland 1846; settled in M. C. 1870.

CONLEY, GEORGE; Vulcan Boiler and Sheet Iron Works; res 124 East Merrill street, Indianapolis. Born in Ohio 1821; settled in M. C. 1833.

Cox, Thomas; Vulcan Sheet Iron Works; res 119 Walnut street, Indianapolis. Born in Ind. 1836; settled in M. C. 1856.

Corridan, Thomas; saloon; 350 South West street, Indianapolis; res same. Born in Ireland 1802; settled in M. C. 1866.

Clump, F. P.; pipeman of Fire Engine Co. No. 6; res Maryland street, Indianapolis. Born in Germany 1838; settled in M. C. 1855.

Corbaley, S. B.; grocer; 414 West Washington street, Indianapolis; res same. Born in M. C. 1834.

Conduitt, Cook & Co.; wholesale grocers; 123 South Meridian street, Indianapolis.

CHAMBERLIN, JAMES; farmer; 2 m s w Indianapolis. Born in Ky. 1807; settled in M. C. 1838. Dem. Christian.

Custer, John; confectioner; 162 West Washington street, Indianapolis. Born in Pa. 1842; settled in M. C. 1870. Rep. Methodist.

CROWDER, B.; carpenter and joiner; res 192 Huron street, Indianapolis. Born in Va. 1838; settled in M. C. 1873. Rep. Protestant.

COOPER, HAMILTON; practical tailor; 11 Indiana avenue, Indianapolis; res 260 West St. Clair street. Born in Ireland 1836; settled in M. C. 1855.

Cox, J. B.; confectioner; 28 Indiana avenue, Indianapolis; res 413 North Mississippi street. Born in England 1826; settled in M. C. 1873.

Cussen, Mrs. G.; dealer in notions; 158 Indiana avenue, Indianapolis.

Cadwallader, Ira & Co.; dealers in boots and shoes; 172 Indiana avenue, Indianapolis.

Case, Wm. H.; firm of Case & Cotton, hardware; 183 Indiana avenue, Indianapolis; res 290 East St. Clair street. Born in M. C. 1847.

Cotton, M. B.; firm of Case & Cotton, hardware; 183 Indiana avenue, Indianapolis; res 290 East St. Clair street. Born in M. C. 1856.

Clifford, Amos; grocer; 201 Indiana avenue, Indianapolis; res 35 Camp street. Born in Ind. 1838; settled in M. C. 1872.

Conlen, Michael; grocer; 323 Indiana avenue, Indianapolis. Born in Ireland 1824; settled in M. C. 1863. Dem. Roman Catholic.

CAVEN, JOHN; attorney at law; 19½ East Washington street, Indianapolis. Born in Pa. 1824; settled in M. C. 1845. Rep.

Chandler, H. C.; engraver on wood; Glenn's Block, Indianapolis; res 278 West Vermont street. Born in Pa. 1842; settled in M. C. 1860. Rep. Unitarian.

Cameron, Dr. J. J.; 15 East Washington street, Indianapolis; res Pleasant street. Born in Pa. 1844; settled in M. C. 1856. Dem. Presbyterian.

Chase, John L.; manager of Wilson Sewing Machine Co.; No. 3 Bates House Block, West Washington street, Indianapolis. Born in Conn. 1844; settled in M. C. 1870. Rep. Unitarian.

Case, D. E.; firm of J. D. Steep & Co., dealers in boots and shoes; No. 5 Bates House Block, West Washington street, Indianapolis; bds Occidental House. Born in Mass. 1846; settled in M. C. 1871.

Coble, G.; grocer; 152 West Washington street, Indianapolis; res 383 West New York street. Born in M. C. 1831. Dem. M. Baptist.

COX, E. T.; State Geologist; office in State House; res 677 North Illinois street. Born in Va. 1821; settled in M. C. 1869.

Curtiss, Rev. Geo. L.; pastor of Asbury M. E. Church, South New Jersey street, Indianapolis; res 238 Virginia avenue. Born in Ohio 1835; settled in M. C. 1873. Rep.

Church, J. N.; firm of Church & Hall, commission merchants; 240 East Washington street, Indianapolis; bds Little House. Born in Ind. 1852; settled in M. C. 1872.

Cook, Wm. F.; ladies' furnishing goods; 276 East Washington street, Indianapolis. Born in Ohio 1844; settled in M. C. 1873.

Craig, Wm.; flouring mills, 354 East Washington street, Indianapolis; res 26 Cherry street. Born in Ky. 1830; settled in M. C. 1861.

Cole, Samuel H.; life insurance agent; 310 East Washington street, Indianapolis.

CHRISTY, L. E.; grocer and teacher; 419 West North street, Indianapolis. Born 1849; settled in M. C. 1865.

Chappell, A. & Bros.; manufacturers of saddles and harness; 262 West Washington street, Indianapolis.

Carlisle, John; Model Mills; 200 West Market street, Indianapolis; res 260 West Washington street. Born in North Ireland 1807; settled in M. C. 1837.

Clark, R. O.; firm of Van Bargen & Clark; res 176 West Michigan street, Indianapolis. Born in Ky. 1821; settled in M. C. 1853.

Cassiday, J. A.; with A. B. Lesh, pork packer; res 135 Park avenue, Indianapolis. Born in Ohio 1836; settled in M. C. 1870.

Cooper, J. W.; proprietor Indiana House, 69 West Market street, Indianapolis. Born in N. Y. 1814; settled in M. C. 1874.

Copeland, J. W. & Co.; importers of millinery and straw goods; 116 South Meridian street, Indianapolis. Born in Mass. 1829; settled in M. C. 1853.

Chapman, John W.; wagonmaker; West Washington street, west of river, Indianapolis. Born in Ind. 1835; settled in M. C. 1858.

Cacher, Frederick; gardener, with Wm. H. Traub. Born in Wurtemberg, Germany, 1811; settled in M. C. 1848.

Culloden, L. P. & Co.; real estate agents; 82½ East Washington street, Indianapolis.

CHISLETT, FREDERICK W.; superintendent of Crown Hill Cemetery; North Indianapolis. Born in Pa. 1827; settled in M. C. 1863.

Crawford, Moses; superintendent Malleable Iron Works; canal and St. Clair street, Indianapolis; res North Illinois street, by toll-gate. Born in Ind.; settled in M. C. 1872.

Crawford, James; secretary Malleable Iron Works; canal and St. Clair street, Indianapolis. Born in Ind. 1838; settled in M. C. 1869.

Cooper, O. P.; toll-gate keeper; North Illinois street, Indianapolis. Born in Ky. 1814; settled in M. C. 1866.

Clark, J. N.; real estate broker; 84 East Washington street, Indianapolis; res 4 m n Washington street. Born in Va.; settled in M. C. 1874.

Carter, Eleazer; gardener and dealer in small fruits; North Indianapolis, on Illinois street. Born in Ind. 1832; settled in M. C. 1867.

Caylor, Allen; dealer in coal, flour and feed; 185 Indiana avenue, Indianapolis; res 458 North West street. Born in M. C. 1842. Rep. Protestant.

Chamberlain, James; farmer; 2 m s w Indianapolis.

Copton, S. M.; firm of H. F. Holmes & Co., bridge builders, and stone work generally; office 91 East Market street, Indianapolis; res 180 North Delaware street.

Chambers, P. L.; wholesale and retail dealer in cigars and tobacco; 11 Massachusetts avenue, Indianapolis; res 73 North Illinois street. Born in N. Y. 1851; settled in M. C. 1873.

Comingore, W. H.; bds North Delaware street, Indianapolis. Born in Ky. 1823; settled in M. C. 1865.

CITIZENS' LIVERY, boarding, and sale stable; 25 East Pearl street, Indianapolis; horses bought and sold at all times; William Hinesly, proprietor; res 83 East Pratt street. Born in M. C. 1830.

CARVIN, J. M.; botanic physician; room, second floor corner of Maryland and Illinois streets, Indianapolis; res 391 East McCarty street. Born in Va. 1820; settled in M. C. 1862.

Clem, Aaron; farmer; 3½ m n e Indianapolis. Born in Va. 1827. settled in M. C. 1838. Rep. Christian.

CHESELDINE & BURNWORTH; manufacturers of carriages and spring wagons of all kinds; 44 East Maryland street, Indianapolis.

Cheseldine, ——.; res 72 East Maryland street, Indianapolis.

CAYLOR, JACOB; restaurant; 33 North Pennsylvania street, Indianapolis; res 187 North Davidson street. Born in Ohio 1833; settled in M. C. 1840. Dem. Protestant.

Crans, James T.; bookkeeper at office of E. S. Folsom, Phœnix Life Insurance Co.; No. 14 Talbott's Block, Pennsylvania street, Indianapolis; res 321 Park avenue. Born in Ohio 1841; settled in M. C. 1868. Rep. Calvinist.

Coalman, Wm. F.; farmer; 4 m n e Indianapolis. Born in Md. 1840; settled in M. C. 1866. Dem. Methodist.

Conda, Wm.; blacksmith; res ½ mile north shoe factory. Born in Ind. 1841; settled in M. C. 1872.

CAMPBELL & GARNER; dealers in fancy groceries and provisions; 24 Malott avenue, Indianapolis.

Garner, O. F.; bds on Ash street, Indianapolis. Born in Ind. 1852; settled in M. C. 1873.

CAMPBELL, M. G.; res on Ash street, Indianapolis. Born in Ind. 1848; settled in M. C. 1873.

Cobb, Branham & Co.; dealers in coal and coke; 17 Virginia avenue, Indianapolis.

Cobb, S. H.; coal dealer; res 107 East St. Joseph street, Indianapolis. Born in Ind. 1837; settled in M. C. 1870.

Colesman, James; bookkeeper with T. A. Goodwin ; 44½ North Pennsylvania street, Indianapolis.

Coe, Henry; secretary of the Indianapolis Fire Insurance Association; room 18 Martindale's Block, North Pennsylvania street, Indianapolis; res 79 East Michigan street. Born in Wis. 1848; settled in M. C. 1873. Rep. Protestant.

COLLOPY & STEWART; proprietors of Union House; 202 South Illinois street, Indianapolis.

COLLOPY, MICHAEL; Indianapolis. Born in N. Y. 1845; settled in M. C. 1872.

COMSTOCK, MRS. H.; hair dresser and manufacturer of switches; all kinds hair goods made to order; 114 Massachusetts avenue, Indianapolis.

Castell, Wm. G.; dealer in confectionery; 105 Massachusetts avenue, Indianapolis; res 360 North Noble street. Born in England 1825; settled in M. C. 1868.

Crompton, E.; manufacturer and dealer in stoves, tin and copper ware; 60 Massachusetts avenue, Indianapolis; res 169 East South street. Born in England 1847; settled in M. C. 1873.

Corliss, C. T.; physician; Miller's Block, corner Illinois and Market streets, Indianapolis; res 169 North Illinois street. Born in N. Y. 1817; settled in M. C. 1856. Dem.

Crane, Geo. W.; superintendent of Indianapolis Wagon Works; res 347 Ash street, Indianapolis. Born in Ohio 1832; settled in M. C. 1865.

Drew, Harry E.; res 702 North Tennessee street, Indianapolis. Born in Ohio 1847; settled in M. C. 1852. Presbyterian.

Dennis & Horton; dealers in wall paper and window shades; 44 North Pennsylvania street, Indianapolis.

Dennis, Chas. C.; res. 338 North New Jersey street, Indianapolis. Born in N. Y. 1829; settled in M. C. 1866.

DONNELLY, JAMES P.; superintendent plumbing and gas fitting at D. Coulter's, 47 South Pennsylvania street, Indianapolis. Born in Ohio 1840; settled in M. C. 1873. Dem.

Davis, Edwin A.; attorney at law; room No. 30 Talbott's Block, North Pennsylvania street, Indianapolis; res 624 North Pennsylvania street. Born in Mass. 1828; settled in M. C. 1860.

Dale, J. C.; dealer in groceries and provisions; 311 Massachusetts avenue, Indianapolis. Born in M. C. 1835.

DROTZ & STEINHAUER; manufacturers of files and rasps, and dealers in saw up-sets and patent saw gummers; 136 South Pennsylvania street, Indianapolis.

DROTZ, EMIL; res 251 Prospect street, Indianapolis. Born in France 1831; settled in M. C. 1854.

Dohn, Philip; wholesale manufacturer and dealer in all kinds of furniture; 244 and 246 South Meridian street, Indianapolis. Born in Germany 1834; settled in M. C. 1861.

DIETZ, C. L.; firm of Goth & Dietz; res 114 Ft. Wayne ave., Indianapolis. Born in Ind. 1851; settled in M. C. 1856.

DAVIS, W. H., PHYSICIAN AND SURGEON; 213 Christian avenue; res 40 Rohampton street, Indianapolis. Born in Ind. 1846; settled in M. C. 1863.

Dyer, Sidney M.; Assistant Secretary of Water Works Co., Indianapolis; res 219 West New York street. Born in Ky. 1850; settled in M. C. 1851.

DAILY EVENING UNION; office 21 North Meridian street, Indianapolis.

DILL & REYNOLDS; dealers in flour, feed and wood; 218 West North street, corner Fayette, Indianapolis.

DILL, E. B.; Indianapolis. Born in Md. 1827; settled in M. C. 1836.

Davis, Ben F.; attorney at law; rooms 4 and 5 Talbott & New's Block, North Pennsylvania street, Indianapolis; res southwest corner East and St. Clair streets. Born in Ohio 1836; settled in M. C. 1871.

Davis, Samuel; tin, copper and sheet iron worker; 18 West Maryland street, Indianapolis. Born in N. Y. 1838; settled in M. C. 1870.

Dunn, W. M.; physician and surgeon; room 23 West Maryland street, Indianapolis. Born in Ind. 1843; settled in M.C. 1854.

Delzell, James; farmer and brick manufacturer; res and yard 4 m n e Indianapolis. Born in Pa. 1816; settled in M. C. 1825. Dem. Protestant.

Dynes, Bradbury & Co.; agents and dealers in real estate; 15 Virginia avenue, Indianapolis.

Dynes, John F.; real estate agent; 15 Virginia avenue, Indianapolis. Born in Ind. 1847; settled in M. C. 1871. Rep.

Doane, T. J.; grocer; 296 East Ohio street, Indianapolis; res 434 South Illinois street. Born in Ind. 1839; settled in M. C. 1874.

Dennerline, John; gardener; North Indianapolis. Born in Germany 1832; settled in M. C. 1854.

DAVIDSON, DORMAN N.; farmer and stock trader; res on Michigan Road, near Crown Hill. Born in M. C. 1841.

DICKMAN, FRANCIS; farmer; 3 m n Circle street on Illinois street. Born in Prussia 1801; settled in M. C. 1837.

Dryer, J. W.; drugs and medicines; 344 East Washington street, Indianapolis; res 630 North Pennsylvania street. Born in Ind. 1840; settled in M. C. 1866.

David, Wm.; farmer; 2 m s w Indianapolis. Born in Va. 1800; settled in M. C. 1829.

DENNY, JACOB; real estate broker; North Indianapolis. Born in Pa. 1822; settled in M. C. 1867.

Dixon, H. B.; manager iron works; 81 and 83 West Washington street, Indianapolis. Born in Ind. 1821; settled in M. C. 1871.

Denton, A. B.; res 331 East South street, Indianapolis. Born in N. Y. 1842; settled in M. C. 1865. Rep. Episcopalian.

Deitrichs & Walker; millinery and fancy goods; 10 East Washington street, Indianapolis.

Dawson, T. E.; auction house; 111 East Washington street, Indianapolis. Born in Del. 1836; settled in M. C. 1859.

Darby, John; confectioner; 11 West Washington street, Indianapolis; res 404 North Illinois street. Born in Va. 1836; settled in M. C. 1858.

DUNN, ISAAC; res Little's Hotel, East Washington street, Indianapolis. Born in Ind. 1846; settled in M. C. 1870.

Daumont, H. & Co.; mirrors and picture frames; 40 West Washington street, Indianapolis.

Daumont, Henry; res Pyle House, Indianapolis. Born in N. Y. 1834; settled in M. C. 1854. Rep. Methodist.

Downey, S. R.; Governor's private secretary; res 575 North Mississippi street, Indianapolis. Born in Ind. 1847; settled in M. C. 1873. Dem. Methodist.

Denny, C. S.; deputy Attorney General; res 359 North Pennsylvania street, Indianapolis. Born in Ind. 1850; settled in M. C. 1870. Rep.

Doherty & McGauley; dealers in gas fixtures; 67 North Illinois street, Indianapolis.

Doherty, C.; res 7 Ellsworth street, Indianapolis. Born in Canada 1849; settled in M. C. 1871. Rep. Methodist.

De Ruiter, D.; produce, oysters, etc.; 61 South Illinois street, Indianapolis; res 47 Fletcher avenue. Born in N. Y. 1844; settled in M. C. 1865. Rep.

Davison & Co.; Buckeye Dining Rooms; 104 South Illinois St., Indianapolis.

Dugen, T.; shoemaker; 136 South Illinois street, Indianapolis; res 305 South Pennsylvania street. Born in Ireland 1819; settled in M. C. 1855. Catholic.

Deitch, C. F.; tobacconist; 151 East Washington street, Indianapolis. Born in Ind. 1848; settled in M. C. 1863.

Danner, S. R.; wagon manufacturer; ¼ m n Exposition building, Indianapolis. Born in Va. 1833; settled in M. C. 1856.

DYNES, L. G.; editor of *The Southside*; 45½ Virginia avenue, Indianapolis; res 24 Fletcher avenue. Born in Ohio 1840; settled in M. C. 1866.

DURBON, R. A. & CO.; pump manufacturers; 193, 195, 197 and 199 South Meridian street, Indianapolis.

DIETZ, FRED; box manufacturer; res 1 m e corporation line.

Davy, Daniel; engineer No. 4 Engine Co. Born in Indianapolis 1848.

Donovan, B.; reel driver No. 4 Engine Co. Born in Ind. 1846; settled in M. C. 1866.

DARROW, BEN C.; firm of Ryan, Darrow & Co.; res 545 North Illinois street, Indianapolis. Born in Mass. 1835; settled in M. C. 1851.

DICKINSON, C. E.; school and church furniture; 36 South Meridian street, Indianapolis; res 213 North Illinois street. Born in Ohio 1845; settled in M. C. 1874.

DOREMUS, GEORGE C.; new southside store, dry goods, notions, hats, caps, and dress goods; 11 Shelby street, Indianapolis. Born in N. J. 1834; settled in M. C. 1866. Dem.

Davis, Joseph; grocer; 486 Vermont street, Indianapolis. Born in 1842; settled in M. C. 1873.

DAMMEYER, CHAS.; with Wm. Cook & Co.; res 310 East Georgia street, Indianapolis. Born in Prussia 1837; settled in M. C. 1854.

Dammeyer & Harmening; grocery, feed and liquors; east end of Washington street, Indianapolis.

DUNCAN, R. B.; attorney at law; second floor, 76 East Washington street, Indianapolis; res 174 Central avenue. Born in N. Y. 1810; settled in M. C. 1820.

Durham, Henry E.; firm of Uhl & Durham; res 704 North Illinois street, Indianapolis. Born in N. Y. 1838; settled in M. C. 1864.

Dickson, C. & Co.; manufacturers of agricultural implements; 90 West Washington street, Indianapolis.

DOWNEY, J. T.; special agent of Northwestern Mutual Life Insurance Company; res 388 West street, Indianapolis. Born in Ohio 1840; settled in M. C. 1869.

DENNIS, BRANSON & ARNOLD; wholesale dealers in teas, cigars, tobacco and liquors; 84 South Meridian street, Indianapolis.

DENNIS, M. P.; res 17 Cherry street, Indianapolis. Born in Ind. 1835; settled in M. C. 1867.

Daggett & Co.; wholesale confectioners; 100 and 102 South Meridian street, Indianapolls.

DELL, WM. & SON; wholesale dealers in coal and lime; office 27 East Georgia street, Indianapolis.

Dollerhide, A.; trader and real estate dealer; res 224 College avenue, Indianapolis. Born in Ind. 1826; settled in M. C. 1826.

DAGGETT & ROTH; architects; office, 23 Vinton's Block, corner Pennsylvania and Market streets, Indianapolis.

DAGGETT, R. P.; firm of Daggett & Roth; res 293 West Vermont street, Indianapolis. Born in Ohio 1847; settled in M. C. 1868.

DONNAN, W.; firm of Wiggins & Donnan; res North Tennessee street, Indianapolis.

DAILEY, H.; attorney at law; office No. 13 Baldwin's Block, Indianapolis; res 126 North Delaware street.

Drew & Poundstone; carriage manufacturers; East Market square, Indianapolis.

DUMONT, JOHN J.; firm of Bartholomew & Dumont; res 120 North Mississippi street, Indianapolis. Born in Ind. 1816; settled in M. C. 1854.

DIETRICH, C.; watchmaker and jeweler; corner of Market and Delaware streets, Indianapolis. Born in Germany 1817; settled in M. C. 1867.

Dunn, Jacob P.; firm of Wm. Love & Co.; notary public; res 410 North Tennessee street, Indianapolis. Born in Ind. 1811; settled in M. C. 1861.

DARK, C. E.; firm of Hammerley & Dark; city shoe store; 8 West Washington street, Indianapolis; res 483 North Illinois street. Born in Ohio 1849; settled in M. C. 1857. Rep. Presbyterian.

DAVIS, H. L.; plumber, gas and steam fitter; 29 South Delaware street, Indianapolis; res 121 East South street. Born in Ohio 1850; settled in M. C. 1852.

DIETZ & REISNER; curriers, and dealers in leather, hides, oil and findings; 21 and 23 South Delaware St., Indianapolis.

Donnelly, Francis; grocer; 34 South Delaware street, Indianapolis. Born in Ireland 1818; settled in M. C. 1850.

Doerre, Wm.; saloon and boarding house; 331 South Delaware street, Indianapolis. Born in Germany 1848; settled in M. C. 1866.

Dickson, Will. C.; secretary Indianapolis Brass and Supply Co.; res 574 North Pennsylvania street, Indianapolis. Born in Pa. 1844; settled in M. C. 1861.

Dickson, Jas. B.; treasurer Indianapolis Brass and Supply Co.; res 574 North Pennsylvania street, Indianapolis. Born in Pa. 1848; settled in M. C. 1861.

Dickson, John; president Indianapolis Brass and Supply Co.; res 578 North Pennsylvania street, Indianapolis. Born in Pa.; settled in M. C. 1861.

Dietz, John; shoemaker; 19 South Delaware street, Indianapolis. Born in Bavaria 1847; settled in M. C. 1871.

Dain & McCullough; real estate and rental agents; 30 North Delaware street, Indianapolis.

Davis, G. H. & Co.; druggists; 531 Virginia avenue, Indianapolis.

DRAPER, M. B.; broker; 73 East Washington street, Indianapolis. Born in Ind. 1848; settled in M. C. 1870.

DUNN, J. T.; real estate broker; 83 East Washington street, Indianapolis. Born in N. J. 1813; settled in M. C. 1861.

Draper, George B.; pawnbroker; 12 Virginia avenue, Indianapolis; res McKernan street. Born in Ind. 1845; settled in M. C. 1873.

DANIEL, HENRY J.; carpenter and builder; 246 Fayette street, Indianapolis. Give him a call.

DAVIS, H. L. & CO.; plumbers, and gas and steam fitters; 29 South Delaware street, Indianapolis.

Dorsey, Wm.; barber; corner Blake and West, Indianapolis. Born in San Domingo 1840; settled in M. C. 1854.

Davis, Robert; brickyard foreman; 1 m s corporation line. Born in Ky. 1840; settled in M. C. 1860.

Disch, Gabriel; gardener; 2½ m s of Circle street. Born in Germany 1823; settled in M. C. 1860.

Dumont, Mrs. Mary; res 2 m s Circle on Meridian street. Born in Ind. 1822; settled in M. C. 1854.

Drew, H. E.; coal dealer; 14 North Pennsylvania street, Indianapolis; res 2 m s Circle. Born in Ohio 1847; settled in M. C. 1856.

DILL, J. B.; dealer in pure drugs and medicines; physicians' prescriptions carefully compounded; 99 Indiana avenue, Indianapolis; res 140 West Vermont street. Born in M. C. 1849. Rep. Christian.

DAVIS, JAMES C.; house, sign and carriage painter; 582 North Mississippi street, Indianapolis; res 275 Christian avenue. Born in Ind. 1831; settled in M .C. 1849. Meth.

Davis, K. M.; grocer; 181 Indiana avenue, Indianapolis. Born in Del. 1830; settled in M. C. 1871. Rep. Methodist.

Dellefield, M ; new and second hand furniture; 187 Indiana avenue, Indianapolis. Born in Hessen, Germany, 1835; settled in M. C. 1864.

Dougherty, Frank L.; foreman No. 8 Hose Reel Co.; res 29 North New Jersey street, Indianapolis. Born in Ind. 1847; settled in M. C. 1858. Rep. Protestant.

Davis, Chas. B.; firm of Davis, Stevenson & Major; real estate agents; 45 East Washington street, Indianapolis; res 181 South New Jersey street. Born in Ky. 1815; settled in M. C. 1831. Rep. Presbyterian.

Denny, Austin F.; attorney at law; 45 East Washington street, Indianapolis; res on Delaware street, second house north of Tinker street. Born in M. C. 1841. Rep. Protestant.

Dorsey, R. S.; wholesale hardware; 110 South Meridian street, Indianapolis.

Dickey, A. H.; attorney at law; 45 East Washington street, Indianapolis; res Palmer's Block, West Maryland street. Born in Ind. 1851; settled in M. C. 1873. Rep. Christian.

Dickson, C.; firm of C. Dickson & Co., wholesale and retail dealers in dyestuffs, acids, factory findings and agricultural implements; 90 West Washington street, Indianapolis; bds Mason House. Born in Ind. 1838; settled in M. C. 1850. Rep. Presbyterian.

Dickson, J. C.; firm of C. Dickson & Co.; res 149 North Meridian street, Indianapolis. Born in Ky. 1816; settled in M. C. 1865.

Dickson, W. E.; firm of C. Dickson & Co.; res 224 Broadway street, Indianapolis. Born in Ind. 1839; settled in M. C. 1865.

Dreher, M.; firm of Dreher & Bollinger, dealers in fancy and dry goods; 250 East Washington street, Indianapolis; res 105 Arsenal avenue. Born in Pa. 1825; settled in M. C. 1858.

Dahne, Chas.; firm of Chas Dahne & Bros., dealers in flour and feed; 300 East Washington street, Indianapolis; res 42 South Liberty street. Born in Prussia 1835; settled in M. C. 1854.

Dahne, Wm.; firm of Chas. Dahne & Bros.; res 215 North Davidson street, Indianapolis. Born in Prussia 1838; settled in M. C. 1855.

Duncan, R. P.; firm of Bird & Duncan, manufacturers of glue; office 85 East State street, Indianapolis; res cor First and Pennsylvania streets. Born in M. C. 1847.

Evans, J. K.; firm of I. P. Evans & Co.; res 360 North Alabama street, Indianapolis. Born in Ohio 1840; settled in M. C. 1863.

Evans, W. R.; firm of I. P. Evans & Co.; res 470 North Delaware street, Indianapolis. Born in Ohio 1834; settled in M. C. 1865.

Evans, I. P.; firm of I. P. Evans & Co.; res Richmond. Born in Ohio 1821.

EVANS, I. P. & CO.; manufacturers of paints, oils, etc.; 124 South Delaware street, Indianapolis.

EHRMANN, L.; firm of Meeger and Ehrmann; res 305 Madison avenue, Indianapolis. Born in Germany 1845; settled in M. C. 1866.

Eagle, J. H,; grocer; 340 North Delaware street, Indianapolis; res 338 North Delaware. Born in Pa. 1817; settled in M. C. 1853.

Eagle, J. D.; with J. H. Eagle; res 338 North Delaware street, Indianapolis Born in Pa. 1847; settled in M. C. 1853.

Eblin, J.; boot and shoemaker; 143 South New Jersey street, Indianapolis.

EGAN, T. P.; draper and tailor; 26 and 28 South Illinois street, Indianapolis; bds Hotel Bates. Born in Ireland 1848; settled in M. C. 1868.

EGAN, E. C.; 26 and 28 South Illinois street, Indianapolis; res corner New Jersey and Walnut streets. Born in Ireland 1844; settled in M. C. 1867. Rep.

EGERTON, CHAS.; saloon and boarding house; 179 South Meridian street, Indianapolis. Born in Germany 1839; settled in M. C. 1866.

EWING, D. B.; physician; 33 Virginia avenue, Indianapolis; bds Circle House. Born in Ohio 1829; settled in M. C. 1858.

Erie and Pacific Dispatch Company; office corner of Virginia avenue and Maryland street, Indianapolis.

EFRAYMSON, JACOB; wholesale and retail dealer in dry goods and notions; 429 and 431 South Meridian street, Indianapolis. Born in Germany 1844; settled in M. C. 1871.

ELLIOTT, C. A.; of Ryan, Darrow & Co.; res 180 North West street, Indianapolis. Born in Ky.; settled in M. C. 1857.

EGAN, TREAT & EGAN; drapers and tailors; 26 and 28 South Illinois street, Indianapolis.

ELRIDGE, JACOB; real estate broker; office Surgical Institute Building, Indianapolis; res Plainfield, Ind. Born in Vt. 1809; settled in M. C. 1840.

EDMUNDS, WM.; firm of Hendricks, Edmunds & Co.; res 118 West Vermont street, Indianapolis. Born in England 1830; settled in M. C. 1859.

ENGLISH, W. H.; President of First National Bank, corner Meridian and Washington streets, Indianapolis; res 60 Circle street.

ENGGARS, H.; merchant tailor; 208 West Washington street, Indianapolis. Born in Germany 1833; settled in M. C. 1862.

Engle & Drew; dealers in all kinds of coal and coke, lath, and lime; yard, west side Military Park; office, 14 North Pennsylvania street, Indianapolis.

Engle, Willis; res 169 Park avenue, Indianapolis. Born in Mich. 1846; settled in M. C. 1865. Indpt. Episcopalian.

Eddy & West; shirt manufacturers and men's furnishing goods; 16 North Pennsylvania street, Indianapolis.

Eddy, Morris R.; res 79 East Ohio street, Indianapolis. Born in Ind. 1842; settled in M. C. 1857.

ENOS, B. V. & SON; architects; room 6 Odd Fellows' Hall, corner Washington and Pennsylvania streets, Indianapolis.

ENOS, B. V.; res 373 North Alabama street, Indianapolis. Born in Del. 1815; settled in M. C. 1853.

ENOS, BEN. H.; Indianapolis. Born in Ohio 1851; settled in M. C. 1853.

ELLIOTT, J. R.; real estate broker; room 13½ North Pennsylvania street, Indianapolis; res 10 Plum street. Born in Ind. 1839; settled in M. C. 1871. Rep. Protestant.

EGLER, WILLIAM; farmer; 1½ miles east of corporation line on Washington street, Indianapolis. Born in Ky. 1810; settled in M. C. 1871. Rep. Protestant.

Elder, John R.; President of Indianapolis Water Works Co.; res 150 North New Jersey, corner New York street.

ENGLISH & OVER; proprietors Victor Foundry and Machine Works, and manufacturers of grain drills, 240 to 246 South Pennsylvania street, Indianapolis.

ENGLISH, J. K.; res 255 North East street, Indianapolis. Born in Md. 1825; settled in M. C. 1830. Rep. Luth.

EVANS, MRS. CRARA; dealer in cigars and confectionery, and news depot; 239 Massachusetts avenue, Indianapolis. Born in Ind. 1844; settled in M. C. 1862.

Elder, Bunger & Co.; manufacturers of roofing and house spouting; 241 Massachusetts avenue, Indianapolis.

Elder, J. W.; res Gosport, Ind.

Ereckson, John; res 330 East Washington street, Indianapolis. Born in Europe 1842; settled in M. C. 1869.

Enos, T. H. K.; dairyman; $2\frac{1}{2}$ m e Indianapolis. Born in Va. 1841; settled in M. C. 1864. Rep. Methodist.

Enclebach, A.; cook; 5 South Illinois street, Indianapolis. Born in Germany 1835; settled in M. C. 1863.

Elliott, J. L.; policeman; 7 and 8, 2d floor, North Illinois St., Indianapolis. Born in Ind. 1841; settled in M. C. 1865. Rep.

ESSMAN, WILLIAM; proprietor ILLINOIS HOTEL; 181, 183 and 185 South Illinois street, Indianapolis. Born in Germany 1825; settled in M. C. 1864.

Emrich, H.; res South New Jersey street, Indianapolis.

Emison, S. A.; lawyer; $91\frac{1}{2}$ East Washington street, Indianapolis.

Ely, J. W.; constable; $91\frac{1}{2}$ East Washington street, Indianapolis; res 34 Camp street.

Ewart, T.; lawyer; 95 East Washington street, 3d floor, Indianapolis; res 219 East North street, Indianapolis. Born in Ohio 1847; settled in M. C. 1874.

EMDEN, MICHAEL; firm of Kahn & Co.; res 19 Madison avenue, Indianapolis. Born in Germany 1844; settled in M. C. 1870.

Ezekiel & Horowitz; dollar store; 39 West Washington street, Indianapolis.

Everett & Homan; plumbers; 47 West Washington street, Indianapolis.

Everett, P. E.; res 33 Ellsworth street, Indianapolis. Born in Ireland 1851; settled in M. C. 1868.

Evans, H. C.; real estate agent; 72½ East Washington street, Indianapolis. Born in Ky. 1836; settled in M. C. 1869. Dem. Presbyterian.

ELBERT, S. A.; physician and surgeon; 61 Indiana avenue; res 229 North Tennessee street. Born in Md. 1832; settled in M. C. 1865. Rep. Methodist.

EGGLESTON, FRANK E.; manager of the Howe Machine Co.; 70 West Washington street, Indianapolis; bds Hotel Bates. Born in Ohio 1847; settled in M. C. 1873. Dem. Protestant.

Eccles, Wm.; dealer in woolen factory goods; 68 West Washington street, Indianapolis; res 96 East New York street.

Emmerick, Henry; firm of John Osterman & Co.; commission merchants; 86 West Washington street, Indianapolis; res 224 West Maryland street. Born in Germany 1835; settled in M. C. 1856. Indpt.

ELDER, R.; firm of Brent & Elder, photographers; 210 and 212 East Washington street, Indianapolis. Born in N. C. 1841; settled in M. C. 1868.

Elder, Benj.; livery, sale and feed stable; 480 East Washington street, Indianapolis.

Emerson, R. B.; firm of Emerson & Beam, manufacturers of doors, sash, blinds and lumber; 225 to 229 West Market street, Indianapolis; res 239 West Market street. Born in N. H. 1812; settled in M. C. 1854.

FLEMINGS, JOHN; farmer; ½ mile north of corporation line, Indianapolis. Born in Ind. 1843; settled in M. C. 1860. Rep. Protestant.

FLEMINGS, MRS. MARY; farmer; ½ mile north of corporation line, Indianapolis. Born in Ind. 1818; settled in M. C. 1830.

FLETCHER, S. K.; res 335 North Pennsylvania street, Indianapolis. Born in M. C. 1840. Rep. Methodist.

Fouts, Samuel; proprietor of saw mill; res ¼ m s e corporation line, Indianapolis. Born in N. C. 1827; settled in M. C. 1850.

FISHER, WILLIAM S.; boot and shoemaker; 15 Massachusetts avenue. Born in England 1824; settled in M. C. 1850.

FURGUSON, W. N.; carpenter and job shop; 41 Massachusetts avenue, Indianapolis. Born in Pa. 1811; settled in M. C. 1852. Rep. Methodist.

Fitch & Anderson; carriage and wagon manufacturers; corner of Noble street and Massachusetts avenue, Indianapolis.

Anderson, J. J.; res 138 John street, Indianapolis. Born in Ohio 1843; settled in M. C. 1870.

Fitch, S. A.; res 38 Park avenue, Indianapolis. Born in Vt. 1835; settled in M. C. 1873.

Frick, John; dealer in fancy groceries and provisions; 301 Massachusetts avenue, Indianapolis. Born in Germany 1819; settled in M. C. 1860.

Foote & Burr; dealers in millinery and fancy goods and notions; 366 St. Clair street, Indianapolis; res 295 North East street.

Foote, Mrs.; res 366 St. Clair street, Indianapolis.

FAUGHT, JAMES L.; dealer in fancy groceries, flour and provisions; 435 East Tinker street, Indianapolis; res 325 Ash street. · Born in Ind. 1835; settled in M. C. 1874. Dem. Christian.

Foster, R. M.; bakery and confectionery; 88 Fort Wayne avenue, Indianapolis. Born in Scotland 1848; settled in M. C. 1868.

Friedgen, C. H.; saloon keeper; 115 Fort Wayne avenue; Indianapolis. Born in Germany 1833; settled in M. C. 1864.

Friedgen, C.; manufacturer and dealer in boots and shoes; 21 North Pennsylvania street, Indianapolis; res 36 North East street. Born in Germany 1836; settled in M. C. 1861.

Fowler, Harry; res 24½ East Washington street, Indianapolis.

FLORIA, J. E.; attorney at law; room 3 Talbott & New's Block, up stairs, North Pennsylvania street, Indianapolis; res 84 Massachusetts avenue. Born in Ind. 1852; settled in M. C 1871. Dem. Methodist.

FRANKLIN, JAMES E.; attorney at law; room 3 Talbott & New's Block, Indianapolis; res 123 North Liberty street. Born in Ky. 1842; settled in M. C. 1867.

Farbis, R. A.; wholesale and retail dealer in flour and feed; 136 and 139 Massachusetts avenue, Indianapolis. Born in N. C. 1818; settled in M. C. 1874. Presbyterian.

Ferguson, T.; stencil cutter and dealer in cigars and tobacco; 111 Massachusetts avenue, Indianapolis. Born in Indiana 1843; settled in M. C. 1843. Episcopalian.

Folsom, E. S.; manager Phœnix Life Insurance Co.; room 14 Talbott & New's Block, North Pennsylvania street, Indianapolis.

Fitchey, Michael G.; chief fire engineer; Hose Co. No. 9; St. Joseph street, Indianapolis.

Featherston, J. R.; physician and surgeon; room, second floor over 24½ Kentucky avenue.

FERTIG, FRANK; house, sign, banner and fresco painter; 24 South Meridian street, Indianapolis; res 496 North Mississippi street. Born in Germany 1828; settled in M. C. 1850.

FLORANDER & LUNDE; blacksmiths; repairing and job work done to order; shop at Southport.

Florander, N. B. S.; brick maker; res Southport. Born in Denmark 1847; settled in M. C. 1868.

FARLEY, T.; saw manufacturer; special attention given to repairing all kinds of saws; 189 South Meridian street, Indianapolis. Born in N. Y. 1837; settled in M. C. 1858.

Fleitz, Chas.; blacksmith; 487 South Meridian street, Indianapolis. Born in Germany 1832; settled in M. C. 1853.

FISHER ERASTUS, with No. 7 Fire Company; 125 East South street, Indianapolis; res 223 South Alabama street. Born in Ind. 1849; settled in M. C. 1863.

FINCH & FINCH; attorneys at law; rooms 9 and 10 Baldwin's Block, second floor, Indianapolis.

Fulmer, L. A.; silver plater; 225 East Washington street, Indianapolis.

FRANKENSTEIN, JACOB; cupping, bleeding, leeching, tooth drawing and barber; shop 249 back, West South street, Indianapolis; res 119 Yeizer street. Born in Germany 1837; settled in M. C. 1862.

Foster, R. S. & Co.; general commission and storage, dealers in cement and plaster; 68 and 70 South Delaware street, Indianapolis.

Foster, R. S.; firm of R. S. Foster & Co.; res 352 North New Jersey street, Indianapolis. Born in Ind. 1834; settled in M. C. 1850.

FLETCHER, W. B.; physician; 107 North Alabama street, Indianapolis.

Francis, Edith; fruit grower; 2½ m s e of Circle, Indianapolis. Born in Va. 1806; settled in M. C. 1837.

Foley, W. W.; physician; 280 North Mississippi street, Indianapolis. Born in M. C. 1843. Indpt. Protestant.

Foley, J. W.; firm of Muir & Foley; 12 West Washington street. Born in Indianapolis 1841. Indpt. Protestant.

FISHBACK, JOHN; president of Indianapolis Sentinel Co.; office, Sentinel Building; res 441 North Meridian street. Born in Ohio 1825; settled in M. C. 1854.

FAY, A. F.; firm of G. F. Adams & Co.; res 335 North Liberty street. Born in N. Y. 1822; settled in M. C. 1866.

FISHER, CHARLES; justice of the peace; 3 Yohn's Block; res 26 West North street. Born in Pa. 1806; settled in M. C. 1834.

FATOUT, H. B.; surveyor and civil engineer; office, 6 and 8 Hubbard's Block, Indianapolis; res Wayne township. Born in M. C. 1851.

FROMMEYER, HENRY; wholesale and retail dealer in china, glass and queensware; 24 South Meridian street, Indianapolis; res 134 North Mississippi street. Born in Germany 1829; settled in M. C. 1849.

FIELD, EDWARD S.; firm of McGilliard, Carpenter & Co., insurance and real estate; res 613 North Illinois street, Indianapolis.

FRY, W. H.; firm of Maxwell, Fry & Co.; res 721 North Meridian street, Indianapolis.

FRANKLIN FIRE INSURANCE CO. OF INDIANAPOLIS; building cor. Circle and Market streets, Indianapolis.

Fuller, James; physician; office 45½ Virginia avenue, Indianapolis; res 104 Fletcher avenue. Born in Vt. 1841; settled in M. C. 1867.

FITZHUGH, L. M. & CO.; dealers in teas, cigars and tobacco; 66 South Meridian street, Indianapolis.

Fitzhugh, L. M., res 76 East New York street. Born in Ind.

Ferger, L.; bakery; 407 West Washington street, Indianapolis. Born in Germany 1833; settled in M. C. 1854.

Feltmann, Geo. H.; shoemaker; 375 South Delaware street, Indianapolis. Born in Germany 1833; settled in M. C. 1865.

Field & Co.; vinegar works; 226 and 228 South Delaware St., Indianapolis.

Field, F. A.; firm of Field & Co., Indianapolis; bds Spencer House. Born in Ohio 1841; settled in M. C. 1873.

Fitzhugh, Dr. T.; physician; room 1, Schrader's Block, 453 Virginia avenue, Indianapolis; res 328 McCarty street. Born in Va. 1835; settled in M. C. 1873.

FORTNER, FLOYD & CO.; wholesale dealers in fancy goods, notions, etc.; 75 South Meridian street, Indianapolis.

FORTNER, A. J.; res 29 School street, Indianapolis. Born in Ind. 1839; settled in M. C. 1867.

FORTNER, S.; res 27 School street, Indianapolis. Born in Ind.; settled in M. C. 1869.

FLOYD, M. H.; res 227 East South street, Indianapolis. Born in Md. 1839; settled in M. C. 1868.

FAHNLEY & McCREA ; importers and jobbers of millinery, straw and fancy goods ; 131 South Meridian street, Indianapolis.

Fatout, Moses; carpenter and contractor; res ½ m e of Indianapolis.

Ferree, W.; dealer in hats and caps; Virginia avenue, Indianapolis. Born in Ind. 1844; settled in M. C. 1872. Rep.

Fisher, John; barber; 412 Virginia avenue, Indianapolis. Born in Switzerland 1846.

FUNKHOUSER, DAVID; physician and surgeon; 35 Market street, Indianapolis; res 40 North Mississippi street. Born in Va.

Forbes & Alcon; watch makers and jewelers; 30 Virginia avenue, Indianapolis.

Forbes, J. R.; res 77 Huron street, Indianapolis. Born in Ind.

Fette, G.; tailoring and repairing; 38 Virginia avenue, Indianapolis; res 229 South Alabama street. Born in Germany 1826; settled in M. C. 1854.

FOUTS, L.; boarding house and restaurant; 65 and 67 North Alabama street, Indianapolis. Born in Va. 1833; settled in M. C. 1874.

Finch & Finch; attorneys at law; 9 and 10 Baldwin's Block, second floor.

Finch, F. M.; res 286 East Ohio street, Indianapolis. Born in N. Y. 1810; settled in M. C. 1865.

Finch, J. A.; res 286 East Ohio street, Indianapolis. Born in Ind. 1842; settled in M. C. 1865.

Fuller, E. & Co.; dealers in pianos, organs, etc.; 4 Circle Hall, Indianapolis.

Fuller, E.; res 118 North Tennessee street, Indianapolis. Born in Mass. 1838; settled in M. C. 1869.

Forsythe, J. T.; res 341 Ash street, Indianapolis. Born in Ind. 1838; settled in M. C. 1873.

Forby, C. H.; dealer in trunks and traveling bags; 115 South Illinois street, Indianapolis.

FEIBLEMAN, MRS. DORA; dealer in notions and fancy goods; 123 South Illinois street, Indianapolis.

Frey, David; dealer in clothing; 129 South Illinois street, Indianapolis; res 63 West Georgia street. Born in Germany 1840; settled in M. C. 1869. Jewish faith.

Frese, C. & Co.; wholesale and retail dealers in hardware and cutlery; 27 West Washington street, Indianapolis.

Frese, Charles; res 27 West Washington street, Indianapolis. Born in Prussia 1834; settled in M. C. 1853.

Featherston, J. R.; physician; 24½ Kentucky avenue, Indianapolis; res 124 North Pennsylvania street. Born in Ky. 1840; settled in M. C. 1865. Dem.

Farnsworth, T. W.; oculist and aurist; 72 East Washington street, Indianapolis. Born in Mass. 1838; settled in M. C. 1865.

Ferguson, C. A.; dealer in watches and jewelry, 44 and 46 East Washington street, Indianapolis; res corner of Tinker and Meridian streets.

Frankem, I. L.; stove dealer; 34 East Washington street, Indianapolis; res 449 North Tennessee street. Born in M. C. 1838.

Foster & Darnall; merchants; 22 East Washington street, Indianapolis.

FLETCHER, S. A. & CO.; BANKERS; 30 and 32 East Washington street, Indianapolis.

First National Bank; 1 East Washington street, Indianapolis.

FEATHERSTON, WM. E.; auction and commission merchant; buys and sells household and other goods; 179 West Washington street, Indianapolis; res 200 North West street. Born in Ky. 1821; settled in M. C. 1828.

Frauer & Bieler; saddle and harness merchants; 109 East Washington street, Indianapolis.

Frauer, R.; res 277 New York street. Born in Germany 1839; settled in M. C. 1854.

Francis, A. E.; saloon; 120 South Illinois street, Indianapolis; res 118 West Georgia street. Born in Ind. 1844; settled in M. C. 1857.

FULLER, W. H.; shaving and hair dressing saloon; opposite Union Depot, Indianapolis. Born in Ind. 1837; settled in M. C. 1870. Rep.

Fletcher, S. A.; res 180 East Ohio street, Indianapolis. Born in Vt. about 1808; settled in M. C. 1831.

Feil, J.; groceries and provisions; 400 South Illinois street, Indianapolis; res 396 South Illinois street. Born in Germany 1836; settled in M. C. 1859. Dem. Catholic.

Fulton, B. F.; grocer; 49 South Illinois street, Indianapolis; res 240 North Illinois street. Born in Ohio 1848; settled in M. C. 1874.

Faulkner, George S.; machinist; No. 1 Engine House, 147 Indiana avenue, Indianapolis. Born in Conn. 1837; settled in M. C. 1867.

Faulkner, Eugene; machinist; No. 1 Engine House, Indianapolis. Born in Conn. 1849; settled in M. C. 1868.

Foster, Jonas; agent Franklin Fire Insurance Co.; res 61 Central avenue, Indianapolis. Born in Ohio 1846; settled in M. C. 1870. Rep. Baptist.

Fritz, Peter; Granger Eating House; 30 West Louisiana street, Indianapolis. Born in Germany 1848; settled in M. C. 1869.

FRANK, JAMES; real estate broker; 35 East Washington street, Indianapolis; res 461 North Tennessee street. Born in Germany 1837; settled in M. C. 1857. Indpt. Catholic.

Frauer, I. C.; druggist; 246 East Washington street, Indianapolis; res 28 North East street. Born in Germany 1841; settled in M. C. 1854.

Feldkamp, R. W.; firm of Feldkamp & Woodford; importers and dealers in wines and domestic liquors; 306 East Washington street, Indianapolis. Born in Hanover, Germany, 1846; settled in M. C. 1869.

Foist, Fred.; firm of Foist & Schweikle; wagon and blacksmith shop; 478 East Washington street, Indianapolis; res 32 North Liberty street. Born in Germany 1835; settled in M. C. 1873.

FELLER, CHARLES; practical watchmaker and jeweler; 226 East Washington street, Indianapolis; res 244 South Missouri street. Born in Ohio 1852; settled in M. C. 1854. Dem. Protestant.

Guyman, John A.; clerk M. M. B. A.; 24 Kentucky avenue, Indianapolis; res 117 West street. Born in Ind. 1847; settled in M. C. 1871. Rep.

GORDON, GEO.; firm of GORDON & HESS, dry goods; 3 Odd Fellows Hall, Indianapolis; res 216 North Delaware street. Born in Ind. 1822; settled in M. C. about 1859.

GORDON, WM.; firm of L. P. Culloden & Co.; real estate agents; 82½ East Washington street, Indianapolis; res 373 North West street. Born in Scotland 1838; settled in M. C. 1873. Indpt. Protestant.

GRAVES, HENRY H.; firm of H. JOHNSON & CO., manufacturers of domestic wines; 194 West Washington street, Indianapolis; res 29 South West street. Born in Ind. 1840; settled in M. C. 1870.

Gordon, Browne & Lamb; attorneys at law; room 8, second floor, McDonald & Roache's Block, Indianapolis.

Graves, P. M.; with T. J. Doan, grocer; 194 West Washington street, Indianapolis; res 29 South West street. Born in Ind. 1846; settled in M. C. 1870.

Goodwin, T. A.; minister and real estate agent; office 44½ North Pennsylvania street, Indianapolis ; res 1¼ m e corporation line, on Washington street. Born in Ind. 1818; settled in M. C. 1854. Rep. Methodist.

Goodyear India Rubber Co.; wholesale and retail dealers in every description of rubber goods ; 12 North Pennsylvania street, Indianapolis.

Garvey, James; ornamental plastering; 90 Massachusetts Ave., Indianapolis ; res between Delaware and Alabama streets. Born in Ireland 1840; settled in M. C. 1873.

GANDOLFO, MRS. FANNIE W.; dress-making; cutting and fitting a specialty; 107 Massachusetts avenue, Indianapolis.

Gillett, Samuel T.; minister of M. E. Church; res 138 Massachusetts avenue, Indianapolis. Born in N. Y. 1809; settled in M. C. 1846.

Gregg, J. A.; wagon maker and repair shop; 226 West North street; res 329 North West street. Born in Ind. 1829; settled in M. C. 1856.

GILBERT, FRM; livery and sale stable; 286 and 288 Massachusetts avenue, Indianapolis; res 224 St. Clair street. Born in Ky. 1824; settled in M. C. 1874. Dem. Spiritualist.

GOTH & DIETZ; dealers in staple and fancy groceries, flour and feed; 489 North New Jersey street, Indianapolis.

GOTH, E. P.; res 453 North New Jersey street, Indianapolis. Born in Ind. 1854; settled in M. C. 1854.

Gale, E. S.; physician and surgeon; 164 Fort Wayne avenue, Indianapolis; res 372 North New Jersey street. Born in Ky. 1821; settled in M. C. 1873.

Garshwiler, W.; livery, sale and feed stable; 130 St. Clair street, Indianapolis.

GUISEY, JOHN C.; dealer in and shipper of oysters, fish, game and poultry; 40 West Maryland street, Indianapolis; res 221 West Maryland street. Born in N. J. 1851; settled in M. C. 1871. Rep. Lutheran.

Gillespie, William J.; res 203 North Illinois street, Indianapolis. Born in M. C. 1843.

GIEZENDANNER, WM.; baker and confectioner; 150 West Vermont street, Indianapolis. Born in Switzerland 1845; settled in M. C. 1860. Protestant.

GORDEN, BEN. F.; printer; res 77 Indiana avenue, Indianapolis. Born in M. C. 1856.

Gorden, Maggie D.; res 77 Indiana avenue.

GARDNER, CONRAD; firm of Gardner & Son, meat market; 100 Indiana avenue, Indianapolis; res 3 m w Circle street. Born in Germany 1828; settled in M. C. 1861. Dem. R. Catholic.

GARDNER, FRED.; firm of Gardner & Son, meat market; 100 Indiana avenue, Indianapolis; res 3 m w Circle street. Born in Ohio 1855; settled in M. C. 1861. Dem.

Gossom, W. H.; salesman in grocery; 201 Indiana avenue; res 38 Camp street. Born in Ky. 1827; settled in M. C. 1869. Conservative. Christian.

Ganter, C.; confectioner; 180 East Washington street, Indianapolis. Born in Baden, Germany, 1820; settled in M. C. 1852.

Grubb, W. C.; insurance agent; 68 West Washington street, Indianapolis; res 310 North Illinois street. Born in Pa. 1842; settled in M. C. 1869. Indpt. Presbyterian.

Green, J. R.; 92 and 94 West Washington street, Indianapolis. Born in Ind. 1851; settled in M. C. 1873. Rep. Christ.

GAUSS, E.; dealer in wooden and willow ware, toys, notions and fancy goods; 174 West Washington street, Indianapolis. Born in Wurtemberg, Germany, 1843; settled in M. C. 1868. Rep. Freethinker.

Graham, R. J.; firm of C. A. Moffat & Co.; 196 West Washington street, Indianapolis. Born in Ind. 1838; settled in M. C. 1871. Rep. Protestant.

GIRTON, CHAS.; pump maker; 214 East Washington street, Indianapolis; res 72 West Maryland street. Born in Ohio 1843; settled in M. C. 1868. Dem. Protestant.

GREIN, JOHN; baker and confectioner; 264 East Washington street, Indianapolis. Born in Germany 1838; settled in M. C. 1845.

GASS, ROBERT; dealer in fancy notions and gents' furnishing goods; 336 East Washington street, Indianapolis. Born in Ireland 1849; settled in M. C. 1873. Presbyterian.

Geisendorff, J. C.; firm of J. C. Geisendorff & Co., proprietors Central Mills; office, corner Circle and Market streets, Indianapolis; res 191 North New Jersey street.

Gallup, W. P.; firm of W. P. & E. P. Gallup, agents for Fairbanks' scales, and dealers in grain; 43 and 45 North Tennessee street, Indianapolis; res 350 North Tennessee street. Born in N. H. 1828; settled in M. C. 1853.

Gallup, E. P.; res 350 North Tennessee street, Indianapolis. Born in N. H. 1836; settled in M. C. 1856.

Gorden, I. S. & Co.; wholesale dealers in saddlery hardware; 118 South Meridian street, Indianapolis; res northwest corner Vermont and Tennessee streets.

Groeschel, August; tailor; near Crown Hill, Indianapolis. Born in Germany 1836; settled in M. C. 1867.

Groeschel, Chas.; gardener; near Crown Hill, Indianapolis. Born in Germany 1832; settled in M. C. 1858.

Gray, Stephen; merchant tailor; 18 North Pennsylvania street, Indianapolis; res 242 North Pennsylvania street. Born in England 1842; settled in M. C. 1868. Indp. Methodist.

Gordon, J. W.; res 475 North Illinois street, Indianapolis.

Green, John C.; druggist; No. 1 Martindale's Block, Pennsylvania street, Indianapolis; res 510 North Delaware street. Born in Ind. 1829; settled in M. C. 1864.

Glazier, Clark & Co.; wholesale and retail dealers in coal, coke and lime, also jobbers in grain, flour, feed and hay; warehouse 146 South Pennsylvania street, Indianapolis.

GRAUMAN, MIRA; city shirt factory and dress making; 108 South Illinois street, Indianapolis.

Grimm & Meyer; dealers in staple and fancy groceries; 203 Massachusetts avenue, Indianapolis.

GRIMM, LOUIS; res 402 North New Jersey street, Indianapolis. Born in Germany 1853; settled in M. C. 1873.

Goldsmith & Co.; dealers in ready made clothing; 101 South Illinois street, Indianapolis.

Goldsmith, Birnhast. Born in Germany 1843; settled in M. C. 1874.

Grauman David; broker; 136 Illinois street, Indianapolis; bds Spencer House. Born in Ky. 1852; settled in M. C. 1872.

Gray, J. W.; proprietor Spencer House, Indianapolis.

Goe, H. N.; dealer in fancy groceries and provisions; 441 North Illinois street, Indianapolis; res 503 North Mississippi St. Born in Ind. 1838; settled in M. C. 1864.

GEORGE, H.; general business manager for L. S. White; 173 East Washington street. Born in Pa. 1838; settled in M. C. 1872. Rep. Presbyterian.

Garrison, J. W.; proprietor Manufacturers and Real Estate Gazette; 60 West Ohio street, Indianapolis. Born in Pa.

GOEBLER, W. M.; cleaning, dyeing and repairing house; 37 North Illinois street, Indianapolis; res 26 Buchanan street. Born in Germany 1835; settled in M. C. 1868.

Gray, Wm.; res 235 North Illinois street, Indianapolis. Born in Ind. 1846; settled in M. C. 1850.

Gray & Beyschlag; successors to H. H. Lee, druggist; Bates House Block, 18 and 20 North Illinois street, Indianapolis.

GOLDSBERRY, S. S.; dealer in fine watches and all kinds of jewelry and silver ware; 11 North Illinois street, Indianapolis; res 259 Virginia avenue. Born in M. C. 1840. Rep. Episcopalian.

Groesley, H.; general commission merchant, 100 South Illinois street; corner Georgia street, Indianapolis; res 413 Washington street. Born in Ohio 1822; settled in M. C. 1874.

GEROLANIUM, JAMES; in the driven well business; res 325 South Illinois street, Indianapolis. Born in Ind. 1848; settled in M. C. 1852. Dem. Christian.

Greany, P. & T.; dealers in groceries, wines and liquors; South Delaware street, Indianapolis.

GALE, J. A.; physician; corner Veach and Shelby streets, Indianapolis; res 372 North New Jersey street. Born in Ind. 1851; settled in M. C. 1873. Rep. Protestant.

Glass, C. C.; grocer; 19 Virginia avenue, Indianapolis. Born in Ind. 1832; settled in M. C. 1870.

GALLAHUE, W. C.; dry goods and notions; 446 Virginia avenue, Indianapolis. Born in 1841; settled in M. C. 1865.

GRAY, G. W.; tailor; custom work done to order; 27 Kentucky avenue, Indianapolis. Born in Va. 1824; settled in M. C. 1862.

Gosset, Francis; farmer and gardener; 2½ m s of Circle street, Indianapolis. Born in Ind. 1836; settled in M. C. 1868.

Gimber, Joseph; gardener; 1 m s of corporation, Indianapolis. Born in Germany 1849; settled in M. C. 1852.

Gimber, Nicholas; 1 m s of corporation, Indianapolis. Born in Germany 1800; settled in M. C. 1852.

GREENMAN, WRIGHT & DUN; proprietors of LITTLE'S HOTEL.; corner Washington and New Jersey streets, Indianapolis.

Greenman, Robert; res Little's Hotel, Indianapolis.

GROOMS, W. E.; printer at office corner Meridian and Circle streets, Indianapolis; bds Sherman House. Born in M. C. 1856. Dem.

Garrison, Edward; toll-gate keeper; East Washington street, ¾ mile east of corporation line, Indianapolis. Born in Ky. 1815; settled in M. C. 1866.

GATES, A. B. & CO.; wholesale dealers in coffees, teas, etc.; 31 East Maryland street, Indianapolis.

GATES, A. B.; res 377 North Mississippi street, Indianapolis. Born in Ind. 1823; settled in M. C. 1869.

Graves, L. W.; farmer; 1½ miles east of corporation line, Indianapolis. Born in Tenn. 1824; settled in M. C. 1861.

GEISEL, HENRY; grocery and provision house; Clifford avenue, east of Woodruff Place, Indianapolis. Born in Germany 1832; settled in M. C. 1849.

GEISEL, W. J.; clerk with Henry Geisel in grocery house, Indianapolis. Born in Indianapolis 1855.

GEHRING, CONRAD; importer and dealer in German scientific books, architects' and engineers' supplies; 127 East Washington street, Indianapolis. Born in Germany 1834; settled in M. C. 1859.

Goldhausen, Franz; German bookseller; 9 and 11 Alabama street, Indianapolis. Born in Germany 1834; settled in M. C. 1869.

GRUNDEN, W. H.; boot and shoe manufacturer; 55 North Alabama street, Indianapolis. Born in Pa. 1822; settled in M. C. 1869.

Geer, S. H.; grocer; 260 South Alabama street, Indianapolis.

GIBSON, W. T. & CO.; general agents American insurance; 77 East Market street, Indianapolis.

GIBSON, W. T.; firm of W. T. Gibson & Co.; res Chicago, Ill.

Gates, Pray & Co.; feed and sale stable; East Market square, Indianapolis.

Gates, A. B.; res 212 East Market street, Indianapolis. Born in Ind. 1825; settled in M. C. 1864.

GLASSEY, WM.; firm of Pease, Robinson and Glassey; res 300 Virginia avenue, Indianapolis.

GRAHAM & HUBBARD; civil engineers; 8 Brouse Block, 92 East Market street, Indianapolis.

GRAHAM, J. M.; firm of Graham & Hubbard; res 283 Pennsylvania street, Indianapolis. Born in Ind. 1850; settled in M. C. 1873.

Green, James; general agent Berkshire Life Insurance Co.; 27 Baldwin's Block, Indianapolis; res 364 North Meridian St. Born in R. I. 1810; settled in M. C. 1853. Rep. Presb.

GUNDELFINGER, B.; firm of B. Gundelfinger & Co., Arcade Clothing House; 6 West Washington street, Indianapolis; res 260 East Ohio street. Born in Germany 1835; settled in M. C. 1860.

GUNDELFINGER, H.; Arcade; res 18 West Vermont street, Indianapolis. Born in Germany 1848; settled in M. C. 1864. Hebrew.

Grove, B.; salesman Wheeler & Wilson sewing machine; 10 West Washington street, Indianapolis. Born in Ohio 1818; settled in M. C. 1836. Rep. Methodist.

GOLDMAN, I. S.; watchmaker and jeweler; special attention paid to repairing and engraving; 78 Virginia avenue, Indianapolis. Born in Ind. 1850; settled in M. C. 1874. Rep. Methodist.

Graves, R.; confectioner; 36 Kentucky avenue, Indianapolis. Born in N. C. 1826; settled in M. C. 1843.

Greek & Rice, carpenters and repairers; pumps, wells and cisterns repaired to order; 131 North Tennessee street, Indianapolis.

Gallup, W. P. & Co.; commission merchants; 43 and 45 North Tennessee street, Indianapolis.

Gentry, Charles; confectioner; 149 North Noble street, Indianapolis.

GARDNER, W. H.; dealer in wrapping paper and paper sacks; 24 South New Jersey street, Indianapolis.

Grafftey, J. F.; shirt maker; 30½ South Illinois street, Indianapolis.

Grafftey, J.; shirt maker; 30½ South Illinois street, Indianapolis.

Gough, Geo.; engineer for Kingan. Born in Ireland 1848; settled in M. C. 1865.

GREEN, W. H.; with Thos. Cottrell, 276 West Washington street, Indianapolis; res 176 Douglass street. Born in Ind. 1847; settled in M. C. 1874.

George, Robert; grocer and liquor dealer; 274 West Washington street, Indianapolis; res 24 North Mississippi street. Born in Ind. 1818; settled in M. C. 1838.

Gibson, D. & T. M.; millers; 352 West Washington street, Indianapolis.

Geis, L. A.; saloon and restaurant; 14 and 16 South Delaware street, Indianapolis. Born in Germany 1843; settled in M. C. 1863.

Grosch, John; proprietor of Mozart Hall, Indianapolis. Born in Germany 1823; settled in M. C. 1848.

Gambold, Thos.; salesman at Wm. Spotts', corner of Delaware street and Virginia avenue, Indianapolis. Born in N. C. 1833; settled in M. C. 1868.

GEHRING, JOSEPH; clerks for Wm. Scott & Co.; res 178 Huron street, Indianapolis. Born in Va. 1843; settled in M. C. 1870.

Goldthwait, Everett; firm of H. Goldthwait & Co.; res 188 California street, Indianapolis. Born in Me. 1851; settled in M. C. 1873.

Goldthwait, H. & Co.; wood dealers; Virginia avenue, Indianapolis.

Gimpel, Michael; grocer and liquor dealer; 353 East street, Indianapolis. Born in Germany 1823; settled in M. C. 1852.

Greer, S. H.; grocer; 70 High street, Indianapolis; res same.

Gibbs, Max; notions, etc.; 406 South Meridian street, Indianapolis; res same. Born in Austria 1834; settled in M. C. 1870.

GEORGE, J. O.; ice cream parlor; 436 South Meridian street, Indianapolis. Born in New Brunswick 1841; settled in M. C. 1874.

Gibson, W. S.; carpenter; res 156 East Market street, Indianapolis. Born in Pa. 1828; settled in M. C. 1863.

GLAZIER, JOHN; foreman No. 4 Engine Co.; Indianapolis; res 316 South Illinois street. Born in M. C. 1852.

Grube, John; hoseman of Engine Co. No. 4; Indianapolis; res 338 South Illinois street. Born in M. C. 1852.

Gates, Jno. J.; firm of Sullivan & Gates; res 212 North California street, Indianapolis.

Gimbel, H. E.; cabinet-maker; 219 East Washington street, Indianapolis. Born in Ohio 1851; settled in M. C. 1854.

GRUM, LEWIS; silver-plater; 225 East Washington street, Indianapolis; res 18 South Pennsylvania street. Born in Pa. 1840; settled in M. C. 1869.

Gorrell, A. W.; res 91 Fletcher avenue, Indianapolis. Born in Va. 1835; settled in M. C. 1856.

Gladen, F. M.; attorney at law; rooms 6 and 8 Hubbard's Bl'k, Indianapolis. Born in M. C. 1851.

Gramling, J. & P.; merchant tailors and dealers in clothing; 35 East Washington street, Indianapolis.

Gramling, J.; res 490 North Delaware street, Indianapolis. Born in Bavaria 1832; settled in M. C. 1862.

Gramling, P.; res 500 North Delaware street, Indianapolis. Born in Bavaria 1828; settled in M. C. 1854.

GOEPPER, F. & CO.; merchant tailors and dealers in clothing and gents' goods; 17 East Washington street, Indianapolis.

GOEPPER, F.; res 373 North Meridian street, Indianapolis. Born in Baden, Germany, 1825; settled in M. C. 1849.

Gilmore, E. T.; dealer in flour and feed; 155 West Washington street, Indianapolis. Born in Canada 1844; settled in M. C. 1871.

GREEN, W. B. & CO.; Cleveland Lightning Rod Co.; office, 193 West Washington street, Indianapolis.

GROVER & BAKER SEWING MACHINE CO.; office, 21 East Washington street, Indianapolis.

GREEN, W. B.; firm of W. B. Green & Co.; bds 193 West Washington street, Indianapolis. Born in Ohio 1837; settled in M. C. 1870.

GALL, ALBERT; dealer in carpets, wall paper, window shades, oil cloth, etc.; 101 East Washington street, Indianapolis; res 131 North New Jersey street. Born in Wisconsin 1842; settled in M. C. 1845.

Griffin, G. O.; dealer and importer of wines and liquors; 187 East Washington street, Indianapolis. Born in Ind. 1839; settled in M. C. 1873.

Hartpence, W.; confectionary stand; corner Washington and Illinois streets, Indianapolis.

HOWLAND, J. A.; baggage master on I. B. & W. R. R.; room No. 8, 22½ South Illinois street, Indianapolis. Born in N. Y. 1848; settled in M. C. 1860. Rep.

Helms, L. A.; dentist; room 14, up stairs, in Franklin Life Insurance Building, Indianapolis. Born in Ohio 1844; settled in M. C. 1865.

HOLLOWELL, J. T.; res 341 South Meridian street, Indianapolis. Born in Ind. 1843; settled in M. C. 1869. Rep. Christian.

Haupt, R.; notion store; 151 East Washington street, Indianapolis; res 17 Chatham street. Born in Prussia 1819; settled in M. C. 1856.

Hadley, H. M.; Deputy Assessor; City Hall, Indianapolis. Born in M. C. 1852.

HADLEY, WM.; City Assessor; office in City Hall, Indianapolis; res 381 North Delaware street. Born in N. C. 1823; settled in M. C. 1853.

Hallenbeck, T. P.; res Cincinnati, Ohio. Born in Pa. 1841.

Hill, J. F.; barber; 28 North Illinois street, Indianapolis; res North Tennessee street. Born in Ohio 1824; settled in M. C. 1864. Rep. Methodist.

HOWARD & SON; cancer doctors; 92 South Illinois street, Indianapolis.

HOWARD, E.; res 822 East Washington street, Indianapolis. Born in Ohio 1815; settled in M. C. 1854. Rep.

HOWARD, W. O.; 92 South Illinois street, Indianapolis. Born in Ind. 1844; settled in M. C. 1854.

Hotz, G. C.; tailor; 124 South Illinois street, Indianapolis. Born in Germany 1833; settled in M. C. 1855.

Heins, S.; dealer in ready-made clothing and furnishing goods; 97 South Illinois street, Indianapolis; res 80 West Maryland street. Born in N. Y. 1848; settled in M C. 1873. Dem.

Hollywood, R. H.; saloon; 131 South Illinois street, Indianapolis. Born in N. Y. 1844; settled in M. C. 1868.

Hallenbeck & Co.; wire works; 39 South Illinois street, Indianapolis.

Hallenbeck, A. H.; res Indianapolis. Born in Pa. 1839; settled in M. C. 1870.

Henninger & Bro.; toy store; 47 South Illinois street, Indianapolis.

Harlan, G. W.; grocer; 49 South Illinois street, Indianapolis; res corner East and Michigan streets.

Haas, S.; clothing; 53 South Illinois street, Indianapolis. Born in Germany 185–; settled in M. C. 1873. Jewish faith.

Hamilton, T. D.; furniture; 139 East Washington street, Indianapolis; res 75 North Illinois street. Born in Pa. 1821; settled in M. C. 1861. Rep. Methodist.

Hamilton, Mrs. M C.; dress-making; 75 North Illinois street, Indianapolis. Born in Ind. 1848; settled in M. C. 1865.

Hadley, W. S.; restaurant; 61 North Illinois street, Indianapolis. Born in N. Y. 1835; settled in M. C. 1874. Dem.

Hardebeck, J. H.; res 389 North Pennsylvania street, Indianapolis. Born in Ohio 1842; settled in M. C. 1874.

Hale, D. B.; physician; 520 East Washington street, Indianapolis. Born in Ohio 1844; settled in M. C. 1872. Rep.

HESS, J. W.; firm of Gordon & Hess; res 385 North Illinois street, Indianapolis. Born in Va. 1835; settled in M. C. 1862. Presbyterian.

- Hereth, J. C.; harness maker; 12 North Delaware street, Indianapolis; res 268 North Alabama street. Born in 1827; settled in M. C. 1852. Rep. Methodist.

HAMILTON, F. W.; Auditor of Marion County; res 115 Park avenue, Indianapolis. Born in Md. 1833; settled in M. C. 1835. Rep.

Haughey, T. P.; President National Bank; res 237 North Meridian street, Indianapolis. Born in Del. 1826; settled in M. C. 1848. Rep. Methodist.

HATCH, V. G.; res 104 College avenue, Indianapolis. Born in N. Y. about 1828; settled in M. C. 1872.

Hawkins, R. O.; res 493 North East street, Indianapolis. Born in Ohio 1848; settled in M. C. 1870. Rep.

HOBBS, WILLIAM H.; firm of Swain & Hobbs; res 112 North Pennsylvania street, Indianapolis. Born in Ind. 1848; settled in M. C. 1868.

Haskins, T. H.; 10 East Washington street, Indianapolis. Born in Ky. 1854; settled in M. C. 1873.

HUBBARD, WM. H.; res corner Meridian and Second streets, Indianapolis. Born in M. C. 1825. Presbyterian.

Hafner, A.; boots and shoes; 127 West Washington street, Indianapolis. Born in Baden 1832; settled in M. C. 1854.

HEIZER, DAVID F.; res 443 North East street, Indianapolis. Born in Va. 1834; settled in M. C. 1834.

Hyde, N. J.; clerk at Capital House; West Washington street, Indianapolis. Born in Wis. 1851; settled in M. C. 1859. Dem.

Hazzard & Webster; real estate brokers; 24½ East Washington street, Indianapolis.

Hazzard, M.; res Indianapolis.

Hannaman, W.; res 2½ m e Indianapolis. Born in Ohio 1806; settled in M. C. 1827.

HUEBNER & BUNTING; architects; rooms 18 and 19, over 95 East Washington street, Indianapolis.

Harrison, R. E.; lawyer; 2d floor, 95 East Washington street, Indianapolis; res 148 Huron street. Born in Ind. 1838; settled in M. C. 1865.

HUEBNER, HENRY R.; res 484 South New Jersey street, Indianapolis. Born in capital city of Saxony; settled in M. C. 1865.

Harrison, Temple C.; lawyer; rooms 8 and 9, over 95 East Washington street, Indianapolis; res 23 Cherry street. Born in Ind. 1834; settled in M. C. 1864.

HILL & NEAL; wholesale and retail druggists; 99 East Washington street, Indianapolis.

Hill, John F.; druggist; res 84 North Alabama street, Indianapolis. Born in Ohio 1812; settled in M. C. 1830.

HASKIT & HETSELGESSER; successors to Haskit & Morris, wholesale and retail druggists; 20 West Washington street, Indianapolis.

HASKIT, W. I.; res 228 North Delaware street, Indianapolis. Born in Ind. 1833; settled in M. C. 1864. Rep. Presby.

HARRISON'S BANK; 15 East Washington street, Indianapolis.

HARRISON, ALFRED; res 252 North Meridian street, Indianapolis. Born in Tenn. 1802; settled in M. C. 1824.

HARRISON, J. C. S.; 262 North Meridian street, Indianapolis. Born in Ind. 1829; settled in M. C. 1847.

HUFF & NICHOL; attorneys at law; office 16½ East Washington street, Indianapolis.

HUFF, SAMUEL A.; firm of Huff & Nichol; bds at Bates House, Indianapolis. Born in S. C. 1811; settled in M. C. 1873.

Herington, Mrs. Sarah; boarding house; 49 North Illinois street, Indianapolis. Born in Ind. 1839; settled in M. C. 1865.

Huff, J. T.; res corner Bellefontaine street and Christian avenue, Indianapolis. Born in Ohio 1841; settled in M. C. 1844. Democrat.

Hill & Myers; boots and shoes; 17 West Washington street, Indianapolis.

Hill, E. C.; res 90 West First street, Indianapolis. Born in Ind. 1830; settled in M. C. 1864.

Hogshire, W. K. & Co.; boots and shoes; 25 West Washington street, Indianapolis.

HAWLISON, WILLIAM; firm of Chas. Mayer & Co.; res 297 North Tennessee street, Indianapolis.

Harowitz, S.; Indianapolis. Born in 1844; settled in M. C. 1873. Circle House.

Homan, H. O.; res 31 Ellsworth street, Indianapolis. Born in N. Y. 1832; settled in M. C. 1868. Dem.

Hanson & Morrow; merchants; 46 North Illinois street, Indianapolis.

HEITKAM, GEO. H.; res 250 North Alabama street, Indianapolis. Born in Germany 1837; settled in M. C. 1853.

HETSELGESSER, L. W.; res 93 North Illinois street, Indianapolis. Dem. Methodist.

Hanson, J. A.; res 327 North Illinois street, Indianapolis. Born in Ind. 1841; settled in M. C. 1873.

HEITKAM & KENNEY; clothing house; Griffith's Block, 38 West Washington street, Indianapolis.

Heims, S.; clothing; 57 South Illinois street, Indianapolis; res 80 Maryland street. Born in Germany 1822; settled in M. C. 1873.

HODGSON, ISAAC; architect; room 6, Griffith's Block, Indianapolis; res 705 North Illinois street. Born in Belfast, Ireland; settled in M. C. 1855.

HODGSON, EDGAR J.; architect; room 6, Griffith's Block, Indianapolis; res 705 North Illinois street. Born in Ind. 1854; settled in M. C. 1855.

HODKINSON & CO.; refiners, agents for carbon, headlight, lubricating and anchor mineral oil; office 22 West Maryland street, Indianapolis.

HODKINSON, S.; Born in Pa. 1843; settled in M. C. 1874.

HEDGES & LYONS; undertakers and wholesale dealers in metalic burial cases, caskets and wooden coffins; 66 West Maryland street, two doors west of Illinois street, Indianapolis.

HEDGES, E.; res 66 West Maryland street, Indianapolis. Born in Ohio 1831; settled in M. C. 1852.

HASTINGS, E. L.; Superintendent State Journal, corner Circle and Market streets, Indianapolis.

Hofmann, Phillip; dealer in fancy groceries and provisions, also proprietor of first class boarding house; near Brightwood, on Pendleton Pike. Born in Germany 1827; settled in M. C. 1863.

Higgins Bent Wood School Furniture Co.; A. B. Judson, secretary; C. J. Higgins, supt.; located at Brightwood.

Hambleton, Robert B.; toll-gate keeper and dealer in cigars and tobacco; 1½ miles northeast terminus Massachusetts avenue. Born in Ohio 1823.

HAUERSEN, WILLIAM; res 297 North Tennessee street, Indianapolis. Born in Germany 1832; settled in M. C. 1854.

Herrington, S. P.; firm of Herrington & Boyd, manufacturers of carriages, buggies and spring wagons; 213 and 215 East Market street, Indianapolis; res 219 East Market street. Born in Ind. 1839; settled in M. C. 1873.

Hunt & Hacker; dentists; office corner Pennsylvania and Vermont streets, Indianapolis.

Haerst, H.; merchant tailor; 38 South Illinois street, Indianapolis; res 65 South Illinois street. Born in Prussia 1825; settled in M. C. 1858.

Hacker, T. S.; res 129 North Illinois street, Indianapolis. Born in Ind. 1851; settled in M. C. 1870.

Hunt, P. G. C.; res at office corner Pennsylvania and Vermont streets, Indianapolis. Born in Ind. 1829.

Hill, Conrad; res 429 East St. Clair street. Born in Germany 1835; settled in M. C. 1869.

Hays, B. D. & Co.; wholesale and retail dealers in all kinds of pine lumber, laths, doors and sash; office 31 east end of Massachusetts avenue, Indianapolis.

Hays, B. D.; res Yandes street, Indianapolis. Born in Ohio 1836; settled in M. C. 1861.

HUBBARD, WM.; dealer in drugs and pure medicines; 44 Malott avenue, Indianapolis; res 48½ Malott avenne. Born in Ind. 1839; settled in M. C. 1872.

HARMON, JOHN; bakery and confectionery; 120 Ft. Wayne avenue, Indianapolis; res same. Born in Me. 1840; settled in M. C. 1874.

Hansen, John N.; grainer; with Webb & Co.; 12 South Pennsylvania street, Indianapolis; res corner Beadle street and Lincoln avenue. Born in Prussia 1834; settled in M. C. 1865.

Haugh & Co.; manufacturers of jail and court house work, iron fronts, wrought and cast iron railing; 68, 70, 74, 76, 78 and 80 South Pennsylvania street, Indianapolis.

Haugh, Joseph R.; res 175 North New Jersey street, Indianapolis.

Haugh, B. F.; res 670 North Pennsylvania street, Indianapolis.

HOFFMAN, W. T.; rag carpet manufacturer; 78 Massachusetts avenue, 2d floor, Indianapolis; res same. Born in Iowa 1841; settled in M. C. 1868.

Hammel, George; res 342 East street, Indianapolis. Born in Ohio 1848; settled in M C. 1859.

Holloway, H. C.; Superintendent of Post Office Department and general manager; Pennsylvania street, Indianapolis; res southwest corner Second and Delaware streets. Born in Ind. 1844; settled in M. C. 1865.

HOGAN & HAMMEL; Avenue Tea Store; dealers in teas, coffee, sugar and foreign fruits, with general grocery stock; corner Massachusetts avenue and New Jersey street, Indianapolis.

Hogan, D. W.; res 173 Massachusetts avenue, Indianapolis. Born in Ky. 1839; settled in M. C. 1872.

Hoss, James J.; real estate broker; office, 78 Massachusetts avenue; res 3½ m n e Indianapolis. Born in Ohio 1833; settled in M. C. 1836. Rep. Methodist.

Hoss, Jacob; retired farmer; 3½ m n e Indianapolis. Born in N. C. 1802; settled in M. C. 1836. Rep. Methodist.

HARPER, SAMUEL; retired farmer; res 1¼ m n e corporation line, Indianapolis. Born in N. C. 1818; settled in M. C. 1836. Rep. Lutheran.

Hibben, W. W.; minister M. E. Church, corresponding editor of Masonic Advocate. Born in Pa. 1811; settled in Ind. 1835.

Hays, I. C. & Son; general insurance agents; over No. 12 North Pennsylvania street.

Hays, I. C.; res 161 Christian avenue, Indianapolis. Born in Ohio 1830; settled in M. C. 1852. Rep. Presbyterian.

Harton, Charles S.; res 258 North Pennsylvania street, Indianapolis. Born in Mass. 1838; settled in M. C. 1874.

Henry, John A.; attorney at law; room 314, second floor, Vinton's Block, Indianapolis; res 83 East St. Clair street. Born in Ohio 1848; settled in M. C. 1873. Rep. Methodist.

Herriott, W. M.; res 112 North Meridian street, Indianapolis. Born in Pa. 1832; settled in M. C. 1874.

Hasket & Kerger; manufacturers of pumps; 34 South Pennsylvania street, Indianapolis.

Hasket, Elijah; res in rear of 272 Washington street, Indianapolis. Born in N. C. 1832; settled in M. C. 1843.

Heard, Thomas; physician and surgeon ; room 1, Odd Fellows' Hall, corner Washington and Pennsylvania streets, Indianapolis. Born in England 1811 ; settled in M. C. 1872. Rep.

Hill, G. W.; res 241 Virginia avenue, Indianapolis. Born in Pa. 1824; settled in M. C. 1873.

HASSON, ED. & CO.; dealers in fashionable hats; 20 North Pennsylvania street, Indianapolis.

Hasson, James; res 423 North New Jersey street, Indianapolis. Born in Ohio 1828; settled in M. C. 1861. Rep. Presb.

HASSON, ED.; res 448 North Meridian street, Indianapolis. Born in Ind. 1851; settled in M. C. 1861. Rep. Presb.

Howland, John D.; Clerk of U. S. Circuit and District Court; room 11, Post Office Building, Indianapolis; res 250 North Tennessee St. Born in Md. 1818; settled in M. C. 1857.

Holloway, Wm. R.; postmaster; Indianapolis; res 144 North Alabama street. Born in Ind. 1836; settled in M. C. 1861.

Hanamon, J. T.; dealer in dry goods, notions, groceries and provisions; corner Columbia street and Home avenue, Indianapolis.

HUTCHINS, H. S.; dealer in fancy groceries and provisions; 401 and 403 North Alabama street, Indianapolis; res 409 North Alabama street. Born in Conn. 1831; settled in M. C. 1855.

Hillman, S. J.; dealer in drugs and pure medicines; corner St. Clair street and Massachusetts avenue, Indianapolis; res on East street.

Hobacker, Gottleib; manufacturer of boots and shoes; 343 North New Jersey street, Indianapolis. Born in Germany 1838; settled in M. C. 1866.

Hoover, Mrs. Mary A.; res 81 Massachusetts avenue, Indianapolis.

HAMLIN, NICHOLAS; res 81 Fort Wayne avenue, Indianapolis. Born in Germany 1852; settled in M. C. 1871.

HADLEY, O. S.; firm of Lecklides & Hadley, attorneys at law; No. 2 Yohn's Block, corner Washington and Meridian streets, Indianapolis; res 221 North Noble street. Born in Ohio 1840; settled in M. C. 1871. Rep. Christian.

Hergd, Fred.; meat market; 234 East Washington street, Indianapolis. Born in Germany 1842; settled in M. C. 1854.

HART, E. F.; clerk with Bowen, Stewart & Co., wholesale and retail book store; 16 and 18 West Washington street, Indianapolis; res 23 Blake street. Born in Glasgow, Scotland, 1838; settled in M. C. 1865. Dem. Catholic.

Hettinger, I. B.; hair dresser and wig manufacturer; 56 Indiana avenue, Indianapolis; res 170 West Market street. Born in Ohio 1844; settled in M. C. 1873. Indp. Methodist.

Hunt, John; painter; No. 1 Engine House, Indianapolis. Born in Ind. 1852; settled in M. C. 1871. Protestant.

Hildebrand, H. W. & Co.; wholesale dealers in lumber; Indiana avenue and canal, Indianapolis; res 308 North Delaware st.

Holte, H. B.; book-keeper with Hildebrand & Co.; bds at Pyle House, Indianapolis. Born in Ind. 1853. Protestant.

HARRYMAN; M. V.; dealer in fine pictures and looking glasses; 10 Indiana avenue, Indianapolis. Born in Ind. 1841; settled in M. C. 1873. Indp. Methodist.

Hammond, J. W.; firm of Brown & Hammond, new and second hand furniture; 173 Indiana avenue, Indianapolis; res 434 Blake street. Born in Ohio 1841; settled in M. C. 1868.

Hatton, J. S.; real estate agent; 182 Indiana avenue, Indianapolis; res 338 North West street. Born in Ind. 1832; settled in M. C. 1864. Rep. Methodist.

Hawkins, E. H.; superintendent city tea and grocery store; 159 Indiana avenue, Indianapolis. Born in England 1832; settled in M. C. 1872. Rep. Episcopalian.

Humphrey, J. W.; grocer; 314 Indiana avenue, Indianapolis. Born in W. Va. 1840; settled in M. C. 1861. Independent. Methodist.

Hoover, W. W.; grocer; 40 Indiana avenue, Indianapolis. Born in M. C. 1826. Rep. M. Baptist.

Held, C.; grocer; 412 and 414 Indiana avenue, Indianapolis. Born in Germany 1825; settled in M. C. 1871. Indpt. Protestant.

- Hogshire, Samuel H.; merchant and farmer; res 452 Blake St., Indianapolis. Born in Ohio 1828; settled in M. C. 1832. Dem. Protestant.

HADLEY, J. W.; firm of Hadley Bros., apothecaries; 317 Indiana avenue, Indianapolis; res 297 California street.

Hurlle, I.; merchant tailor; 170 East Washington street, Indianapolis. Born in Baden, Germany, 1832; settled in M. C. 1854.

Hurley, Patrick; livery and hack business; 309 California street, Indianapolis. Born in Ireland 1829; settled in M. C. 1856. Dem. Catholic.

HOLDEN, JOHN W.; manufacturer of picture frames; 174 East Washington street, Indianapolis; bds 138 East New York street. Born in N. C. 1841; settled in M. C. 1868. Dem. Christian.

Hutton, A. P.; carpenter and joiner; res 351 North Mississippi street, Indianapolis. Born in N. C. 1843; settled in M. C. 1873. Dem. Protestant.

Haywood, Alfred; artificial limbs and braces for deformities; 172 East Washington street, Indianapolis; res 310 East New York street. Born in Pa. 1831; settled in M. C. 1853. Rep. Protestant.

Hyde, A. R.; real estate agent; 35 East Washington street, Indianapolis; res 291 North Noble street. Born in Ohio 1824; settled in M. C. 1854.

Heron, Alex.; secretary State Board of Agriculture; office, State House, Indianapolis; res 413 North Illinois street. Born in Md. 1830; settled in M. C. 1872.

HENDERSON, ED.; dealer in new and second-hand furniture, stoves, carpets, bedding, etc.; 184 West Washington street, Indianapolis. Born in Ind. 1832; settled in M. C. 1872. Methodist.

HERRINGTON, ISAAC H.; manufacturer and dealer in harness, saddles, etc.; 78 West Washington street, Indianapolis; res 231 North California street. Born in Ind. 1837; settled in M. C. 1869. Rep. Protestant.

HARDEN, R. E.; manufacturer brick moulds; 216 East Washington street, Indianapolis; res 87 North Noble street. Born in Ohio 1828; settled in M. C. 1852. Rep. Methodist.

HILL, JOHN F.; barber and hair dresser; 218 East Washington street, Indianapolis. Born in Ohio 1845; settled in M. C. 1872. Rep. Methodist.

Hall, J. E.; firm of Church & Hall, commission merchants; 240 East Washington street, Indianapolis; res 2 m e Indianapolis. Born in Ind. 1849; settled in M. C. 1870.

HADLEY, W. C.; firm of Hadley Bros., apothecaries; 317 Indiana avenue, Indianapolis; res 297 California street. Born in Ind. 1852; settled in M. C. 1874. Methodist.

Hutchins, H. H.; boot and shoe manufacturer; 222 East Washington street, Indianapolis; res 256 East Market street. Born in Conn. 1824; settled in M. C. 1851.

Hess, Josiah M.; dealer in fruit cans, sealing wax, etc.; 292 East Washington street, Indianapolis. Born in Pa. 1830; settled in M. C. 1869.

Hust, Geo. C.; meat market; 564 East Washington street, Indianapolis. Born in Bavaria, Germany, 1830; settled in M. C. 1865.

Helman, J. A.; of Indianapolis Coffin Co.; res corner Eighth and Tennessee streets.

Hofman, Jacob; grocer; corner West and Second streets, Indianapolis. Born in Germany 1842; settled in M. C. 1859.

Hereth, G. L.; druggist; 174 Indiana avenue, Indianapolis.

Hutton, E. L.; meat market; 414 West North street, Indianapolis. Born in Ind. 1843; settled in M. C. 1854.

HILD, WM.; firm of C. F. Hild, dealers in produce and groceries; 152 Blake street, Indianapolis; res 287 North Davidson street, Indianapolis. Born in Nassau, Germany, 1847; settled in M. C. 1858.

HILD, C. F.; firm of C. F. Hild & Bros.; res 287 North Davidson street, Indianapolis.

Hampton, J. D.; manufacturer of carriage and buggy bodies; 186 West Market street, Indianapolis; res 340 West Vermont street. Born in Ind. 1826; settled in M. C. 1866.

HAGERHORST, C. M.; wholesale and retail dealer in groceries, provisions, canned fruits, fresh meats, &c.; 223 West Ohio street, Indianapolis. Born in Prussia 1830; settled in M. C. 1840.

Hohlt, Wm.; gardener; North Indianapolis. Born in Germany 1838; settled in M. C. 1856.

Hohlt, Henry; gardener; North Indianapolis. Born in Germany 1850; settled in M. C. 1868.

Hanna, Sam.; street contractor; res 292 Christian avenue, Indianapolis. Born in Ind. 1850; settled in M. C. 1870.

Hamilton, David P.; locomotive engineer; res 154 South New Jersey street, Indianapolis. Born in Philadelphia 1830; settled in M. C. 1867. Methodist.

HOLLER, E. TH.; dealer in Madison ale, Pittsburg pale ale, porter and lager beer, in bottles or kegs; 37 South Delaware street, Indianapolis. Born in Germany 1842; settled in M. C. 1870.

Hasket, E.; firm of Hasket & Kiger, pump manufacturers; 34 South Pennsylvania street, Indianapolis; res 272 East Washington street. Born in N. C. 1829; settled in M. C. 1843. Rep. Protestant.

Harden, Richard; barber; 10 South Pennsylvania street, Indianapolis. Born in Ky. 1843; settled in M. C. 1868.

Hancock, Harrison; wholesale and retail dealer in confectionery; 16 South Pennsylvania street, Indianapolis. Born in Ohio 1851; settled in M. C. 1867. Dem. Protestant.

HERR, JOHN; toll gate keeper on the Bluff, Indianapolis and Leavensworth gravel roads. Born in Pa. 1835; settled in M. C. 1857.

Hoefgen, John; brick manufacturer and trader; 1 mile south of corporation line, Indianapolis.

Hellman, Lewis; block south of toll-gate on Meridian street, Indianapolis.

Harming, William; farmer; 2½ miles southeast of Circle street, Born in Germany 1813; settled in M. C. 1840.

Hansing, Henry; farmer; 1 mile southeast of corporation line. Indianapolis. Born in Germany 1840; settled in M. C. 1843.

Hitchcock, C. B.; Dean Bros.' steam pump manufactory; Madison avenue; res 84 South Mississippi street, Indianapolis. Born in Mass. 1846; settled in M. C. 1871.

Hartley, Thos.; with Chappell, 262 West Washington street, Indianapolis. Born in Ind. 1842; settled in M. C. 1874.

HOLLINGSWORTH, ZEPH.; feed, livery and sale stable; 277 West Washington street, Indianapolis; res 331 West Washington street. Born in M. C. 1843.

Heid, Henry; express driver; res 577 Michigan street, Indianapolis. Born in Germany 1836; settled in M. C. 1864. Lutheran.

Herrman, F. J.; undertaker; 26 South Delaware street, Indianapolis. Born in France 1817; settled in M. C. 1854.

HALE & BILLINGS; house and sign painters; 47 South Delaware street, Indianapolis

Harmining, C.; groceries and liquors; 283 South Delaware St., Indianapolis; res same. Born in Germany 1819; settled in M. C. 1846. Dem. Lutheran.

HANSON, M.; shoe store; 363 South Delaware street, Indianapolis; res Madison avenue. Born in Denmark 1837; settled in M. C. 1864.

Hereth, J. C.; saddle and harness shop; 12 North Delaware St., Indianapolis; res 268 North Alabama street. Born in Europe, 1827; settled in M. C. 1852.

Hereth & Co.; manufacturers and dealers in harness, saddles, etc.; 24 North Delaware street, Indianapolis.

HALL BROS.; manufacturers of folding lounges and spring mattresses; 147 and 149 North Delaware St., Indianapolis.

Hall, T. Q.; firm of Hall Bros.; res 125 East Walnut street, Indianapolis. Born in Ind. 1835; settled in M. C. 1851.

Hall, B. R.; firm of Hall Bros.; res 181 North Delaware street, Indianapolis. Born in Ind. 1850; settled in M. C. 1851.

Hawk, W. V. & Co.; real estate brokers; 28 North Delaware street, Indianapolis.

Hawk, W. V.; firm of W. V. Hawk & Co.; res 32 College avenue, Indianapolis. Born in Ky. 1822; settled in M. C. 1866. Dem. Christian.

Hawk, J. K.; res 52 College avenue, Indianapolis. Born in 1849; settled in M. C. 1866. Methodist.

HARTROD, LEWIS; saloon and restaurant; corner Shelby street and Virginia avenue, Indianapolis; res same. Born in Prussia 1842; settled in M. C. 1856.

HERINGTON & BOYD; carriage works; 213 and 215 East Market street, Indianapolis. If you want cheap jobs give them a call.

Haines & Bro.; wholesale and retail dealers in portable gaslight fixtures; 33 and 35 Kentucky avenue, Indianapolis.

Hartman & Dreier; blacksmiths and wagon ironers; 197 South East street, Indianapolis.

Hill & Long; manufaeturers of doors, frames, etc.; 113 and 115 South East street, Indianapolis.

HOLLWEG & REESE; importers of china, glass and queensware; 96 and 98 South Meridian street, Indianapolis.

HOLLWEG, LOUIS; firm of Hollweg & Reese; res 240 East Market street, Indianapolis. Born in Germany; settled in M. C. 1858.

HOLLAND, T. F. & CO.; importers of teas, tobaccos, syrups and groceries; 27 and 29 East Maryland St., Indianapolis.

HOLLAND, T. F.; firm of T. F. Holland & Co.; res 383 North Illinois street, Indianapolis. Born in M. C. 1838.

Harvey, Preston; farmer and dairyman; 1½ miles north of corporation, Indianapolis. Born in N. C. 1834; settled in M. C. 1847.

HANIMAN, WM.; res 1 mile east of corporation, Indianapolis.

HENDRICKS, THOS. A.; Governor of the State of Indiana; office in State Building, corner Washington and Tennessee streets, Indianapolis; res 407 North Tennessee street, corner of St. Clair street. Born in Tenn. 1819; settled in M. C. 1860.

Huber, Jacob; firm of Becker & Huber; res 125 Davidson street, Indianapolis. Born in Germany 1837; settled in M. C. 1864.

HEITKAM, P. G.; dealer in all kinds of furniture; upholstering done to order, and cash paid for old furniture; 67 East Washington street, Indianapolis. Born in Germany 1829; settled in M. C. 1853. Dem.

Hunt, A. L. & Co.; real estate brokers; 73 East Washington street, Indianapolis.

Hunt, A. L.; firm of A. L. Hunt & Co., Indianapolis. Born in Ohio 1824; settled in M. C. 1840. Rep. Protestant.

Hunt, W. W.; firm of A. L. Hunt & Co.; Indianapolis. Born in Mo. 1849. Rep. Protestant.

HOLLAND, B. B.; firm of T. F. Holland & Co.; res 22 West St. Clair street, Indianapolis. Born in M. C. 1852.

HOLLAND, J. H.; firm of T. F. Holland & Co.; res 27 and 29 West Maryland street, Indianapolis. Born in M. C.

Hahn & Bals; wholesale liquor dealers; 33 East Maryland st., Indianapolis.

HALL, WILL. C.; with Bowen, Stewart & Co., Indianapolis. Born in Md. 1852; settled in M. C. 1870.

HANNA, O. J. R.; Treasurer of National Surgical Institute, Indianapolis; res 382 North Meridian street. Born in Ohio 1847; settled in M. C. 1869.

HOLLIDAY, W. J. & CO.; wholesale and retail dealers in iron, steel and heavy hardware, 59 South Meridian street, Indianapolis.

HOLLIDAY, W. J.; res 241 North Meridian street, Indianapolis. Born in Va. 1832; settled in M. C. 1856.

HENDRICKS, EDMUNDS & CO.; wholesale dealers in boots and shoes; 79 South Meridian street, Indianapolis.

HENDRICKS, V. K.; firm of Hendricks, Edmunds & Co.; res 455 North Meridian street, Indianapolis. Born in Pa. 1832; settled in M. C. 1859.

Hibben, Kennedy & Co.; wholesale dry goods; 97 and 99 South Meridian street, Indianapolis.

HAMMERSTEIN, J.; firm of Hammerstein Bro. & Co.; Superintendent of Indianapolis Lithograph Institute, Indianapolis.

HAMMERSTEIN, N. & S.; proprietors of Indianapolis Lithograph Institute, Indianapolis.

Holbrook, H. C.; wholesale liquor dealer; 129 South Meridian street, Indianapolis.

HAY, WM. H.; firm of Jones & Hay, real estate and insurance; res 222 North Tennessee street, Indianapolis. Born in Ind. 1834; settled in M. C. about 1865.

HUFFER, J. M.; saddle and harness maker; 23 South Meridian street, Indianapolis; res 69 Fletcher avenue. Born in Ohio 1826; settled in M. C. 1860.

Hildebrand & Fugate; dealers in hardware and cutlery; 35 South Meridian street, Indianapolis.

HAWTHORN, MORRIS, GORRELL & JONES; china, glass and queensware; 37 South Meridian street, Indianapolis.

HEDGES, ISAAC L.; firm of Renihan, Long & Hedges; res 300 South Meridian street, Indianapolis. Born in Ohio 1829; settled in M. C. 1850.

Heath, Sylvester; res 35 Chatham street, Indianapolis. Born in Ind. 1847; settled in M. C. 1866.

HOSBROOK & FATOUT; civil engineers and surveyors; 6 and 8 Hubbard Block, Indianapolis.

HOSBROOK J. A.; firm of Hosbrook & Fatout; res 477 North Illinois street, Indianapolis. Born in Ohio 1850; settled in M. C. 1872.

HOSBROOK, D. B.; firm of Hosbrook & Fatout; res 91 Laurel street, Indianapolis. Born in Ohio.

Hays, Barton S.; artist; 43 Hubbard Block, Indianapolis; res 708 North Tennessee street. Born in Ohio 1826; settled in M. C. 1858.

HARDING, G. C.; editor of *The Sunday Herald;* 23 Circle street, Indianapolis; res 20 Pratt street.

HESPELT, CHAS.; baker and confectioner; 372 Virginia avenue, Indianapolis. Born in Germany 1842; settled in M. C. 1862.

HOWLAND, POWELL; farmer; $1\frac{1}{2}$ m n e corporation line. Born in N. Y. 1799; settled in M. C. 1839.

HAERLE, W.; wholesale and retail dealer in fancy dry goods; 4 West Washington street, Indianapolis. Born in Germany 1838; settled in M. C. 1857.

Hammerly, J. M.; firm of Hammerly & Dark; 8 West Washington street, Indianapolis. Born in Ohio 1843; settled in M. C. 1871.

HAYS, JOSEPH; wholesale and retail tobaccos; 71 East Washington street, Indianapolis; res 160 South New Jersey street. Born in Ind. 1853; settled in M. C. 1862.

HOSTON, T. C.; manager of the Wheeler and Wilson Sewing Machine Co.; 10 West Washington street, Indianapolis; res 284 North Tennessee street. Born in Ohio 1848; settled in M. C. 1871. Rep.

Heddrick, Chas. E.; wood carver; 219 East Washington street, Indianapolis. Born in Ind. 1845; settled in M. C. 1845.

Hamilton, James A.; deputy sheriff; res 105 Park avenue, Indianapolis. Born in M. C. 1843.

- Harding, R. N.; deputy sheriff of Marion county; Indianapolis.

HARRISON, B.; firm of Harrison, Hines & Miller; res 299 North Alabama street, Indianapolis. Born in Ohio 1833; settled in M. C. 1854.

HINES, C. C.; firm of Harrison, Hines & Miller; res 428 North Tennessee street, Indianapolis. Born in N. Y. 1830; settled in M. C. 1854.

HARRISON, HINES & MILLER; attorneys at law; office in Wright's Block, East Market street, Indianapolis.

HARDESTY, JOHN O.; editor of the Sun; office, corner of Meridian and Washington streets, Indianapolis; res 35 West St. Joseph street. Born in Indianapolis 1843.

Hindman, Robert; boot and shoe shop; 222 North Merrill St., Indianapolis. Born in Ky. 1814; settled in M. C. 1832.

Herberich, M. G.; boot and shoemaker; 57 East South street, Indianapolis; res same. Born in Germany 1834; settled in M. C. 1873.

HATHAWAY, H. F.; proprietor of Bloomington House, Indianapolis. Born in N. Y. 1836; settled in M. C. 1861.

HAYS, E. M. & CO.; dealers in boots and shoes; 75 East Washington street, Indianapolis.

Hays E. M.; firm of E. M. Hays & Co.; res 160 South New Jersey street, Indianapolis. Born in Germany 1819; settled in M. C. 1861.

Hensley, John; farmer; 2¾ m n Indianapolis.

Hague, J. F.; boot and shoemaker; 10 Virginia avenue, Indianapolis. Born in Ind. 1833; settled in M. C. 1873.

HIATT, JAMES M.; minister Christian Church; res 159 Park avenue, Indianapolis. Born in Ind. 1836; settled in M. C. 1853.

HAHN, LOUIS; meat market; 48 Virginia avenue, Indianapolis. Born in Germany 1825; settled in M. C. 1855.

HARTLEY, W. J.; willow-ware manufactory; 46 Virginia avenue, Indianapolis; res 22 Wyoming street. Born in N.Y. 1843; settled in M. C. 1870.

HESSLING, B.; merchant tailor; 15 South Alabama street, Indianapolis. Born in Germany 1831; settled in M. C. 1856.

Hamlin, Carlin; firm of Jacob T. Wright & Co., real estate office; rooms 1 and 2 Baldwin's Block, Indianapolis.

Heller, James E.; attorney at law; office 13 Baldwin's Block, Indianapolis; res 297 Winston street. Born in Ind.

HUBBARD, C. A.; firm of Graham & Hubbard; res 171 Christian avenue, Indianapolis. Born in Mass. 1851; settled in M. C. 1872.

Hibbard, A. W.; real estate broker; 27 Baldwin's Block, Indianapolis. Born in Va. 1830; settled in M. C. 1872.

Hanna, Caldwell & Co.; wholesale grocers; 52 South Meridian street, Indianapolis.

Hanna, S. C.; firm of Hanna, Caldwell & Co.; res 184 Broadway, Indianapolis. Born in Pa. 1832; settled in M. C. 1857.

HOUSTON & CO.; wholesale dealers in tobacco, cigars and teas; corner Meridian and Louisiana streets, Indianapolis.

HOUSTON, JOHN T.; firm of Houston & Co.; res 214 South Alabama street, Indianapolis.

HANNA & KNEFLER; attorneys at law; 32 North Delaware street, opposite Court House, Indianapolis.

HANNA, JOHN; firm of Hanna & Knefler; res Greencastle.

HARTMAN, HERMAN; dealer in groceries, dry goods and notions, flour, feed, etc.; 150 Madison avenue; res 14 Mulberry street, Indianapolis. Born in M. C. 1849.

Haig, M.; saloon; Madison avenue, Indianapolis. Born in Germany 1823; settled in M. C. 1861.

Hadley, D. E.; office 191 Virginia avenue, Indianapolis; res 195 Virginia avenue. Born in Ind. 1845; settled in M. C. 1867.

Harder, A.; painter and contractor; 38 South East street, Indianapolis. Born in Germany 1838; settled in M. C. 1873.

Hagedora, H.; meat market; corner East and McCarty streets, Indianapolis; res same. Born in Germany 1843; settled in M. C. 1866.

Hoover, J. J.; tin shop; 438 Meridian street, Indianapolis; res same. Born in Pa. 1836; settled in M. C. 1871.

Harper, W. S.; ice cream parlor; 460 South Meridian street, Indianapolis; res same. Born in Ind. 1842; settled in M. C. 1854.

Haldy, C.; cigar manufacturer; 471 South Meridian street, Indianapolis; res same. Born in Germany 1853; settled in M. C. 1863.

Harttrodt, Herman; proprietor Alleghany House; corner Kentucky avenue and Sharp street, Indianapolis. Born in Germany 1838; settled in M. C. 1856.

HACKNEY, JOSEPHINE; milliner and dress maker; 23 West South street, Indianapolis; res same. Born in Ind. 1842; settled in M. C. 1861.

Hufmann, M.; grocer; 470 South Meridian street, Indianapolis.

INDIANAPOLIS WOOL HOUSE; J. C. Alvord; wool dealer; 14 and 16 West Pearl near Meridian street, Indianapolis bds at Hotel Bates. Born in Ind. 1847; settled in M. C. 1847.

Ives, James O.; proprietor of Hotel Bates; corner Washington and Illinois streets, Indianapolis.

Irish, W. W.; proprietor of the Revere House, 45 North Illinois street, Indianapolis. Born in Ohio 1828; settled in M. C. 1873.

Indianapolis One Stave Barrel Factory; west of Military Park, Indianapolis; John G. Blake, president; H. H. Fulton, vice president; J. B. Newcomb, secretary, H. Clay Dowell, superintendent.

Indianapolis Elevator Co.; west of river, Indianapolis; Wm. P. Gallup, president; John C. Wright, secretary.

Idler, Clinton; master mechanic of Vandalia machine shops; res 171 West South street, Indianapolis. Born in Pa. 1827; settled in M. C. 1849.

Indianapolis Coffin Shops; West street and Canal, Indianapolis.

Irwin, John S.; manager of United States Life Insurance Co.; 3 Glenn's Block, East Washington street, Indianapolis.

Iliff, J. A.; firm of Iliff Bros.; dealers in hats and caps; 42 West Washington street, Indianapolis; res East Washington street, opposite Deaf and Dumb Institute. Born in N. J. 1845; settled in M. C. 1854.

Iliff, Chas. E.; res 73 North Alabama street, Indianapolis.

Irwen, V. Q.; real estate broker; 30½ West Washington street, Indianpolis; res 471 North Pennsylvania street. Born in Ind. 1829; settled in M. C. 1872. Rep.

Indianapolis National Bank; 1 Odd Fellows' Hall, East Washington street, Indianapolis.

Indianapolis Boot and Shoe Manufacturing Establishment; ½ m n e corporation line, Indianapolis; John L. Miller, president; F. D. Somerby, vice president; L. W. Williams, manager.

Iaus, William; dealer in all kinds of meat; 153 Ft. Wayne avenue; res same. Born in Germany 1851; settled in M. C. 1871.

Indianapolis Malleable Iron Works; corner St. Clair street and canal; C. Spiegel, president; J. M. Crawford, secretary and treasurer; M. Crawford; superintendent.

Irwin, J. D.; farmer and trader; res at Southport. Born in Ind. 1824; settled in M. C. 1844. Protestant.

Irwin, J. B.; dairyman; dealer in milk and butter; res n of corporation line, Indianapolis. Born in Va. 1827; settled in M. C. 1870. Liberal.

Indiana Dental Depot; Moore, Herriott & Co.; dealers in dental goods; rooms 10, 11 and 12, 2d floor Vinton's Block, 48 North Pennsylvania street, Indianapolis.

• INDIANAPOLIS LITHOGRAPH INSTITUTE; 145 South Meridian street, Indianapolis.

Indianapolis Paper Company; wholesale dealers in and manufacturers of paper sacks; 25 East Maryland street, Indianapolis.

INDIANAPOLIS & ST. LOUIS RAILROAD; office South Alabama street; General Superintendent, Ed. King; General Agent, P. Peas; President, E. W. Woodward.

Indianapolis Brass Supply Company; wrought iron pipes, fittings, etc.; 106, 108 and 110 South Delaware street, Indianapolis.

Indianapolis Saw Works; 189 South Meridian street, Indianapolis.

Ingersoll, Frank; foreman hook and ladder No. 2; bds at 255 South Alabama street, Indianapolis. Born in Ind. 1839; settled in M. C. 1840.

Isensee, Albert; bell hanger and locksmith; 16 Virginia avenue. Born in Ind. 1842; settled in M. C. 1843.

Israel, Levi; grocer; 428 South Meridian street. Born in Germany 1847; settled in M. C. 1871.

Ingraham, C. B.; photographer; 324 East Washington street; res 265 North Tennessee street. Born in Me. 1820; settled in M. C. 1866. Episcopalian.

INLOW & HEIZER; wholesale dealers in cigars and fine cut tobacco, groceries, etc.; 141 West Washington street, Indianapolis.

INLOW, J. W.; res 77 East Vermont street, Indianapolis. Born in Ky. 1843; settled in M. C. 1870.

JOACHIM, J. C.; butcher and dealer in all kinds of meat; 117 Fort Wayne avenue, Indianapolis. Born in D. C. 1838; settled in M. C. 1868.

Johnson, Mrs. Jane; dealer in cigars and tobacco; 36 North Illinois street, Indianapolis. Born in Ky.; settled in M. C. 1869. Dem. Catholic.

Johnson, Isaac; res 1½ m e Maywood P. O. Born in Ind. 1842.

Jones, Robert A.; res 299 Winston street, Indianapolis. Born in Ohio 1831; settled in M. C. 1861.

JOSSELYN, ALASON K.; dealer in real estate; res ½ mile east of corporation line, on National Road, Indianapolis. Born in N. Y. 1844; settled in M. C. 1869. Rep. Prot.

Joseph, George W. & Co.; real estate agents and brokers; 25 Martindale's Block, second floor, Pennsylvania street, Indianapolis.

Joseph, Geo. W.; res 808 North Tennessee street, Indianapolis. Born in Mass. 1836; settled in M. C. 1860.

JONES, J. G.; physician and druggist; corner Pennsylvania street and Madison avenue, Indianapolis. Born in Ohio 1849; settled in M. C. 1874. Rep. Methodist.

JOHNSON, ERECKSON & BROWN; proprietors of Union Furniture Co.; 44 Massachusetts avenue, Indianapolis.

JOHNSON, AUGUST; res 514 East Washington street, Indianapolis. Born in Europe 1844; settled in M. C. 1871.

Jones & O'Neal; proprietors of Massachusetts Avenue House; 42½ Massachusetts avenue, Indianapolis.

Jones, Thomas; Indianapolis Born in Mass. 1831; settled in M. C. 1850.

JOYCE, JOHN; Washington Street Marble Works; 212 West Washington street, Indianapolis. Call and see samples.

JOYCE, JOHN. Born in Ireland 1847; settled in M. C. 1865.

Jefferson House; 61 and 63 East South street, Indianapolis.

Jester, Valentine; 297 West Washington street, Indianapolis.

Jacobi, Fred.; meat shop; 387 South Delaware street, Indianapolis; res 67 Wyoming street. Born in Germany 1823; settled in M. C. 1855.

Jacobi, August; res 67 Wyoming street, Indianapolis. Born in Germany 1845; settled in M. C. 1867.

Jacqumine, Frank; at City Brewery, Indianapolis; res Madison avenue.

Jenks, L. B.; at Indianapolis Vinegar Works. Born in California; settled in M. C. 1872.

JAMESON, FUNKHOUSER & JAMESON; physicians and surgeons; office 35 East Market street, Indianapolis.

JAMESON, HENRY; firm of Jameson, Funkhouser & Jameson, physicians and surgeons; Indianapolis. Born in M. C. 1848.

JAMESON, P. H.; firm of Jameson, Funkhouser & Jameson, physicians and surgeons; res 163 North Tennessee street, Indianapolis. Born in Ind. 1824; settled in M. C. 1843.

Johnson, T. A. H.; firm of Barnard & Johnson; res 155 Broadway, Indianapolis. Born in M. C. 1843.

JOHNSON, GREEN C.; proprietor of barber shop; under Indianapolis Publishing House; res 29 Douglass street. Born in Canada 1831; settled in M. C. 1852.

JACKSON, R.; firm of WM. LOVE & CO.; notary public; res East South street, Indianapolis. Born in Ind. 1837; settled in M. C. 1871.

JONES & HAY; real estate and insurance office; 21 South Meridian street, Indianapolis.

JONES, BARTON D.; firm of JONES & HAY; res 188 North Delaware street. Born in District of Columbia 1829; settled in M. C. 1855.

JOHNSON, J. W.; contractor, brick mason and cistern builder, etc.; res 127 West First street, Indianapolis. Born in Vt. 1837; settled in M. C. 1866.

Johnston & Lilly; organic chemists; 55 East Maryland street, Indianapolis.

Johnston, John F.; firm of Johnston & Lilly; res 751 North Pennsylvania street, Indianapolis. Born in England 1827; settled in M. C. 1851.

Jones, John; merchandise broker; 25 East Maryland street, In dianapolis.

Johnston, Wm. W., firm of Murphy, Johnston & Co.; res 546 North Meridian street, Indianapolis.

JOHNSON, W. P.; of National Surgical Institute; res North Pennsylvania street, Indianapolis.

JONES, A., SEN.; ex-treasurer of State and president Indiana- polis Rolling Mill Co.; Indianapolis. Born in N. C. 1812; settled in M. C. 1859.

JONES, E. S.; farmer and stock raiser; Washington township, 3 m n Indianapolis. Born in Ind. 1853; settled in M. C. 1859.

JOHNSON & SONS; grocers and farmers; business room 749 East Washington street, Indianapolis. The place for bar- gains.

JOHNSON, SAMUEL; firm of Johnson & Sons ; farmer; 1½ m e corporation line. Born in M. C. 1822. He now lives on the farm that he was born on.

JOHNSON, CHAS. E.; firm of Johnson & Sons ; farmer; 1½ m e corporation line. Born in M. C. 1849.

JOHNSON, W. H. H.; firm of Johnson & Sons. Born in M. C. 1855.

JONES, C. B.; proprietor Alabama House; 61, 63 and 65 North Alabama street, Indianapolis.

JONES, JOHN G.; physician and druggist; corner of Madison avenue and Huron street, Indianapolis. Born in Ohio 1849; settled in M. C. 1874.

Judkins, L. D.; photographer; 16½ East Washington street, Indianapolis. Born in Me.; settled in M. C. 1869.

Johnson & Kelsey; attorneys at law; office No. 4 Blackford's Block, corner Washington and Meridian sts, Indianapolis.

Johnson, E. T.; firm of Johnson & Kelsey, Indianapolis. Born in Ky.; settled in M. C. 1864.

Jones, J. L.; retail dealer in boots and shoes; 91 East Washington street; res 430 North New Jersey street. Born in Va. 1797; settled in M. C. 1863. Rep. Christian.

JULIAN, BROWN & JULIAN; attorneys at law; office 95 East Washington street, Indianapolis.

JULIAN, JACOB B.; res Irvington. Born in Indiana Territory 1815; settled in M. C. 1872.

JULIAN, JOHN F.; res Irvington. Born in Ind.; settled in M. C. 1873.

Judah & Lamme; attorneys at law; office over 95 East Washington street, Indianapolis.

Judah, J. M.; res 163 North Tennessee street, Indianapolis. Born in Ind. 1848; settled in M. C. 1867.

Johnson, T. E.; attorney at law; 31 West Washington street, Indianapolis; res 139 St. Mary's street. Born in Md. 1837; settled in M. C. 1864. Indpt. Methodist.

JOHNSTON, W. J.; firm of Johnston & Bro.; wholesale and retail dealers in stoves, tin and copper ware; Capital Galvanized Iron Works; 62 East Washington street, Indianapolis; res 184 East Vermont street. Born in M. C. 1837. Presbyterian.

JOHNSTON, S. A.; firm of Johnston Bros.; res 220 North New Jersey street, Indianapolis. Born in Ind. 1835; settled in M. C. 1837. Presbyterian.

JOHNSTON, O. W.; with Johnston Bros.; 62 East Washington street, Indianapolis; res 222 North New Jersey street. Born in M. C. 1853. Presbyterian.

JORDAN, LEWIS; firm of Jordan & Jordan, attorneys at law; room No. 1, 82½ East Washington street, Indianapolis; res 352 North Meridian street. Born in Ind. 1833; settled in M. C. 1860. Dem.

JOHNSTON, JAMES; firm of Colden & Johnston, real estate
brokers; office, 94½ East Washington street, Indianapolis;
res 285 Union street. Born in Ind. 1831; settled in M. C.
1870. Indpt. Protestant.

Johnson, W. II.; manufacturer of domestic liquors; West Washington street, Indianapolis; res corner Fayette and St. Clair
streets. Born in Ind. 1837; settled in M. C. 1870.

JACKSON, JOHN; dealers in ladies' and children's paper dress
patterns; 39½ East Washington street, Indianapolis; res 40
North East street. Born in England 1825; settled in M. C.
1870. Rep. Presbyterian.

Jackson, Mrs. L. L.; teacher of dress and garment cutting,
dress making, paper patterns, etc.; 39½ East Washington
street; res 40 North East street.

Judd, Chas. S.; photographer; 45 East Washington street, Indianapolis; res 55 Hoyt avenue. Born in Arkansas 1844;
settled in M. C. 1872. Dem. Episcopalian.

Jenkins, Wm.; candy maker; 39 Hosbrook street, Indianapolis.

Judd, Frederick; grocer; 239 Blake street, Indianapolis.

Jarvis, C. H.; livery, sale and feed stable; West Washington
street, Indianapolis. Born in Ohio 1832; settled in M.
C. 1873.

Jay, L.; grocer; West Washington street, Indianapolis.

Johnson, David; farmer and contractor of public improvements;
2½ m s w Indianapolis. Born in M. C. 1831.

Jones, Jesse; general agent; room over 19 West Washington
street, Indianapolis; res 488 North Illinois street. Born in
Va. 1813; settled in M. C. 1833. Rep. Methodist.

Klingensmith, I.; attorney at law; 115 East Washington street,
Indianapolis; res 704 North Tennessee street. Born in Pa.
1827; settled in M. C. 1829.

KAHN, DAVID; res 283 East Market street, Indianapolis.
Born in Ind. 1853; settled in M. C. 1864.

KAHN, DAVID & Co.; dealers in gents' furnishing goods, trunks, valises, etc.; 83 East Washington street, Indianapolis.

Knippenberg, Henry; saw manufacturer; 210 to 226 South Illinois street, Indianapolis; res 128 West Ohio street. Born in Germany 1843; settled in M. C. 1866.

KOEHNE, CHAS.; firm of H. LIEBER & CO., dealers in picture moulding and frames; 82 East Washington street, Indianapolis; res 467 North Delaware street. Born in Germany 1833; settled in M. C. 1859. Indpt.

KENNY, JOHN; firm of JOHN KENNY & CO., real estate brokers; room 3, 82 East Washington street, Indianapolis; res 163 West South street. Born in Ohio 1828; settled in M. C. 1873. Rep. Christian.

Kruger, Charles D.; flour and feed merchant; 149 East Washington street, Indianapolis; res 368 West New York street. Born in Ohio 1846; settled in M. C. 1851.

KING, D. W.; merchant tailor; 161 East Washington street, Indianapolis. Born in England 1820; settled in M. C. 1870.

KELLEY, P. H.; dealer in drugs and medicines; 756 North Illinois street, Indianapolis; bds 726 North Tennessee street. Born in N. Y. 1841; settled in M. C. 1866. Rep. Presbyterian.

KAIEN & CO.; merchant tailors; Anderson, Madison county.

KAIEN, EDWARD; res 36 Bollivar street, Anderson, Madison county. Born in Ireland 1829; settled in M. C. 1861.

Kelley, Mrs. M.; dressmaker; 67 North Illinois street, second floor, Indianapolis; res same.

Kitchen, John M.; physician and surgeon; office, room 2, second floor, Vinton's Block, opposite Post Office, North Pennsylvania street, Indianapolis; res 145 North Pennsylvania street. Born in Ohio 1826; settled in M. C. 1851.

17

King, James; boot and shoemaker; 133 Indiana avenue, Indianapolis. Born in Ky. 1803; settled in M. C. 1860. Rep. Methodist.

King, James H.; boot aud shoemaker; 133 Indiana avenue; Indianapolis; res 131 Indiana avenue. Born in Ind. 1845; settled in M. C. 1860. Protestant.

Kurts, II. P.; blacksmith; 410 Indiana avenue, Indianapolis. Born in Ohio 1828; settled in M. C. 1850. Indp. Methodist.

Kahn, Leon; dry goods merchant; 45 and 47 East Washington street, Indianapolis; res 164 North East street. Born in France 1832; settled in M. C. 1864. Rep. Hebrew.

Kersting, Benj.; saloon and restaurant; 82 West Washington street, Indianapolis. Born in Pa. 1844; settled in M. C. 1871.

Kingsbury, J. G.; firm of J. G. Kingsbury & Co., publishers of the Indiana Farmer; 76 West Washington street, Indianapolis; res 179 East New York street. Born in Ind. 1832; settled in M. C. 1870. Presbyterian.

Knotts, N. R.; house and sign painter; res 390 North West street, Indianapolis. Born in Pa. 1825; settled in M. C. 1852. Indp. Protestant.

King, Rev. H. N.; pastor Blackford street M. E. Church, Indianapolis. Born in Ind. 1840; settled in M. C. 1873. Rep.

Kelley, J. M.; grocer; 248 East Washington street, Indianapolis; res 318 North Noble street. Born in Ohio 1834; settled in M. C. 1871.

KOEPPEN, ROBERT; manufacturer of picture frames and fancy wood work; 272 East Washington street, Indianapolis. Born in Berlin, Prussia, 1849; settled in M. C. 1868.

Keppel, Martin; eating house and restaurant; 36 West Louisiana street, Indianapolis. Born in Pa. 1840; settled in M. C. 1856.

Kocher, Edmund; farmer; west of river, Washington street. Born in Pa. 1831; settled in M. C. 1852.

Koers, Wm.; farmer; 2 m n w Circle street, Indianapolis. Born in Ireland 1814; settled in M. C. 1867.

KAHN, ADOLPHUS; firm of KAHN & CO., Boston Clothing House; gents' furnishing goods; 9 West Washington street, Indianapolis; res 363 North New Jersey street. Born in Germany 1844; settled in M. C. 1865.

Kenney, Thos.; firm of G. H. Heitkam & Kenney, clothing house; 38 West Washington street, Indianapolis; res 58 West street. Born in Ireland 1833; settled in M. C. 1855. Liberal Dem. Catholic.

Kiefer, L. F.; firm of L. F. Kiefer & Son, clock and watchmakers; 2 Odd Fellows' Hall, East Washington street, Indianapolis; res 463 North Delaware street. Born in Bavaria 1811; settled in M. C. 1867. Lutheran.

Kiefer, Louis A.; firm of L. F. Kiefer & Son; res 463 North Delaware street, Indianapolis. Born in Ohio 1844; settled in M. C. 1868. Lutheran.

Kelley, C.; res 424 West New York street, Indianapolis. Born in Ireland 1838; settled in M. C. 1862. Dem. Catholic.

Kilgore, J. D.; dentist; 70 North Illinois street; Indianapolis.

Keene, E. S.; jeweler; corner Bates House, Indianapolis. Born in Penn. 1838; settled in M. C. 1871. Rep. Presbyterian.

Kretsch, Peter; manufacturer and dealer in cigars and tobacco; 141 South Illinois street, Indianapolis.

KEELEY, SAMUEL; sanitary policeman; No. 6 Franklin Life Insurance Block, South Illinois street, Indianapolis; res 25 Sullivan street. Born in Ind. 1826; settled in M. C. 1847. Dem. Methodist.

KELLEY, L. L.; dealer in groceries and provisions; 275 South Illinois street, Indianapolis; res 134 North Pennsylvania street. Born in Ind. 1851; settled in M. C. 1871. Rep. Methodist.

KETTENBACH, H. C. & W. F.; dealers in hardware, cutlery, mechanics' tools, doors, sash, etc.; 123 East Washington street, Indianapolis.

KETTENBACH, H. C.; res 356 North Noble street, Indianapolis. Born in Nassau, Germany, 1844; settled in M. C. 1853.

KETTENBACH, W. F.; res 360 North Noble street, Indianapolis. Born in N. Y. 1850; settled in M. C. 1853.

Kindleberger & Pritchard; physicians; office and res 79 East Vermont street, Indianapolis.

Kindleberger, T. J.; Indianapolis. Born in Penn. 1805; settled in M. C. 1841.

KING, JAMES; harness maker; 264 Massachusetts avenue, Indianapolis; res 178 East South street. Born in Ohio 1840; settled in M. C. 1873. Rep. Universalist.

KEEPERS, JOHN; blacksmith and horse shoeing; 299 Massachusetts avenue, Indianapolis. Born in Ind. 1822; settled in M. C. 1874.

KOSE, C. W.; dealer in dry goods and notions, hats and caps; 371 South Delaware street, near McCarty street, Indianapolis; bds 112 Davidson street. Born in Germany 1851; settled in M. C. 1867.

KEIGHTLEY, E. T.; proprietor of Palace Drug Store, dealer in pure drugs and medicines; 102 to 106 Massachusetts avenue, Indianapolis; res 820 East Washington street. Born in Ky. 1833; settled in M. C. 1872.

Kuhn, Philip J.; dealer in staple and fancy groceries; 160 Fort Wayne avenue, Indianapolis; res same. Born in Germany 1818; settled in M. C. 1848.

Kline, I. G.; barber and hair dresser; 162 Ft. Wayne avenue, Indianapolis. Born in Germany 1837; settled in M. C. 1862.

KNIGHT, EDWARD; merchant tailor; 124 Ft. Wayne avenue, Indianapolis; res same. Born in Mass. 1812; settled in M. C. 1872.

Kramer, Henry; butcher and dealer in all kinds of meat; 80 Ft. Wayne avenue, Indianapolis; res same. Born in Germany 1829; settled in M. C. 1856.

KNIGHT, MRS. J.; dealer in fancy goods and notions; 124 Ft. Wayne avenue, Indianapolis.

Kevers, John H.; dealer in fancy groceries, provisions and flour; 525 North Mississippi street; res same. Born in Germany 1828; settled in M. C. 1854.

Kealing, Samuel; dairyman; 2½ m e Indianapolis. Born in Ind. 1836; settled in M. C. 1855.

Keyser, George W. & Smith ; plumbers, gas and steam fitters; 61 North Pennsylvania street, Martindale's Block, Indianapolis.

Keyser, George W.; res. 171 Blake street, Indianapolis. Born in Penn. 1847; settled in M. C. 1861. Methodist.

Keller, Paul; cabinet maker; 56 Massachusetts avenue, Indianapolis; res same. Born in Germany 1824; settled in M. C. 1868.

KLINE, NICHOLAS; manufacturer of boots and shoes; 283 Massachusetts avenue, Indianapolis; res 361 North Spring street. Born in Germany 1824; settled in M. C. 1853.

Kipp, Robert; Indianapolis. Born in Germany 1847; settled in M. C. 1867.

KLINE, LOUIS; fireman at No. 2 Engine House, Massachusetts avenue, Indianapolis. Born in Ind. 1852; settled in M. C. 1852.

KIEROLFS, SEMANUELL; manufacturer of children's carriages; 135 Massachusetts avenue, Indianapolis; res up stairs, same place. Born in N. Y. 1833; settled in M. C. 1874.

KINDLER, C.; locksmith and bell-hanger; locks and door-plates on hand; 25 Massachusetts avenue, Indianapolis; res 215 North Noble street. Born in Germany 1830; settled in M. C. 1855.

KING, IKE; firm of RAYMOND & KING; res Huron street, five doors e Noble, n side. Born in Ohio 1846; settled in M. C. 1863.

Krider, R. G.; manufacturers' agent and commission dealer in
boots and shoes; 145½ South Meridian street, Indianapolis.

KAUFMAN, B.; wholesale dealer in cigars; 28 West Louisiana
street, Indianapolis.

Kaiser, G.; physician; office corner Illinois and Louisiana Sts.,
Indianapolis.

KNEFLER, FRED.; firm of Hanna & Knefler; res corner
Washington street and Highland avenue, Indianapolis.

Keeling, Adam; custom blacksmith shop; on National Road, 1
m e of corporation, Indianapolis.

Keeling, Peter; farmer; 1½ m e corporation, Indianapolis. Born
in Germany 1829; settled in M. C. 1846. Lutheran.

KING, EDWARD; farmer and railroader; res 1½ m e Indianapolis.

Ketcham, J. L.; assistant cashier of Indiana Banking Co.; res
759 East Washington street, Indianapolis. Born in M. C.
1844. Rep. Presbyterian.

Knecht, H.; dealer in cutlery, concave razors, shears, etc.; 24
Virginia avenue, Indianapolis. Born in Germany 1843;
settled in M. C. 1864.

Koller, Chas.; dealer in groceries; 25 South Alabama street, Indianapolis; res same. Born in Indianapolis 1848.

KREGELO, DAVID; undertaker; 75 East Market street, Indianapolis; res 228 North West street. Born in Md. 1812;
settled in M. C. 1839.

Kregelo, Chas. E.; at 75 East Market street, Indianapolis.
Born in Indianapolis 1843.

KALTENBACH, J. C.; boot and shoemaker; 79 East Market
street, Indianapolis. Born in Ohio 1854; settled in M. C.
1874.

KAUFMAN, MAX; firm of Mayer, Bro. & Co.; res East
Market street, Indianapolis. Born in Ohio; settled in M.
C. 1873.

KAISER, CHRIST; harness maker; 458 South Meridian street,
Indianapolis. Born in Germany 1850; settled in M. C. 1874.

KIEFER, A.; wholesale druggist; 68 South Meridian street, Indianapolis; res 388 North Illinois street. Born in Germany 1828; settled in M. C. 1863.

KEMPF, R.; dealer in saddles, harness and horse clothing; repairing done to order; all work warranted; 458 South Meridian street, Indianapolis; res same. Born in Germany 1848; settled in M. C. 1867.

KLEINE, FRED.; saloon; 474 South Meridian street, Indianapolis. Born in Germany 1843; settled in M. C. 1853.

KLARE, FRED.; firm of Klare & Schroeder, saloon; 584 South Meridian street, Indianapolis. Born in Germany 1832; settled in M. C. 1852.

KLARE & SCHRŒDER; saloon and bowling alley; 584 and 586 South Meridian street, Indianapolis.

Kistner, Henry; shoe shop; 471 South Meridian street, Indianapolis. Born in Germany 1828; settled in M. C. 1857.

Kelly, Wm.; grocer; 335 South West street, Indianapolis; res same. Born in Ireland 1837; settled in M. C. 1870.

Kelly, John. Born in Ireland 1824; settled in M. C. 1873.

Kerr, W. M.; liveryman; 222 West Washington street, Indianapolis. Born in N. C. 1844; settled in M. C. 1874.

Kaughman, A.; Riverside drug store, 501 West Washington street, Indianapolis. Born in England 1828; settled in M. C. 1861.

Kenar, M.; saloon and billiard parlor; West Georgia street, Indianapolis.

Knarger, Geo.; saloon and billiards; 60 South Delaware street, Indianapolis. Born in Europe 1845; settled in M. C. 1854.

Kaufman, Geo.; saloon; 76 South Delaware street, Indianapolis. Born in Germany 1823; settled in M. C. 1852.

Kropp, Jacob; groceries and liquors; 425 Madison avenue, Indianapolis. Born in Germany 1837; settled in M. C. 1873.

KEUGER, C. H.; grocer; 439 Virginia avenue, Indianapolis. Born in Germany 1840; settled in M. C. 1843.

Kelly, O.; firm of W. V. Hawk & Co.; res 153 Park avenue, Indianapolis. Born in Ind. 1831; settled in M. C. 1872. Rep.

KENNINGTON, ROBERT; dealer in groceries, flour and provisions; No. 44, corner of Bicking and Delaware streets, Indianapolis; res same. Born in Ireland 1832; settled in M. C. 1853.

KENNEDY, P. A. B.; attorney at law; 46 North Delaware street, Indianapolis; res 448 Huron street. Born in Ind. 1845; settled in M. C. 1873.

Kingston, Samuel; hosiery and shirt manufactory; 78 South Delaware street, Indianapolis. Born in Ireland 1836; settled in M. C. 1864.

Kelsey, Isaac M.; firm of Johnson & Kelsey; Indianapolis. Born in Ind. 1844; settled in M. C. 1869. Rep. Prot.

KEEFFE, P. O.; firm of Watterson & Keeffe; res 90 Indiana avenue, Indianapolis. Born in Ireland 1834; settled in M. C. 1867.

Kistner, John; boot and shoe manufacturer; 189 West Washington street, Indianapolis. Born in Ohio 1848; settled in M. C. 1852.

Krause & Riemenschneider; dealers in hosiery; 115 E. Washington street, Indianapolis.

LYON, VIRGIL; with L. I. Mossler & Bro.; 37 East Washington street, Indianapolis. Born in Ind. 1836; settled in M. C 1869. Rep. Universalist.

LEMON, D. A.; dealer in groceries and all kinds of country produce, wood and willow ware; 187 West Washington street, Indianapolis; res 196 North Tennessee street. Born in M. C. 1844.

Lelewer, Isaac; fur manufacturer and hat dealer; 97 East Washington street, Indianapolis; res 137 West New York street. Born in Prussia 1840; settled in M. C. 1867.

LEVY, HENRY; dealer in new and second-hand clothing; 199 East Washington street, Indianapolis. Born in England 1837; settled in M. C. 1864.

LUTZ, GUS; dealer in cigars and tobacco; 44 Indiana avenue, Indianapolis; res Pearl street. Born in Ohio 1846; settled in M. C. 1868.

Lockwood, W. G.; real estate broker; 91½ East Washington street, Indianapolis; res 514 North New Jersey street. Born in 1833; settled in M. C. 1858.

Lyman, L. R.; boarding house; 53 Malott avenue, Indianapolis.

LUDLOW, W. F.; butcher and meat dealer; corner Christian avenue and Peru street, Indianapolis; res 91 Ash street.

Lacy, Frank; farmer; 2½ m n e Indianapolis.

Lancaster, R. P.; farmer; 3 m n e Indianapolis. Born in Ohio 1813; settled in M. C. 1859. Rep. Methodist.

Leach, Jesse C.; farmer; 4 m n e Indianapolis. Born in Va. 1830; settled in M. C. 1854. Dem. Methodist.

Lich, Rev. H. G.; pastor German M. E. Church, corner New York and New Jersey streets, Indianapolis; res 185 East New York street. Born in Germany 1831; settled in M. C. 1851.

LEMON, PETER H.; Deputy Clerk of Marion Co.; res 458 East Georgia street. Born in Indiana Territory, Knox Co., 1813; settled in M. C. 1863. Indpt Granger.

LEMON, ALBERT E.; Deputy Clerk Marion county; res 458 East Georgia street. Born in Ind. 1840; settled in M. C. 1864.

LEE, J. N.; agent Land Department Mission, Fort Scott and Gulf R. R.; bds Little's Hotel.

Ludlum, J. E.; firm of Powell, Ludlum & Powell; res 49 Chatham street, Indianapolis. Born in Ohio 1832; settled in M. C. 1854.

Leary, P. C. & Co.; grocers; 229 West Washington street, Indianapolis.

Leary, James; firm of Leary & Co.; res 229 West Washington street, Indianapolis. Born in Ind. 1852; settled in M. C. 1864.

Luft, Wm.; shoe shop; 248 West Washington street, Indianapolis. Born in Germany 1853; settled in M. C. 1858.

Langenberg, Henry; firm of Langenberg & Co.; res South Meridian street, Indianapolis. Born in Germany 1818; settled in M. C. 1861.

LOCH, JOHN; saloon and boarding house; 439 West Washington street, Indianapolis; res same. Born in Prussia 1841; settled in M. C. 1862.

LANG, GEORGE; 439. Born in Wurtenburg, Germany, 1851; settled in M. C. 1852.

Lester, Wm. H.; druggist at Riverside drug store, 501 West Washington street, Indianapolis. Born in Ind. 1840; settled in M. C. 1872.

LAUGHLIN & CROSIER; dealers in choice family groceries, etc.; southeast corner of Deleware and Duncan streets, Indianapolis.

LAMBERT, J. M.; of the Ray House, Indianapolis. Born in Tenn. 1828; settled in M. C. 1848. Protestant.

LAMBERT, A. H.; of the Ray House, Indianapolis. Born in Ind. 1849; settled in M. C. 1869. Protestant.

Laughlin, J. C.; firm of Laughlin & Crosier; res 225 South Alabama street, Indianapolis. Born in N. Y. 1850; settled in M. C. 1867.

Lieber, P.; City Brewery; South Meridian street, Indianapolis.

Loeper, J. W.; at City Brewery, Indianapolis; res 519 Madison avenue.

LORD, JOHN P.; real estate broker; 97 Baldwin's Block, East Market street, Indianapolis. Born in Ind. 1849; settled in M. C. 1858.

LORD, C. M.; real estate broker; 97 East Market street, Indianapolis. Born in Ind. 1851; settled in M. C. 1857.

LORD, JOHN M.; real estate broker; 97 East Market street, Indianapolis; res 654 North Meridian street. Born in Vt.; settled in M. C. 1858.

LOVE, WILLIAM & CO.; real estate brokers; 48 Baldwin's Block, North Delaware street, Indianapolis.

LOVE, WILLIAM; firm of Wm. Love & Co.; res 434 North Delaware street, Indianapolis. Born in Ky.; settled in M. C. 1860.

Long, George; firm of G. W. Alexander & Co., real estate brokers; res 272 Blake street, Indianapolis. Born in M. C. 1853.

LANDIS, M. M.; firm of Hanna, Caldwell & Co.; res North Pennsylvania street, Indianapolis.

LEAK, J. B.; secretary of Surgical Institute; res 132 North Tennessee street, Indianapolis.

Lilly, Ely; firm of Johnston & Lilly; res 451 North Tennessee street, Indianapolis. Born in Md. 1838; settled in M. C. 1860.

LANGSENKAMP, WILLIAM; coppersmith and manufacturer of brewer and salt kettles, gas generators, soda founts, etc.; 96 South Delaware street, Indianapolis; res 184 South Delaware street. Born in Germany 1836; settled in M. C. 1854.

LAYMAN, CAREY & CO.; wholesale dealers in hardware; Nos. 85 and 87 South Meridian street, Indianapolis.

Layman, Jas. T.; firm of Layman, Carey & Co.; res 545 North Alabama street, Indianapolis. Born in Ind. 1844; settled in M. C. 1865.

LAMARCHE, MRS. LIZZIE; confectionery and news stand 152 Madison avenue, Indianapolis. Born in Germany 1838; settled in M. C. 1871.

Lamarche, N.; confectionery; 152 Madison avenue, Indianapolis; res same. Born in France 1835; settled in M. C. 1871.

LUDLUM, E. S.; dealer in first-class brands of imported and domestic cigars and finest brands of tobacco; 19 Virginia avenue, Indianapolis; res Chatham street.

LEWIS, T. A.; general manager of Erie and Pacific Dispatch Co.; corner Virginia avenue and Maryland street, Indianapolis.

Lynn, W. C.; local agent Erie and Pacific Dispatch Co.; res 23 West St. Clair street, Indianapolis. Born in Ind. 1841; settled in M. C. 1863.

Lehr, Lewis; bakery; 473 South Illinois street, Indianapolis; res same. Born in Germany 1840; settled in M. C. 1860.

Lahmann, Chas.; grocer; 430 Virginia avenue, Indianapolis. Born in Germany 1828; settled in M. C. 1855. Dem.

Ludlow, J. C.; dealer in sash, doors and blinds; 32 South New Jersey street, Indianapolis.

Lame & Son; carpenters and builders; 30 South New Jersey street, Indianapolis.

LEWIS & WHITEHEAD; dealers in fine marble monuments and tombstones; 48 and 50 Kentucky avenue, Indianapolis. Whitehead born in England 1841; settled in M. C. 1871.

Lawless & Caulfield; grocers; 138 South Noble street, Indianapolis.

Laut, H. W.; grocer; 350 South Noble street, Indianapolis. Born in M. C. 1851.

LINCE, C.; groceries, cigars, tobacco and beer; 250 Davidson street, Indianapolis.

LAKE, JOSEPH P.; carpenter and builder; corner of Clifford avenue and Watts street, Indianapolis. Born in M. C. 1841.

LONG, ROB.; firm of RENEHAN, LONG & HEDGES; res 15 Circle street, Indianapolis. Born in Ohio; settled in M. C. 1868.

Lane, Joseph; manufacturer of toilet and bar soap; West Indianapolis. Born in Mass. 1822; settled in M. C. 1874.

Ludorff, L. & Co.; dealers in notions, fancy goods and gents' furnishing goods; 42 South Meridian street, Indianapolis.

LONG & LEHMAN; FEED, SALE and LIVERY STABLE; 13 Circle street, Indianapolis.

LANDERS, FRANK; firm of HIBBEN, KENNEDY & CO.; is a member of Congress of the Seventh District, elected October, 1874.

LYNN, P. A.; firm of ROSS & LYNN; res 573 North Tennessee street, Indianapolis. Born in Ind. 1845; settled in M. C. 1862.

LIZIUS, C. B. & CO.; editors and publishers of the Indiana Deutsche Zeitung; 92 East Market street, Indianapolis.

Lutz, G. W.; physician; 270 West Washington street, Indianapolis; res 389 North Pennsylvania street. Born in Ind. 1849; settled in M. C. 1874.

LEVISON, CHARLES; business manager of Guttenburg Co., 25 South Delaware street, Indianapolis; bds at Circle House. Born in Prussia, Germany, Sept. 3d, 1827; settled in M. C. 1871; came to the United States in 1864.

Lemon, J. A.; dealer in family groceries; 298 North Pennsylvania street, Indianapolis; res same. Born in M. C. 1851.

Lamotte, Joseph; wholesale and retail dealer in stoves, tinware, and roofing; 192 Massachusetts avenue, corner North and East streets, Indianapolis. Born in France 1814; settled in M. C. 1855.

Lamotte, Chas.; Indianapolis. Born in France 1846; settled in M. C. 1855.

LEACH & SCHAUB; dealers in choice family groceries and all kinds of provisions; 110 and 118 Massachusetts avenue, Indianapolis.

Lewis, Mrs. M.; physician; room No. 1, second floor, Shively Block, Massachusetts avenue, Indianapolis; res same.

LATHROPE, Mrs. E. F.; dressmaker; 129 Massachusetts avenue, Indianapolis; res same.

Lowry, Wiley M.; dealer in drugs and medicines; 65 Massachusetts avenue, Indianapolis; res 73 Massachusetts avenue. Born in N. C. 1822; settled in M. C. 1857.

Louis, Anderson; res 271, corner North and Vanervoy streets, Indianapolis. Born in Ky. 1835; settled in M. C. 1864.

LANDIS, P. K.; insurance agent; rooms 22 and 24 Hubbard's Block, Indianapolis; res 364 East St. Clair street. Born in Ohio 1848; settled in M. C. 1872.

LANDIS, P. K.; with Meridian Printing Co.; 33 North Illinois street, Indianapolis.

Loftin, Samuel; farmer, merchant and trader; 5 m s w Indianapolis. Born in N. C. Dem. Protestant.

Loftin, T. W.; farmer and trader; 5 m s w Indianapolis. Born in M. C. 1851. Dem. Protestant.

Louis, Ranponi; confectionery stand; corner Washington and Pennsylvania streets, Indianapolis. Born in Italy 1835; res Pennsylvania street.

LEEDS, H. B.; manager R. G. Dun & Co., Mercantile agency; 3 and 4 Wiley's Block, Indianapolis; res 492 North Mississippi street. Born in Pa. 1845; settled in M. C. 1872. Rep. Protestant.

Lukenbach, A.; res 55 Malott avenue, Indianapolis. Born in Pa. 1841; settled in M. C. 1874. Dem. Presbyterian.

Lee, Chas. N.; insurance agent; with E. B. Martindale, room 13, Martindale's Block, North Pennsylvania street, Indianapolis; res 148 Blackford street. Born in Ohio 1830; settled in M. C. 1861. Rep. Christian.

Leck, R. M.; dealer in millinery and fancy goods, hats, and all kinds of trimming; 42 South Illinois street, Indianapolis. Born in Scotland 1840; settled in M. C. 1860. Rep. Presbyterian.

Longakes & Johnson; dealers in fresh oysters, game and fruits; 71 North Illinois street, Indianapolis.

LEPPERTS, L.; hair dressing and shaving saloon; 174 South
  Illinois street, Indianapolis; res 181 South Tennessee street.
  Born in Europe 1830; settled in M. C. 1872.

Longakes, Isaac; res 1½ m s w of Indianapolis.　Born in Pa.
  1840; settled in M. C. 1842.　Indpt.　Protestant.

LEE, H. H.; dealer in teas, coffee, sugar and spices, China Tea
  Store, corner Illinois and Ohio streets, Indianapolis; res 189
  North Illinois street.　Born in Ohio 1836; settled in M. C.
  1856.　Rep.　Unitarian.

Lampher, Mark E.; revenue clerk; 45 North Illinois street, Indianapolis.　Born in Del. 1811; settled in M. C. 1869.　Rep.
  Methodist.

LeRoy, W. Braden; General Secretary Young Men's Christian
  Association, 35 North Illinois street, Indianapolis.

Lyons, J. A.; wholesale and retail dealer in stoves, tinware and
  general house furnishing goods; 26 North Illinois street,
  Indianapolis; res 286 Virginia avenue.　Born in Ireland
  1847; settled in M. C. 1872.

LATSON, M. W.; manager of Connecticut General Life Insurance Co. for Indiana; office, 5 and 6 Claypool Block, corner Washington and Illinois streets, Indianapolis.　Born in
  Mich. 1845; settled in M. C. 1872.　Rep.

Lilly, J. O. D.; firm of J. O. D. Lilly & Son; Capital City Varnish Works, corner Kentucky avenue and Mississippi street,
  Indianapolis; res corner Second and Tennessee streets.
  Born in N. Y. 1822; settled in M. C. 1858.　Dem.　Episcopalian.

Langbein, Joseph; dealer in toys, fancy goods and notions; 200
  East Washington street, Indianapolis.　Born in Germany
  1819; settled in M. C. 1849.

LAUER, CHAS.; wholesale dealer and jobber in all kinds of
  Havana and domestic cigars; 202 East Washington street,
  Indianapolis.　Born in Bavaria 1837; settled in M. C. 1854.

Lindsay, Wm. I.; traveling agent for Howe Sewing Machine
  Company, Indianapolis; bds at Hotel Bates.　Born in Ohio
  1847; settled in M. C. 1874.　Rep.　Protestant.

Levette, Gilbert M.; assistant geologist; office State House, Indianapolis; bds at Mason House. Born in Pa. 1832; settled in M. C. 1851.

Lather, John; grocer; 505 North West street, Indianapolis. Born in Germany.

Lines, J. W.; dealer in boots and shoes; 37 West Washington street, Indianapolis; res 130 West Vermont street. Born in Ind. 1833; settled in M. C. 1861. Rep.

Latham, Henry; Cashier Indianapolis National Bank, No. 1 Odd Fellows Hall, Indianapolis; res 614 East Washington street. Born in Ohio 1844; settled in M. C. 1854. Rep. Presbyterian.

LIEBER, H.; firm of H. Lieber & Co., dealers in pictures, moulding and frames; 82 East Washington street, Indianapolis; res 404 North Delaware street. Born in Germany 1832; settled in M. C. 1854. Independent.

LENTZ, CHRISTIAN F.; gardener; west of river, Vermont street, Indianapolis. Born in Germany 1825; settled in M. C. 1852.

LENTZ, CHRISTIAN; gardener; west of river, Vermont St., Indianapolis. Born in Indianapolis 1852.

Leonard, Myron; secretary Udell Ladder Co.; res corner Michigan Road and Udell street, Indianapolis. Born in Vt. 1838; settled in M. C. 1874.

LECKLIDER, JOHN T.; firm of Lecklider & Hadley, attorneys at law; room 2, Yohn's Block, corner Washington and Meridian streets, Indianapolis. Born in Ohio 1840; settled in M. C. 1873. Rep. Presbyterian.

LYNCH, M. W.; city police; res 80 Indiana avenue. Born in Ireland 1840; settled in M. C. 1865. Dem.

Lee, Wm. N.; firm of Ira Cadwallader & Co., boots and shoes; 172 Indiana avenue, Indianapolis; res 213 North Illinois street. Born in Ind. 1841; settled in M. C. 1873. Dem.

Langsdale, Geo. H.; firm of Langsdale & Son, commission merchants; 230 East Washington street, Indianapolis. Born in M. C. 1840.

LINTNER, A. B.; firm of A. B. Lintner & Co., dealers in dry goods, notions, ladies' and gents' furnishing goods; 182 Indiana avenue, Indianapolis; res 269 North West street. Born in Pa. 1850; settled in M. C. 1856. Methodist.

LINTNER, C. H.; firm of C. H. Lintner & Co., the cheap boot and shoe store; 184 Indiana avenue, Indianapolis; res 285 Indiana avenue. Born in Pa. 1830; settled in M. C. 1856. Rep. Methodist.

Loucks, John M.; carpenter and joiner; 200 Virginia avenue, Indianapolis. Born in M. C. 1849. Rep. Methodist.

Langsdale, Joshua M. W.; firm of Langsdale & Son, commission merchants; 230 East Washington street, Indianapolis; res 225 East Ohio street.

Lacy, William; dealer in coal and plasterers' findings; 350 East Washington street, Indianapolis; res 41 Ash street. Born in Ind. 1821; settled in M. C. 1872.

Lindmann, Frank; grocer; 206 East Washington street, Indianapolis; res 79 North New Jersey street. Born in Ohio 1844; settled in M. C. 1853.

Liebrich, Lewis; grocer; 318 West North street, Indianapolis. Born in Germany 1826; settled in M. C. 1849.

Lambert, J. R. Jr.; drugs and medicines; corner of Michigan and Blake streets, Indianapolis. Born in Ind. 1838; settled in M. C. 1871.

Lobb, John; grocer; 206 North Blake street, Indianapolis. Born in England 1806; settled in M. C. 1870.

Lesh, A. B.; pork packer and dealer in provisions; 84 West Market street, Indianapolis; res 750 North Tennessee street. Born in Ind. 1828; settled in M. C. 1861.

Lowe, George; manufacturer of carriages and buggies; 71 and 73 West Market street, Indianapolis; res 321 North Pennsylvania street. Born in Pa. 1823; settled in M. C. 1846.

Mowl, G.; merchant tailor; 76 Massachusetts avenue, Indianapolis; res 698 Massachusetts avenue. Born in England 1840; settled in M. C. 1871.

McBride, ———; res 274 North Liberty street, Indianapolis. Born in Ireland.

Meyer, C. F.; dealer in pictures and looking-glasses of all kinds; 42 Massachusetts avenue, Indianapolis; res 227 North Liberty street. Born in Germany 1834; settled in M. C. 1850.

Messersmith, Peter; farmer; $3\frac{1}{2}$ miles northeast of Indianapolis. Born in Va. 1806; settled in M. C. 1831. Dem. Meth.

McLAIN, W. D.; MANAGER OF THE SINGER MANUFACTURING CO.; Singer Sewing Machine Co.; 72 and 74 West Washington street, Indianapolis.

MOORE, W. G.; physician and surgeon; 262 Mass. avenue, Indianapolis; res 323 Virginia avenue. Born in M. C. 1847.

Martin, L.; dealer in groceries, provisions, feed and flour; 300 Massachusetts avenue, Indianapolis; res 274 East St. Clair street. Born in Pa. 1847; settled in M. C. 1851.

McCoy, J. A. C.; physician and surgeon; 16 Malott avenue Indianapolis; res 132 Columbia avenue. Born in Ind. 1827; settled in M. C. 1870.

MOORE, GEO. W.; dealer in cigars, tobacco and confectionery; 4 Malott avenue, Indianapolis; res 65 California avenue. Born in Ind. 1833; settled in M. C. 1867. Rep. Methodist.

Meyer, H. B.; dealer in family groceries and provisions, wines and liquors; 109 Hill avenue, Indianapolis.

Murphy, Mrs. Annie; dealer in notions and hair goods; 395 North New Jersey street, Indianapolis.

MEIER, LEWIS; dealer in dry goods, boots and shoes; 196 Fort Wayne avenue, Indianapolis; res 123 Fort Wayne avenue. Born in Germany 1840; settled in M. C. 1862. Lib. Rep. Common sense.

Mothershead, Morris & Co.; stove manufacturers, Brightwood.

MONNINGER, DANIEL; dealer in organs and pianos; 28 Kentucky avenue, Indianapolis; res 386 North Tennessee street. Born in Germany 1831; settled in M. C. 1857.

MAYER, CHARLES & CO.; importers and jobbers of toys, notions and fancy goods, also fancy china ware, glass, etc.; 29 West Washington street, Indianapolis.

Mull & Bond; sale, boarding and livery stables; 19, 21 and 23 West Pearl street, Indianapolis. Horses kept by the day, week or month.

Mull, J. H.; res 273 North Tennessee street, Indianapolis. Born in 1823; settled in M. C. 1838.

MAGUIRE & GILLESPIE; Capital Coffee and Spice Mills; agents for Royal Baking Powder; 26 West Maryland street, Indianapolis.

MAGUIRE, D.; res 78 East Ohio street, Indianapolis. Born in M. C. 1836.

MAYER, CHARLES; res 285 North Illinois street, Indianapolis. Born in Germany 1819; settled in M. C. 1838.

McBRIDE & CONATY; wholesale and retail dealers in flour, feed, etc.; 64 West Maryland street, Indianapolis.

Miner, W. W.; book-keeper for Mills & Bro., corner Meridian and Railroad streets, Indianapolis; res 3 m n e Indianapolis.

McDonald, Mrs. Mary E.; proprietress of boarding house; 215 West North street, Indianapolis.

Manlove, William R.; attorney at law; office 24 Baldwin's Block, corner Delaware and Market streets, Indianapolis. Born in Ind. 1842.

Moore, Thomas; farmer; 1¾ m e corporation line. Born in Ireland 1811; settled in M. C. 1832. Dem. Protestant.

Metzger, Alexander; real estate and general insurance agent; No. 5 Odd Fellows Hall, Indianapolis; res 385 North Pennsylvania street. Born in Germany 1825; settled in M. C. 1851.

Morrow & Trusler; attorneys at law; 3 and 4, on second floor, Vinton's Block, Indianapolis.

Morrow, Wilson; res 282 North Pennsylvania street, Indianapolis. Born in Ind. 1823; settled in M. C. 1865. Rep. Methodist.

Maurice & Spohr; manufacturers and dealers in boots and shoes; 7 North Pennsylvania street, Indianapolis.

Maurice, J. N.; res 29 Fayette street, Indianapolis. Born in France 1837; settled in M. C. 1858.

MEYER, CHRIST. D.; res 402 North New Jersey street, Indianapolis. Born in Germany 1853; settled in M. C. 1873.

Medert, John A.; wholesale and retail dealer in all kinds of foreign and domestic cigars; 183 Massachusetts avenue, Indianapolis. Born in Germany 1833; settled in M. C. 1873.

Murphy, Timothy; boot and shoemaker; 109 Massachusetts avenue, Indianapolis; res same. Born in Ireland 1821; settled in M. C. 1854.

MERALLAS, MRS. M. C.; dealer in cigars, confectionery and notions; 92 Massachusetts avenue, Indianapolis. Born in N. Y. 1817; settled in M. C. 1869.

Moss, Mrs. Martha; dress maker; over No. 70, room 7, Massachusetts avenue, Indianapolis; res same. Born in England 1822; settled in M. C. 1831.

MEYER, CHARLES F.; manufacturer of and dealer in cigars and tobacco; 11 North Pennsylvania street, Indianapolis; res 323 North Delaware street. Born in Indianapolis 1852.

McKay, M. H.; real estate agent; 3 Odd Fellows' Hall, corner Washington and Pennsylvania streets, Indianapolis; res 156 Ash street. Born in Ohio 1841; settled in M. C. 1866.

Mitchell, Simeon; deputy clerk internal revenue; room 15, postoffice building, North Pennsylvania street, Indianapolis; res 771 North Mississippi street. Born in Ind. 1832; settled in M. C. 1866. Rep. Methodist.

MARTINDALE, ELIJAH B.; attorney at law, insurance and loan office; room 13, Martindale's Block, North Pennsylvania street, Indianapolis; res 666 North Meridian street. Born in Ind. 1828; settled in M. C. 1862. Rep. Presb.

MARTINDALE, J. B. & CO.; managers of the Western Law and Collection Association, also of the John McKillop & Co. Commercial Agency, and publisher of Martindale's U. S. Law Directory; rooms 15 and 19 Martindale's Block, North Pennsylvania street, Indianapolis.

MARTINDALE, J. B.; bds at Hotel Bates.

MANHEIMER, L. & BRO.; jewelers; all kinds of jewelry, watches and clocks repaired, and warranted; 83 East Washington street, Indianapolis.

MANHEIMER, LOUIS; res 139 North Alabama street, Indianapolis. Born in Ky. 1853; settled in M. C. 1863.

MANHEIMER, JOSEPH C.; res 139 North Alabama street, Indianapolis. Born in Ind. 1851; settled in M. C. 1863.

McLain, M. G.; lawyer; 91½ East Washington street, Indianapolis.

Morris, M. F.; 91½ East Washington street, Indianapolis; res 504 North Mississippi street, Indianapolis. Born in N. Y. 1849.

Miller, E. T.; druggist; 9 South Illinois street, Indianapolis. Born in Pa. 1822; settled in M. C. 1866.

Morrow, William; corner Illinois and Washington streets, Indianapolis. Born in Ind. 1849; settled in M. C. 1862.

Martin, Mrs. Caroline; restaurant; 19 North Illinois street, Indianapolis. Born in Germany 1840; settled in M. C. 1864.

McKERNAN, D. S.; real estate broker; room 3, second floor, in Claypool's Block, Indianapolis; res 408 North Illinois street. Born in Ohio 1840; settled in M. C. 1848. Dem. Catholic.

Mai, A.; jeweler; 43 South Illinois street, Indianapolis. Born in Germany 1838; settled in M. C. 1866.

MORRISON, WILLIAM HENRY; civil engineer and surveyor; 56½ North Illinois street, Indianapolis. Born in Ind. 1823. Dem.

McLENE & NORTHROP; jewelers and watchmakers; corner Washington and Illinois streets, Indianapolis.

MUTZ, C. M.; physician and surgeon; office, No. 4, second floor, Franklin Life Insurance Building, Indianapolis. Born in Ind. 1851; settled in M. C. 1871. Dem.

Morris & Carter; barbers; 135 South Illinois street, Indianapolis.

Moore, D. L.; general agent; 138 South Illinois street, Indianapolis. Born in N. Y. 1850; settled in M. C. 1872.

Myers, L.; barber; 93 South Illinois street, Indianapolis; res 274 South West street. Born in Germany 1837; settled in M. C. 1871. Dem.

McCUNE & SON; wholesale and retail dealers in teas, coffees, sugars and spices; 224 East Washington street and 100 North Illinois street, Indianapolis; res 221 East Ohio St.

McHutchan & McMillan; dealers in millinery and fancy goods; 64 North Illinois street, Miller's Block, Indianapolis.

McMILLAN, A. M.; res 124 North Tennessee street, Indianapolis. Born in Scotland 1848; settled in M. C. 1872. Rep. Presbyterian.

Mason, B.; restaurant; 83 and 85 North Illinois street, Indianapolis; res 191 West Maryland street. Born in Va. 1813; settled in M. C. 1861. Rep. Methodist.

Merrill, W. H. D.; dealer in gas fixtures; 68 North Illinois St., Miller's Block, Indianapolis; res 141 West New York St. Born in Ind. 1838; settled in M. C. 1838.

Martin, C. B.; restaurant; 19 North Illinois street, Indianapolis.

Marsh, W. S.; res 94 North Mississippi street, Indianapolis. Born in Ky. 1821; settled in M. C. 1863. Rep. Meth.

MERRIFIELD, C. E. & S. S.; dealers in agricultural implements; agents for Buckeye reaper and mower; 79 West Washington street, Indianapolis.

MERRIFIELD, S. S.; res 169 Broadway, Indianapolis. Born in Ind. 1836; settled in M. C. 1871. Methodist.

MERRIFIELD, C. E.; res 336 Park avenue, Indianapolis. Born in Ind. 1840; settled in M. C. 1866. Episcopalian.

McOuat, Foote & Co.; dealers in stoves and house furnishing goods; 61 and 63 West Washington street, Indianapolis.

MOSES, L. W.; optician and dealer in optical goods; 50 East Washington street, Indianapolis; res 87 East Michigan St. Born in Conn. 1826; settled in M. C. 1856.

MICK BROS.; real estate brokers; 16½ East Washington street, Indianapolis.

Mick, J. F.; res 669 North Alabama street, Indianapolis. Born in Ohio 1831; settled in M. C. 1862. Methodist.

McVEY, WM.; firm of R. R. Rouse & Co.; res 61 West Michigan street, Indianapolis. Born in Ind. 1824; settled in M. C. 1828.

Mick, W. E.; res 159 Christian avenue, Indianapolis. Born in Ohio 1833; settled in M. C. 1863. Methodist.

MOSSLER, L. I. & BRO.; One Price Clothing House; 37 East Washington street, Indianapolis.

MOSSLER, L. I.; res 130 North East street, Indianapolis. Born in Prussia 1837; settled in M. C. 1859. Jewish faith.

MOSSLER, SOLOMON; res 130 North East street, Indianapolis. Born in Prussia 1835; settled in M. C. 1859. Jewish faith.

Morgan, S. W.; firm of Stewart & Morgan; res 214 North Illinois street, Indianapolis. Born in Ohio 1831; settled in M. C. 1862. Dem. Episcopalian.

MERRILL, HUBBARD & CO.; publishers and dealers in BOOKS AND STATIONERY; No. 5 East Washington street, Indianapolis.

MERRILL, SAMUEL; res 170 East Merrill street, Indianapolis. Born in M. C. 1831. Rep. Presbyterian.

McKernan, J. H.; real estate agent; 51½ West Washington street, Indianapolis; res 68 Circle street. Born in Del. 1815; settled in M. C. 1845. Dem. Catholic.

MARTIN, LUTHER R. & CO.; real estate and loan brokers; office, No. 10 East Washington street, Indianapolis.

MARTIN, DANIEL; res 91 East Michigan street, Indianapolis. Born in Ohio 1839; settled in M. C. 1869. Baptist.

Martin, L. R.; res 91 East Michigan street, Indianapolis. Born in Md. about 1834; settled in M. C. 1856.

MYERS, J. M.; res 258 North Tennessee street, Indianapolis. Born in Ind. 1838; settled in M. C. 1849.

Martin & Hopkins; insurance agents; 34 and 36 West Washington street, Indianapolis.

Martin, H. C.; res 166 Bellefontaine street, Indianapolis.

McCLELLAN, J. I.; firm of Breedlove and McClellan; res 218 West New York street, Indianapolis. Born in Ind. 1821; settled in M. C. 1865.

McMasters & Boice; lawyers; 64½ East Washington street, Indianapolis.

McMasters, J. L.; res 398 North Delaware street, Indianapolis. Born in Ohio 1843; settled in M. C 1870. Rep.

MARTIN, J. O.; secretary of M. M. B. S. of Ind.; 24 Kentucky avenue, Indianapolis; res 416 North Pennsylvania street. Born in N. Y. 1838; settled in M. C. 1865.

MILNER & MITCHELL; attorneys at law; 94 East Washington street, Indianapolis.

MITCHELL, J. R.; firm of Milner & Mitchell; office, 94 East Washington street, Indianapolis.

MILNER, JOHN; firm of Milner & Mitchell; office 94 East Washington street, Indianapolis.

Myers, D. E.; res 100 East Washington street, Indianapolis. Born in Ohio 1842; settled in M. C. 1870. Christian.

MINICK, D. E.; real estate and loan broker; room 2, 17 West Washington street, Indianapolis; res 310 South Illinois St., Indianapolis. Born in Dayton, Ohio, 1821; settled in M. C. 1852. Dem.

Mayhew, J. N.; optician; 50 East Washington street, Indianapolis. Born in Ind. 1839; settled in M. C. 1844. Rep.

McCURDY, GEO. W.; auction and commission house, 1 Occidental Hotel, Indianapolis; res 344 North Alabama street. Born in Ind. 1837; settled in M. C. 1852. Rep.

MOSSLER, L. H.; One Price Clothing House, 13 West Washington street, Indianapolis; res 90 North East street. Born in Prussia 1837; settled in M. C. 1862. "NEW IRON BLOCK."

Myres, S. H.; firm of Hill & Myres; room 25 West Washington street, Indianapolis.

McDowell, J.; book-keeper for Bowen & Stewart; res 238 South Alabama street, Indianapolis.

MYERS, J. M. & CO.; real estate brokers; 25 West Washington street, opposite Trade Palace, Indianapolis.

MARTIN & BEHRENDT; dealers in fancy and staple goods, grain, flour and feed; 172 South Illinois street, Indianapolis.

McCann, Miss Mary; dealer in cigars, tobacco and candies; 200 South Illinois street, Indianapolis. Born in Va. 1835; settled in M. C. 1869.

Meredith, E.; foreman of saw works; South Illinois street, Indianapolis; res 235 South Mississippi street. Born in England 1828; settled in M. C. 1863. Dem.

Merrick, W. M.; livery stable; corner Illinois and South streets, Indianapolis. Born in Ind. 1838; settled in M. C. 1863. Rep. Methodist.

Mueller, E.; grocer; 182 East Washington street, Indianapolis. Born in Germany 1830; settled in M. C. 1856.

Moore, S. G.; physician; 527 North Illinois street, Indianapolis. Born in Ind. 1844; settled in M. C. 1874.

Millinery store, 13 South Illinois street, Indianapolis. Proprietor refused to give his name.

MEIGS, CHARLES; res Christian avenue, Indianapolis. Born in Pa. 1846.

MACY, DAVID; President I. P. & C. R. R. Co.; office 101 East Washington street, Indianapolis; res 298 North Delaware street. Born in N. C. 1810; settled in M. C. 1852.

Malott, V. T.; Treasurer I. P. & C. R. R. Co.; 101 East Washington street; res 288 North Delaware street. Born in Ky. 1838; settled in M. C. 1847.

Marot, J. R.; dealer in furniture; 87 East Washington street, Indianapolis. Born in Pa.

Marot, L.; furniture salesman; 87 East Washington street, Indianapolis. Born in Pa. 1825; settled in M. C. 1874.

McCutcheon, J. C.; firm of Hanna, Caldwell & Co.; res North Meridian street, Indianapolis.

MAYER, BRO. & CO.; wholesale dealers in cigars and tobacco; 56 South Meridian street, Indianapolis.

MAYER, JOSEPH; firm of MAYER, BRO. & CO.; res 81 East street, Indianapolis. Born in Germany 1844; settled in M. C. 1863.

MAYER, L.; firm of MAYER, BRO. & CO.; res East street, Indianapolis. Born in Germany 1847; settled in M. C. 1865.

METZNER, A.; Eagle Pharmacy; corner Virginia avenue and Washington street, Indianapolis; res Coburn street. Born in Germany 1834; settled in M. C. 1864. Rep.

MANUFACTURERS' AND REAL ESTATE EXCHANGE; office 92 East Market street, Indianapolis; organized Nov. 26th, 1873; membership 120; see statistics.

MILLER, W. H. H.; firm of Harrison, Hines & Miller; res 185 Broadway, Indianapolis. Born in N. Y. 1840; settled in M. C. 1874.

Morris, S. V.; firm of Anderson & Morris, attorneys at law and real estate brokers; 49 South Pennsylvania street, Indianapolis. Born in M. C. 1833. Rep.

Miller, Mrs. Ella; toll-gate keeper on Bethel pike.

Martin, George W.; carriage and wagon maker; 1 m s corporation, Indianapolis. Born in M. C. 1852.

Munson, W. L.; dealer in new and second-hand furniture; 139 East Washington street, Indianapolis; res 61 North New Jersey street. Born in N. J. 1818; settled in M. C. 1860.

MOTHERSHEAD, MORRIS & CO.; manufacturers and wholesale dealers in stoves, tinware, etc.; No. 32 South Meridian street, Indianapolis.

Mothershead, J. L.; res corner Ohio and Alabama streets, Indianapolis. Born in Indianapolis.

Morris, A. W.; bds Hotel Bates. Born in Indianapolis.

MADSEN, C. L. F.; carpenter and contractor; res 371 West North street, Indianapolis. Born in Denmark 1836; settled in M. C. 1865.

Mayo, E. H.; res 562 North Pennsylvania street, Indianapolis. Born in Ohio 1837; settled in M. C. 1863.

MAYO & BERGUNDTHAL; iron, steel and hardware; 86 and 88 South Meridian street, Indianapolis.

Murphy, Johnson & Co.; wholesale dry goods and notions; 51 and 53 South Meridian street, Indianapolis.

Murphy, John; firm of Murphy, Johnson & Co.; res 166 North Meridian street, Indianapolis. Born in Ohio 1828; settled in M. C. 1856.

Miller & Bro.; celebrated chemical paint; 76 East Maryland street, Indianapolis.

MINICH, J. A.; physician and surgeon, National Surgical Institute, Indianapolis.

Miller, W. R.; physician and surgeon, National Surgical Institute, Indianapolis.

McLain, L. C.; physician, National Surgical Institute, Indianapolis.

Mullaney, Hayes & Co.; wholesale liquor dealers; 143 South Meridian street, Indianapolis.

Mooney, Taylor & Smith; manufacturers and dealers in leather; 147 South Meridian street, Indianapolis.

MADDUX, THOS.; firm of Huston & Co., tobacconists; res Cincinnati.

Morris, N.; general collecting agent; collections made throughout the State; office, 85½ East Washington street, Indianapolis; res 414 South Illinois street. Born in Cal. 1857; settled in M. C. 1871.

MOORE, JOSEPH A. & BRO.; brokers; money loaned on mortgage; 90 East Market street, Indianapolis.

MOORE, JOSEPH A.; res 613 North Pennsylvania street, Indianapolis. Born in Ohio 1840.

MOORE, THOS. C.; firm of Moore & Bro.; res 477 North Pennsylvania street, Indianapolis. Born in Ind. 1845; settled in M. C. 1858.

Manufacturers and Real Estate Exchange; East Market street, Indianapolis.

McCOY, H. & CO.; miners of block coal and dealers in all kinds of coal and coke; office s w corner Delaware and Market streets, Baldwin's Block, Indianapolis.

McCOY, H.; res 809 North Meridian street, Indianapolis. Born in Va. 1837; settled in M. C. 1870.

Mathews, Samuel; attorney at law; 30 Baldwin's Block, corner Delaware and Market streets, Indianapolis.

Munson, E. A.; insurance office; 40 North Delaware street, Indianapolis; res 429 North Meridian street.

Morrow & McDonald; fire insurance office; No. 1 Glenns' Block, East Washington street, Indianapolis.

Morrow, W. L.; firm of Morrow & McDonald; res 248 Fletcher avenue, Indianapolis. Born in Ohio.

McDonald, J. B.; firm of Morrow & McDonald; res 74 Forest avenue, Indianapolis. Born in Mich. 1848; settled in M. C. 1872.

Mendenhall, H. W.; note broker and collector; office 41 North Delaware street, Indianapolis.

MACAULEY, DANIEL; General Agent of Massachusetts Life Insurance Company; office 18 Baldwin's Block, Indianapolis; res 324 North Meridian street. Born in N. Y. City 1840.

Miller, W. B.; farmer; 3 m n Exposition Building, Indianapolis. Born in Ohio 1840; settled in M. C. 1873.

MOORE, JOHN; farmer and stock raiser; 1 m e corporation line. Born in Ireland 1806; settled in M. C. 1831.

Manford, C. B.; dealer in Burge's stone cement; 645 North Illinois street, Indianapolis. Born in Ind. 1835; settled in M. C. 1865.

Mayer, John F.; manufacturer of umbrellas and parasols; 69 East Washington street, Indianapolis. Born in Germany 1822; settled in M. C. 1852.

McDOUGAL, E. R.; brick manufacturer; 73 East Washington street, Indianapolis; yard 1¼ m s e Indianapolis. Born in Indianapolis 1828. Rep. Protestant.

Martin, Lyman & Co.; real estate dealers; 75½ East Washington street, Indianapolis.

Martin, E. M.; firm of Martin & Co.; res Hillside avenue, Indianapolis. Born in Ind. 1850; settled in M. C. 1871. Rep. Protestant.

Martin, L.; firm of Martin & Co.; res Hillside avenue, Indianapolis. Born in Ind. 1840; settled in M. C. 1850. Rep. Protestant.

MUNHALL, L. W.; dentistry; first class work; 35½ East Market street, Indianapolis. Born in Ohio 1843; settled in M. C. 1861.

Muecke, Wm.; house and sign painter; 14 Virginia avenue, Indianapolis; res 129 Huron street. Born in Prussia 1844; settled in M. C. 1864.

MOSSLER, A. I. & CO.; dealers in ladies' and gents' furnishing goods and notions; 20 and 22 Virginia avenue, Indianapolis.

MOSSLER, A. I.; res 266 East Market street, Indianapolis. Born in Prussia 1840; settled in M. C. 1858.

McFarland & Sebern; grocers; 50 Virginia avenue, Indianapolis.

Moore, John O.; attorney at law; 9 and 10 Baldwin's Block, Indianapolis. Born in M. C. 1849.

McGINNIS, GEN. G. F.; office 13 Baldwin's Block, Indianapolis; res 629 Meridian street. Born in Boston, Mass., 1826; settled in M. C. 1850.

Maurice & Spohr; professional boot makers; 13 North Meridian street, Indianapolis.

McDougall Bros. & Butler ; 33 North Illinois St., Indianapolis.

McDougall, G. P.; res 13 West North street, Indianapolis. Born in M. C. 1844.

McDougall, F. W.; res 13 West North street, Indianapolis. Born in M. C. 1850.

McLAUGHLIN, FRANK ; 23 South Meridian street, Indianapolis; res 319 Huron street. Born in Mass. 1843; settled in M. C. 1869.

Meridian National Bank; 30 South Meridian street, Indianapolis; Wm. P. Gallup, president ; J. D. Howland, vice president; John G. Kennedy, cashier.

Mitchel & Rammelsburg Furniture Co.; 41 and 43 South Meridian street, Indianapolis.

Morris, N. N.; firm of Wright & Morris; res 325 North Liberty street, Indianapolis. Born in Ill. 1837; settled in M. C. 1871.

Morris, V. K.; firm of Wright & Morris ; res 323 North Alabama street, Indianapolis. Born in Ind. 1838; settled in M. C. 1872.

Mills, T. P.; real estate; rooms 6 and 8 Hubbard Block, Indianapolis. Born in Ohio 1833; settled in M. C. 1839.

McCarty, Nicholas; rooms 19 and 12 Hubbard Block, corner of Washington and Meridian streets, Indianapolis; res North Pennsylvania street.

McGILLIARD, CARPENTER & CO.; insurance and real estate agency; 16 South Meridian street, Indianapolis.

McGILLIARD, M. V.; firm of McGilliard, Carpenter & Co.; res 468 North East street, Indianapolis.

Maxwell, Fry & Thurston; dealers in iron, steel, blacksmith tools, etc.; 34 South Meridian street, Indianapolis.

Miller, A. J.; druggist. Born in Ind. 1854; settled in M. C. 1871.

MILLIKAN, JOHN S.; groceries and provisions, also all kinds of liquors; 255 South Tennessee street, Indianapolis; res same. Born in Ohio 1841; settled in M. C. 1871.

Millikan, John S.; house mover; 255 South Tennessee street, Indianapolis; res same.

Mitchell, Jas.; saloon; 276 South Missouri street, Indianapolis; res same. Born in Ireland 1840; settled in M. C. 1869.

McGuff, Martin; driver Hose Co. No. 7; bds Ray House, Indianapolis. Born in Ohio 1852; settled in M. C. 1870.

Martindale, W.; dealer in coffee, teas, etc.; 404 Virginia avenue, Indianapolis. Born in Ind.; settled in M. C. 1863.

MOORE, F. M.; dealer in stoves, tinware, etc.; 192 Virginia avenue, Indianapolis. Builders' work done to order; job work of all kinds. Born in Ind. 1839; settled in M. C. 1867.

MANSFIELD & JENKINS; horse shoeing; shop, 26 South New Jersey street, Indianapolis.

Meyer, W. N. A.; grocer; 100 South Noble street, Indianapolis.

Moore, Geo.; apothecary; corner New York and Noble streets, Indianapolis.

McKENZIE, J. A.; clothing house; No. 30 West Washington street, Indianapolis; res 466 North Meridian street. Born in Ohio 1831; settled in M. C. 1872. Rep. Episcopalian.

Morrison, A. T.; clerk in bank; res 622 North Alabama street, Indianapolis. Born in M. C. 1838.

Mueller, L. H.; druggist; 249 East Washington street, Indianapolis. Born in Germany 1842; settled in M. C. 1865.

Metzger, Conrad; manufacturer of boots and shoes; 301 East Washington street, Indianapolis. Born in Prussia 1846; settled in M. C. 1865.

MECGER & EHRMANN; dealers in groceries, flour and feed; 505 Madison avenue and 578 South East street, Indianapolis.

MECGER, HENRY; firm of MECGER & EHRMANN; res .578 East South street, Indianapolis. Born in Germany 1847; settled in M. C. 1872.

MEYER, JOHN; GROCERY AND PROVISION STORE; 1 Shelby street, Indianapolis, res same. Born in Germany 1851; settled in M. C. 1872.

Meyer, Henry; with John Meyer; Indianapolis. Born in Cincinnati 1853; settled in M. C. 1855.

Moore, John; dealer in custom made boots and shoes; 457 Virginia avenue, res same. Born in Ireland 1842; settled in M. C. 1873.

Mann, J. B.; grocer; 7 Virginia avenue, Indianapolis; res same. Born in Ky. 1826; settled in M. C. 1835.

McIntire, J.; firm of Butsch & Dickson; res 25 South West street, Indianapolis. Born in Ohio; settled in M. C. 1862.

McGrath, T. W.; dealer in boots and shoes; 445 South East street, Indianapolis. Born in Mass. 1839; settled in M. C. 1865.

Muse, James; the model pharmacy; 540 South East street, Indianapolis; res 508 South East street.

Meany, John; saloon and boarding house; 181 and 183 South Meridian street, Indianapolis. Born in Ireland 1817; settled in M. C. 1863.

MEYER, WM.; grocer; 490 and 492 Union street, Indianapolis. Born in Germany 1830; settled in M. C. 1855.

Martin E.; druggist; corner South Meridian street and Russel avenue, Indianapolis. Born in Germany 1842; settled in M. C. 1868.

McDonall, James; grocer; 296 South West street, Indianapolis. Born in Ireland 1825; settled in M. C. 1872.

MORRIS, J. W.; firm of Roll & Morris, carpets and wall paper; 30, 32 and 34 South Illinois street, Indianapolis; res 210 Park avenue. Born in M. C. 1846. Rep. Presbyterian.

Martin, J. T.; tin shop; 253 West Washington street, Indianapolis; res 21 West street. Born in M. C. 1845.

MEIKEL, JOHN P.; brewery; 297 West Washington street, Indianapolis; res 213 West Maryland street.

MEIKEL, PHILIP; machinist and engineer; 397 West Washington street, Indianapolis. Born in Germany 1832; settled in M. C. 1849.

MILLIGAN, FRANCIS; wagon maker; Indianapolis. Born in Tenn. 1840; settled in M. C. 1865.

Martin, J. L.; saloon and billiards; 192 West Washington St., Indianapolis; res same. Born in Ind. 1829; settled in M. C. 1862.

McFarland, C. A.; firm of McFarland & Sebern; res 75 Fletcher avenue, Indianapolis. Born in M. C. 1840.

MOZART HALL; by JOHN GROSCH; wine and beer saloon; South Delaware street, Indianapolis.

Memgis, Frank; cigars and tobacco; 182 South Delaware street, Indianapolis; res same. Born in Germany 1817; settled in M. C. 1854.

Mugge, J. D.; groceries, feed and liquors; 373 South Delaware street, Indianapolis; res 38 Wyoming street. Born in Germany 1823; settled in M. C. 1852.

McWHORTER, WM.; farmer; North Indianapolis, near Crown Hill. Born in Md. 1831; settled in M. C. 1838.

MYERS, C.; foreman brass department Indianapolis Brass and Supply Co.; res 70 South Liberty street. Born in Cincinnati, Ohio; settled in M. C. 1858.

MORBACK, P.; shoe store; 30 South Delaware street, Indianapolis; res 117 Merrill street. Born in France 1826; settled in M. C. 1867.

McCullough, Wm.; firm of Dain & McCullough; res 37 Broadway, Indianapolis. Born in Ohio 1833; settled in M. C. 1871.

McCLURE, JACOB H.; carpenter and builder; North Indianapolis, corner Armstrong street and east of Michigan Road. Born in Ky. 1828; settled in M. C. 1847.

McClintock, Thos. A.; farmer; North Illinois street, Indianapolis, 3½ miles north of Circle street. Born in M. C. 1844.

Myers, Allen; farmer and dairyman; 4 miles north of Circle on Illinois street, Indianapolis. Born in Ind. 1837; settled in m. C. 1872.

Miller, Jacob; farmer; 2½ miles southwest of Indianapolis P. O. Born in Ohio.

MARTIN, W. W.; bookkeeper Weed Sewing Machine Co.; 42 North Pennsylvania street, Indianapolis; bds Revere House. Born in N. Y. 1852; settled in M. C. 1873.

MORE, P. H.; practical piano maker and tuner of musical instruments; 66 Indiana avenue, Indianapolis. Born in Birmingham, England; settled in M. C. 1865. Rep.

MOODY, CHAS. W.; firm of Moody Bros., druggists; 52 and 54 Indiana avenue, Indianapolis. Born in Ohio 1846; settled in M. C. 1863. Indpt. Methodist.

MOODY, E. R.; firm of Moody Bros., druggists; 52 and 54 Indiana avenue, Indianapolis; res 128 West Vermont street. Born in Ohio 1839; settled in M. C. 1863. Rep. Meth.

Meyer, Christian; cigar manufacturer; 26 Indiana avenue, Indianapolis; res 17½ Virginia avenue. Born in Germany 1851; settled in M. C. 1873.

McChesney, Edward; railroader; 454 North Tennessee street, Indianapolis. Born in M. C. 1846. Rep. Episcopalian.

Markle, C.; grocery and feed store; 149 Indiana avenue, Indianapolis. Born in Ohio 1819; settled in M. C. 1872. Rep. Presbyterian.

Matthews, Edward; confectioner; 183 Indiana avenue, Indianapolis. Born in Germany 1842; settled in M. C. 1868.

MATTHEWS, JOSHUA; house, sign and carriage painter; 585 Mississippi street, Indianapolis; res 14 Lenox street. Born in M. C. 1847. Indpt. Presbyterian.

MAYO, WM. E.; furniture repairing, upholstering and chair caning; 254 Indiana avenue, Indianapolis. Born in Ind. 1843; settled in M. C. 1872. Indpt. Methodist.

MONNINGER, CONRAD; cigar manufacturer and saloon keeper; 390 Indiana avenue, Indianapolis; res 388 Indiana avenue. Born in Bavaria 1828; settled in M. C. 1858.

Mansur, Isaiah; banker; n e corner Washington and Alabama streets, Indianapolis; res n e corner Meridian and Vermont streets. Born in Ind. 1824; settled in M. C. 1847.

Major, Stephen F.; firm of Davis, Stevenson & Major; res 78 Prospect street, Indianapolis.

MILLER, A. R.; firm of Burr & Miller, real estate agents; 45 East Washington street, up stairs, Indianapolis; res 15 East New York street. Born in Ohio 1827; settled in M. C. 1862. Rep. Episcopalian.

May, Edwin; architect; office 5 and 6 Glenn's Block, East Washington street, Indianapolis; res 175 North Pennsylvania street. Born in Mass. 1823; settled in M. C. 1839. Dem.

Miller, R. A.; watchmaker and jeweler; 268 East Washington street, Indianapolis.

McGinnis, John; groceries, flour and feed; 280 East Washington street, Indianapolis. Born in Ireland 1832; settled in M. C. 1860.

McKay, R. J.; grocer and commission merchant; No. 298 East Washington street, Indianapolis.

Marine, A. C.; with R. J. McKay; 298 East Washington street; res 71 Lockerbie street, Indianapolis. Born in N. C. 1819; settled in M. C. 1871.

Mitchel, Jacob; clothier, gents' furnishing goods; 2 Bates House Block, Indianapolis. Born in Germany 1832; settled in M. C. 1854. Conservative. Hebrew.

Martin, P. J.; firm of Martin, Maguire & Co.; dry goods; 164 and 166 West Washington street, Indianapolis; bds Occidental Hotel. Born in Ireland 1848; settled in M. C. 1862. Liberal. R. Catholic.

Maguire, Chas.; firm of Martin, Maguire & Co.; dry goods; 164 and 166 West Washington street, Indianapolis; res 176 West Ohio street. Born in Ireland 1844; settled in M. C. 1866. Liberal. Episcopal.

Moore, S. H.; firm of Moore & Wiley, druggists; 172 West Washington street, Indianapolis; res 361 West Vermont street. Born in Ind. 1829; settled in M. C. 1873. Rep. Methodist.

Matz, John; boot and shoemaker; 286 West Washington street, Indianapolis. Born in Germany 1834; settled in M. C. 1863. Dem. R. Catholic.

Miles, J. A.; restaurant; 188 West Washington street, Indianapolis. Born in Ohio 1828; settled in M. C. 1871. Indpt.

Moffatt, C. A.; manufacturer of show cases; 196 West Washington street, Indianapolis; res 222 North Blackford street. Born in N. Y. 1830; settled in M. C. 1861. Rep. Prot.

Mettee, S. E.; railroader; res 63 Huron street, Indianapolis. Born in Md. 1814; settled in M. C. 1861. Rep. Meth.

McCUNE, H. B.; firm of McCune & Son, wholesale and retail dealers in teas, coffees, sugars and spices; 224 East Washington, and 100 North Illinois streets, Indianapolis; res 221 East Ohio street. Born in Pa. 1825; settled in M. C. 1871.

McGauly, James; firm of Doherty & McGauley, gas fitters; 67 North Illinois street, Indianapolis.

McCORMACK, HEZEKIAH S.; real estate agent; 5 Black-ford's Block, over First National Bank, Indianapolis; res 173 Winston street. Born in Ind. 1819; settled in M. C. 1820. Rep. Methodist.

McCready, E. S.; stoves and tinware; 270 East Washington street, Indianapolis; res 268 East Market street. Born in M. C. 1847.

Munson, David; lightning rods; 220 East Washington street, Indianapolis; res 228 East Market street.

MAUER, J. P.; firm of J. P. Mauer & Son, dealers in groceries, produce, flour and feed; corner Blake and Elizabeth streets, Indianapolis. Born in Germany 1815; settled in M. C. 1848.

MAUER, H. J.; firm of J. P. Mauer & Son; corner Blake and Elizabeth streets, Indianapolis. Born in M. C. 1852.

Mitchem, Rev. Nathan; minister A. M. E. Church; res 214 West Vermont street, Indianapolis. Born in Ky. 1814; settled in M. C. 1873. Rep.

Moosman, Samuel; baker; 121 Blake street, Indianapolis. Born in Germany 1839; settled in M. C. 1872.

Maus, C.; brewer of lager beer; west end New York street, Indianapolis; res 20, Agnes street. Born in France 1815; settled in M. C. 1864.

Maus, M.; brewer; res 20 Agnes street, Indianapolis. Born in Ind. 1853; settled in M. C. 1864.

Maus, A.; foreman at brewery; res 28 Agnes street, Indianapolis. Born in Ohio 1844; settled in M. C. 1864.

Maus, F.; clerk at brewery; res 20 Agnes street, Indianapolis. Born in Ind. 1851; settled in M. C. 1864.

MOUNTS, GEO. F.; proprietor of Park House; 66 North Missouri street, Indianapolis. Born in Ind. 1854; settled in M. C. 1874.

MANHATTAN MARBLE WORKS; office at Indianapolis, 208 West Market street.   John G. Blake, president; res 308 North Tennessee street; John T. Macauley, vice-president; res 526 North Illinois street; Wm. W. Blake, secretary and treasurer; res 308 North Tennessee street; P. Rafferty, superintendent; bds Capital House.

Macauley, J. T.; manufacturer of the improved artificial stone; office and works corner Market street and canal, Indianapolis; res 526 North Illinois street.

Mason, Benj.; firm of Mason, Pettit & Co., dealers in coal and lime; 94 West Market street, Indianapolis; res 191 West Maryland street.

McKee & Branham; wholesale dealers in boots and shoes; 108 South Meridian street, Indianapolis.

Miley, John; west of the river on Washington street, Indianapolis.   Born in Germany 1816; settled in M. C. 1864.

Miley, John S.; with Conduit & Cook, South Meridian street, Indianapolis; res 36 East Cherry street.

MARTIN, JOHN H.; farmer and gardener; 2 m n w Circle. Born in Ohio 1815; settled in M. C., Wayne township, 1837, when the city could boast of only 400 inhabitants and 400 outside the city.

MARTIN, THOS. S.; farmer; 2 m n w of Circle, west of river. Born in M. C. 1846.

MARTIN, HENRY D.; 2 m w Circle, west of river.   Born in M. C. 1849.

McDIARMID, DUNCAN; foreman at Crown Hill Cemetery, North Indianapolis.   Born in Scotland 1840; settled in M. C. 1865.

Neal, Smith & Co.; dealers in new and second-hand furniture; 87 South Illinois street, Indianapolis.

Naltner, Martin; saloon keeper; 262 South Illinois street, Indianapolis.   Born in Germany 1837; settled in M. C. 1856.

New, G. W.; physician; office 15 Miller's Block, North Illinois street, Indianapolis; res 426 North Illinois street. Born in Ind. 1819; settled in M. C. 1860. Rep. Christian.

Nilius, Charles; merchant tailor; cleaning and repairing; 144 South Illinois street; res same. Born in Prussia 1831; settled in M. C. 1865. Dem.

NEIMAN, MRS. LAHA.; boarding house; 209 South Illinois street, Indianapolis. Born in Pa. 1828; settled in M. C. 1852.

Nichols, N. C.; foreman of the bending and saw department at Woodburn Sarven Wheel Factory, Indianapolis; res 124 Buchanan street. Born in Ind. 1840; settled in M. C. 1869. Rep. Methodist.

Nolan, R. G.; foreman of No. 4 Engine Co.; res corner Norwood and Eddy streets, Indianapolis. Born in Ind. 1848; settled in M. C. 1871. Dem. Catholic.

Neerman, Christian; manufacturer and dealer in all kinds of boots and shoes; 269 Massachusetts avenue, Indianapolis; res over No. 269 Massachusetts avenue. Born in Germany 1837; settled in M. C. 1857.

NOLAN, EDWARD; manufacturer of boots and shoes; 164 West Michigan street, Indianapolis; res same. Born in Ireland 1844; settled in M. C. 1872.

NICOLAI BROS.; dealers in house furnishing goods, pressed and japanned ware; 81 Fort Wayne avenue, Indianapolis.

NICOLAI, CHARLEY; res 81 Fort Wayne avenue, Indianapolis. Born in Germany 1852; settled in M. C. 1871.

Netzel, Henry; bookkeeper; res 285 North Illinois street, Indianapolis. Born in Germany 1848; settled in M. C. 1866.

Nichols, Willard C.; deputy clerk of the United States Circuit and District Courts, room 10, Post Office Building; res 212 East Vermont street, Indianapolis. Born in Ohio 1847; settled in M. C. 1858.

Nettler, L.; dining room; 44 South Illinois street, Indianapolis; res same. Born in Miss. 1829; settled in M. C. 1864.

NICOLAI, HENRY; butcher and meat dealer; 62 Massachusetts avenue, Indianapolis; res 89 Broadway street. Born in Ind. 1843; settled in M. C. 1851.

Nesbit, Wm. T.; livery, feed and sale stable; 28 and 30 South Pennsylvania street, Indianapolis; res 38 College avenue. Born in Ind. 1840; settled in M. C. 1840. Rep. Presbyterian.

Neuerburg, Leonard; manufacturer of brick; yard 1 m e corporation line; res on National Road. Born in Germany 1845; settled in M. C. 1865.

NOLAN, MICHAEL; boot and shoe manufacturer; 98½ Indiana avenue, Indianapolis. Born in Dublin, Ireland, 1823; settled in M. C. 1856. Dem. Catholic.

NEWELL, R. A.; contractor and builder; 123 Indiana avenue, Indianapolis; res 88 West Ohio street. Born in Del. 1834; settled in M. C. 1867. Dem. Protestant.

Neff, D.; physician; 250 Indiana avenue, Indianapolis; res 323 California street. Born in Va. 1832; settled in M. C. 1871. Democrat.

Neab, Conrad; plumber, gas and steam fitter; 6 Bates House Block, Indianapolis.

Nickum, J. R.; firm of Parrott, Nickum & Co., cracker bakers, 188 East Washington street, Indianapolis; res 26 Lockerbie street. Born in Md. 1821; settled in M. C. 1861. Rep. Protestant.

Newcomb, T. M.; manager of the Great Atlantic and Pacific Tea Company; Bates House Block, Indianapolis; bds at Pyle House. Born in Ohio 1853; settled in M. C. 1873.

Naughton, Patrick; grocer; 210 East Washington street, Indianapolis; res 213 East Ohio street. Born in Ireland 1842; settled in M. C. 1858.

Nicoli, Lew.; firm of Nicoli & Reynolds, dealers in hats and caps; 244 East Washington street, Indianapolis; res 89 Broadway street. Born in Ohio 1846; settled in M. C. 1853.

Neal & Allen; dealers in new and second-hand furniture; 229 East Washington street, Indianapolis.

New, John C.; cashier First National Bank; res 272 North Pa. street, Indianapolis. Born in Ind. 1831; settled in M. C. 1846.

Norris, John; proprietor of Eagle shoe store; 23 East Washington street, Indianapolis. Born in Ireland 1829; settled in M. C. 1869.

Newman, David; dealer in clothing and gents' goods; 145 West Washington street. Born in Germany 1844; settled in M. C. 1864.

NEEF, HERBERT; photographer; 121 West Washington St. Indianapolis; res 731 North Illinois street. Born in Ohio 1828; settled in M. C. 1855.

Naughton, Peter; dealer in groceries; southwest corner Illinois and McCarty streets, Indianapolis. Born in Ireland 1848; settled in M. C. 1867. Dem. Catholic.

Neal, A. C.; bds Little's Hotel, Indianapolis. Born in Ohio.

Nelson, J. D.; boot and shoe manufacturer; 21 Circle street, Indianapolis. Born in Pa. 1832; settled in M. C. 1871.

Norton, Pierce; firm of Bixby & Norton; bds Sherman House, Indianapolis. Born in Ind. 1850; settled in M. C. 1873.

NOLAND, W. W.; firm of Batty, Noland & Tarkington; res 181 Home avenue, Indianapolis. Born in Ind. 1825; settled in M. C. 1870.

NIXON, CYRUS T.; secretary of Manufacturers' and Real Estate Exchange; office 92 East Market street, Indianapolis; res 85 Bradshaw street. Born in Ind. 1831; settled in M. C. 1873.

Nelson, J. M.; druggist; 408 South Meridian street, Indianapolis; res same. Born in M. C. 1847.

Nolan, T.; hoseman of No. 4 Engine Co.; Indianapolis. Born in Ireland 1846; settled in M. C. 1866.

Newbacker, L.; foreman in Brass and Supply Works, Indianapolis. Born in Austria 1840; settled in M. C. 1866.

NORTON, JOHN; saloon keeper; 167 West Washington street, Indianapolis; res 18 South Mississippi street. Born in Ireland 1849; settled in M. C. 1869.

Nihans, J. L.; firm of Zimmer & Nihans, grocers; res 349 South Delaware street, Indianapolis. Born in Germany 1828; settled in M. C. 1864.

Nelson, H. L.; watchmaker; 48 North Delaware street, Indianapolis. Born in Pa. 1834; settled in M. C. 1860.

NICHOL, JOSEPH W.; firm of Huff, Nichol & Co.; res 292 North Meridian street, Indianapolis. Born in Ind. 1836; settled in M. C. 1866.

Nicholi, Charles; saddler and harness maker; 326 East Washington street, Indianapolis. Born in Prussia 1799; settled in M. C. 1843.

Norman, J. B.; contractor and plasterer; Irvington. Born in Ky. 1835; settled in M. C. 1853.

NEIMAN, JOSEPH; dealer in groceries and provisions; 422 West North street, Indianapolis; res 354 Douglass street. Born in Pa. 1821; settled in M. C. 1849.

Nelson, James; dairyman; 2 miles northwest of Circle street, Indianapolis. Born in Denmark 1833; settled in M. C. 1865.

Nowland, John H. B.; author of Early Reminiscences of Indianapolis. Born in Ky. 1814; settled in M. C. 1820.

Northway, John; contractor and plasterer; res 306 East North street, Indianapolis. Born in Ind. 1828; settled in M. C. 1838.

Nichols, T. M.; dentist; 25 West Washington street, Indianapolis; res North Illinois street. Born in Ky. 1823; settled in M. C. 1851.

NEWBY, FRANK S., general railroad and steamship ticket agent; No. 1 Spencer House, South Illinois street, Indianapolis; res 158 Bellefontaine street. Born in Ind. 1839; settled in M. C. 1871. Rep. Friend.

Nichols & Jackson; livery, sale and commission stable; 4 East Maryland street, Indianapolis. Born in Ohio 1832; settled in M. C. 1873.

Overman, E. C.; grocer; 34 Indiana avenue, Indianapolis; res 132 North Tennessee street.   Born in Ind. 1819.   Rep. Quaker.

Ott, L. F.; watchmaker; 32 Indiana avenue, Indianapolis; res Wabash street.   Born in Germany 1848; settled in M. C. 1869.

Olleman, Ezra A.; firm of J. G. Kingsbury & Co., editors of *The Indiana Farmer*, 76 West Washington street, Indianapolis; res 237 West Ohio street.

Osterman, John; firm of John Osterman & Co., commission merchants; 86 West Washington street, Indianapolis; res 549 North Illinois street.

Office of McDonald & Butler, attorneys at law; No. 1 and 2 McDonald & Butler's Block, North Pennsylvania street, Indianapolis.

OFFICE OF INDIANAPOLIS GAS LIGHT AND COKE CO.; corner South Pennsylvania and Maryland streets; S. A. Fletcher, President; L. Vanlaningham, Secretary; res 274 North Alabama street.   Born in Ind. 1817; settled in M. C. 1827.   Rep.   Methodist.

OVER, EWALD; res 417 North Tennessee street, Indianapolis.   Born in Germany.   Rep.   Lutheran.

OWENS, E. J. Mrs.; dealer in all kinds of ladies' and gents' clothing, new and second handed, 133 Massachusetts avenue, Indianapolis.   Born in Va. 1819; settled in M. C. 18—.

ORIEN, MARKS; boot and shoemaker; 272 South Illinois street; res same.   Born in Ireland 1832; settled in M. C. 1873.

Office of O'Brien & Kelley; wholesale and retail dealers in choice brands of cigars and tobacco; 51 South Illinois street, Indianapolis.

O'Neill, M.; firm of O'Neill, Haerst & Wernring, merchant tailors; 38 South Illinois street, Indianapolis; res 143 East McCarty street.   Born in Ireland 1818; settled in M. C. 1846.   Dem.   Catholic.

O'Neill, Haerst, & Wernring; merchant tailors; 38 South Illinois street, Indianapolis.

Osgood, M. J.; manufacturer and wholesale dealer in black walnut and white wood lumber, and all kinds of fancy woodwork; office and yard corner Massachusetts and Clifford avenues, Indianapolis.

O'Brian & Lewis; blacksmiths and horse shoers; corner North and Fayette streets, Indianapolis.

O'Brian, Michael; res 500, corner California and Vaneroy Sts. Born in Ireland 1849; settled in M. C. 1873.

OGAN, J. R.; marble and granite works; 24 West Maryland street, Indianapolis; res 30 West Maryland street.   Born in Ohio 1840; settled in M. C. 1871.

OSGOOD, J. B.; house, sign and ornamental painter; 16 West Maryland street, Indianapolis; res 187 South Alabama St. Born in Mass. 1806; settled in M. C. 1853.   Dem.   Univ.

OHMER, N. & G.; proprietors Union Depot Dining Hall and Restaurant, in Union Depot, Indianapolis.

OSLER, JOHN; proprietor barber shop; 235 East Washington street, Indianapolis; res 87 South Liberty street.   Born in Ohio 1839; settled in M. C. 1871.

Osler, James; barber; 235 East Washington street, Indianapolis. res 87 South Liberty street.   Born in Ohio 1857; settled in M. C. 1871.

OUTLAND & BIBB; proprietors barber shop; 22 South Meridian street, Indianapolis.

OUTLAND, EDWARD E.; firm of Outland & Bibb; Indianapolis.   Born in Ind. 1830; settled in M. C. 1863.

Orr, G. W.; manager of delivery department of American Express Co.; 46 and 48 South Meridian street, Indianapolis. Born in M. C. 1843.

Ohleyer, Geo.; basket manufacturer; 456 South Meridian street, Indianapolis.   Born in Germany 1833; settled in M. C. 1864.

Otwell, Francis; policeman; res West Washington street, Indianapolis.   Born in Ky. 1809; settled in M. C. 1861.

Oliver, C.; tobacconist and liquor dealer; 288 West Washington street, Indianapolis. Born in England 1833; settled in M. C. 1857.

Oehler, A.; jeweler; 20 South Delaware street, Indianapolis. Born in Germany 1834; settled in M. C. 1858.

Overgfell, H.; boot and shoemaker; 366 South Delaware street, Indianapolis. Born in Germany 1851; settled in M. C. 1871.

Otto, Fred.; manufacturer of cigars; 7 Shelby street, Indianapolis. Born in Germany 1844; settled in M. C. 1872. Dem. Protestant.

Pries, H. J.; State agent for McCormick's reaper and mower and dealer in agricultural implements; 212 East Washington street, Indianapolis; res 189 East Ohio street.

Prange, Chas.; firm of Prange & Co., dealers in dry goods; 318 East Washington street, Indianapolis; res 92 East Michigan road. Born in Germany 1833; settled in M. C. 1855.

Prange, Anthony; firm of Prange & Co.; res 112 North Davidson street. Born in Germany.

PARRY, M; manufacturer and dealer in boots and shoes; 322 East Washington st., Indianapolis. Born in England 1833; settled in M. C. 1867.

Perrin, Geo. K.; attorney at law; 45 East Washington street, Indianapolis; res 293 North New Jersey street. Born in Vt. 1827; settled in M. C. 1855.

Pettit, Wm. B.; firm of Mason, Pettit & Co., coal and lime dealers; 94 West Market street, Indianapolis; res 325 North Illinois street. Born in Ohio 1846; settled in M. C. 1870.

Pettit, Frank R.; firm of Mason, Pettit & Co., coal and lime dealers; 94 West Market street, Indianapolis; res 325 North Illinois street. Born in Ohio 1853; settled in M. C. 1870.

Pfaff, W. A.; firm of John C. Burton & Co., wholesale dealers in boots and shoes; 14 South Meridian street, Indianapolis.

Pfaff, John W.; firm of John C. Burton & Co., Indianapolis.

PFAFFLIN, WM.; dealer in staple and fancy groceries; 200 North Mississippi street, corner Indiana avenue, Indianapolis. Born in Wurtemburg, Germany, 1847; settled in M. C. 1867. Dem. Lutheran.

Perkins, J. H.; dry goods and tailoring; 162 Indiana avenue, Indianapolis. Born in Ind. 1842; settled in M. C. 1864.

Posner, Morris; merchant tailor; 189 Indiana avenue, Indianapolis. Born in Prussia 1837; settled in M. C. 1870.

Parrott, Horace; firm of Parrott, Nickum & Co., cracker bakers; 188 East Washington street, Indianapolis; res 349 North Delaware street. Born in Ky. 1820. Rep.

Parkman, Chas. B.; secretary of Indianapolis Rolling Mill Co.; 13 East Washington street, Indianapolis; res 230 North West street. Born in Mass.; settled in M. C. 1858. Rep. Presbyterian.

Paxton, R. S.; insurance agent; 68 West Washington street, Indianapolis; res 310 North Illinois street. Born in Pa. 1813; settled in M. C. 1870. Rep. Presbyterian.

POTTAGE, CHAS. E.; manager of B. Pottage's hardware store; wholesale and retail dealer; 84 West Washington street, Indianapolis; res 98 North Mississippi street. Born in Ohio 1835; settled in M. C. 1835.

POTTAGE, BENJAMIN; wholesale and retail dealer in hardware; 84 West Washington street, Indianapolis; res 127 West Market street. Born in England 1798; settled in M. C. 1835.

Paster, Fred; saloon keeper; 144 Indiana avenue, Indianapolis. Born in Germany 1825; settled in M. C. 1859. Protestant.

PALMER, N. B.; retired; res 57 West Maryland street. Born in Conn. 1790; settled in M. C. 1834.

PALMER, B. M.; farmer; 2 m w Indianapolis. Born in Ind. 1830; settled in M. C. 1834.

PATTERSON, R. H.; Deputy Treasurer of Marion County; bds at 149 North Meridian street, Indianapolis. Born in Indianapolis 1841. Protestant.

PORTER, EDWARD B.; firm of Yohn & Porter, dealers in books and stationery; 4 East Washington street, Indianapolis; res 249 North Alabama street. Born in Indianapolis 1851. Rep. Methodist.

Porter, O. F.; firm of A. M. Porter & Co., dealers in cigars and tobacco; 33 West Washington street, Indianapolis; res 50 Cherry street. Born in Ky. 1846; settled in M. C. 1862.

Perine, P. R.; Deputy County Assessor; 17½ West Washington street, Indianapolis; res 783 North Illinois street. Born in Ind. 1817; settled in M. C. 1857. Rep. Methodist.

Potter, N. C.; Cashier St. Louis Life Insurance Co.; 53 West Washington street, Indianapolis; res 169 Massachusetts avenue. Born in Ind. 1842; settled in M. C. 1865. Indp. Methodist.

Powell, Ludlum & Powell; real estate brokers; 26 North Delaware street, Indianapolis.

Powell, G. W.; firm of Powell, Ludlum & Powell; res 328 North Alabama street, Indianapolis. Born in Ind. 1850; settled in M. C. 1859. Rep.

Powell, David; firm of Powell, Ludlum & Powell; res 638 North Alabama street, Indianapolis. Born in Ind. 1828; settled in M. C. 1859. Rep.

Poor, A. P.; commission merchant, and dealer in provisions and feed; 45 Virginia avenue, Indianapolis; res 258 South Meridian street. Born in Minn. 1829; settled in M. C. 1867.

PICKERILL, GEO. W.; physician and surgeon; 31 Virginia avenue, Indianapolis; bds at corner of Plumb and Cherry streets. Born in Ind. 1837; settled in M. C. 1856. Careful attention given to chronic diseases of the blood, throat or lungs.

Poehler, Fred.; firm of W. & F. Poehler; res corner High and Coburn streets, Indianapolis. Born in Germany 1850; settled in M. C. 1851.

Poehler, W. & F.; groceries and liquors; corner High and Coburn streets, Indianapolis.

Peck, Edwin J.; retired from business; res 264 North Illinois street, Indianapolis. Born in Conn. 1796; settled in M. C. 1833. Presbyterian.

Pettis, Dickson & Co.; New York Store, Glenn's Block, Indianapolis.

PULLEN, JOHN W.; brickmason and contractor; res 140 East McCarty street, Indianapolis. Born in Va. 1830; settled in M. C. 1849.

Pray, William; firm of Gates, Pray & Co.; res 223 East Market street, Indianapolis. Born in Ind.; settled in M. C. 1864.

PEASE, ROBINSON & GLASSEY; real estate brokers; 88 East Market street, Indianapolis.

PEASE, T. W.; firm of Pease, Robinson & Glassey; res 160 Fort Wayne avenue, Indianapolis.

POTTS, MRS. MARY A.; photograph studio; 78 West North street, Indianapolis; res same. Born in Md. 1820; settled in M. C. 1834.

Perry, J. C.; firm of Robertson & Perry; wholesale grocers; res 320 North Alabama street, Indianapolis.

Pattison & Finley; wholesale dealers in queensware; Talbott's Block, North Pennsylvania street, Indianapolis.

Pfau & Ward; wholesale dealers in liquors; 141 South Meridian street, Indianapolis.

Pee, George W. & Co.; notions, white goods, etc.; 137 and 139 South Meridian street, Indianapolis.

Paver, J. M.; news stand, corner Meridian and Louisiana streets, Indianapolis. Born in Ohio 1839; settled in M. C. 1867.

PRINGLE, W. W.; attorney at law; office 85½ East Washington street; res South Noble street.

Ponsue, Joseph; blacksmith; 1 mile east of Indianapolis. Born in Germany 1834; settled in M. C. 1865.

Parker, R. R.; men's furnishing goods; 32 West Washington street, Indianapolis; res 378 North Meridian street.

PORTER, ALBERT G.; attorney at law; office n e corner of Washington and Meridian streets, Indianapolis; res 501 North Tennessee street. Born in Ind. 1824; settled in M. C. 1845.

PRITCHARD, C. W.; manager of Provident Life and Trust Co. of Philadelphia; office 15 Hubbard Block, Indianapolis; res 302 North Delaware street. Born in Ind. 1834; settled in M. C. 1873. Minister Society of Friends.

- Powell, G. W.; firm of Cooper & Powell; bds Illinois street, Indianapolis. Born in Canada 1853; settled in M. C. 1874.

Plumb, H. H.; firm of Geo. W. Black & Co.; res 49 South Pennsylvania street, Indianapolis. Born in N. Y. 1835; settled in M. C. 1861. Rep. Methodist.

Peak & Bro.; dealers in flour, feed, etc.; 146 Virginia avenue, Indianapolis.

Power, J. S.; dry goods and millinery; 186 Virginia avenue, Indianapolis. Born in Ireland 1850; settled in M. C. 1870.

Painter, J. M.; tea store; Virginia avenue, Indianapolis. Born in Ohio 1836; settled in M. C. 1871.

PAULI, HENRY; superintendent of Manufacturers' and Carpenters' Union; manufacturers of doors, blinds, sash, etc.; dealers in rough and dressed lumber, laths and shingles; 38, 40 and 42 South New Jersey street, Indianapolis.

Pearson & Campbell; attorneys at law; room 4 Ætna Building, over 17 North Pennsylvania street, Indianapolis.

Peas, Sanford; Western Feed Store; 265 West Washington St., Indianapolis. Born in Conn. 1841; settled in M. C. 1872.

POIVIER, J. B.; member Hook and Ladder Co. No. 2; bet Delaware and South streets, Indianapolis. Born in Ohio 1849; settled in M. C. 1860.

Preble, J. G.; real estate broker; 16½ East Washington street, Indianapolis. Born in Ohio 1816; settled in M. C. 1872. Rep. Protestant.

PALMATEER, J. W.; special agent for the St. Louis Life Insurance Co.; 53 West Washington street, Indianapolis. Born in Ohio 1837; settled in M. C. 1874. Rep. Meth.

POWELL, WILLIAM; firm of Powell & Steadman, general agents; 164 South Illinois street, Indianapolis; res 215 West Ohio street. Born in Ky. 1824; settled in M. C. 1847. Rep. Methodist.

Pink, Gustave; variety store; 115 West Washington street, Indianapolis. Born in Germany 1847; settled in M. C. 1868. Mosaic.

Potter, M. A.; manufacturer of household goods; 5 Griffith's Block, Indianapolis; bds 197 North Alabama street. Born in Mich. 1855. Rep. R. Baptist.

Perrine, T. F.; real estate broker; 30½ West Washington street, Indianapolis; res corner Tennessee and Seventh streets. Born in Ind. 1844; settled in M. C. 1859. Indpt.

PATTISON, W. A.; firm of W. A. & I. N. Pattison; wholesale and retail druggists; 100 East Washington street, Indianapolis; res North Illinois street. Born in Ind. 1824; settled in M. C. 1855. Methodist.

Pattison, I. N.; druggist; res 138 North New Jersey street, Indianapolis. Born in Ind. 1840; settled in M. C. 1871. Rep. Protestant.

PATTISON, W. A. & I. N.; wholesale and retail druggists; a full line of fresh drugs always on hand; 100 East Washington street, Indianapolis.

PEELLE, S. J.; firm of Tipton & Peelle, attorneys at law; office 100 East Washington street, Indianapolis; res 135 North Illinois street. Born in Ind. 1843; settled in M. C. 1869. Presbyterian.

Pyburn, Mrs. A.; wholesale and retail dealer in confectionery; Post Office news stand, North Pennsylvania street, Indianapolis; manufactory 129 North Pennsylvania street.

PHILADELPHIA BRICK YARDS; 1 m from terminus Massachusetts avenue, near Brightwood; S. K. Fletcher and Robert Thomas, proprietors.

Parker, John B. W.; farmer; 3 m e Indianapolis. Born in M. C. 1841. Dem.

POTHART, AUGUST; brick manufacturer; res and yard 1½ m e Indianapolis. Born in Germany 1836; settled in M. C. 1855.

Pearson, J. C.; attorney at law; 4 Ætna Building, Indianapolis. Born in Ind. 1841; settled in M. C. 1871; bds North Delaware street. Rep. Protestant.

Pearson, George C.; salesman with M. A. Stowell; 46 North Pennsylvania street, Indianapolis. Born in Pa. 1851; settled in M. C. 1870. Rep. Presbyterian.

Perry Brothers; dealers in drugs and pure medicines; corner Pennsylvania and Market streets, Indianapolis.

Perry, Ross W.; bds Hotel Bates, Indianapolis. Born in Mich. 1850; settled in M. C. 1872.

Perry, Joseph R.; res 235 East Vermont street, Indianapolis. Born in England 1840; settled in M. C. 1869.

Page, J. P.; manufacturer of boots and shoes; 10 North Pennsylvania street, Indianapolis; res 599 South East St. Born in England 1831; settled in M. C. 1869.

PATTERSON, C. H.; livery, feed and sale stable; Michigan street, between Alabama and New Jersey, Indianapolis; res 140 Massachusetts avenue. Born in M. C. 1854.

Planing mill of Builders' and Manufacturers' Association; manufacturers of sash, doors and blinds, and dealers in all kinds of lumber, lath and shingles; mill 225 to 235 North Delaware street; yard 329 Massachusetts avenue, Indianapolis. C. Eden, president; John L. Avery, secretary.

Peel, Louis; dealer in fancy groceries and provisions; 552 North Mississippi street, Indianapolis; res same. Born in Germany 1843; settled in M. C. 1872.

Poehler, Christian; dealer in groceries and provisions, also all kinds of meat; 155 West First street, Indianapolis; res same. Born in Germany 1840; settled in M. C. 1856.

Phipps, Silas; farmer; 3½ m n e Indianapolis.

POUEL, IRA; firm of J. R. Budd & Co.; Indianapolis. Born in Ind. 1839.

Pogue, James; farmer; 4½ m n e Indianapolis. Born in M. C. 1844.

Phipps, Charles R.; assistant treasurer at the Indianapolis Savings Bank; North Pennsylvania street, Indianapolis; res 66 Arsenal avenue. Born in M. C. 1843.

Pyle, John; confectionery and restaurant; 17 North Pennsylvania street, Indianapolis; res corner Second and Tennessee streets. Born in Pa. 1819; settled in M. C. 1855.

Perrine, T. B.; general engraver; rooms 22 and 23 Talbott & New's Block, third floor, North Pennsylvania street, Indianapolis; res same. Born in Ind. 1834; settled in M. C. 1854. Protestant.

Phipps, L. M.; deputy collector Internal Revenue; room No. 15 Post Office Building, North Pennsylvania street, Indianapolis; res 282 Christian avenue. Born in M. C. 1834. Rep. Methodist.

Philips, Mrs. A.; manufacturer and dealer in ladies' and children's shoes; 108 Massachusetts avenue, Indianapolis; res 457 Virginia avenue.

Phillips, E. R.; commission merchant; 40 Massachusetts avenue, Indianapolis. Born in Ohio 1844; settled in M. C. 1871.

Platz, V.; brass instruments; 17 Massachusetts avenue, Indianapolis. Born in Wis. 1840; settled in M. C. 1859.

Preefer, H.; dealer in dry goods and notions of all kinds; 38 Malott avenue, Indianapolis; res 40 Malott avenue. Born in Germany 1835; settled in M. C. 1872.

Petti, John J. B.; physician and surgeon; Ohio street, Indianapolis; bds Revere House. Born in Ind. 1847; settled in M. C. 1869. Rep. Protestant.

PETTIJOHN & CLARK; physicians and surgeons; 69 North Illinois street, Indianapolis.

Palmer, Edw. L.; dealer in books and stationery; 66 South Illinois street, Indianapolis; res 136 West Vermont street. Born in Ind. 1834; settled in M. C. 1835. Indpt.

Prosser, John; Philadelphia dye house; res 602 North Mississippi street, Indianapolis. Born in South Wales 1828; settled in M. C. 1818. M. Baptist.

Phipp, A.; res 82 South Illinois street, Indianapolis. Born in Ky. 1832; settled in M. C. 1871.

Paulmane, E. L.; dealer in watches, clocks and jewelry; 118 South Illinois street, Indianapolis; res 479 South Missouri street. Born in Europe 1845; settled in M. C. 1871.

Purdy, I. C.; foreman of yard of Woodburn Sarven Wheel Co.; res 57 Eddy street, Indianapolis. Born in Ky 1841; settled in M. C. 1871.

Parmer, F. C.; clerk at Spencer House, Indianapolis. Born in N. Y. 1842; settled in M. C. 1872. Rep. Protestant.

Quinn, Thomas; South street Hook and Ladder Co., Indianapolis. Born in Ireland 1848; settled in M. C. 1868.

QUEISSER, F. F.; meat market; fresh meat always on hand; 368 Virginia avenue. Born in 1848.

Ridgway, J. F.; physician and surgeon; room 1, 2d floor Miller's Block, North Illinois street, Indianapolis; res 366 North West street. Born in Ohio 1830; settled in M. C. 1866. Rep. Unitarian.

RIKHOFF & CO.; wholesale dealers in pure Kentucky copper-distilled whisky; 81 South Illinois street, Indianapolis.

Rockwell, Silas; bakery and confectionery; 105 South Illinois street, Indianapolis. Born in N. Y. 1816; settled in M. C. 1864. Rep.

Richter, F. B.; dealer in groceries, provisions, flour and feed; corner Russell avenue and Illinois street, Indianapolis. Born in Germany 1829; settled in M. C. 1858.

Rice, George H.; res corner Bellefontaine street and Christian avenue, Indianapolis. Born in Maryland 1841; settled in M. C. 1863. Rep. Protestant.

ROSS, JAMES; firm of John B. Stumph & Co., Indianapolis.

Rodibaugh, O.; dealer in groceries and provisions: corner Illinois and Tinker streets, Indianapolis.

RUSSELL, A. A.; dealer in threshing machines, horse powers and portable steam engines; 197 West Washington street, Indianapolis. Born in Vt. 1833; settled in M. C. 1873.

Ray, John W.; secretary and treasurer of Indianapolis Savings Bank; res 249 North Alabama street, Indianapolis.

Rudy, E. H.; dealer in groceries, notions and provisions; 106 Hill avenue, Indianapolis; res same. Born in Pa. 1840; settled in M. C. 1849.

Rossener, Charles; blacksmith and horse shoer; 368 St. Clair street, Indianapolis; res 30 Ash street. Born in Germany 1842; settled in M. C. 1849.

Resener, C. F.; manufacturer of boots and shoes; 374 St. Clair street, Indianapolis; res same. Born in Prussia 1834; settled in M. C. 1849.

RHEINSCHILD, JOHN; manufacturer of boots and shoes; 151 Fort Wayne avenue, Indianapolis; res 119 Broadway. Born in Germany 1844; settled in M. C. 1865.

REYNOLDS, —.; res 248 West Third street, Indianapolis. Born in Ind. 1850; settled in M. C. 1871.

RICHEY, MRS. ELECTA; proprietor boarding house; 78 West Maryland street, Indianapolis.

Randall, C. F.; life insurance agent; 1 and 2, over 18 North Pennsylvania street, Indianapolis; res 525 North Alabama street. Born in N. Y. 1830; settled in M. C. 1870. Rep. M. Baptist.

Richardson, Benjamin A.; cashier Gaslight and Coke Co. Born in N. Y. 1843; settled in M. C. 1865. Rep. Presbyterian.

Reeves, J. N. D.; res 146 Buchanan street, Indianapolis. Born in Ind. 1844; settled in M. C. 1873.

Reeves & Hill; manufacturers of regalia and Lodge supplies for Odd Fellows, Masons, Druids, Knights of Pythias, Red Men and Good Templars; 9 and 10 Odd Fellows Hall, Indianapolis.

REID, B. W.; gold, silver and nickel plater; rooms 22 and 23 Talbott & New's Block, North Pennsylvania street, Indianapolis; bds Little's Hotel. Born in Canada 1851; settled in M. C. 1873.

• RIDENOUR, J. M.; real estate general agent; room 14, second floor, Martindale's Block, North Pennsylvania street, Indianapolis; res 650 East Washington street. Born in Ohio 1820; settled in M. C. 1867.

REMINGTON SEWING MACHINE CO.; 57 North Pennsylvania street, Indianapolis; L. M. COYNER, Jr., agent; res 132 Pennsylvania street. Born in Va. 1844; settled in M. C. 1866.

RANPONI, LOUIS; confectionery stand, corner Washington and Pennsylvania streets, Indianapolis; res Pennsylvania st. Born in Italy 1835; settled in M. C. 1870.

RYAN, FRANK; silk hat manufacturer and repairer; 27 South Illinois street, Indianapolis. Born in N. Y. 1847; settled in M. C. 1873. Rep. Catholic.

Raymond, Nathan; res 805 North Tennessee street, Indianapolis. Born in N. Y.; settled in M. C. 1871.

Raymond, Andrew; res Indianapolis. Born in N. Y. 1845; settled in M. C. 1871.

RUTH, ROBERT; saloon and loan office; 97 North Illinois street, Academy of Music Building, Indianapolis; res 77 North Liberty street. Born in Germany 1843; settled in M. C. 1862.

RAYMOND & CO.; dealers in drugs, medicines, paints, oils and dye-stuff; 98 North Illinois street, Thompson's Block, Indianapolis.

RAYMOND, N. Born in N. Y. 1817; settled in M. C. 1872. Dem. Presbyterian.

Ripley, Wm. I.; dealer in teas and groceries; 47 and 49 North Illinois street, Indianapolis.

REILLY, J. W.; wholesale and retail dealer in millinery, ribbons, laces and fancy goods; 63 North Illinois street, Indianapolis. Born in N. Y. 1830; settled in M. C. 1870. Rep. Catholic.

Rentsch & Kipp; dealers in groceries, dry goods and fancy notions, flour and feed; 273, 275 and 277 Massachusetts avenue, Indianapolis; res same.

Rentsch, Ferdinand; Indianapolis. Born in Germany 1843; settled in M. C. 1868.

RESENER, A. F.; dealer in flour and feed; 301 Massachusetts avenue, corner East and North streets, Indianapolis; res 320 East Vermont street. Born in Europe 1838; settled in M. C. 1849.

Rienan, ——.; res 120 Columbia avenue, Indianapolis.

ROBARDS, WALLACE; farmer; 3 m n e Indianapolis. Born in Ky. 1818; settled in M. C. 1865. Rep. Protestant.

Ryan, James R.; dealer in teas and fancy groceries; 70, 72 and 74 Massachusetts avenue, Indianapolis.

ROBERTS, ALICK; city gas inspector; City Hall, Indianapolis; res 44 Broadway. Born in Scotland 1848; settled in M. C. 1871. Catholic.

Romberg & Steinmetz, upholsterers and dealers in fine furniture and bedding, wholesale and retail; 117 East Market street, Indianapolis.

Romberg, Henry; res 418 North East street, Indianapolis.

Ross, A. P.; car recorder of I. P. & C. R. R.; office 101 East Washington street, Indianapolis. Born in Vt. 1837; settled in M. C. 1858.

Rentsch, H.; grocer; 125 East Washington street, Indianapolis.

Raschig, C. M.; wholesale dealer in cigars and tobacco; 11 East Washington street, Indianapolis. Born in Ohio 1838; settled in M. C. 1855.

ROBERTS, JOSEPH P.; attorney at law; office 91 East Washington street, Indianapolis; res 167 West Third street. Born in Ind. 1850; settled in M. C. 1869. Rep.

RADCLIFFE, N. B.; architect draftsman, with D. A. Bohlen; 95 East Washington street, Indianapolis. Born in Md. 1853; settled in M. C. 1872.

Raap, Sebastian; boot and shoe dealer; 189 East Washington street, Indianapolis. Born in Germany 1834; settled in M. C. 1854.

Rouschen, W. H.; res 366 South Illinois street, Indianapolis. Born in Germany 1824; settled in M. C. 1863.

Russel & Co.; manufacturers of threshing machines, horse powers and portable steam engines; factory at Massilon, Ohio; branch office 197 West Washington street, Indianapolis.

ROOT, DELOSS & CO.; manufacturers of stoves, hollow ware, jobbing and architectural castings; 8 Louisiana street, Indianapolis.

ROOT, DELOSS; firm of Deloss Root & Co.; res 570 North Meridian street, Indianapolis. Born in N. Y. 1819; settled in M. C. 1850.

ROOT, J. B.; firm of Deloss Root & Co.; res 511 North Illinois street, Indianapolis. Born in N. Y. 1822; settled in M. C. 1850.

ROOT, G. R.; wholesale and retail dealer in coal and coke of all kinds; northwest corner Delaware and Market streets, Indianapolis. Born in Pa. 1844; settled in M. C. 1865.

Roth, Matthew; firm of Daggett & Roth; res 6 Buchanan street, Indianapolis. Born in Germany 1840; settled in M. C. 1861.

Ridgeway, O. N.; watchmaker; 34 Virginia avenue, Indianapolis. Born in Ind. 1843; settled in M. C. 1867.

ROSS & LYNN; dealers in all kinds of coal and coke; office, southwest corner Circle and Market streets, Indianapolis.

ROSS, J. H.; firm of Ross & Lynn; res 294 North Tennessee street, Indianapolis. Born in Ky. 1820; settled in M. C. 1849.

Royse, J. T.; furniture and queensware; 80 East Market street, Indianapolis; res 71 East St. Clair street. Born in Ind. 1842; settled in M. C. 1871.

ROSE, E. G.; physician; office, 38 West Market street, Indianapolis. Born in Ohio 1846; settled in M. C. 1873.

Routh, J. R.; real estate agent and broker; 75 College avenue, Indianapolis. Born in Ind. 1829; settled in M. C. 1871.

Ray & Doster; grocers; 100 South Noble street, Indianapolis.

Reichwein, Phil; saloon and beer garden; 350 East Market street, Indianapolis.

Rothioc & Co.; manufacturers of wheelbarrows and wagon stock; 278 Davidson street, Indianapolis.

REASNER, A. & W.; dealers in grain, provisions and groceries; 587 and 589 East Washington street, Indianapolis.

REASNER, W. F.; res 635 East Washington street, Indianapolis. Born in Ind. 1841; settled in M. C. 1865.

REASNER, A.; res 635 East Washington street, Indianapolis. Born in Ind. 1850; settled in M. C. 1870.

Reed, Henry A.; real estate agent; 75½ East Washington street, Indianapolis. Born in Pa. 1842; settled in M. C. 1865.

RUCKLE, N. R.; PRESIDENT INDIANAPOLIS JOURNAL CO., and ex-sheriff of Marion Co.; res 48 North Alabama street, Indianapolis; office Journal Building. Born in Md. 1838; settled in M. C. 1852.

Rottler & Schultz; saddlery and harness; 18 South Meridian street, Indianapolis.

RENIHAN, LONG & HEDGES; undertakers; 15 Circle street, Indianapolis.

RENIHAN, JAMES; firm of Renihan, Long & Hedges; res 48 South Tennessee street, Indianapolis. Born in Ireland 1829; settled in M. C. 1853.

REED, ENOS B.; editor of *The People;* 25 South Delaware street, Indianapolis; res 241 North West street. Born in N. J. 1822; settled in M. C. 1869.

Ransdell, D. M.; firm of Smock & Ransdell; res 483 North Tennessee street, Indianapolis. Born in M. C. 1842.

Robinson, J.; firm of Pease & Robinson; res 300 Virginia avenue, Indianapolis.

Richie, W. W.; publisher; 10 East Washington street, Indianapolis. Born in Pa. 1844; settled in M. C. 1872.

RICHARDSON, GEO. W.; attorney at law; 29 Baldwin's Block, Indianapolis. Born in Mass. 1835; settled in M. C. 1874.

Reed, John; wholesale leather and shoe findings; 64 South Meridian street, Indianapolis. Born in Pa. 1816; settled in M. C. 1874.

Rosebrock, Henry & Co.; brick manufacturers; south of toll gate, South Meridian street.

Ransford, Wm. P.; firm of Ransford & Denton. Born in N. Y. 1821; settled in M. C. 1870.

Rupp, Wm.; merchant tailor, 13 East Washington street, Indianapolis. Born in Germany 1829; settled in M. C. 1852.

ROTHSCHILD, HENRY; dealer in clothing; 125 West Washington street, Indianapolis; res 207 South Illinois street, Indianapolis. Born in Prussia 1834; settled in M. C. ——.

Ricker, G.; Secretary and Treasurer of Western Furniture Co.; res 238 South New Jersey street, Indianapolis. Born in Germany 1834; settled in M. C. 1854.

Richardson, J. F.; firm of Chamberlin & Co.; res in Ohio.

RUPP, JOHN; groceries and provisions, also fine assortment of liquors; 201 Kentucky avenue, Indianapolis; res same. Born in Germany 1837; settled in M. C. 1856.

ROHR, JOSEPH; saloon, the finest assortment of liquors always on hand; 293 Kentucky avenue, Indianapolis; res same. Born in Germany 1833; settled in M. C. 1860.

Roy, H. J.; saloon keeper and bottler of Cincinnati lager beer; 86 East South street, Indianapolis; res same. Born in Germany 1833; settled in M. C. 1864.

Rifenberick, Wm.; boarding house and restaurant; 13 Madison avenue, Indianapolis. Born in Pa. 1826; settled in M. C. 1873.

Robinson, J. R.; driver of fire engine No. 6; res 84 Bright St., Indianapolis. Born in Ind. 1842; settled in M. C. 1851.

RICE, MARTIN H.; editor and publisher Masonic Advocate; 24 Kentucky avenue, Indianapolis; res 148 North East St. Born in Vt. 1829; settled in M. C. 1869. Dem.

Reaume, J. A.; gents' furnishing goods; 24 South Illinois st., Indianapolis. Born in Canada 1828; settled in M. C. 1861. Dem. Catholic.

Roll & Morris; carpets and wall paper; 30, 32 and 34 South Illinois street, Indianapolis.

Robinius, T.; shoe store; 223 West Washington street, Indianapolis; res 222 West Maryland street. Born in France 1827; settled in M. C. 1856. Dem. Catholic.

Rout, Thos.; with V. Meier, 225 and 227 West Washington street, Indianapolis. Born in England 1812; settled in M. C. 1863. Dem.

REDMOND, T.; res 346 West Washington street, Indianapolis. Born in Ireland 1830; settled in M. C. 1860.

RICHARDS, J. H.; proprietor of Richards House, Indianapolis. Born in Ohio 1837; settled in M. C. 1867.

Rehling, Wm.; shoe store; 255 South Delaware street, Indianapolis; res 259 South Delaware street. Born in Europe 1820; settled in M. C. 1849.

RAY HOUSE; 2 squares southeast of Union Depot, corner of Delaware and South streets, Indianapolis. J. M. and A. H. Lambert, proprietors.

Rusch, C. A.; manufacturer and dealer in malt; 214 and 216 South Delaware street, Indianapolis. Born in Prussia 1830; settled in M. C. 1867.

Rose, J. N.; shoe shop; Parker's Block, Indianapolis. Born in Ohio 1821; settled in M. C. 1865. Dem. Christian.

RODEWALD, HENRY; grocery and provisions; 519 Virginia avenue, Indianapolis; res same. Born in Germany 1826; settled in M. C. 1854.

REINECKE; J. F.; groceries, flour and feed; 355 Virginia avenue, Indianapolis; res same. Born in Germany 1851; settled in M. C. 1866.

Rothert, J. H.; groceries and feed; 346 Virginia avenue, Indianapolis. Born in Ky. 1843; settled in M. C. 1856.

ROSEBROCK & ELLRECHT; dealers in all kinds of groceries and feed; 578 and 580 Virginia avenue, Indianapolis. Give them a call.

ROHLER, F. W.; boots and shoes made to order on short notice; 49 Kentucky avenue, Indianapolis. Born in Germany 1845; settled in M. C. 1873.

Russell & Son; dealers in all kinds of castings; corner Market and Davidson streets, Indianapolis.

ROSE, F. W.; physician; 38 West Market street, Indianapolis; res same. Born in Va. 1819; settled in M. C. 1873.

ROBERTSON & PERRY; wholesale grocers; 74 and 76 South Meridian street, Indianapolis.

ROBERTSON, A. M.; of Robertson and Perry; bds Hotel Bates. Born in Ind. 1841; settled in M. C. 1863.

RYAN, DARROW & CO.; wholesale dealers in boots and shoes; 78 South Meridian street, Indianapolis.

RYAN, T. F.; of RYAN, DARROW & CO.; bds Hotel Bates, Indianapolis. Settled in M. C. 1856.

REESE, CHAS. E.; of Hollweg & Reese; res 240 East Market street. Born in Germany 1841; settled in M. C. 1855.

Routh, J. B.; of Indianapolis Paper Co.; res 234 Bright street, Born in Ind. 1834; settled in M. C. 1874.

Rawl, E. & Sons; dealers in hides, tallow and wool; 80 and 82 East Maryland street, Indianapolis.

RAYMOND & KING; horse shoeing and job work neatly done; 60 East Maryland street, Indianapolis.

RAYMOND, S.; of RAYMOND & KING; res over gas office, room 3, Indianapolis.   Born in Ohio;   settled in M. C. 1862.

Robinson, F. M.; book keeper for Byram & Cornelius; 101 to 105 South Meridian street, Indianapolis.

Rickback, Geo.; gardener; ½ m e corporation, Indianapolis.

Reinken, Henry; cigar maker and tobacconist; 266 East Wash. street, Indianapolis.   Born in Germany 1830; settled in M. C. 1859.

REMY, A. C.; firm of A. C. Remy & Co., wholesale and re- tail dealers in flour, grain, produce, and general brokers and commission merchants; 308 East Washington street, Indianapolis; res 51 Central avenue.   Born in Ind. 1827; settled in M. C. 1870.

Riechenmeyr, Henry; dealer in flour and feed; 253 East Wash- ington street, Indianapolis; res 115 East St. Joseph street. Born in Germany 1827; settled in M. C. 1854.

Reichter, Wm.; grocer; 520 East Washington street, Indian- apolis.   Born in Germany 1818; settled in M. C. 1854.

Rasener, Frederick Wm.; dealer in groceries and dry goods; 552 East Washington street, Indianapolis; res 62 Michigan Road.   Born in Germany 1824; settled in M. C. 1836.

Rassel, Nick; grocer; 598 North West street, Indianapolis.

Recker, Peter; grocer; 494 West North street, Indianapolis. Born in Germany 1828; settled in M. C. 1856.

Rozier, A.; grocer; corner Vermont and Blackford streets, In- dianapolis.

Rowland, John; grocer; corner New York and Blackford streets, Indianapolis.

Rodewald, H. H.; grocer; 113 North Agnes street, Indian- apolis.

Rickard, H.; firm of Rickard, Kirby & Co., wholesale dealers in hats, caps and millinery goods; 112 South Meridian st., Indianapolis.

Reeves, T. P.; boot and shoemaker; 15½ Indiana avenue, Indianapolis; res 130 Agnes street. Born in Pa. 1819; settled in M. C. 1874.

RAUCH, JOHN; manufacturer and dealer in domestic cigars and tobacco; 160 Indiana avenue, Indianapolis. Born in Ind. 1850; settled in M. C. 1873. Liberal German. Cath.

Ross, Frank; grocer; 63 Indiana avenue, Indianapolis; res 65 Indiana avenue. Born in Ohio 1846; settled in M. C. 1854. Rep. Protestant.

Roney, E. H.; street paver and contractor; res 256 Fletcher avenue, Indianapolis. Born in Ohio 1851; settled in M. C. 1871.

Ruddell, J. H.; attorney at law and real estate agent; 35½ East Washington street, Indianapolis; res 673 North Meridian street. Born in M. C. 1840. Rep. Protestant.

Rockwood, Wm. O.; treasurer Indianapolis Rolling Mill Co.; 13 East Washington street, Indianapolis; res 276 North Illinois street. Born in Mass. 1814; settled in M. C. 1853. Rep. Presbyterian.

Reynolds, Chas. E.; firm of Nicholi & Reynolds, dealers in hats, caps and furs; 244 East Washington street, Indianapolis; res 327 North Alabama street. Born in Ohio 1848; settled in M. C. 1853. Friend.

ROSENTHAL, HENRY; clothing, merchant tailoring, and gents' furnishing goods house; 242 East Washington street, Indianapolis; res 82 North East street. Born in Wurtemberg, Germany, 1826; settled in M. C. 1863.

Rollar, Jacob; gatekeeper at Crown Hill Cemetery, Indianapolis. Born in Germany 1822; settled in M. C. 1862.

Reynolds, W. L.; carpenter and joiner; 4 miles north Indianapolis P. O. Born in Va. 1839; settled in M. C. 1858.

Roberts, H. W.; marble works; corner of Pendleton Pike and Clifford avenue, Indianapolis.

Ross, D.; Excelsior Mills, Bridgeport; res 84 White avenue, Indianapolis. Born in Va. 1836; settled in M. C. 1866.

Robinson, James; farmer; 2½ miles southwest of Indianapolis P. O. Born in Ky. 1821; settled in M. C. 1867.

Rosenberg, John; merchant tailor; 198 East Washington street, Indianapolis; res 119 South East street. Born in Germany 1837; settled in M. C. 1866.

Riley, A. J.; minister; corner of Shoemaker and Lula streets, North Indianapolis. Born in Ohio 1828; settled in M. C. 1873. M. Baptist.

RICHARDSON FRANK; manager Weed Sewing Machine Co.; 42 North Pennsylvania street, Indianapolis; res 444 North New Jersey street. Born in Ind. 1840; settled in M. C. 1861.

Rooker, Cal.; attorney at law. Born in Indianapolis 1824. Rep. Methodist.

Richards, E. N.; clerk in county treasurer's office; res 476 North Mississippi street, Indianapolis. Born in Mass. 1835; settled in M. C. 1866. Rep. Christian.

RITTER, ELI F.; firm of Ritter, Walker & Ritter, attorneys at law; office 82 East Washington street, Indianapolis; res 375 Central avenue. Born in Ind. 1838; settled in M. C. 1865. Rep. Methodist.

RITTER, LEVI; firm of Ritter, Walker & Ritter; res Irvington. Born in Ind. 1830; settled in M. C. 1872. Rep. Meth.

Reisner, G. A.; firm of Hogshire & Co., dealers in boots and shoes; 25 West Washington street, Indianapolis; res 241 North Tennessee street. Born in Va. 1836; settled in M. C. 1858. Indpt. Methodist.

Rheinheimer, N.; dealer in clothing; res 230 East New York street, Indianapolis.

Reagan, D. J.; firm of D. J. Reagan & Co., real estate brokers; No. 5 Griffith's Block, second floor, Indianapolis; res 623 North Illinois street. Born in Ohio 1838; settled in M. C. 1862. Indpt. Methodist.

ROSS, JAMES; proprietor of barber shop; 55 South Illinois street, Indianapolis, res same. Born in Ky. 1847; settled in M. C. 1862. Dem. Protestant.

ROUSE, R. R.; firm of R. R. Rouse & Co., driven wells, and dealers in all kinds of pumps and brass goods, 63 South Illinois street, Indianapolis. res 31 West Maryland street. Born in N. Y. 1838; settled in M. C. 1868. Jackson Dem. Methodist.

Rowan, S. L.; real estate agent; res 501 Eighth street, Indianapolis. Born in Ind. 1849; settled in M. C. 1872. Indep. Christadelphian.

ROBERTSON, F.; firm of Robertson & Schindler, dealers in dry goods and notions; 94 and 96 East Washington street, Indianapolis; res 70 East St. Clair street. Born in Ind. 1844; settled in M. C. 1867. Rep. Protestant.

Remy, C. H.; attorney at law; 48½ East Washington street, Indianapolis; res 51 Central avenue. Born in Ind. 1852; settled in M. C. 1870. Rep.

Reed, A. T.; firm of A. Reed & Co., mineral water manufacturers; 475 Indiana avenue, Indianapolis. Born in Mo. 1833; settled in M. C. 1866.

Rassfeld, F.; groceries and liquors; 414 Indiana avenue, Indianapolis. Born in Prussia 1849; settled in M. C. 1869.

RILEY, S. H.; druggist and apothecary; physicians' prescriptions carefully compounded; 417 Indiana avenue, Indianapolis. Born in Ind. 1836; settled in M. C 1874.

REYNOLDS, DAVID; miller, and wholesale and retail dealer in flour; 78 East Maryland street, Indianapolis; res 2¾ m n e Indianapolis. Born in Ind. 1840; settled in M. C. 1873.

Surber, Thomas; dairyman; 2 m n e Indianapolis. Born in Ind. 1831; settled in M. C. 1846. Rep. Protestant.

SPRINGER, JAMES F. & CHARLES E.; manufacturers of brick; yard on S. K. Fletcher's farm, 1¼ m n e corporation line, Indianapolis.

SPRINGER, JAMES F. Born in M. C. 1852.

SPRINGER, CHARLES E. Born in M. C. 1854.

Stienaker, H.; manufacturer of brick; res and yard 1 m e corporation, Indianapolis. Born in Germany 1848; settled in M. C. 1869. Dem.

Spann, John M.; real estate and insurance agent; over 50 East Washington street, Indianapolis; res n e corner Delaware and Linden streets. Born in M. C. 1850. Rep. Prot.

SPANN, JOHN S. & CO.; real estate and insurance agents; over No. 50, corner Washington and Pennsylvania streets, Indianapolis.

Spann, T. H.; real estate and insurance agent; over No. 50, corner Washington and Pennsylvania streets, Indianapolis; res 439 North Pennsylvania street. Born in M. C. 1848. Rep. Presbyterian.

Solomon, J. & M.; original loan office; 25 South Illinois street, Indianapolis.

Solomon, J.; res 229 East Ohio street, Indianapolis. Born in Ireland 1834; settled in M. C. 1860.

Smith, C. A.; res corner New Jersey and Washington streets, Indianapolis. Born in Ohio 1846; settled in M. C. 1874. Neutral. Protestant.

Smith & Pott; dealers in groceries and provisions; 79 North Illinois street, Indianapolis.

Smith, B. K.; res 2 m n e corner Massachusetts avenue and New Jersey streets, Indianapolis. Born in M. C. 1842.

Steward, F. M.; milk depot, 71 North Illinois street, Indianapolis; dealer in fresh country milk and butter. Born in Ohio 1850; settled in M. C. 1872. Rep. Christian.

Schwartz, Joseph; manufacturer of hoop skirts, also dealer in notions and fancy goods; 52 North Illinois street, cor Market, Indianapolis; res 231 North Mississippi street.

Smith, James; dealer in miscellaneous books, newspapers and fine stationery; 25 North Illinois street, Indianapolis; res same.

Stern & Lovinger; dealers in fancy goods, notions, ladies' and gents' furnishing goods; 22 and 24 North Illinois street, Bates House Block, Indianapolis.

Stern, R.; res 22 and 24 North Illinois street, Indianapolis. Born in Germany 1846; settled in M. C. 1869.

SCUDDER, JOHN & BROS.; livery, feed and sale stable; 36 West Ohio street, Indianapolis.

Scudder, Isaac; born in Ohio 1848; settled in M. C. 1856.

SCUDDER, JOHN; res 36 West Ohio street, Indianapolis. Born in Ohio 1840; settled in M. C. 1856.

Sulgrove, James W. & Co.; wholesale and retail manufacturers of saddles and harness; 40 South Illinois St., Indianapolis.

Stirk, D. P.; cancer doctor; 48 South Illinois street, up stairs, Indianapolis. Born in Pa. 1839; settled in M. C. 1854. Rep. Protestant.

Seitz, Charles; dealer in fancy and staple groceries; 112 South Illinois street, Indianapolis; res same. Born in Germany 1839; settled in M. C. 1865. Lutheran.

Stanridge & Herdman; real estate agents; 22 South Illinois St., Indianapolis.

Stanridge, H. J., res 123 Lockerbie street, Indianapolis. Born in Ind. 1829; settled in M. C. 1858. Rep.

Sheridan & Todd; dealers in dry goods, millinery, notions and fancy goods; 103 South Illinois street, Indianapolis.

Sheridan, P. H.; res 162 North Mississippi street, Indianapolis. Born in Ireland 1848; settled in M. C. 1867.

Solomon, J.; star loan office; 111 South Illinois street, Indianapolis.

Solomon, Henry; saloon keeper; 27 South Illinois street, Indianapolis; res 56 South Pennsylvania street. Born in England 1837; settled in M. C. 1869.

Schopp, George; manufacturer and dealer in boots and shoes; 180 South Illinois street, Indianapolis. Born in M. C. 1848. Dem. Catholic.

Sindlinger, Godfrey; butcher. Born in Penn. 1824; settled in M. C. 1864.

Steward, M.; proprietor of the Union Hotel; 202 South Illinois street, Indianapolis. Born in Ohio.

Schellschmidt, Fred.; dealer in boots and shoes; 159 East Washington street, Indianapolis; res same. Born in Prussia 1834; settled in M. C. 1854.

Smith, T. W.; boot and shoemaker; 58 Massachusetts avenue, Indianapolis; res 419 East St. Clair street. Born in England 1835; settled in M. C. 1856.

Scott & Smith; dealers in groceries and provisions; corner Delaware street and Massachusetts avenue, Indianapolis.

Scott, A. A.; res 224 East Market street, Indianapolis.

Smith, C. D.; res 119 East New York street, Indianapolis. Born in Ohio 1836; settled in M. C. 1873.

STEPHENS, R. E.; sewing machine repairing office; dealer in needles and attachments for all machines; 19 Massachusetts avenue, Indianapolis; res 170 East Vermont street. Born in Ill. 1845; settled in M. C. 1870.

SELLERS, JOHN; dealer in foreign and domestic cigars, chewing and smoking tobacco; 306 Massachusetts avenue, Indianapolis; bds 70 Plum street. Born in M. C. 1845.

SINKER, DAVIS & CO.; Western Machine Works; 101 to 149 South Pennsylvania street.

Smith, W. J.; dealer in staple and fancy groceries and flour; 300 New Jersey street, Indianapolis; res 363 Indiana Ave. Born in Ohio 1839; settled in M. C. 1872.

STOWELL, M. A.; dealer in music, Chickering pianos, organs and melodeons; 46 North Pennsylvania street, Indianapolis; res 78 W. Michigan street. Born in Mass. 1815; settled in M. C. 1854.

Stanton, Ambrose P.; attorney at law; room 1, Vinton's Block, Indianapolis; res 781 North Illinois street. Born in Ind. 1834; settled in M. C. 1863.

Smith, W. M.; res corner Delaware and Ohio streets, Indianapolis.

Seaton, W. D.; dealer in hats, caps, and furs; 25 North Pennsylvania street, Indianapolis; res 181 Park avenue. Born in Ind. 1845; settled in M. C. 1865.

Stiles, H. D. & Co.; art emporium; 27 North Pennsylvania street, Indianapolis.

Stiles, H. D.; res 129 North Illinois street. Born in Mich. 1850; settled in M. C. 1870.

SMITH, J. W.; general agent Florence sewing machines; 27 North Pennsylvania street, Indianapolis; res 426 North New Jersey street. Born in England 1837; settled in M. C. 1863.

SPOONER, BENJAMIN J.; U. S. Marshal, district of Ind.; res Lawrenceburg.

Schellschmidt, Adolf.; teacher of music and dealer in musical instruments; 157 East Washington street, Indianapolis; res 246 East Ohio street. Born in Prussia 1829; settled in M. C. 1854.

Schulmeyer, Louis; dealer in drugs and pure medicines; corner Illinois and First streets, Indianapolis; res same. Born in Germany 1835; settled in M. C. 1852.

SAYLOR, WM. J.; catcher at old Rolling Mill, Indianapolis; res 272 South Pennsylvania street. Born in Pa. 1846; settled in M. C. 1864.

Shindler, Wm.; janitor Y. M. C. A. building; 35 North Illinois street, Indianapolis.

STREET, E. S.; book-keeper at No. 13 North Illinois street, Indianapolis; bds at the Alabama House, Alabama street. Born in Canada 1831; settled in M. C. 1860.

Smith, J. W.; bakery and confectionary; 206 South Illinois st., Indianapolis; res same. Born in Md. 1829; settled in M. C. 1873. Rep. Methodist.

STUMPH, JOHN B. & CO.; dealers in liquors and wines; 183 East Washington street, Indianapolis.

STUMPH, JOHN B.; res 459 East Market street, Indianapolis. Born in Germany 1820; settled in M. C. 1843.

Stewart; dealer in drugs and medicines; 40 East Washington street, Indianapolis; res 265 North Illinois street. Born in Ind. 1824; settled in M. C. 1863. Rep. Methodist.

Springer, David; carpenter and stair builder; res 13 Chatham street, Indianapolis. Born in Pa. 1806; settled in M. C. 1850.

SILVER, SAMUEL O.; dealer in fancy groceries and provisions; 221 Massachusetts avenue, Indianapolis; res same. Born in Ind. 1846.

Southard, George; agent Indianapolis, Peru & Chicago Railway; res Massachusetts avenue station, Indianapolis. Born in M. C. 1844.

Stumpf & Hill; carriage and repair shops and general blacksmithing business; corner Christian avenue and Peru street, Indianapolis.

Shea, Michael; manufacturer of boots and shoes; 58 Malott avenue, Indianapolis. Born in Ireland 1847; settled in M. C. 1871.

Shields & Rienan; dealers in fancy groceries, provisions and meats; 20 Columbia avenue, Indianapolis.

Shields, R. C.; res 120 Columbia avenue, Indianapolis. Born in Ohio 1851; settled in M. C. 1871.

SULLIVAN, O. H.; physician and surgeon; rooms 3 and 4, second floor, Foote's Block, over 24½ Kentucky avenue, Indianapolis; res same. Born in Tenn. 1851; settled in M. C. 1853.

SCHAUF, WILLIAM; res 483 Alabama street, Indianapolis Born in M. C. 1853.

Swart, John B.; dealer in groceries and fancy goods of all kinds; 219 Massachusetts avenue, Indianapolis; res same. Born in England 1838; settled in M. C. 1865.

Schoonover, J. S.; res 290 Lincoln avenue, Indianapolis.

SCHMIDT, F. & BRO.; manufacturers of Schmidt's French Liquid Bluing and White Rose Baking Powder; 66 Massachusetts avenue, Indianapolis; res 175 East Market street.

SCHMIDT, AUGUST; butcher and dealer in all kinds of meat; 223 Massachusetts avenue, Indianapolis. Born in Germany 1845; settled in M. C. 1854.

Schuinehart, Edmon; boot and shoemaker; 197 Massachusetts avenue, Indianapolis; res 132 St. Mary street. Born in Md. 1816; settled in M. C. 1850. Protestant.

Sindlinger, J. M.; house, sign and ornamental painting; 7 Massachusetts avenue, Indianapolis.

Schmidt, C. A.; res 175 East Market street, Indianapolis. Born in N. Y. City 1851; settled in M. C. 1872.

Schmidt, F.; res 175 East Market street, Indianapolis. Born in N. Y. 1849; settled in M. C. 1869.

Smith, J. G.; res 98 Peru street, Indianapolis. Born in Ind. 1851; settled in M. C. 1870.

Spohr, J. G.; bds at Circle House, Indianapolis. Born in Germany 1846; settled in M. C. 1866.

Swing & Woolen; dealers in flour and feed; 1 Massachusetts avenue, Indianapolis.

Swing, W. W.; res 40 Blake street, Indianapolis. Born in Ohio 1834; settled in M. C. 1866.

Stueker, Martin; proprietor of Marion Hotel, 18 South Pennsylvania street, Indianapolis. Born in Ind. 1839; settled in M. C. 1871.

Steel, Marion; student at law; room 23 South Pennsylvania st., Indianapolis. Born in Ind. 1849; settled in M. C. 1869. Presbyterian.

Slevin, Maria M.; dress maker; 89 Pennsylvania street, Indianapolis.

STEINHAUR, M.; res 172 East South street, Indianapolis. Born in Ohio 1846; settled in M. C. 1864. Rep. Lutheran.

Stokely, Benj.; res 164 Winston street, Indianapolis. Born in Pa. 1832; settled in M. C. 1860.

Shover & Christian; contractors and builders; 124 East Vermont street, Indianapolis.

Shover, T. E.; res 451 North Delaware street, Indianapolis.

SCHROEDER, CHARLEY; blacksmithing and general repairing; horse shoeing a specialty; 144 Fort Wayne avenue, Indianapolis; res 193 Harrison street. Born in Germany 1843; settled in M. C. 1870.

Sherman & Comingore; wholesale dealers in feathers, rags, beeswax and produce; 21 West Maryland street, Indianapolis.

Spickelmier, J.; proprietor boarding house; 36 West Maryland street, Indianapolis. Born in Ky. 1829; settled in M. C. 1874. Rep. Baptist.

Stoops, F. M.; res Omer street. Born in M. C.

Summers, J. W.; carpenter and builder; res 1½ m n e corporation line, Indianapolis. Born in Pa. 1845; settled in M. C. 1871.

Shearer, John; farmer and stock raiser; 3 m n e Indianapolis, on Center gravel road. Born in Ohio 1825; settled in M. C. 1829. Rep. Methodist.

Stilz, J. George; dealer in agricultural implements and seeds; 78 East Washington street, Indianapolis; res Stilz's Grove, southeast of city. Born in Pa. 1834; settled in M. C. 1857. Rep. Episcopalian.

Smith, Chas. W.; firm of Smith & Hawkins, attorneys at law; 48½ East Washington street, Indianapolis; res 382 North Tennessee street. Born in Ind. 1846; settled in M. C. 1867. Rep. Methodist.

Stewart & Morgan; wholesale and retail druggists; 38 and 40 East Washington street, Indianapolis.

STEDMAN, H. S.; publisher and dealer in sheet music, books and musical merchandise; 36 East Washington street, Indianapolis; res 413 North New Jersey street. Rep. Presbyterian.

STEWART, DANIEL; firm of Stewart & Morgan; res 263 North Illinois street, Indianapolis. Settled in M. C. 1862. Meth.

SMITH, WALTER S.; superintendent Marion county schools; office in court house; bds Pyle House.

Spaulding, J. L.; steam laundry, west of Indianapolis.

Seibert, S. M. & Sons; blacksmiths and wagon makers; 302 East Washington street, Indianapolis; res 11 North Liberty street. Born in Pa. 1817; settled in M. C. 1831.

Seibert, C. W.; born in Indianapolis 1852.

Seibert, T. B.; born in Indianapolis 1849.

Seibert, R. S.; born in Indianapolis 1848; res Greer street.

STITZ, FRED; firm of Fred Stitz & Co., manufacturers and wholesale and retail dealers in cigars and tobacco; 328 East Washington street, Indianapolis; res 36 North East street. Born in Wurtemberg, Germany, 1844; settled in M. C. 1862.

Shoemaker, John F.; trunk manufacturer; 342 East Washington street, Indianapolis; res 388 East Market street. Born in Ohio 1840; settled in M. C. 1856.

Stein, F.; barber and hair dresser; 262 East Washington street, Indianapolis. Born in Germany 1839; settled in M. C. 1863.

STAPP, JAMES H.; attorney at law; 45½ East Washington street, Indianapolis; res corner Howard and Seventh streets. Born in Ky. 1814; settled in M. C. 1830. Rep. Meth.

Schweikle, J. F.; firm of Faist & Schweikle, carriage and wagon makers; 478 East Washington street, Indianapolis; res 29 Chatham street. Born in Germany 1837; settled in M. C. 1870.

Sparks, C.; grocer; west of river, Washington street, Indianapolis.   Born in N. J. 1837; settled in M. C. 1870.

Speir, Fred.; dealer in groceries and dry goods, 546 East Washington street, Indianapolis.   Born in Germany 1832; settled in M. C. 1856.

Schwier, C. II.; firm of C. H. Schwier & Co., dealers in dry goods and groceries, 576 East Washington street, Indianapolis.   Born in Germany 1831; settled in M. C. 1854.

Schwier, C. F.; firm of C. H. Schwier & Co.; res 568 East Washington street, Indianapolis.   Born in Germany 1847; settled in M. C. 1866.

Smith S.; with Benj. Elder, 480 East Washington street; Indianapolis; res 506 East Washington street.   Born in Ohio 1829; settled in M. C. 1874.

SCOTT, GEO. W.; proprietor of Empire feed and sale stable, 72 West Market street, Indianapolis; res 117 North Mississippi street.   Born in N. Y. 1843; settled in M. C. 1873.

Schaub, John; horse shoer and carriage and wagon maker, west of river, Washington street, Indianapolis.   Born in Germany 1848; settled in M. C. 1853.

SCHURMAN, CHARLES; real estate broker; room 5 Odd Fellows Hall, Indianapolis; res corner Schurman's avenue and Crawfordsville road.   Born in Indianapolis 1852.

SCHMALHOLZ, S.; firm of Fred. Stitez & Co., manufacturers and wholesale and retail dealers in cigars and tobacco, 328 East Washington street, Indianapolis; res 64 North Noble street.   Born in Bavaria 1848; settled in M. C. 1854.

Socwell, H. M.; wholesale and retail grocer; 232 East Washington street, Indianapolis; res 300 East Market street.   Born in N. J. 1830; settled in M. C. 1859.

Schutter, Christian; grocer; corner North and Blake streets, Indianapolis.   Born in Germany 1820; settled in M. C. 1846.

Smith, Warren P.; saddle and harness maker; North Indianapolis.   Born in Mass. 1832; settled in M. C. 1873.

Swan, B. C.; gardener; North Illinois street, 3½ miles from P. O. Born in Ohio 1842; settled in M. C. 1873.

Scott, Henry M.; United States gauger; res 36 Broadway street, Indianapolis. Born in Ohio 1840; settled in M. C. 1859.

Shewey, A. C.; firm of Shewey & Henry; map company; corner Pennsylvania and Market streets, Indianapolis. Born in Va. 1845; settled in M. C. 1874.

Stiwalt, V. B.; real estate broker; 72 East Washington street, Indianapolis; res 67 Vine street. Born in Ohio 1837; settled in M. C. 1873. Rep. Protestant.

STOUT, DAVID E.; popular hat house; 76 East Washington street, Indianapolis; res 18 Central avenue. Born in M. C. 1845. Rep. Protestant.

STAUB, JOSEPH; merchant tailor; No. 2 Odd Fellows' Hall, Indianapolis; res 200 North Noble street. Born in Germany 1825; settled in M. C. 1853.

SCHINDLER, ROBERT; firm of Robertson & Schindler; dealers in dry goods and notions; 94 and 96 East Washington street, Indianapolis; res 247 East Washington street. Born in Germany 1844; settled in M. C. 1849.

Sullivan, T. S.; res corner Tennessee and Ohio streets, Indianapolis. Episcopalian.

SHIDLER, I. M.; res 84 College avenue, Indianapolis. Born in Ohio 1820; settled in M. C. 1871. Presbyterian.

Sturgis, I. A. & Co.; lawyers; 16½ East Washington street, Indianapolis.

Sturgis, I. A.; res 413 West New York street, Indianapolis. Born in Pa. 1830; settled in M. C. 1872.

SWAIN & HOBBS; real estate agents; over 8 East Washington street, Indianapolis.

SWAIN, DAVID F.; res 258 North Pennsylvania street, Indianapolis. Born in Ohio 1845; settled in M. C. 1865.

Shaw, Andrew; farmer; North Indianapolis. Born in Ind. 1838.

Siersdorfer, L.; boots and shoes; 41 East Washington street, Indianapolis; res 185 Virginia avenue.   Born in Germany 1839; settled in M. C. 1863.

Sickels, W. W.; insurance agent; 6 Blackford's Block, Indianapolis; res North East street.   Born in Ind. 1831; settled in M. C. 1831.

Secrest, Chas.; general collector; room 3, 45 East Washington street, Indianapolis; res 319 South Alabama street.   Born in Ky. 1808; settled in M. C. 1846.   Rep.   Christian.

SEIDERS, WM. H.; local and State insurance agent; 35 East Washington street, Indianapolis; res 374 North West St. Born in Me. 1825; settled in M. C. 1864.   Rep.   Meth.

Stewart, John H.; real estate broker; 1 Glenn's Block, Indianapolis; res 735 North Meridian street.   Born in Ind. 1826; settled in M. C. 1872.   Rep.   Methodist.

Sweetser, J. N.; attorney at law; 19½ East Washington street, Indianapolis; res 614 North Pennsylvania street.   Born in Ind. 1830; settled in M. C. 1837.   Rep.   Christian.

Steep, J. D.; wholesale and retail dealer in boots and shoes; 5 Bates House Block, Indianapolis; bds Hotel Bates.   Born in Pa. 1847; settled in M. C. 1871.

Stout, F. & T.; wholesale and retail liquors and tobacco; 160 West Washington street, Indianapolis; res 194 North California street.   Settled in M. C. 1853.

Surface, J. M.; firm of Witt & Surface, wholesale and retail druggists; 182 West Washington street, Indianapolis; res 26 North Mississippi street.   Born in Ind. 1847; settled in M. C. 1864.   Rep.   Methodist.

SLUSHER, HENRY; practical watchmaker and jeweler; watches and clocks neatly cleaned on short notice; 190 West Washington street, Indianapolis.   Born in Ind. 1838; settled in M. C. 1841.   Liberal. ·

Schurr, Leonard, Sen.; dealer in watches and clocks; 76 Indiana avenue, Indianapolis.   Born in Germany 1816; settled in M. C. 1854.

Schurr, Leonard, Jr.; dealer in watches and clocks; 76 Indiana avenue, Indianapolis. Born in Germany 1848; settled in M. C. 1854.

Shaw, M. B.; with M. V. Haryman, dealer in fine pictures and looking glassses; 10 Indiana avenue, Indianapolis; res 81 East St. Clair street. Born in N. C. 1831; settled in M. C. 1871. Rep.

Shilling, W. E.; trunk and box maker; 98 Indiana avenue, Indianapolis; res 191 Douglas street. Born in Ohio 1844; settled in M. C. 1865. Rep. Methodist.

Santo, Edward; grocer; 204 Indiana avenue, Indianapolis. Born in Germany 1829; settled in M. C. 1856. Rep. Catholic.

Schildmeier, Fred.; merchant tailor; 182 East Washington St., Indianapolis. Born in Germany 1827; settled in M. C. 1842.

Stevenson, Thos. H.; firm of Davis, Stevenson & Major, real estate agents; 45 East Washington street, Indianapolis; res 135 North Illinois street. Born in Ind. 1843; settled in M. C. 1873. Rep. Presbyterian.

Salter, Wm. H.; photographer; 45 East Washington street, Indianapolis; res 233 East Michigan street. Born in Ind. 1839; settled in M. C. 1864.

Smith, John G.; justice of the peace; room 3, 45 East Washington street, Indianapolis; res 162 North New Jersey St. Born in N. J. 1812; settled in M. C. 1852. Rep. Meth.

SHILLING, R. L ; manufacturer of trunks, traveling bags and valises; 55 West Washington street and 12 Kentucky avenue, Indianapolis; res 299 North New Jersey street. Born in Ohio 1828; settled in M. C. 1863. Rep.

Sharpe, A. W.; cigars and tobacco; 57 West Washington street, Indianapolis; res 193 South New Jersey street.

STATE SENTINEL OFFICE, corner of Meridian and Circle streets, Indianapolis.

Schofield, G. K.; carriage salesman; 139 West Washington St., Indianapolis; res 452 North Delaware street. Born in Ind. 1853; settled in M. C. 1870.

SAILORS, J. L. & CO.; merchant tailoring, dry goods, notions and fancy goods; No. 177 West Washington street, Indianapolis.

Sailors, James L.; res on William street, bet Illinois and Tennessee streets, Indianapolis. Born in Ind. 1832; settled in M. C. 1864. Rep. R. Baptist.

Sulzer, W. T.; Clerk of Court; res 90 North Mississippi street, Indianapolis. Born in Ky. 1852; settled in M. C. 1873. Rep. Lutheran.

Schrader, F.; dealer in boots and shoes, 85 West Washington street, Indianapolis; res 126 North Mississippi street. Born in Md. 1837; settled in M. C. 1844.

Stevenson & Co.; real estate agents; 30½ West Washington st., Indianapolis.

Stevenson, D. H.; res Sherman House, Indianapolis. Born in Ind. 1846; settled in M. C. 1872. Rep.

Storey, New & Co.; dealers in hardware; 64 East Washington street, Indianapolis.

Story, J. M.; res Franklin. Born in Ind. 1840; settled in M. C. 1873. Christian.

Scott, J. N.; lawyer; 72½ East Washington street, Indianapolis; res 199 North Delaware street. Born in Ohio 1836; settled in M. C. 1866.

STRAUSS, L.; res 15 North Meridian street, Indianapolis. Born in Prussia 1845; settled in M. C. 1865.

Smith & Co.; real estate agents; room 3, 2d floor, corner Washington street and Kentucky avenue, Indianapolis.

Smith, R. L.; res 418 North California street, Indianapolis. Born in Ohio 1844; settled in M. C. 1863. Rep. Meth.

STEDMAN, P.; firm of Powell & Stedman; res 413 North New Jersey street, Indianapolis. Born in N. Y. 1827; settled in M. C. 1857. Rep.

SPADES, M. H.; dealer in dry goods, notions, fancy articles, and *real hair;* 5 and 7 West Washington street, Indianapolis; res 560 North Pennsylvania street. Born in Ohio 1845; settled in M. C. 1865.

SPADES, J. C.; Indianapolis; bds Circle House. Born in Ohio 1847; settled in M. C. 1870.

SAILORS, M. P.; res 34 South West street, Indianapolis. Born in Ind. 1850; settled in M. C. 1864.

Stout & Son; groceries; 175 West Washington street, Indianapolis.

SCHOLL, CHARLES; Clerk of Supreme Court, Indianapolis; res 90 North Mississippi street. Born in Prussia 1832; settled in M. C. 1872.

Siegel, S.; bds at 207 South Illinois street, Indianapolis. Born in Ohio 1855; settled in M. C. 1869. Dem. Hebrew faith.

Steinmetz, P.; res 78 North New Jersey street, Indianapolis. Born in Germany.

SPRINGER, DR J. E.; manager of the Indiana department of the Security Life Insurance Co.; office, 95 East Washington street, Indianapolis; res 115 Meek street. Born in Ky. 1824; settled in M. C. 1856.

Smock, R. M.; clerk; res 390 North Delaware street, Indianapolis. Born in M. C. 1841. Rep. Presbyterian.

SMOCK, PETER; JUSTICE OF THE PEACE; office 91½ East Washington street, Indianapolis; res between Delaware and Alabama streets on the south side of Sixth street. Born in Ky. 1812; settled in M. C. 1821.

Smith & Hannaman; brokers in large loans and dealers in all kinds of municipal bonds of Indiana, and financial agents for railroads; office 95 East Washington street, Indianapolis.

Smith, Francis; res n w corner Third and Tennessee streets, Indianapolis. Born in England.

Schultz, H. C.; firm of Rottler & Schultz, saddlery and harness; res 214 Indiana avenue, Indianapolis. Born in Europe 1844; settled in M. C. 1873.

SELF, BERRY; with Ed. Hasson & Co., dealers in hats, caps, furs, etc., 20 North Pennsylvania street, Indianapolis; res ½ m e Woodruff Place. Born in Ky. 1845; settled in M. C. 1864. Rep. Christian.

SMITH, N. R.; firm of L. S. AYRES & CO., 26 and 28 West Washington street, Indianapolis; res 442 North Illinois St. Born in Vt. 1831; settled in M. C. 1867. Rep. Congregationalist.

Speer, J. K.; advertising agent for Sentinel Co.; Indianapolis. Born in N. C. 1831; settled in M. C. 1870.

Soehner, Chas.; dealer in pianos and organs; 20 East Washington street, Indianapolis.

Scovil & Sparrow; wholesale dealers in watches, jewelry, etc.; 18 Hubbard Block, Indianapolis.

Share, Geo. K. & Co.; saddlery hardware and carriage goods; 40 South Meridian street, Indianapolis.

Share, Geo. K.; res 314 West New York street, Indianapolis. Born in N. Y. 1837; settled in M. C. 1863.

SLOANE, E. W.; superintendent American Express Co., Western Division; 46 and 48 South Meridian street, Indianapolis; res 451 North Tennessee street. Born in Ohio 1821; settled in M. C. 1861.

SUNDAY HERALD; office 23 Circle street, Indianapolis.

SCHLEY, GEORGE J.; firm of Reed, Schley & Shellman, proprietors of the "People," Indianapolis. Born in Md. 1836; settled in M. C. 1857.

SHELLMAN, HARRY J.; firm of REED, SCHLEY & SHELLMAN, proprietors of the "People," Indianapolis. res 735 North Pennsylvania street. Born in Md. 1843; settled in M. C. 1868.

SCHAUB, HENRY; dealer in all kinds of drinks; 364 Virginia avenue, Indianapolis.

Schulz, Henry; tobacco and cigars; 282 Virginia avenue, Indianapolis.

Starch, A.; dealer in boots and shoes; 25 North New Jersey street, Indianapolis. Born in Germany 1828; settled in M. C. 1854.

Stokes & Wread; barbers; 74 Virginia avenue, Indianapolis.

Snider, H. & Co.; druggists; 199 South East street, Indianapolis. Born in Ind. 1849.

Saltmarsh, W. L.; carpenter and builder; 40 Kentucky avenue, Indianapolis. Born in Ind. 1831; settled in M. C. 1847.

Schinn & Souders; druggists; 41 Kentucky avenue, Indianapolis.

Swain & Black; carriage manufacturers; 25 South Tennessee street, Indianapolis.

STOBO, THOMAS; carriage and wagon shop; 100 Kentucky avenue, Indianapolis.

SIMS & SMITHERS; refiners of coal tar, and manufacturers of roofing and sheeting, anything in their line promptly attended to; 69 West Maryland street, Indianapolis.

Shafer & McClain; planing mill and lumber yard; 26 Winston street, Indianapolis.

Stuckmeyer, Chas.; meat market; 104 South Noble street, Indianapolis. Born in Ohio 1850.

Smith, Fred, grocer; 351 North Noble street, Indianapolis.

Surm, H.; coal and lumber yard; corner of Ohio and Davidson streets, Indianapolis.

Sellers, W. W.; grocer; No. 186 Madison avenue, Indianapolis; res 115 Madison avenue. Born in Ohio 1829; settled in M. C. 1871.

Schmitt, A.; painter; res 230 South Pennsylvania street, Indianapolis. Born in France 1833; settled in M. C. 1859.

Scherer, P.; barber shop; 14 South Delaware, street, Indianapolis. Born in Germany 1839; settled in M. C. 1874.

Selman, A. G. & Son; physicians and surgeons; 21 Virginia avenue, Indianapolis; res 401 North New Jersey street.

22

Schicketanz; Jacob; grocer and liquor dealer; corner East and Coburn streets, Indianapolis; res 489 South New Jersey st.

Schmidt, C. F.; brewery; Schmidt's Square, Indianapolis.

Schwoomeyer & Co.; grocers; 397 South Meridian street, Indianapolis.

Schwoomeyer, C. H.; firm of Schwoomeyer & Co., Indianapolis. Born in Germany 1825; settled in M. C. 1852.

Selman, A. G. Born in Ala. 1822; settled in M. C. 1864.

Selman, J. W. Born in M. C. 1848.

Stein, Joseph; shoe store; 410 South Meridian street, Indianapolis. Born in Germany 1846; settled in M. C. 1861.

Schmitt, J.; cigar manufacturer; 418 South Meridian street, Indianapolis. Born in Germany 1845; settled in M. C. 1858. Dem. Catholic.

SCHROEDER, WM.; firm of KLARE & SCHROEDER; res corner Ray and Meridian streets, Indianapolis. Born in Germany 1837; settled in M. C. 1861.

Sluth, H. C.; with Klare & Schroeder, 588 South Meridian st., Indianapolis. Born in Ind. 1848; settled in M. C. 1873.

Sherer, Adam; boot and shoemaker; 336 South West street, Indianapolis. Born in Germany 1839; settled in M. C. 1864.

SOGEMIER, WM.; dealer in groceries, provisions, flour and feed, also china and glassware; 495 South Meridian street, Indianapolis; res same. Born in Germany 1831; settled in M. C. 1859.

Strong, M. H.; grocer; 25 West South street, Indianapolis. Born in N. Y. 1843; settled in M. C. 1872.

Shelton, G.; pipeman of Engine Co. No. 4, Indianapolis. Born in M. C. 1844.

Sherwood, W. O.; Captain of Fire Co. No. 6; 275 West Washington street, Indianapolis. Born in N. Y. 1835; settled in M. C. 1853.

Sullivan & Gates; merchant millers, Ætna Mills; 354 and 356 West Washington street, Indianapolis.

Sullivan, W. H.; firm of Sullivan & Gates, Indianapolis; res 475 North Meridian street. Born in Ky. 1836; settled in M. C. 1856.

Stormer, S. B.; pipeman of Fire Co. No. 6, Indianapolis; res 261 West Washington street. Born in Ind. 1847; settled in M. C. 1852.

SHOEMAKER, J. C.; President Franklin Fire Insurance Company; office corner Circle and Market streets, Indianapolis; res 506 North Meridian street. Born in Ind. 1826; settled in M. C. 1871.

SCHOEN, A.; proprietor of Indianapolis Excelsior Dye Works; gents' clothing cleaned, dyed, repaired, altered and neatly pressed. I have had twenty years' experience in the business, and can do the very best and neatest work done in the city. All work warranted good, and satisfaction guaranteed. Office 30 Circle street.

Schneider, Conrad; saloon; 69 Wyoming street, Indianapolis. Born in Germany 1821; settled in M. C. 1846.

Schroeder, Henry; horse-shoeing; 19 North Alabama street, Indianapolis. Born in Prussia 1837; settled in M. C. 1858.

Simmons, D.; secretary of Simmons Edge Tool Co., Indianapolis; res 673 North Delaware street, Indianapolis. Born in N. Y. 1839; settled in M. C. 1873.

Smock & Ransdell; real estate brokers; 84 East Market street, Indianapolis.

Smock, Wm. C.; firm of Smock & Ransdell; res 340 North Delaware street, Indianapolis.

SHACKELFORD & McCOY; sole agents and proprietors in the West for Dr. J. C. Wills' World Worm Candy; manufactured at Indianapolis.

Stubbs, G. W.; attorney at law; 13 Hubbard Block, Indianapolis. Born in Ind. 1837; settled in M. C. 1871.

SCHOFIELD, NAT. M.; firm of Anderson, Bullock & Schofield; res 452 North Delaware street, Indianapolis. Born in Pa. 1815; settled in M. C. 1867.

SCHOFIELD, J. B.; firm of Anderson, Bullock & Schofield; res 491 North Tennessee street, Indianapolis. Born in Ind. 1844; settled in M. C. 1865.

SMITH, J. H.; agent for Miller Brothers' celebrated Chemical Paint; room 75 East Maryland street, Indianapolis; res 295 Indiana avenue. Born in Ohio 1825; settled in M. C. 1867.

Shaw Carriage Co.; office, 26 to 34 East Georgia street, Indianapolis; B. C. Shaw, president; Irvin Robins, vice president; T. C. Reading, superintendent; Ralph Tousey, treasurer and secretary.

SEVERIN, OSTERMEYER & CO.; wholesale dealers in groceries; 55 and 57 South Meridian street, Indianapolis.

Smith, J. B.; confectioner; 65 South Meridian street, Indianapolis. Born in Mich. 1839; settled in M. C. 1861.

SHERMAN HOUSE; opposite Union Depot, Indianapolis. McCarty & Jenks, proprietors.

Sherman House Barber Shop, Indianapolis; L. D. Sirrona, proprietor.

Stanridge & Hendman; real estate brokers; 22 South Illinois street, Indianapolis.

Sweeney, Daniel; with J. T. Martin & Co.; 253 West Washington street, Indianapolis. Born in N. Y. 1851; settled in M. C. 1856.

SUTHERLAND, LEVY; wagon and carriage maker, back of 281 and 283 West Washington street, Indianapolis; res 59 East McCarty street. Born in M. C. 1827.

SHEPHERD, JAMES M.; at brewery, 297 West Washington street, Indianapolis; res 215 West Maryland street. Born in N. Y. 1843; settled in M. C. 1862. Dem.

Simcox, J. W ; 262 West Washington street, Indianapolis. Born in Ind. 1828; settled in M. C. 1837.

Shaffer, A. C.; shoemaker; 264 West Washington street, Indianapolis. Born in Pa. 1849; settled in M. C. 1868:

Smith, Chas.; tinner; 135 East Washington street, Indianapolis. Born in Md. 1842; settled in M. C. 1873.

SCHAUB, JOHN; blacksmith; Indianola; work done to order
and guaranteed. Born in Germany 1840; settled in M. C.
1865.

Sebern, J. W.; grocer; 50 Virginia avenue, Indianapolis; res
272 Fletcher avenue. Born in M. C. 1849.

Sharpe, Joseph K.; leather and shoe findings; 49 South Delaware street, Indianapolis; res North Pennsylvania street.
Born in Conn. 1818; settled in M. C. 1845.

Schwabacher, & Selig; wholesale liquors and cigars; 41 South
Delaware street, Indianapolis.

Schmidt, J. H.; restaurant; 31 South Delaware street, Indianapolis. Born in Germany 1851; settled in M. C. 1867.

Spotts, Wm.; commission merchant, dealer in feed, flour and
grain; corner Delaware street and Virginia avenue, Indianapolis. Born in Pa.; settled in M. C. 1853.

Shortle, E. Y.; firm of R. S. Foster & Co.; 68 and 70 South
Delaware street. Born in Ohio 1838; settled in M. C.
1855.

Schweinsbercer, Wm.; meat dealer; 329 South Delaware street,
Indianapolis. Born in Germany 1832; settled in M. C.
1858.

SPONSEL, HENRY; grocer and liquor dealer; 349 Madison
avenue, Indianapolis; res same. Born in Germany 1842;
settled in M. C. 1862.

Sanborn, A. W.; cigar and tobacco dealer; 16 North Delaware
street, Indianapolis. Born in Me. 1847.

SOUTH-SIDE TIN STORE; E. F. Moore, proprietor; dealer
in all kinds of stoves and tinware; corner of Shelby street
and Virginia avenue, Indianapolis; res 496 Virginia avenue.
Born in Ind. 1847; settled in M. C. 1873. Rep. Prot.

Sisco, David; blacksmith; corner Dougherty street and Virginia
avenue, Indianapolis. Born in Va. 1837; settled in M. C.
1872.

Stuckmeyer, A.; meat market; 533 Virginia avenue, Indianapolis. Born in Ohio 1848; settled in M. C. 1849.

Schrader, Christian; grocer and liquor dealer; 453 Virginia avenue, Indianapolis. Born in Germany 1824; settled in M. C. 1850.

STOLART, FRANK; horse buyer and real estate agent; 421 South Delaware street, Indianapolis. Born in Prussia 1839; settled in M. C. 1871.

SCOTT, JOHN; manufacturing jeweler; 10 West Market St., Indianapolis. Born in N. Y. 1841; settled in M. C. 1870.

Surface, D. F. M.; proprietor of wagon shop; south of toll-gate, South Meridian street, Indianapolis. Born in Ind. 1842; settled in M. C. 1872. Rep.

Thompson, J. F.; saloon keeper and billiards; basement under 21 and 23 South Illinois street, Indianapolis. Born in Ireland 1839; settled in M. C. 1865.

TALBERT, C. S.; dentist; No. 9 Claypool Block, corner Washington and Illinois streets, Indianapolis. Born in Ohio 1850; settled in M. C. 1872. Rep. Protestant.

Talbott, Mrs. & Davis; dress and cloak makers; 50 South Illinois street, second floor, over Weber's jewelry store, Indianapolis.

Tarkingron, M. S.; dealer in pure drugs and medicines, fancy articles and pure liquors; 199 South Illinois street, Indianapolis. Born in Ind. 1848; settled in M. C. 1874.

Thomas, W. H.; collector and trader; res Hill avenue, Indianapolis. Born in N. Y. 1842; settled in M. C. 1856.

Tipton, W. A.; firm of Tipton & Peelle; attorneys at law; 100 East Washington street, Indianapolis; res 53 Arsenal avenue. Born in Ind. 1833; settled in M. C. 1871.

Thrasher, Joseph; photographer; 94 East Washington street, Indianapolis; res 21 North East street. Born in Ind. 1834; settled in M. C. 1872.

THE SINGER MANUFACTURING CO., Singer Sewing Machines; W. D. McLAIN, agent; 72 and 74 West Washington street, Indianapolis.

The Sewing Machine Cabinet Company; manufacturers of all kinds of sewing machines, Wheeler & Wilson's factory, Indianapolis. Sheldon Morris, Pres.; M. E. Morris, Secy.

Tilman, John W.; dealer in fancy groceries and provisions; 2 Malott avenue, Indianapolis; res same place. Born in Ind. 1844; settled in M. C. 1858.

Trimpe, Harman; manufacturer of boots and shoes; 309½ West street, Indianapolis; res same. Born in Germany 1842; settled in M. C. 1873.

TRAUB, ISRAEL; dealer in fancy groceries and provisions; 500 North Alabama street, Indianapolis; res 490 North Alabama street. Born in Germany 1808; settled in M. C. 1850.

Templeton, Mrs. L.; dress maker; 21½ West Maryland street, Indianapolis.

Tully, Mrs. E.; proprietor boarding house; 17 West Maryland street, Indianapolis.

Tompkins, J. H.; farmer; 3 m n e Indianapolis. Born in Va. 1839; settled in M. C. 1868. Dem. Episcopalian.

Tompkins, Wm. B.; farmer; 3 m n e Indianapolis. Born in Va. 1840; settled in M. C. 1870. Episcopalian.

Tucker & Smith; retail dealers in cloaks, white goods, linens, laces, notions and trimmings; 9 North Pennsylvania street, Indianapolis.

Tucker, H. S.; res 318 North Alabama street, Indianapolis. Born in Me. 1844; settled in M. C. 1864.

Taggart, Samuel; millwright; office, 132 South Pennsylvania st., Indianapolis; res 118 North Mississippi street. Born in N. Y. 1817; settled in M. C. 1852.

Todd Bros. & Bigelow; office, rooms 16 and 17 on second floor, Martindale's Block, North Pennsylvania street, Indianapolis.

Todd, R. N.; res 78 West Market street, Indianapolis.

TAYLOR, J. F.; architectural and ornamental draughtsman of all kinds of plaster work; 80 Massachusetts avenue, Indianapolis; res 179 East New York street.

Todd, L. L.; res 464 North East street, Indianapolis.

Trow, J. J.; Merchant Lunch Room; 10 West Pearl street, Indianapolis. Born in Mass.

THOMAS, ROBERT; res at brick yard. Born in Ireland 1830; settled in M. C. 1860. Rep. Methodist.

Topp, Frederick; gardener; North Illinois street, 3 m n P. O., Indianapolis. Born in Germany 1820; settled in M. C. 1848.

Thompson, W. H.; carriage trimmer; 178 Indiana avenue, Indianapolis; res 476 West New York street. Born in Ohio 1839; settled in M. C. 1869. Rep.

Tibbetts, James I.; druggist; 186 Indiana avenue, Indianapolis; res 258 North Tennessee street. Born on Maderia Island 1849; settled in M. C. 1865.

Tanner, W. F.; shoe and boot maker; 217 Indiana avenue, Indianapolis. Born in Georgia 1843; settled in M. C. 1865.

Taylor, Sam; general insurance agent; 68 West Washington street, Indianapolis; res West New York street. Born in England 1832. Baptist.

THOMPSON, E.; firm of Brackin & Thompson, dealers in lumber, lath, shingles, dressed flooring and siding; yard 180 West Market street, Indianapolis; res in Stanton's Addition, s e part of city. Born in Indianapolis 1831.

TRAUB, JOHN J.; gardener; west of river, on Washington street, Indianapolis. Born in Ind. 1841; settled in M. C. 1849.

TRAUB, JACOB; gardener; west of river, on Washington St., Indianapolis. Born in Germany 1811; settled in M. C. 1849.

TRAUB, ALFORD; gardener; west of river, on Washington street, Indianapolis. Born in Indianapolis 1853.

TRAUB, WM. H.; gardener; west of river, on Washington street, Indianapolis. Born in Ind. 1843; settled in M. C. 1849.

Thayer, A. T.; trader; corner Udell street and Michigan Road, Indianapolis. Born in S. C. 1836; settled in M. C. 1874.

Thomas, James C.; bricklayer and contractor; res 301 Indiana avenue, Indianapolis. Born in Ohio 1820; settled in M. C. 1853.

Thomas, C. L.; grocer; West Washington street, Indianapolis. Born in Ky. 1819; settled in M. C. 1832.

Terry, E.; firm of Indianapolis Coffin Co.; res 443 North Meridian street, Indianapolis.

Tuttle, Orrin; reel driver, No. 1 Engine, Indianapolis. Born in N. Y. 1836; settled in M. C. 1848. Protestant.

Test, Charles; U. S. store keeper at Baker's Sons' distillery; res 97, corner Vermont and Tennessee streets. Born in Ind. 1843; settled in M. C. 1860.

TILFORD, J. M.; President of Indianapolis Printing and Publishing House, corner Meridian and Circle streets; res Irvington. Born in Ky. 1811; settled in M. C. 1853. Christian.

TILFORD, SAMUEL; book-keeper Indianapolis Printing and Publishing House, corner Meridian and Circle streets; res Irvington.

Thayer, Geo. V.; firm of J. M. Meyer & Co., real estate brokers; 25 West Washington street, Indianapolis; res 498 North Pennsylvania street. Born in S. C. 1845; settled in M. C. 1849.

Thompson, C. W.; with Martin & Hopkins, 34 and 36 West Washington street, Indianapolis; res 373 North Pennsylvania street. Born in N. Y. 1850; settled in M. C. 1873. Rep. Episcopal.

Tuttle, B. F.; merchandise broker; 25 East Maryland street, Indianapolis.

THOMSON, M. C.; livery and feed stable; Indianola; first class accommodations and satisfaction guaranteed. Born in 1837; settled in M. C. 1874.

THE PEOPLE; published every Sunday morning; 25 South Delaware street, Indianapolis.

Tousey, W. G.; pork and beef packer; Pennsylvania street, Indianapolis.

Taylor, Rand & Taylor; attorneys at law; 24 East Washington street.

TODD & SHIDELER; JOHN M. TODD, ISAAC M. SHIDELER; real estate brokers; 24½ East Washington street, Indianapolis.

TODD, JOHN M.; res 157 Bellefontaine street, Indianapolis. Born in Pa. 1834; settled in M. C. 1861.

Thompson, Lemon, Mason & McLaughlin; real estate brokers; 16½ East Washington street, Indianapolis.

Thumbert, W.; confectioner; 51 West Washington street, Indianapolis.

Tilt, T. C.; wholesale liquor dealer; 191 West Washington St., Indianapolis. Born in Ireland 1841; settled in M. C. 1863.

Tutewiler, Henry W.; City Treasurer; 181 East Washington street, Indianapolis; res 401 North Mississippi street. Born in Indianapolis.

Tremont House; corner South and Meridian streets, Indianapolis; George Miller, proprietor.

Thompson, J. S.; grocer; 589 and 591 South Meridian street, Indianapolis. Born in Ohio 1843; settled in M. C. 1873.

TOOLE, JOHN R.; with No. 7 Engine Co.; 125 East South street, Indianapolis; bds Ray House. Born in Ind. 1852; settled in M. C. 1856.

Traub, Chas.; house and sign painter; 229 Park avenue, Indianapolis. Born in Germany 1834; settled in M. C. 1851.

Traub, Jacob; house and sign painter; 229 Park avenue, Indianapolis. Born in Germany 1840; settled in M. C. 1851.

Thompson, J. A.; dealer in fish, oysters and game; 2 Virginia avenue, Indianapolis. Born in Me. 1837; settled in M. C. 1873.

Tounsen, R. D.; agent for Cleveland Iron Fence; 6 Virginia avenue, Indianapolis. Born in Pa. 1847; settled in M. C. 1872.

Talbott, R. L.; firm of W. S. Wooten & Co.; res 136 East North street, Indianapolis. Born in Va. 1827; settled in M. C. 1860.

Thalman, John; bakery; 75 North Alabama street, Indianapolis.

Turner, Gustave; proprietor barber shop; 31 West Market St., Indianapolis. Born in Ky. 1807; settled in M. C. 1833.

Trueblood, N. A.; with Smock & Ransdell; res 399 North East street, Indianapolis. Born in Ind. 1834.

Tompkins, J. H. F.; Shaw Carriage Works; res 3 miles northeast of Indianapolis. Born in Va. 1838; settled in M. C. 1868. Dem. Episcopalian.

TOUT & KROPS; commission merchants and dealers in grain, flour and feed; 29 South Meridian street, Indianapolis.

TEN EYCK, H. B.; general agent of American Fire Insurance Co.; 18 South Meridian street, Indianapolis; res 258 Pennsylvania street. Born in N. Y. 1811; settled in M. C. 1874.

TEN EYCK, W. C.; agent American Fire Insurance Co.; 18 South Meridian street, Indianapolis. Born in Ohio 1850; settled in M. C. 1874.

Taggart, Bros.; bakery; 20 South Meridian street, Indianapolis.

Tarlton, John & J. A.; wholesale fish dealers; 26 South Meridian street, Indianapolis.

Tarlton, John; res 492 North Tennessee street, Indianapolis. Born in Ky. 1824; settled in M. C. 1840.

Tarlton, J. A.; res 960 North Illinois street, Indianapolis. Born in Ky. 1831; settled in M. C. 1840.

Thurston, W. B.; firm of Maxwell, Fry & Thurston; res No. 79 West New York street, Indianapolis. Born in R. I. 1816; settled in M. C. 1839.

TURNER, A. H.; dealer in cigars and tobacco of best brands; 76 Virginia avenue, Indianapolis. Born in Ind. 1828; settled in M. C. 1863.

Thomas Bros.; grocers; corner of Ohio and East streets, Indianapolis.

Tull, J. H.; painter; 52 Kentucky avenue, Indianapolis. Born in Ind. 1832; settled in M. C. 1856.

TARKINGTON, W. C.; firm of Batty, Noland & Tarkington, Indianapolis; res 154 North Meridian street. Born in Ind. 1818; settled in M. C. 1864.

Thornton, E. C.; firm of Fitzhugh & Co., Indianapolis; bds at 76 East New York street. Born in Ohio 1850; settled in M. C. 1869.

Thornton, Frank.; firm of Fitzhugh & Co., Indianapolis; bds at 44 North Alabama street. Born in Ohio 1847; settled in M. C. 1873.

TALBOTT, C. H. & CO.; wholesale hat house, 89 and 91 South Meridian street, Indianapolis.

Talbott, C. H.; res 566 North Delaware street, Indianapolis.

TUMEY, TAYLOR; farmer; 3 m n Indianapolis. Born in Ind. 1850; settled in M. C. 1873.

Tuttle, Samuel; farmer; 1½ m e Indianapolis. Born in Ky. 1833; settled in M. C. 1874.

TREAT, A. J.; firm of Egan, Treat & Eagan, Indianapolis; res 230 North Meridian street. Born in Conn. 1838; settled in M. C. 1864. Rep.

TIDELIS, S.; at beer garden, 211 West Washington street, Indianapolis. Born in Austria 1837; settled in M. C. 1852.

Tarrar, John; shoemaker; 266 West Washington street, Indianapolis. Born in England 1840; settled in M. C. 1856.

TEN EYCK, RICHARD F.; shoe shop; 340 West Washington street, Indianapolis. Born in Ohio 1836; settled in M. C. 1848.

TEN EYCK, J. A.; fancy grocery; 340 West Washington st., Indianapolis; res same. Born in Ohio 1830; settled in M. C. 1848.

UNVERZAGT, HERMAN H.; gardener; North Indianapolis. Born in Germany 1829; settled in M. C. 1850.

Udell, C. G.; president Udell Ladder Co.; res Shoemaker St., North Indianapolis. Born in N. Y. 1830; settled in M. C. 1873.

Udell Ladder Co.; Daniel G. Williams, vice-president and treasurer; res 236 College avenue, Indianapolis. Born in N. H. 1838; settled in M. C. 1850.

Uphaus, Henry; with Farrars; 266 West Washington street, Indianapolis; res 6 Wisconsin street. Born in M. C. 1851.

Uhl & Durham; cigar manufacturers; 19 South Meridian St., Indianapolis.

Uhl, Peter; firm of Uhl & Durham; res 781 North Tennessee street, Indianapolis. Born in Germany 1845; settled in M. C. 1856.

Vanstan, John; boot and shoe maker; 91 East Washington St., Indianapolis; res 47 Yeiser street. Born in Ireland 1829; settled in M. C. 1866.

Vogt, Fred J.; res 224 West Washington street. Born in Germany 1835; settled in M. C. 1858.

Vansickle, Alexander; pres. Atlas Engine and Boiler Works; 14 Hubbard Block, Indianapolis; res 660 North Meridian street. Born in N. Y.; settled in M. C. 1864.

Vehling, Fred.; grocer; corner South and New Jersey streets, Indianapolis.   Born in Germany 1811; settled in M. C. 1848.

VULCAN BOILER AND SHEETIRON WORKS; manufacturers of all descriptions of sheet, boiler and galvanized iron work, also builders of hot air furnaces; special attention given to boiler repairing; old engines and boilers bought and sold; 326 South Delaware street.

Voltz, Anthony; captain No. 7 Fire Co.; 125 East South street, bds at Ray House, Indianapolis.   Born in Ind. 1847; settled in M. C. 1869.

VANCAMP, G. C. & SON; commission merchants and fruit packers; 75 and 77 West Washington street, Indianapolis.

Vancamp, G. C.; res 176 North California street, Indianapolis. Born in Ind. 1817; settled in M. C. 1860.   Rep.   Presb.

Vœgtle, Jacob; dealer in stoves, tinware and tinners' stock; 103 East Washington street, Indianapolis.   Born in Germany 1837; settled in M. C. 1859.

Vandyke, W. W.; real estate broker; Baldwin's Block, Indianapolis.   Born in Ind. 1844; settled in M. C. 1869.   Rep. Methodist.

Victor Sewing Machine Company; office 18 North Delaware street, Indianapolis.

VIEDHABER, G.; butcher shop; 663 Virginia avenue, Indianapolis; res same.   Born in Germany 1849; settled in M. C. 1865.

Vondersaar, Lewis, grocer; 577 Virginia avenue, Indianapolis; res 571 Virginia avenue.   Born in Pa. 1852; settled in M. C. 1854.

VIEKIR, FRED.; blacksmith; horse shoeing done to order; 269 Daugherty street and Virginia avenue, Indianapolis; res Georgia street.   Born in Germany 1851; settled in M. C. 1868.

Vinedge, Jones & Co.; wholesale dealers in boots and shoes; 93 and 95 South Meridian street, Indianapolis.

VANNATHAN, F.; dealer in confectionery and fruit; corner Meridian and Louisiana streets, Indianapolis.

Vance, John J.; watchmaker; 69 East Washington street, Indianapolis. Born in Pa. 1850; settled in M. C. 1859. Rep.

Vanloon, A.; dealer in cigars and confectionery; 3 Virginia avenue, Indianapolis; res same. Born in Ohio 1816; settled in M. C. 1872.

Vencills, Adam; dealer in fancy groceries, flour and provisions; 126 Fort Wayne avenue, Indianapolis. Born in W. Va. 1826; settled in M. C. 1874.

Vansicle & Stoops; dealers in fancy groceries, also feed and flour; 58 Clifford avenue, Indianapolis.

Vansicle, George W.; res 2 Brookside avenue, Indianapolis. Born in M. C. 1844.

Voss, G. H.; attorney at law; rooms 9, 10 and 11 Talbott & New's Block, up stairs; res North Illinois street, Indianapolis. Born in Ohio 1822; settled in M. C. 1868. Rep. Christian.

VANDYKE, J. G.; dealer in cigars and tobacco; 86 South Illinois street, Indianapolis; res 84 South Illinois street. Born in Ohio 1854; settled in M. C. 1870. Rep. Methodist.

VANDYKE, C.; proprietor of the Irving House; 84 South Illinois street, Indianapolis. Born in New Jersey 1828; settled in M. C. 1870.

Vondergotten, Henry; hair dressing and shaving saloon; 140 South Illinois street, Indianapolis; res 279 North Liberty street. Born in Germany 1826; settled in M. C. 1863.

VanVorhis, F. I.; res 223 North Alabama street, Indianapolis. Born in Ind. 1840; settled in M. C. 1870.

Vieira, M. J.; hair dresser and wig maker; 56 Indiana avenue, Indianapolis; res 92 Massachusetts avenue. Born in Portugal 1842; settled in M. C. 1871. Rep. Catholic.

Vandegrift, Henry; agent I., C. & L. R. R.; North street station, Indianapolis; res 260 North Mississippi street. Born in Pa. 1818; settled in M. C. 1837. Dem.

VANHORN, S. E.; job printing; visiting and business cards a specialty; 174 East Washington street, up stairs, Indianapolis. Born in Ohio 1847; settled in M. C. 1870. Prot.

Vanantwerp, G. W.; horse-shoeing shop; 24 North East street, Indianapolis; res 60 State street. Born in N. Y. 1833; settled in M. C. 1860.

VONNEGUT, CLEMENS; wholesale and retail dealer in hardware and cutlery; 184 and 186 East Washington street, Indianapolis; res 508 East Market street. Born in Muenster, Germany, 1824; settled in M. C. 1852.

VANBERGEN, WM. H.; carpenter and builder; shop corner Missouri and Wabash streets, Indianapolis; res 75 West Michigan street. Born in Ind. 1829; settled in M. C. 1855.

Voorhees, Jacob; plasterer and contractor; res 58 Arch street, Indianapolis. Born in Indianapolis 1835.

Vielhaber, D.; boot and shoe manufacturer; 204 East Washington street, Indianapolis.

VESTAL, JOHN; Deputy Treasurer of State, Indianapolis. Born in Ind. 1832; settled in M. C. 1873.

Weber, Fred.; watchmaker and jeweler; 50 South Illinois street, Indianapolis; res 774 East St. Joseph street. Born in Switzerland 1837; settled in M. C. 1808. Protestant.

WECHSLER, DAVID; butcher and dealer in meats; 307 Massachusetts avenue, Indianapolis; res 424 South Illinois street. Born in Germany 1826; settled in M. C. 1839.

Woolen, G. V.; physician and surgeon; 20 West Ohio street, Indianapolis. Born in Ind. 1840; settled in M. C. 1840. Rep. M. Baptist.

Ward Bros.; dealers in drugs and pure medicines; 196 Fort Wayne avenue, Indianapolis.

Ward, B.; res 389 New Jersey street, Indianapolis. Born in Ind. 1832; settled in M. C. 1866.

Ward, M. Born in Ind. 1840; settled in M. C. 1869.

Williams, I. K.; dealer in fancy groceries and provisions, flour and feed; corner Home avenue and Ash street, Indianapolis; res 192 Ash street. Born in Ind. 1831; settled in M. C. 1873.

Whiting, T. M.; bleacher of straw goods of all kinds; 26 Kentucky avenue, Indianapolis.

Winings, Dan P.; salesman with H. S. Hutchens, 401 North Alabama street, Indianapolis. Born in Ohio 1849; settled in M. C. 1853.

WRIGHT, ISAAC; blacksmith and general custom shop; 118 Fort Wayne avenue, Indianapolis; res 734 East Tinker St. Born in Ind. 1849; settled in M. C. 1874.

Wertman, J. S.; attorney at law; room No. 7 Talbott & New's Block, second floor, Indianapolis. Born in Ohio 1845; settled in M. C. 1873.

Webb, Ira C. & Co.; house and sign painting; 12 South Pennsylvania street, Indianapolis.

Webb, Isaac; res 267 West Vermont street, Indianapolis. Born in N. Y. 1838; settled in M. C. 1862.

Waterman & Van Vorhis; physicians and surgeons; office 30 East Ohio street, Indianapolis.

Waterman, L. D.; res 22 Pennsylvania street, Indianapolis.

Woodson, Mrs. Clarissa A., tailoress; 140 West First street, Indianapolis.

Williamson, Ira D.; livery and sale stable, 37 and 39 West Pearl street, Indianapolis; res 180 Broadway. Born in Ind. 1825; settled in M. C. 1869.

Walter, John E.; farmer and dairyman; 2½ m n e Indianapolis. Born in Ohio 1826; settled in M. C. 1837. Rep. Meth.

Walter, D. M.; physician and surgeon; office with Todd & Bigelow; office corner Market and Delaware streets, Indianapolis. Born in Ind. 1846. Rep. Methodist.

23

Walter, C. G.; farmer and trader; res 2½ m n e Indianapolis. Born in M. C. 1849. Rep. Protestant.

White, A. R. & Co.; White's Pulmonaria, White's Bitters; 102 and 106 Massachusetts avenue, Indianapolis.

Ward, Richard; manufacturer of and dealer in Ward's Liniment; res 3 m e Indianapolis. Born in Ind. 1819; settled in M. C. 1873. Rep. Christian.

WÓLFE, JACOB; farmer; 3½ m n e Indianapolis. Born in Ky. 1818; settled in M. C. 1830. Dem. Universalist.

WALLACE, WILLIAM; attorney and counsellor at law; office 4 Odd Fellows' Hall, Indianapolis; res 84 East Michigan street.

Warrick, J. W.; attorney at law; 100 East Washington street, Indianapolis; bds at 121 North Delaware street. Born in Ind. 1850; settled in M. C. 1874. Christian.

Wagner, Geo. W.; builder; 94½ East Washington street, Indianapolis; res 112 Peru street.

Woodford, Jas. E.; firm of Feldkamp & Woodford, dealers in and importers of wines and all kinds of liquors; 306 East Washington street, Indianapolis; res 293 North Meridian street.

Wilson, W. P.; grocer; 414 West New York street, Indianapolis. Born in Ky. 1835; settled in M. C. 1873.

Wright, M. H.; dealer in stoneware; 146 West Louisiana street, Indianapolis.

Wachtstetter, John M.; gardener; Vermont street, west of the river, Indianapolis. Born in Germany 1831; settled in M. C. 1853.

Weikert, John; real estate broker; 16 North Meridian street, Indianapolis; res North Indianapolis. Born in Pa. 1821; settled in M. C. 1859.

Watts, D. M.; dealer in dry goods and groceries; corner Shoemaker and Lula streets, North Indianapolis. Born in M. C. 1843.

White, John F. & George Hicks; dairymen and traders; North Tennessee street, Indianapolis.

West, Geo. H.; clerk in Auditor's office; res North Illinois st., Indianapolis. Born in N. Y. 1830; settled in M. C. 1846.

Watters, W. W.; farmer; 2 m w Indianapolis. Born in Ind. 1822; settled in M. C. 1828.

Woollen, Wm. M.; grocer; 101 Indiana avenue, Indianapolis; res 288 North Tennessee street. Born in Ky. 1824; settled in M. C. 1833. Rep. Christian.

WERT, F. A.; firm of F. A. Wert & Co., dealers in stoves and tinware; 121 Indiana avenue, Indianapolis; res 169 Bright street. Born in Indianapolis 1846. Rep. Meth.

WEDDINGTON, E. E.; firm of F. A. Wert & Co., dealers in stoves and tinware; 121 Indiana avenue, Indianapolis. Born in Ind. 1853; settled in M. C. 1873. Rep. Methodist.

Westefeld, A.; house and sign painter; 15½ Indiana avenue, Indianapolis; res 69 Alabama street.

WOERNER, L.; dealer in groceries and provisions; 154 Indiana avenue, Indianapolis. Born in Baden, Germany, 1834; settled in M. C. 1854.

Wallace, A. R.; dry goods merchant; 188 Indiana avenue, Indianapolis; res 228 California street. Born in Ind. 1834; settled in M. C. 1874. Dem. Protestant.

Waller, Bernhard; shoemaker; 151 Indiana avenue, Indianapolis. Born in France 1820; settled in M. C. 1854.

Willis, J.; dealer in stoves and tinware; 448 Indiana avenue, Indianapolis. Born in Ind. 1843; settled in M. C. 1864. Indpt. Episcopalian.

WATTS, JAMES E.; general store; corner Blake street and Indiana avenue, Indianapolis. Born in M. C. 1832. Rep. Protestant.

Witthoeft, Fred.; grocery and saloon; 329 Indiana avenue, Indianapolis. Born in Germany 1827; settled in M. C. 1864. Dem. Protestant.

Wehle, Lucas; boot and shoe manufacturer; 194 East Washington street, Indianapolis; res 212 East Ohio street. Born in Germany 1835; settled in M. C. 1857.

Woollen, Wm. W., Jr.; attorney at law; 35½ East Washington street, Indianapolis; res 160 College avenue. Born in M. C. 1838. Rep. M. Baptist.

Williams, E. H.; firm of Billingsley & Williams; wholesale fruit and produce merchants; 76 West Washington street, Indianapolis; res 130 Broadway street. Born in Ind. 1839; settled in M. C. 1865.

Whitehill, James B.; 92 and 94 West Washington street, Indianapolis. Born in Ohio 1849; settled in M. C. 1873. Dem. Pretestant.

Wiley, M. W.; firm of Moore & Wiley, druggists; 172 West Washington street, Indianapolis; res 303 Indiana avenue. Born in Ind. 1844; settled in M. C. 1862. Dem. Christian.

Witt, B. F.; firm of Witt & Surface, wholesale and retail druggists; 182 West Washington street, Indianapolis; res 364 North New Jersey street.

Wells, G. A.; dentist; 15 East Washington street, Indianapolis; res 181 North New Jersey street. Born in N. Y.; settled M. C. 1856.

Wallace, Wm. J.; ex-clerk of Marion county; Indianapolis.

Wright, Isaac; clerk in county treasurer's office, Indianapolis; bds 224 North Alabama street. Born in Md. 1804; settled in M. C. 1868. Rep. Friend.

WALKER, L. C.; firm of Ritter, Walker & Ritter, attorneys at law; office 82 East Washington street, Indianapolis; res 320 North Alabama street. Born in Ohio 1837; settled in M. C. 1873. Rep. Presbyterian.

WALKER, J. L.; manufacturer and dealer in stoves and house furnishing goods; 31 West Washington street, Indianapolis; res 169 North Mississippi street. Born in M. C. 1849. Presbyterian.

Wood, D. L.; firm of D. L. Wood & Co., State agents for Mutual Benefit Life Insurance Co.; 19½ West Washington St., Indianapolis; res 417 North Pennsylvania street. Born in N. Y. 1830; settled in M. C. 1866. Rep. Presbyterian.

WOOLLEN, WEBB & CO.; BANKERS; 15 WEST WASHINGTON STREET, INDIANAPOLIS.

WOOLLEN, WM. W.; firm of Woollen, Webb & Co.; res 172 East Ohio street, Indianapolis. Born in Md. June 21st, 1828; settled in M. C. March 1st, 1864. Dem. Presb.

WEBB, WILLIS S.; firm of Woollen, Webb & Co.; res 440 North Meridian street, Indianapolis. Born in Ind. 1820; settled in Indianapolis 1865. Dem. Baptist.

Wagner, Abram; clerk in office of Secretary of State; corner Washington and Tennessee streets, Indianapolis. Born in Ind. 1845; settled in M. C. 1873. Rep. Universalist.

Wildman, James A.; Auditor of State; res 415 North Pennsylvania street, Indianapolis. Born in Ind. 1834; settled in M. C. 1873. Rep.

Wiley, L. C.; real estate broker; 72 East Washington street, Indianapolis; res 37 West St. Joseph street. Born in Ohio 1820; settled in M. C. 1873. Rep. Methodist.

Wylie, Andrew; dealers in periodicals and stationery; 13 North Pennsylvania street, Indianapolis; res 37 South Benton St. Born in Scotland 1815; settled in M. C. 1864.

WEED SEWING MACHINE CO.; 42 North Pennsylvania street, Indianapolis; FRANK RICHARDSON, Manager; res 444 North New Jersey street. Born in Ind. 1840; settled in M. C. 1861. Rep. M. Baptist.

Wright & Son; pump makers; 48 South Illinois street, Indianapolis.

White, Edward; publisher; room 1 in Talbott & New's Block, Pennsylvania street, Indianapolis; res 368 West New York street. Born in N. Y. 1846; settled in M. C. 1874. Liberal.

Woelz, Charles A.; wholesale and retail confectionery, toys and fancy candies of all kinds; corner of Delaware street and Massachusetts avenue, Indianapolis.

WATSON, THOMAS N.; barber and hair dresser; 26½ Massachusetts avenue, Indianapolis; res same. Born in Ind. 1840; settled in M. C. 1873.

WOOD, J. S.; dealer in fancy groceries, flour and provisions; 399 North Illinois street, Indianapolis; res same. Born in Ohio 1832; settled in M. C. 1836.

WELLS, O. T.; dealer in cigars and tobacco; 61 North Illinois street and 18 North Meridian street, Indianapolis; res 384 West New York street. Born in Ind. 1854; settled in M. C. 1871.

Webb, J.; res 308 Chestnut street, Indianapolis. Born in Ohio 1810; settled in M. C. 1867. Neutral. Christian.

Weaver, W. W. & Son; undertakers; 39 North Illinois street, nearly opposite Bates House, Indianapolis; res 233 North Illinois street. Born in Pa. 1808; settled in M. C. 1836. Neutral. Methodist.

Woodward, John; wholesale and retail dealer in choice brands of cigars and tobacco; 15 North Illinois street, opposite the Bates House, Indianapolis.

WILKINSON, JOHN; merchant tailor; 32 North Illinois st., Indianapolis; res 121 West New York street. Born in Scotland 1817; settled in M. C. 1868. Rep. Presby.

White, T. G.; book-keeper with Rikhoff & Co., Indianapolis; res 63 Minerva street. Born in Ohio 1817. Dem. Prot.

Ward, A. S. & Co.; general railroad ticket agents; 128 South Illinois street, Indianapolis.

Ward, A. S.; res 111 Fort Wayne avenue, Indianapolis. Born in N. Y. 1848; settled in M. C. 1870. Rep. Protestant.

WISHMEIER, C. F.; wholesale and retail dealer in groceries and produce; 197 and 199 Massachusetts avenue, corner of East street, Indianapolis.

WISHMEIER, CHARLES; res 300 North Winston street, Indianapolis.

WISHMEIER, CHR.; res 300 North Winston street, Indianapolis. Born in M. C. 1848.

WISHMEIER, WM.; res 300 North Winston street, Indianapolis. Born in M. C. 1851.

WISHMEIER, CHARLES. Born in Germany 1820; settled in M. C. 1840. Lutheran.

Worden & Morrow; proprietors of the Occidental Hotel; corner Illinois and Washington streets, Indianapolis.

Worden, Wm. Born in Pa. 1822; settled in M. C. 1874.

Williams, Chas. C.; res 20 West Michigan street, Indianapolis. Born in Ind. 1851; settled in M. C. 1851. Rep. Meth.

Wheeler, W. A.; dealer in stoves and tinware; 56 North Illinois street, Miller's Block, Indianapolis. Prompt attention given to repairing.

Wheeler, W. A.; res 153 North Tennessee street, Indianapolis. Born in N. Y. 1846; settled in M. C. 1867. Rep. Prot.

WAMBACH, WILLIAM; proprietor of the Globe House; 201 South Illinois street, Indianapolis. Born in Germany 1819; settled in M. C. 1868. Dem. Catholic.

Woodburn Sarven Wheel Co.; manufacturers of the Sarven patent wheel; South Illinois street, Indianapolis.

Westover, J. M.; proprietor of boarding house; 255 South Pennsylvania street, Indianapolis. Born in N. Y. 1813; settled in M. C. 1858.

Wright, George; dairyman; 2 m e Indianapolis. Born in Wales 1827; settled in M. C. 1866. Rep. Protestant.

WEIR, GEORGE; tailor; 202 South Illinois street, Indianapolis; res same. Born in Germany 1825; settled in M. C. 1856.

WHITE, L. S.; dealer in photographic materials; 173 East Washington street, Indianapolis.

Worland, Wm. & Son; grocers; 649 Virginia avenue, Indianapolis.

Wasson, H. P.; firm of Close & Wasson, dry goods dealers; corner Washington and Meridian streets, Indianapolis; res 181 California street. Born in Md. 1846; settled in M. C. 1865.

Woechter, Paul; dealer in silk and felt hats; 94 Virginia avenue, Indianapolis. Born in 1825; settled in M. C. 1873.

Wolfe & Tiner; dealers in groceries; 200 Virginia avenue, Indianapolis.

WHITFORD, F. & SON; dealers in hardware, cutlery and farming implements; 654 Virginia avenue, Indianapolis. Give them a call.

Woelke & Co.; Indianapolis; iron fencing and grading done to order.

Wymond & Helfer; carriage works; 26, 28, 30 and 32 South Tennessee street, Indianapolis.

WATERMAN & VAN VORHIS; physicians; office 300 East Ohio street, Indianapolis; Waterman's res 3d floor, over 22 North Pennsylvania street; Van Vorhis's res 223 North Alabama street.

WISLING, C.; grocer; 330 North Noble street, Indianapolis. First-class groceries at the lowest cash price.

Woodruff, J. O.; proprietor of Woodruff Place; office 17 Baldwin's Block, North Delaware street, Indianapolis; res Woodruff Place. Born in N. Y. 1840; settled in M. C. 1868.

WHARTON, J. W.; real estate broker; office in Surgical Institute Building, Indianapolis; res 68 Spann avenue. Born in Ohio 1849; settled in M. C. 1873.

Wands, Dr. W.; office No. 3 Franklin Life Insurance Building, Indianapolis; res 330 East Vermont street.

Whitton, R. L.; druggist; 269 West Washington street, Indianapolis; res 267 West Washington street. Born in England 1845; settled in M. C. 1859.

Whitehead, Wm.; grocer; 430 West Washington street, Indianapolis. Born in England 1840; settled in M. C. 1843.

Wells, Edmond; shoemaker; 28 South Delaware street, Indianapolis; res 191 South New Jersey street. Born in M. C. 1838.

Wuands, Elex.; shoemaker; 28 South Delaware street, Indianapolis. Born in Scotland 1819; settled in M. C. 1845.

WEINREICH, WM. G.; saloon; 80 South Delaware street, Indianapolis. Born in Germany 1828; settled in M. C. 1869.

WHEATLEY, H. H.; sash and door manufacturer, res 311 South East street, Indianapolis. Born in Ind. 1831; settled in M. C. 1848.

Writtlinger, J.; dealer in groceries and liquors, Indianapolis. Born in Germany 1835; settled in M. C. 1860.

Wilmot, A.; agent Victor Sewing Machine Co., 18 North Delaware street, Indianapolis. Born in Ohio 1820; settled in M. C. 1873.

WIGGINS, GEORGE W.; firm of Wiggins & Donnan; res 30 Sinker street, Indianapolis. Born in N. Y. 1840; settled in M. C. 1865.

WIGGINS & DONNAN; stove and tinware manufacturers; 35 South Alabama street, Indianapolis.

Wright, C. E.; physician and surgeon; 107 North Alabama st., Indianapolis.

WARING, ISAAC; firm of W. T. Gibson & Co.; res 274 North Mississippi street, Indianapolis. Born in Conn. 1828; settled in M. C. 1865.

Wright, B. C.; claim agent, rooms 3 and 4 Baldwin's Block, Indianapolis. Born in Ind. 1844; settled in M. C. 1860.

Wright, Jacob T. & Co.; real estate brokers, rooms 1 and 2 Baldwin's Block, Indianapolis.

Wright, Jacob T.; res 275 North Delaware street, Indianapolis. Born in Ohio 1816; settled in M. C. 1852.

Washington, J. M.; electro plating emporium; 10 West Market street, Indianapolis; res 18 West Georgia street. Born in Pa. 1824; settled in M. C. 1869.

Wilkens & Co.; folding and bed lounges and spring mattresses of all kinds; 78 East Market street, Indianapolis.

Wilkens, John H.; firm of Wilkens & Co.; res 217 Broadway street, Indianapolis. Born in Indianapolis.

Wright, Frank M.; attorney at law; office, 25 and 26 Baldwin's Block, Indianapolis; res 311 North Pennsylvania street. Born in Pa. 1848; settled in M. C. 1854.

Wiles, Bro. & Co.; wholesale grocers; 149 South Meridian St., Indianapolis.

Washburn, C.; contractor and builder; 65 Peru street, Indianapolis. Born in Vt. 1826; settled in M. C. 1865.

WEIAND, ELY; farmer; 1 m n corporation. Born in M. C. 1855.

Wright, Willis; farmer; ¾ m e corporation line, Indianapolis.

Wallace, John; farmer and brick manufacturer; 1½ m e corporation line, Indianapolis.

WALLACE, V.; physician and surgeon; 83 East Washington street, Indianapolis. Born in N. Y. 1842; settled in M. C. 1874. Rep. Liberal.

Wright & Co.; real estate dealers; 75½ East Washington street, Indianapolis.

Wright, C. A.; Indianapolis. Born in Mich. 1833; settled in M. C. 1859. Rep. Protestant.

Wright, L. G.; firm of Wright & Co.; Indianapolis. Born in Mich. 1843; settled in M. C. 1873.

Weir, Wm.; dealer in monuments and tombstones; 44 Virginia avenue, Indianapolis. Born in Scotland; settled in M. C. 1855.

Willcox & Garret; carpenters; East Market street, opp Journal Office, Indianapolis.

WOOTON, W. S. & CO.; school furniture; 23 South Alabama
street, Indianapolis.

WOOTON, W. S.; of Wooton & Co.; res Prospect street, Indianapolis.

Wissen, Joseph; manufacturer of boots and shoes; 440 South
Meridian street, Indianapolis. Born in Germany 1844;
settled in M. C. 1872.

Walter, W. F.; 474 South Meridian street, Indianapolis. Born
in Ind. 1852; settled in M. C. 1873.

Walter, H. W.; policeman 12th ward; res 447 South Meridian
street, Indianapolis. Born in Ohio 1848; settled in M. C.
1872.

WALTER, GEO.; saloon and boarding house; 249 West South
street, Indianapolis. Born in France 1833; settled in M.
C. 1862.

White, James; saloon; 370 South West street, Indianapolis.
Born in Ireland 1849; settled in M. C. 1855.

Wallace, Andrew; wholesale grocer; 52 and 54 South Delaware
street, Indianapolis. Born in Ireland 1816; settled in M.
C. 1844.

Wallace, Wm. P.; with Andrew Wallace; res 158 East Market
street, Indianapolis. Born in Ind. 1843; settled in M. C.
1844.

Waterman, C.; Rolling-mill Grocery; dealer in groceries, flour
and feed; corner South and Tennessee streets, Indianapolis.

Wiggins, J. S.; pork and beef packer; 27 and 29 South Pennsylvania street, Indianapolis. Born in Ind. 1839; settled in
M. C. 1865.

WEINBERGER, H.; proprietor of eating house and restaurant;
10, 12 and 14 West Louisiana street, opposite Union Depot, Indianapolis; res same. Born in Bavaria, Germany,
1826; settled in M. C. 1856.

Wallace, J. H.; brick manufacturer; 2 m s Circle street, Indianapolis. Born in N. C. 1834; settled in M. C. 1873.

Wilmington, Edward; Deputy County Auditor; res 124 St. Mary street, Indianapolis. Born in Ohio 1836; settled in M. C. 1844. Rep. Methodist.

Woodbridge, John; firm of Woodbridge & Co., dealers in glass and queensware; 34 West Washington street, Indianapolis; res 147 North Pennsylvania street. Born in Ohio.

Wright, Arthur L.; real estate dealer; 224 North Alabama st., Indianapolis. Born in Ind. 1835; settled in M. C. 1853.

Wright & Morris; real estate brokers; 6 and 8 Hubbard Block, Indianapolis.

Wright, Willis; firm of Wright & Morris; resides out of city.

Witt & Corbaley; attorneys and claim agents; office 10 and 12 Hubbard Block, Indianapolis.

Witt, B. F.; firm of Witt & Corbaley; res 364 North New Jersey street, Indianapolis. Born in Ohio; settled in M. C. 1861.

White, J. J.; produce and provision broker; room 35 Hubbard Block, Indianapolis; res 552 North Meridian street. Born in Va. 1845; settled in M. C. 1874.

WHITE & BLUE; designers and wood engravers; room 47 Hubbard Block, corner Meridian and Washington streets, Indianapolis.

WHITE, W. G.; firm of White & Blue; res 55 Bates street, Indianapolis. Born in Ky. 1853.

WEAVER, J. P.; manufacturer of paper boxes; 26 South Meridian street, Indianapolis; res 220 North Noble street. Born in M. C. 1840.

WOOLLEN, W. W.; vice president of the Franklin Fire Insurance Co.; res 172 East Ohio street, Indianapolis; office at Woollen & Webb's bank.

WOOD, HENRY & CO.; feed and sale stable and coal yard; 17 and 19 Circle street, Indianapolis.

WOOD, HENRY; firm of HENRY WOOD & CO.; res 279 South East street, Indianapolis. Born in Ky. 1817; settled in M. C. 1864.

Wood, W. S.; wholesale and retail dealer in coal oil, burning fluid, lamp burners, etc.; 39 Virginia avenue, Indianapolis. Born in Mass. 1848; settled in M. C. 1872.

Wells, J. B. & Co.; printers, binders and blank book manufacturers; 39 and 41 Virginia avenue, Indianapolis.

Wells, Joseph; firm of J. B. Wells & Co.; res 77 West Washington street, Indianapolis. Born in M. C.

WEIS, PETER & CO.; dealers in dry goods, groceries, provisions, queensware, flour, feed, pottery, etc.; southeast corner East and McCarty streets, Indianapolis.

Wiegman, C.; dealer in groceries, provisions and feed; corner of East and Buchanan streets, Indianapolis. Born in Germany 1835; settled in M. C. 1858.

Wachstetter, Chas.; saloon and restaurant; 186 South Meridian street, Indianapolis. Born in Germany 1845; settled in M. C. 1856.

Weiland, W. C.; firm of Schwoomeyer & Co.; res 159 Union street, Indianapolis. Born in Germany 1840; settled in M. C. 1855.

Wolfrom Bros.; dealer in stoves and tinware; 197 East Washington street, Indianapolis.

WRIGHT, JOSEPH; res Little's Hotel, Indianapolis.

WILLIAMSON, J. W.; physician and surgeon; 205 East Washington street, Indianapolis; bds at Little's Hotel. Born in Ohio 1821; settled in M. C. 1873.

Wade, Frank P.; general ticket agent I. P. & C. R. R.; 101 East Washington street, Indianapolis. Born in Ohio 1846; settled in M. C. 1870.

Wellman, R. G.; bookkeeper Cleveland Lightning Rod Co.; 193 West Washington street, Indianapolis. Born in Ohio 1836; settled in M. C. 1870.

Walker, Pease & Co.; real estate dealers; office 16½ East Washington street, Indianapolis.

WALLICK, J. F.; Superintendent Western Union Telegraph Co.; office No. 7, 2d floor, s e corner Washington and Meridian streets, Indianapolis; res 36 West Michigan street. Born in Pa. 1830; settled in M. C. 1852. Rep.

Watterson & Keeffe; dealers in stoves, queensware, glassware, etc.; 169 and 171 West Washington street, Indianapolis.

Watterson, J. F.; res 31 Indiana avenue, Indianapolis. Born in Pa. 1833; settled in M. C. 1870.

Webster, John L.; firm of Hazzard & Webster; res on Prospect street, Indianapolis. Born in Va. 1823; settled in M. C. 1873.

Western Furniture Co.; wholesale and retail dealers in furniture; 105 East Washington street, Indianapolis.

Weir, A. B.; assistant secretary Citizens Mutual Benefit Association of Indianapolis; office 123 East Washington street, Indianapolis.

WILEY, E. W.; general agent of Grover & Baker Sewing Machine Co.; office 21 East Washington street, Indianapolis; res 287 East Market street. Born in Mass. 1842; settled in M. C. 1868.

YACHMAN, HERRMAN; dealer in notions, men's furnishing goods and merchant tailor; 312 East Washington street, Indianapolis. Born in Prussia 1827; settled in M. C. 1864.

Youse, G. D.; dealer in wines and brandies; 507 West Washington street, end river bridge, Indianapolis. Born in Ind. 1847; settled in M. C. 1874.

YOHN, ALBERT B.; firm of Yohn & Porter; dealers in books and stationery; 4 East Washington street, Indianapolis; res 35 Central avenue. Born in M. C. 1847. Rep. Meth

York, B.; clerk of Criminal Court; res 300 East North street, Indianapolis. Born in Ind. 1847. Rep.

YOHN, CHARLES G.; firm of Yohn & Porter; 4 East Washington street, Indianapolis; res 37 Central avenue. Born in Indianapolis 1849. Rep. Methodist.

Yohn, James C.; merchant; res 206 North Delaware street, Indianapolis. Born in Md. 1818; settled in M. C. 1834. Rep. Methodist.

Yocum, John N.; manufacturer of boots and shoes; No. 18 Malott avenue, Indianapolis; res 734 Sheldon street. Born in Pa. 1808; settled in M. C. 1872.

Yoke, R. A.; farmer and dairyman; 2 miles southeast of Circle street, Indianapolis. Born in Ky. 1808; settled in M. C. 1829.

Zimmer & Neihaus; grocers; 299 South Delaware street, Indianapolis.

Zimmer, Peter; firm of Zimmer & Neihaus; res 299 South Delaware street, Indianapolis. Born in Prussia 1839; settled in M. C. 1864.

ZIMMERMAN, C.; slate and metallic roofer, and dealer in roofing slate; 37 and 39 South Alabama street, Indianapolis; res 612 East Washington street. Born in Pa. 1825; settled in M. C. 1850.

Zawistowski, A. G.; furniture repairer; 64 Massachusetts avenue, Indianapolis.

Zimmerman, H. A.; proprietor of dining hall; 68 Massachusetts avenue, Indianapolis. Born in Md. 1835; settled in M. C. 1873.

Zumbush, Theodore; dealer in clocks and jewelry; res 54 South Pennsylvania street, Indianapolis. Born in Germany 1827; settled in M. C. 1854.

Zellers, Henry; superintendent mattress factory, for Spiegel, Thoms & Co.; corner Wabash and Osage streets, Indianapolis; bds Capital House. Born in Pa. 1832; settled in M. C. 1852.

DECATUR TOWNSHIP.

DECATUR TOWNSHIP is located in the southwest corner of Marion county, and is bounded on the north by Wayne township, on the east by White River, which forms the boundary between this and Perry townships, on the south by Morgan and Johnson, and on the west by Hendricks county, and contains an area of 30 square miles.

The surface is slightly rolling or level, with a few small bluffs on White River.

The soil of the greater part of the township is good, yet not so rich as some other parts of the county, yet is better adapted to blue grass than the rich black soil.

It is watered by White River and spring branches. Timber, building material and gravel beds are plentiful, and the enterprizing citizens are making good use of them.

This is the smallest township in the county in area, population and wealth. The present population is very near 1700. The vote in October, 1874, was, Dem., 95; Rep., 238; total, 333; Rep. majority 143.

Post offices, Valley Mills and West Newton.

EARLY SETTLERS.

John and Absalom Dollarhide were among the first settlers of Decatur township, and were with the commissioners when Indianapolis was laid off in 1820. James Sulgrove settled in this township in 1822; William Daniel was born in this township in 1825. Joseph Allen settled in 1824, J. F. Coppock in 1824, Seth Newby in 1824, and the McCreery family in 1824.

CHURCHES, LODGES, &C.

Center Meeting House of Friends; 2½ m s Bridgeport; membership about 75. Samuel Starbuck and Robert Furnas, overseers Sabbath School; average, 40; value of church property, $500.

Bethel M. E. Church; 1½ m n Valley Mills; membership, 106; Rev. J. Wharton, pastor. Sabbath school average, 60; James Huffman, superintendent; value of church property, $800.

Olive Branch First Evangelical Lutheran Church; 2 m w Maywood; membership, 15; Rev. O. Brown, pastor. Sabbath school average, 30; Hiram Rhoads, superintendent; value of church property, $1,500.

Friends Church; West Newton; membership, 240; value of church property, $3,000.

West Newton M. E. Church; membership, 78; value of church property, $1,500; J. S. Walls, pastor. Sabbath school average, 50; David Williams, superintendent.

West Newton Lodge, F. & A. M., U. D.; postoffice, West Newton; membership, 10.

DIRECTORY OF DECATUR TOWNSHIP.

Amick, Wm.; farmer; ½ m s e Bridgeport. Born in Ind. 1851; settled in M. C. 1871. Christian.

Allen, Joseph, Jr.; farmer and stock raiser; 2½ m n w Newton. Born in M. C. 1833. Rep. Friend.

Armstrong, T. F.; wagon maker; West Newton. Born in Pa. 1816; settled in M. C. 1840. Dem. Methodist.

Allen, M.; farmer; ½ m n e West Newton. Born in M. C. 1832. Rep. Friend.

Allen, Preston; farmer and stock raiser; 3 m n w West Newton. Born in Ohio 1821; settled in M. C. 1825. Rep. Friend.

ALLEN, WESLEY; physician and surgeon; West Newton. Born in M. C. 1836. Rep. Methodist.

Allen, Jesse; farmer; ¼ m n e West Newton. Born in M. C. 1855. Rep. Protestant.

ALLEN, JOSEPH; retired farmer; West Newton. Born in Va. 1794; settled in M. C. 1824. Rep. Friend.

Allen, Joseph; farmer and stock trader; 2½ m n w West Union. Born in M. C. 1833.

Basset, John; farmer; 1 m n Valley Mills. Born in Ky. 1817. Rep. Protestant.

Barnett, A.; farmer; 1½ m n West Newton. Born in M. C. 1831. Rep. Friend.

Barnett, Willis; farmer; 1½ m s e West Newton. Born in Ind. Rep. Protestant.

Barnett, Thomas; West Newton. Born in Ohio 1817; settled in M. C. 1827. Rep. Friend.

Baker, Jesse; general work; West Newton. Born in Ky. 1818; settled in M. C. 1873. Rep. Methodist.

Beeler, J. V.; farmer; 1 m e Friendswood.   Born in Ind. 1826;
    settled in M. C. 1853.   Minister Christian Church.

Breedlove, John; toll gate keeper; West Newton.   Born in N.
    C. 1846; settled in M. C. 1871.   Rep.   Methodist.

Breedlove, John; boot and shoe maker; West Newton.   Born in
    N. C. 1834; settled in M. C. 1871.   Rep.   Methodist.

Breedlove, John; boot and shoe maker; West Newton.   Born
    in N. C. 1798; settled in M. C. 1873.   Rep.   Methodist.

Boatright, Wm. ; farmer; 8 m s w Indianapolis.   Born in M.
    C. 1837.   Dem.   Methodist.

Bailey, G. W.; farmer; 1 m w Valley Mills.   Born in Ohio
    1822; settled in M. C. 1830.   Protestant.

Burk, George; gardener and huckster; Valley Mills.   Born in
    Ky. 1822; settled in M. C. 1865.   Rep.   Methodist.

Beasley, Thomas; ¾ m n e Valley Mills.   Born in N. C. 1831;
    settled in M. C. 1840.   Dem.   Protestant.

Baker, Thomas; tanner and carpenter; 1½ m n w Valley Mills.
    Born in Pa. 1804; settled in M. C 1853.   Dem.   Prot.

Compton, Stephen; farmer; 2 m s e Bridgeport.   Born in Ohio
    1834; settled in M. C. 1868.   Protestant.

Chamberlain, John; farmer; Maywood.   Born in Ky. 1815;
    settled in M. C. 1853.   Dem.   R. Baptist.

Clark, Thomas; farmer; 1 m e Valley Mills. Born in 1821; settled in M. C. 1873. Dem.

Cavnaugh, John; farmer; 1 m w Valley Mills. Born in Ireland; settled in M. C. 1854. Dem. Catholic.

Cavenaugh, James; farmer; 1 m w Valley Mills. Born in Ireland; settled in M. C. 1854. Dem. Catholic.

Cox, Mitchel; farmer; 1 m s West Newton.

CATT, GEORGE; farmer; 1 m s West Newton. Born in Ohio 1811; settled in M. C. 1865. Dem. Christian.

Catt, Wm.; farmer; 1 m s West Newton. Born in Indiana 1845; settled in M. C. 1865. Dem. Christian.

Carpenter, James; farmer; 1½ m s Bridgeport. Born in N. C. 1832; settled in M. C. 1873. Rep. Protestant.

Compton, J.; farmer and stock raiser; 1½ m s Bridgeport. Born in Ohio 1836; settled in M. C. 1862.

Carson, Elwood; farmer; ¼ m w Valley Mills. Born in M. C. 1843. Rep. Friend.

COPPOC, ISAAC; blacksmith and general custom shop; West Newton. Wagons made to order, and horses shod in the best of style. Born in M. C. 1836. Rep. Friend.

Coppoc, J. F.; farmer; ½ m n w West Newton. Born in M. C. 1827. Rep. Protestant.

Card, W. N.; farmer; ¾ m n w West Newton. Born in Ind. 1840; settled in M. C. 1861. Rep. Friend.

Coomer, Jeremiah; 1¼ m s e Friendswood. Born in N. C. 1794; settled in M. C. 1837. Rep. Baptist.

Carson, Amos; carpenter; ½ m s e Valley Mills. Born in M. C. 1834. Rep. Friend.

Doan, Amos; farmer; 1 m s w Valley Mills. Born in Ind. 1828; settled in M. C. 1856. Rep. Friend.

Dollarhide, Noah; dry goods clerk; West Newton.

DEARING, M. M.; horticulturist and dealer in all kinds of small fruit; ½ m s e Valley Mills. Born in Ky. 1841; settled in M. C. 1872. Rep. Friend.

Darnell, Wm.; farmer; 2 m s w Maywood. Born in M. C. 1825. Methodist.

Defolt, H. B.; farmer; 1 m n e Valley Mills. Born in Ohio 1842; settled in M. C. 1872. Dem. Protestant.

David, B. F.; farmer; 2 m n w Valley Mills. Born in Ky. 1828; settled in M. C. 1830. Rep. Protestant.

Dillon, Oliver; farmer; 2¾ m s Bridgeport. Born in Ind. 1840; settled in M. C. 1869.

EAST, JOHN; farmer; Maywood. Born in N. C. 1843; settled in M. C. 1874.

Edwards, J. ; farmer; 2 m n w West Newton. Born in Ind. 1841. Rep. Friend.

Edwards, G. L. ; farmer; 2 m e Valley Mills. Born in Ind. 1831 ; settled in M C. 1872. Dem. Methodist.

Edwards, Miles ; farmer; 2 m e West Newton. Born in M. C. 1851. Rep. Protestant.

Edwards, Joshua ; farmer; 2 m e West Newton. Rep.

Ely, Levi ; farmer; 2 m s w Maywood. Born in Ind. 1848 ; settled in M. C. 1874. Dem. Methodist.

Ellis, John W. ; dealer in dry goods and fancy groceries ; Valley Mills. Born in Ind. 1840; settled in M. C. 1859. Rep. Methodist.

Edwards, Joshua ; farmer; 2 m e West Newton. Born in N. C. 1804 ; settled in M. C. 1837. Rep. Baptist.

Foltz, Joseph; farmer; 1½ m n Valley Mills. Born in Ohio 1833. Rep.

Fling, George; farmer; 1½ m n Valley Mills. Born in Ohio 1848; settled in M. C. 1850. Rep. Protestant.

Fergeson, Clark; farmer; 3 m n e Valley Mills. Born in Ohio 1821. Rep. Friend.

Fergeson, Robert; farmer; 3 m n e Valley Mills. Born in M. C. 1854. Rep. Friend.

Flynn, Patrick; farmer; 2 m s w Valley Mills. Born in Ireland 1830; settled in M. C. 1858. Dem. Catholic.

Fogarty, Edmun; farmer; 2 m s w Valley Mills. Born in Ireland; settled in M. C. 1853. Dem. Catholic.

France, B.; farmer; 1½ m s e Friendswood. Born in N. C. 1834; settled in M. C. 1874. Rep. Protestant.

FURNAS, JOSEPH; farmer; 3 m n e Friendswood. Born in Ohio 1805; settled in M. C. 1829. Rep. Friend.

FURNAS, ROBERT; farmer; 2½ m w Valley Mills. Born in Ohio 1812; settled in M. C. 1864. Rep. Friend.

FURNAS, JOHN W.; nurseryman and fruit grower; Valley Mills. Born in M. C. 1835. Rep. Friend.

Faris, Wm. H.; farmer; 1½ m s e Bridgeport. Born in Ky. 1849; settled in M. C. 1873. Rep. Protestant.

Forsha, A. A.; carpenter and builder; West Newton. Born in Ohio 1845; settled in M. C. 1856. Rep. Protestant.

Furnas, R. W.; farmer and insurance agent; 3 m n Friendswood. Born in M. C. 1848. Rep. Protestant.

GEORGE, J. R.; farmer; ½ m s w West Newton. Born in O. 1828; settled in M. C. 1837. Rep. Friend.

George, Lewis; farmer; 1 m n e Valley Mills. Born in Ohio 1821; settled in M. C. 1845. Rep. Friend.

GREGG, A. W.; lumber dealer; 2½ m s w Maywood. Born in
Pa. 1825; settled in M. C. 1873. Rep. Methodist.

GEORGE, J. F.; stock dealer; 5½ m s w Indianapolis. Born
in Ohio 1841; settled in M. C. 1847. Rep. Protestant.

George, Isaiah; farmer; 1¼ m s e Valley Mills. Born in Ohio
1805; settled in M. C. 1839. Rep. Friend.

Garrettson, George W.; farmer; 2 m s w Maywood. Born in
M. C. 1841. Dem. Methodist.

Green, H. E.; dealer in dry goods and groceries; West Newton.
Born in N. Y.

GIBSON, JAMES; blacksmith; West Newton. Born in Ind.
1852; settled in M. C. 1873. Rep. Methodist.

George, Joel; farmer; ¾ m s w West Newton. Born in Va.
1804; settled in M. C. 1853. Rep. Protestant.

Hoffman, Elijah; farmer; 1½ m s Bridgeport. Born in Ind.
1847. Rep. Methodist.

Harmon, Patrick; farmer; 6 m s w Indianapolis. Born in Ireland. Catholic.

Hoffman, Henry; farmer; 1 m n Valley Mills. Born in M. C.
1831. Rep. Methodist.

Hawkins, Isaac; farmer; 2½ m s Bridgeport. Born in M. C. 1830. Rep. Friend.

Hayworth, C. W.; farmer; ¾ m s e West Newton. Born in Ind. 1835. Rep. Methodist.

Haskins, L. M.; miller; West Newton. Born in Ind. 1848; settled in M. C. 1859. Rep. Friend.

Hayworth, John; farmer; West Newton. Born in M. C. 1841. Rep. Friend.

Hilt, Wm.; farmer; 1½ m n w West Newton. Born in Ind. 1846; settled in M. C. 1870. Dem. Methodist.

Hayworth, J. W.; farmer; ¾ m s e West Newton. Born in M. C. 1849. Rep. Protestant.

HANCH, J. N.; farmer; Maywood. Born in M. C. 1850. Dem. Protestant.

Horton, Alfred; farmer; 1 m s West Newton. Rep. Friend.

Horton, Joseph ; painter ; West Newton. Born in M. C. 1847. Rep. Protestant.

Horton, Dr. ; physician and surgeon ; West Newton. Born in Ind. 1842. Rep. Friend.

Horton; Cyrus ; farmer ; ½ m n w West Newton. Born in M. C. 1830. Rep. Friend.

Hayworth, C. W. ; butcher and meat dealer ; ½ m s e West Newton. Born in M. C. 1835. Rep. Methodist.

Hall, John M.; farmer; ½ m w West Newton. Born in M. C. 1829. Rep. Methodist.

Haskins, R. G.; sawyer; West Newton. Born in N. C. 1837; settled in M. C. 1858. Rep. Friend.

Horten, Wm.; carpenter; West Newton. Born in Ohio 1815; settled in M. C. 1824. Rep. Friend.

Hayley, Enoch; farmer; 1½ m n e West Newton. Born in M. C. 1847. Dem. Protestant.

Huls, Joseph; farmer; 1 m s w Maywood. Born in Ky. 1821; settled in M. C. 1832.

Hoffman, H. G.; farmer; 3 m s e Bridgeport. Born in Ind. 1836; settled in M. C. 1838. Rep. Protestant.

Hoffman, John; farmer; 1½ m n w Valley Mills.

Healy, Dennis; farmer; 1 m n e Valley Mills. Born in Ireland 1820; settled in M. C. 1855. Dem. Catholic.

HAWKINS, J. F.; farmer and butcher; 1¼ m n e Valley Mills. Born in Ohio 1834; settled in M. C. 1860. Dem. Meth.

INGLING, APOLLO S.; farmer; 2½ m s e Bridgeport. Born in N. J. 1842; settled in M. C. 1854. Rep. Friend.

Jenkins, C. M.; tile factory; 2 m n w Valley Mills. Born in Ohio 1844; settled in M. C. 1854. Rep. Friend.

Jackson, William; farmer; 1 m n West Newton. Born in Ind. 1842; settled in M. C. 1871. Rep. Friend.

Johnson, Caleb; farmer and stock raiser; 1½ m n West Newton. Born in Ind. 1819; settled in M. C. 1839. Rep. Friend.

Johnson, J. W.; farmer; 1 m n West Newton. Born in M. C. 1853. Rep. Friend.

Jones, B. F.; farmer; 1 m n West Newton. Born in Ky. 1851; settled in M. C. 1871. Rep. Methodist.

Jackson, H. C.; farmer; 1½ m s e West Newton. Born in Ind. 1850; settled in M. C. 1874. Rep. Friend.

Johnson, Silas; farmer; 1 m s w Valley Mills. Born in M. C. 1835. Rep. Friend.

Jackson, Joel; dealer in groceries and provisions, and postmaster; West Newton. Born in M. C. 1835. Rep. Meth.

JACKSON, Z. S.; farmer; 1½ m s w Friendswood. Born in N. C. 1803; settled in M. C. 1828. Rep. Protestant.

Jessup, J. L.; farmer and minister; ½ m e Friendswood. Born in N. C. 1821; settled in M. C. 1841. Rep. Friend.

Jessup, Wm.; farmer; 2 m w West Newton. Born in Ind. 1829; settled in M. C. 1860. Dem. Protestant.

KENWORTHY, R.; tile manufacturer, merchant and P. M.; Valley Mills. Born in Ind. 1839.

Kenworthy, Harmon; farmer; 1¼ m n w Valley Mills. Born in M. C. 1837. Friend.

Kinman, W. P.; farmer; West Newton. Born in Ohio 1844; settled in M. C. 1854. Rep. Protestant.

Kitchem, D. L.; farmer; 1¼ m n e West Newton. Born in Ky. 1837; settled in M. C. 1869. Rep. Protestant.

Kenworthy, Wm.; retired farmer; Valley Mills. Born in S. C. 1804.

Killough, E. T.; 1¾ m w Valley Mills. Born in M. C. 1835. Rep. Methodist.

Kenworthy, J. F.; farmer and stock raiser; 2½ m n w Valley Mills. Born in M. C. 1851. Rep. Friend.

Layton, J.; farmer; 1 m n Valley Mills. Born in Ohio 1835; settled in M. C. 1837. Rep. Protestant.

Landers, S. C.; farmer; 2 m n Valley Mills. Born in 1847; settled in M. C. 1871. Dem. Methodist.

LUCE, L. H.; farmer; ½ m n w West Newton. Born in Ind. 1847; settled in M. C. 1864. Rep. Christian.

Lenard, John; farmer; 4 m n w West Newton.

Leeman, William; farmer; 2 m w Valley Mills. Born in M. C. 1833. Rep. Methodist.

Leeman, James; farmer; 2 m w Valley Mills. Born in M. C. 1831. Rep. Methodist.

Likes, Wm.; plasterer and brick mason; ¼ m n e West Newton. Born in Va. 1863. Rep. United Brethren.

Long, P. E.; farmer; 1 m s e Friendswood. Born in N. C. 1835; settled in M. C. 1870. Rep. Methodist.

Meredith, John; farmer; ¾ m from Bridgeport. Born in N. C. 1847; settled in M. C. 1871.

Mills, W. A.; tile manufacturer; 2 m n w Valley Mills. Born in M. C. 1849. Rep. Friend.

McCreary, Noah; farmer; Valley Mills. Born in Ohio 1823; settled in M. C. 1824. Methodist.

MENDENHALL, I. J.; writing school teacher; 2 m n w Valley Mills. Born in N. C. 1854; settled in M. C. 1872. Rep.

MILHOUSE, ISAAC; horticulturist; Valley Mills. Born in Ohio 1832; settled in M. C. 1850. Rep. Friend.

MILHOUSE, ROBERT; farmer; Valley Mills. Born in Ohio 1806; settled in M. C. 1835. Rep. Friend.

Mann, W. S.; farmer; 2½ m w West Newton. Born in Ind.; settled in M. C. 1871. Rep.

Mendenhall, John; farmer; West Newton. Born in M. C. 1848. Rep. Protestant.

Mendenhall, B.; farmer; West Newton. Born in M. C. 1850; Rep. Friend.

Mendenhall, Levi; farmer; West Newton. Born in M. C. 1853. Rep. Friend.

Mendenhall, A.; farmer; 1½ m n w West Newton. Was not at home.

Miryer, G.; farmer; 1½ m s w Maywood. Born in Germany 1846; settled in M. C. 1874. Dem. Lutheran.

Mills, Seth; physician and surgeon; Valley Mills. Born in Ohio 1841; settled in M. C. 1842. Friend.

Mills, Amos; farmer and horticulturist; 1 m n w West Newton. Born in Ohio 1828; settled in M. C. 1833. Rep. Friend.

Mendenhall, Wesley; farmer; 1½ m n w West Newton. Born in Ind. 1841; settled in M. C. 1841. Rep. Friend.

Mills, Mark; retired farmer; 1 m n West Newton. Born in S. C. 1804; settled in M. C. 1833.

Marlin, Albert; carriage and wagon manufacturer; West Newton. Born in N. J. 1837; settled in M. C. 1865. Rep. Methodist.

Miller, David; house painter; West Newton. Born in Ohio 1845; settled in M. C. 1868. Rep. Friend.

Mill, W. P.; dealer in dry goods and groceries; West Newton. Born in Ohio 1846; settled in M. C. 1873. Rep. Friend.

Mendenhall, Richard C.; farmer; 2 m s West Newton. Born in M. C. 1844. Rep. Protestant.

Mendenhall, J. L.; proprietor threshing machine; ½ m e Friendswood. Born in M. C. 1845. Rep. Protestant.

Mullin, L.; general work; 1 m n e Valley Mills. Born in Ind. 1832; settled in M. C. 1849. Dem.

Mendenhall, Ely; farmer; 1½ m w West Newton. Born in M. C. 1825. Rep. Friend.

Mendenhall, William; farmer; 1½ m s w West Newton. Born in Ohio 1810. Rep. Friend.

Mills, Wm.; farmer; 1 m s West Newton. Born in S. C. 1793; settled in M. C. 1854. Rep. Friend.

Mills, A.; farmer; 1 m s West Newton. Born in Ohio 1844; settled in M. C. 1854. Rep. Friend.

Mills, W. P.; dealer in dry goods and groceries; West Newton.

Mills, Joel; farmer; West Newton. Born in M. C. 1835. Rep. Friend.

McAdams, J. B.; carpenter; 1¼ m s Bridgeport. Born in N. C. 1830; settled in M. C. 1872. Rep. Protestant.

MILHOUSE, JOHN; farmer; 1 m s Bridgeport. Born in Ind. 1844; settled in M. C. 1844. Rep. Friend.

Mills, Daniel; farmer and stock raiser; 2 m s e Bridgeport. Born in Ohio 1827; settled in M. C. 1838. Rep. Friend.

Miller, J. W.; farmer; 1½ m n w Valley Mills. Born in Ky. 1847; settled in M. C. 1873. Dem. Protestant.

Mullin, Henry; farmer; 2 m n e Valley Mills. Born in Ind. 1823; settled in M. C. 1856. Dem. Methodist.

Nuson, E. ; farmer ; 1 m n w West Newton ; was not at home

NEWBY, SETH.; farmer ; 1½ m s e Bridgeport. Born in M. C. 1824. Rep. Friend.

PARNELL, HENRY ; farmer ; 1½ m s e Bridgeport. Born in Ind. 1846. Rep. Friend.

Parker, J. T. ; farmer; 2 m n Landersdale.

Palmer; J. A. ; carpenter and builder ; West Newton. Born in Ky. 1828 ; settled in M. C. 1866. Rep. Methodist.

Price, Ellis ; farmer ; 2 m e Valley Mills. Born in M. C. 1851.

Price, Jesse ; farmer and carpenter ; 1½ m s e Valley Mills. Born in N. J. 1820; settled in M. C. 1844. Dem. Prot.

Pfaff, Wesley ; farmer and trader ; ¼ m e West Newton. Born in 1849 ; settled in M. C. 1859. Rep. Methodist.

Russell, Joshua; farmer; West Newton. Born in Ind. 1817;
    settled in M. C. 1838. Rep. Friend.

Ritter, James; farmer; West Newton. Born in Ind. 1841;
    settled in M. C. 1867. Dem. Methodist.

Rose, Henry; farmer; West Newton. Born in Germany 1846;
    settled in M. C. 1866. Dem.

Ritter, E. J.; farmer; 1½ m e Valley Mills. Born in Ind.
    1828; settled in M. C. 1853.

RARDEN, A.; farmer; 1½ m n e Valley Mills. Born in
    Tenn. 1820; settled in M. C. 1871. Rep. Friend.

Ritter, C. A.; medical student; Valley Mills. Born in Ind.
    1851; settled in M. C. 1857. Rep. Friend.

Reynolds, Jesse; farmer; 1½ m n w West Newton.

REAGAN, REASON; farmer; 1 m n West Newton. Born in
    Ohio 1844; settled in M. C. 1851. Rep. Friend.

RATLIFF, NATHAN; farmer and stock raiser; 1¼ m n
    Friendswood. Born in Ind. 1824; settled in M. C. 1864.
    Rep. Friend.

Robeson, G. S.; farmer; 6 m s w Indianapolis. Born in M. C.
    1843. Rep. Protestant.

Riggs, Geo. W.; carpenter and builder; 2 m n e Valley Mills.
    Born in Ohio 1846; settled in M. C. 1853. Dem. Prot.

Roberson, George; farmer; 2 m s Sunny Side. Born in M. C.
    1843.

Stanton, James; farmer; 1 m s w Valley Mills. Born in Ohio 1820; settled in M. C. 1848. Rep. Friend.

Spray, J.; farmer; West Newton. Born in Ohio 1827; settled in M. C. 1865. Rep. Friend.

Sawyers, Iredell; farmer; 1 m n Laudersdale. Born in N. C. 1816; settled in M. C. 1840. Dem. Protestant.

Sellers, J. B.; farmer; 8 m s w Indianapolis. Born in Ohio 1844. Dem. Protestant.

Scott, Isom; farmer; 1 m s Valley Mills. Born in Ohio 1823; settled in M. C. 1834. Rep. Friend.

Scott, Wm.; farmer; Valley Mills. Born in M. C. 1848. Rep. Methodist.

Scott, John; farmer; ¾ m n Valley Mills. Born in Ohio. Rep. Methodist.

Sanders, Wm.; farmer; Valley Mills. Born in Ohio 1819; settled in M. C. 1832. Rep. Friend.

Serley, Martin; farmer; 1 m n w Valley Mills.

SANDERS, S. W.; farmer; 1½ m n West Newton. Born in M. C. 1849. Rep. Friend.

SPRAY, WILLIAM W.; farmer; 1½ m n West Newton. Born in Ohio 1848. Rep. Friend.

Spray, Amos; farmer; 3 m s Bridgeport. Born in M. C. 1844. Friend.

SMITH, SHELBY; farmer; 2 m s e Bridgeport. Born in Ky. 1818; settled in M. C. 1873. Rep. Methodist.

SMITH, AMOS M.; farmer; 2 m s e Bridgeport. Born in Ky. 1856; settled in M. C. 1873. Rep. Protestant.

Starbuck, Isaac; farmer; 2 m s Bridgeport. Born in Ind. 1849; settled in M. C. 1874. Rep. Friend.

Shelley, Daniel; farmer; 2 m n Valley Mills. Born in M. C. 1836. Rep. Methodist.

SCOTT, LOUIS C.; farmer; ½ m s Valley Mills. Born in M. C. 1852. Rep. Friend.

Seerley, Silas; farmer; 2 m n e Valley Mills. Born in M. C. 1848. Rep. Protestant.

Seerley, Martin L.; farmer; 1¾ m n w Valley Mills. Born in M. C. 1846. Rep.

Seerley, Martin; farmer; 1¾ m n w Valley Mills. Born in 1818. Rep.

Strode, Samuel; farmer; 2 m w Maywood. Born in Ky. 1831; settled in M. C. 1857. Dem. Methodist.

Sandlen, L.; farmer; 1½ m e Maywood. Born in N. C. 1819; settled in M. C. 1851. Rep. Methodist.

Sanders, Eli; farmer and stock raiser; 2 m s w Valley Mills. Born in Ohio 1815; settled in M. C. 1832. Rep. Friend.

Stanton, James; farmer; 1½ m s w Valley Mills. From home.

Sanders, John; farmer and stock raiser; ¾ m n e West Newton. Born in M. C. 1837. Rep. Friend.

Sanders, Wm. H.; farmer; 1½ m n e West Newton. Born in M. C. 1842. Rep. Friend.

Scott, Josiah; farmer; ½ m s Valley Mills. Born in M. C. 1850. Rep. Protestant.

Stone, James; farmer; 1½ m n e West Newton. Born in Ky. 1822; settled in M. C. 1872. Dem. Christian.

Stanton, Lewis B.; blacksmith and job worker; West Newton. Born in Ind. 1840; settled in M. C. 1868. Rep. Friend.

Shelley, S. S.; butcher; West Newton. Born in M. C. 1837. Rep. Methodist.

Sebastin, Marion; farmer; 1½ m e Friendswood. Born in Ky. 1828; settled in M. C. 1872. Dem. Christian.

Turley, John H.; huckster; West Newton. Born in Ind. 1844; settled in M. C. 1873. Dem. Christian.

Twining, E.; farmer; 1 m w Valley Mills. Born in Mass. 1824. Dem. Protestant.

Thomas, Wm. S.; farmer; 3 m s w Maywood. Born in M. C. 1840. Rep. Methodist.

Thomas, Edward; farmer; 3 m s w Maywood.   Born in Ky.
    1814; settled in M. C. 1833.   Rep.   Methodist.

VANNIDA, P. H., Jr.; farmer; 5½ m s w Indianapolis.   Born
    in Ohio 1844; settled in M. C. 1857.   Dem.   Presbyterian.

VANNIDA, P. H.. Sen.; 5½ m s w Indianapolis.   Born in Eu-
    rope 1813; settled in M. C. 1857.   Dem.   Presbyterian.

Willson, J. M.; farmer; 2½ m n e West Newton.   Born in M.
    C. 1826.   Rep.

Warren, Allen; farmer and carpenter; 2½ m n e West Newton.
    Born in Pa. 1844; settled in M. C. 1850.   Rep.

WILSON, G. J.; farmer and stock raiser; 1 m s w Valley
    Mills.   Born in Ohio.   Dem.   Methodist.

Wills, James A.; blacksmith; Maywood.   Born in Va. 1848;
    settled in M. C. 1872.

Whitson, Wm.; farmer; ½ m w Valley Mills.   Born in M. C.
    1843.   Rep.   Protestant.

WHITSON, J. J.; horticulturist; 1½ m s w Valley Mills.
    Born in Ind. 1830; settled in M. C. 1865.   Rep.   Prot.

Wilson, J. M.; farmer; 2 m n e West Newton.   Born in Ind.
    1826.

Wilson, Elijah; farmer; 2½ m e West Newton. Born in New Jersey 1811; settled in M. C. 1854. Rep. Protestant.

Wilson, H. J.; farmer; 2 m n Landersdale. Born in New Jersey 1835; settled in M. C. 1854. Rep. Protestant.

WAREN, E. B.; farmer; 1 m s e West Newton. Born in Tenn. 1834; settled in M. C. 1853. Protestant.

Weatherly, W. A.; farmer; West Newton. Born in N. C. 1830; settled in M. C. 1858. Rep. Friend.

Werld, Adam; farmer; 7 m s e Indianapolis. Born in Germany 1821; settled in M. C. 1871. Lutheran.

Williams, David; farmer; 1 m w West Newton. Born in M. C. 1839. Rep. Methodist.

Whitson, Willis; farmer; 1 m s West Newton. Born in M. C. 1849. Rep. Friend.

Wall, P. S.; minister M. E. Church. Born in West Va. 1823; settled in M. C. 1863. Rep.

Warren, John M.; farmer and carpenter; ¾ m w Valley Mills. Born in Tenn. 1832; settled in M. C. 1849. Rep.

Wilson, J. W.; blacksmith; Valley Mills. Born in Ind. 1842; settled in M. C. 1842. Methodist.

Wright, P. M.; farmer; 1½ m n e Valley Mills. Born in M. C. 1826. Rep. Methodist.

WILSON, HOWARD; farmer and stock raiser; 2½ m n Valley Mills. Born in M. C. 1843. Rep. Methodist.

Williamson, Samuel; farmer; 2 m n Valley Mills. Born in Ohio 1844; settled in M. C. 1849. Dem. Methodist.

Worth, John; farmer; 1½ m n w Valley Mills. Born in Ky. 1807; settled in M. C. 1832. Dem. Methodist.

WISEMAN, JOEL; farmer; 2½ m s Bridgeport. Born in Ind. 1837; settled in M. C. 1858. Protestant.

Worth, A. F.; farmer; 2½ m n w Valley Mills. Born in Ky. 1816; settled in M. C. 1838. Rep. Methodist.

Whitson, William; farmer; 1 m s West Newton. Born in Ohio 1809; settled in M. C. 1834. Rep. Friend.

ZEISLER, FREDERICK; farmer; 2 m n Valley Mills. Born in Germany 1834; settled in M. C. 1859. Dem. Meth.

FRANKLIN TOWNSHIP.

FRANKLIN TOWNSHIP is located in the southeast corner of Marion county, and is bounded on the north by Warren township, on the east by Hancock and Shelby counties, on the south by Johnson county, and on the west by Perry township, and contains about forty-two square miles.

The surface is rolling, and the soil rich. It is watered by Sugar Creek, Buck Creek and spring branches.

The farmer and stock raiser are amply rewarded for their labors, and the general improvements would indicate that the services of the mechanic demand good prices.

The citizens of this township are kind and generous, and take considerable interest in all public enterprises, and in the education of the young and rising generation. The public roads are in good order, and a great portion of them are graveled and turnpiked, which speaks well for her enterprising citizens.

Neat schoolhouses are numerous, and morality and intelligence are on the advance.

The present population of the township is about twenty-five hundred. The vote as taken from the official returns of October, 1874, for Secretary of State, is, Dem., 301; Rep., 184, Stout, Indpt., 4; total, 488; Dem. majority, 114.

Postoffices, Acton, Gallaudet.

Below will be found the names of some of the early settlers: James John Vandeman, J. H. Vandeman, Ashley Sutherland,

Willis Smither, W. C. Adair, John Smock, David Morris, T. J.
McCollum, J. P. McClain, Rev. Fisher, T. J. Carroll, Harris
Adams.

CHURCHES.

M. E. Church, Acton; F. S. Turk, pastor; membership, 200;
propable value of church property, $7,000.   Acton circuit has
four Sabbath schools; twenty-five teachers enrolled and 225
scholars, average attendance of schools, about 150.

Acton Missionary Baptist Church; H. McCalip, pastor; membership, 104.

Acton Missionary Baptist Sabbath School; superintendent, J.
McCollum; attendance of school, 40; number enrolled, 120.

New Bethel Missionary Baptist Church; pastor, F. M. Buchannan; membership, 209.   Sabbath school superintendent, F.
M. Buchannan; number of scholars enrolled, 128; average attendance of school, 50.   Postoffice, Gallaudet.

DIRECTORY OF FRANKLIN TOWNSHIP.

ADAIR, W. C.; retired from business; Poplar Grove.   Born in
Indiana Territory 1803; settled in M. C. 1824.

ARNOLD, JAMES M.; 5 m s e Indianapolis.   Born in 1820.

Arnold, Milton; 2¼ m s w New Bethel.   Born in M. C. 1851.

Anderson, Stephen H.; retired farmer; 5 m e Southport.   Born
in Ky. 1815; settled in M. C. 1833.

Ayers, Milton; wagon maker; Acton.   Born in Ind. 1821; settled in M. C. 1859.   Rep.

Anderson, Wm.; farmer; 1½ m n w Acton.   Born in England
1820; settled in M. C. 1854.

Anderson, Wm. A.; farmer; 2 m n w Acton. Born in England 1820; settled in M. C. 1854.

Adams, G. W.; farmer; ¼ m w New Bethel. Born in M. C. 1848.

Adams, Harrison; farmer; ¼ m n New Bethel. Born in Ky. 1813; settled in M. C. 1826.

BALDWIN, BENJAMIN; farmer; ¼ m s Gallaudet. Born in Va. 1820; settled in M. C. 1866.

Baldwin, Thomas; ¼ m s Gallaudet. Born in Ky. 1853; settled in M. C. 1866.

Barnett, Howard; farmer; 1½ m s Acton. Born in Va. 1850 ; settled in M. C. 1871.

Brady, Annie; 1½ m s Gallaudet.

BRADLEY, G. W.; farmer; 3 m w Gallaudet. Born in Ky. 1840; settled in M. C. 1874.

Butcher, Geo.; farmer; 3 m w Gallaudet. Born in England 1844; settled in M. C. 1866.

Butcher, Geo.; farmer; 3 m w Gallaudet. Born in England 1821; settled in M. C. 1860.

BELCHER, JOHN; farmer; 2 m n w Acton. Born in Ind. 1853; settled in M. C. 1853.

Brumley, J. D.; merchant; New Bethel. Born in M. C. 1835.

Brumley, John A.; farmer; 4 m n Gallaudet.   Born in M. C. 1832.

Berry, Walker James, farmer; 3 m n w Acton.   Born in M. C. 1851.

BERRY, MILES, farmer; 3 m n w Acton.   Born in M. C. 1849.

Brumley, Howard W.; farmer; 3¼ m n Gallaudet.   Born in M. C. 1844.

Bush, Geo. A.; farmer; 2 m s w Julietta.   Born in 1851; settled in M. C. 1868.

Baughman, William; farmer; 4 m n Acton.   Born in Ind. 1853; settled in M. C. 1870.

Brinkman, Henry; farmer; 2 m n w Gallaudet.   Born in 1815; settled in M. C. 1854.

Brinkman, Henry, Jr.; farmer; 2 m n w Gallaudet.   Born in Ind. 1850.

Barlow, John; farmer; 3 m s w Acton.   Born in Ky. 1821.

BEEKLY, WM.; farmer; 2 m s Acton.   Born in Va. 1801; settled in M. C. 1859.

BATTS, WM.; farmer; 3 m s w Acton.   Born in Ky. 1831; settled in M. C. 1859.   Dem.   Baptist.

BUDD, A. B.; jeweler and watchmaker; 1½ m e Acton.   Born in Ind. 1851.   Dem.   Universalist.

BOHNAT, PATRICK; wagonmaker; New Bethel. Born in Germany 1842; settled in M. C. 1874.

Buchannan, F. M.; pastor M. Baptist Church, New Bethel. Born in Ind. 1842; settled in M. C. 1864.

BROWN, GEO.; 2 m n w Gallaudet. Born in England 1843; settled in M. C. 1866.

Baker, Henry; farmer; 2 m n w Gallaudet. Born in Prussia 1831; settled in M. C. 1861.

BICKERSTAFF, JOHN; farmer; ½ m n Acton. Born in Ind. 1824; settled in M. C. 1869.

Bellis, Caleb; retired farmer; Acton. Born in Ky. 1811; settled in M. C. 1824. Dem. M. Baptist.

Bellis, Lewis; farmer. Born in Ind. 1839.

Burton, Harrison; carpenter; 1 m s e Acton. Born in Pa. 1839; settled in M. C. 1873.

Button, Timothy; farmer; 4½ m w Acton. Born in Ind. 1846; settled in M. C. 1868. Dem. Christian.

BUELL, JEREMIAH; farmer; 4½ m s e Southport. Born in Ind. 1820; settled in M. C. 1874.

CLEMENS, WM. J.; painter; Acton. Born in Ind. 1845; settled in M. C. 1856. Rep.

CLARK, ALEXANDER; farmer; Acton. Born in Ky. 1839; settled in M. C. 1852. Dem.

COLLY, WM. J.; farmer; 2½ m s w Acton. Born in Va. 1811; settled in M. C. 1835. Rep.

Crouch, Sam.; blacksmith; 3 m s w Acton. Born in M. C. 1850. Dem.

Crouch, Ben.; farmer; 2 m n w Acton. Born in Ind. 1830; settled in M. C. 1831. Dem. Methodist.

CRAFT, MRS. MARY; 1½ m n w Acton. Born in N. J. 1812; settled in M. C. 1856.

Craft, Jas. T.; Acton. Born in Ind. 1850; settled in M. C. 1856.

Campbell, T. D.; farmer; New Bethel. Born in Ind. 1834; settled in M. C. 1858.

Cranch, Geo. W.; farmer; 4¼ m s w Acton. Born in Ky. 1849; settled in M. C. 1870.

Cummins, Geo. D.; farmer; ½ m s Gallaudet. Born in Ky. 1836; settled in M. C. 1863.

Cox, Reuben; farmer and trader; 2 m s w Gallaudet. Born in Ky. 1837; settled in M. C. 1870.

Clark, J. M.; farmer; 2¼ m s Gallaudet. Born in Ky. 1847; settled in M. C. 1872.

Collins, Andrew; farmer; 2 m s w Gallaudet. Born in Ohio 1814; settled in M. C. 1842.

Clark, Wm.; farmer; 2 m s w Gallaudet. Born in Ind. 1850; settled in M. C. 1850.

Collins, Isaac; farmer; 2½ m w Gallaudet. Born in Ohio 1809; settled in M. C. 1847.

Collins, Ephraim; farmer; 2¼ m w Gallaudet. Born in Ind. 1846.

Cleaver, W. D.; toll gate keeper; 3½ m e Southport. Born in Ind. 1843; settled in M. C. 1864.

CARRON, JOHN; farmer; New Bethel. Born in Ky. 1852; settled in M. C. 1868.

CORYMAN, T. J.; farmer; 1½ m n w Gallaudet. Born in N. H. 1848; settled in M. C. 1873.

CARROLL, ARCHIBALD; farmer; 1½ m n w Gallaudet. Born in Ky. 1820; settled in M. C. 1854.

CAMERON, HENRY; farmer; 4 m s w Acton. Born in N. J. 1849; settled in M. C. 1874.

CROMLEY, DANIEL; farmer; 5½ m n Acton. Born in S. C. 1847; settled in M. C. 1869.

CRANE, JAMES N.; carpenter; New Bethel. Born in Ind. 1850; settled in M. C. 1873.

CREAM, J. C.; farmer; 5 m n Acton. Born in Ky. 1851; settled in M. C. 1872.

CORNIN, JOHN; farmer; 4½ m n w Acton. Born in Iowa 1839; settled in M. C. 1869. Dem. Christian.

Carney, Martin; farmer; 3 m n w Acton. Born in Pa. 1829; settled in M. C. 1847.

Carney, John S.; farmer; 3 m n w Acton. Born in M. C. 1854.

CRESS, JOHN; farmer; ¼ m s Gallaudet. Born in Ky. 1832; settled in M. C. 1873.

Carney, Mrs. Nancy; 3 m s w Acton. Born in N. Y. 1799; settled in M. C. 1851.

CLARK, JOSEPH K.; farmer; 3 m w Acton. Born in Ky. 1810; settled in M. C. 1850.

Clark, G. M.; farmer; 3 m w Acton. Born in M. C. 1852.

Copeland, Henry; farmer; 3 m w Acton. Born in Va. 1827; settled in M. C. 1851.

Collins, E. H.; farmer; 1¼ m s Gallaudet. Born in 1838; settled in M. C. 1842.

Cleveland, E.; farmer; 9 m s e Indianapolis. Born in 1836.

CARSON, CHAS.; farmer; 3¼ m s w Gallaudet. Born in Ohio 1844; settled in M. C. 1871.

CARSON, JAMES P.; farmer; 1½ m s e Gallaudet. Born in Ind. 1837; settled in M. C. 1837.

CARSON, ANDREW; farmer; 1½ m s e Gallaudet. Born in M. C. 1840.

Carroll, James; farmer; 1½ m w Gallaudet. Born in Ky. 1837; settled in M. C. 1859.

Catterson, Noah; 4 m n e Gallaudet. Born in M. C. 1851.

Cook, Mrs.; ½ m n New Bethel. Born in M. C. 1829.

Cunningham, K.; farmer; ½ m n Gallaudet. Born in Va. 1816.

Crook, Robert; farmer; ½ m Gallaudet.

- Cooper, Wm.; saddler and harness maker; Acton. Born in England 1828; settled in M. C. 1860.

CRIM, H. C.; carpenter; 5 m n Acton. Born in N. Y. 1838; settled in M. C. 1873.

CASEY, M. J.; farmer; 4 m s e Southport. Born in 1848; settled in M. C. 1870.

Classey, H.; farmer; 3 m s e Southport. Born in Ireland 1842; settled in M. C. 1864.

CARROLL, T. J.; retired farmer; 2½ m n Acton. Born in Indiana Territory 1810; settled in M. C. 1818.

CRAVENS, DAVID G.; farmer; 3 m e Southport. Born in Ind. 1844; settled in M. C. 1871.

CARTWRIGHT, P. S.; farmer and brick molder; 1½ m s Acton. Born in Ind. 1851; settled in M. C. 1873.

Dewitt, D. M.; teacher; Acton. Born in Ky. 1831; settled in M. C. 1873. Rep. Universalist.

DAVIS, HENRY; farmer; 1 m n Gallaudet. Born in Ind. 1838; settled in M. C. 1850. Rep. M. Baptist.

Douglass, Booker; farmer; ¼ m s Gallaudet. Born in Va. 1837; settled in M. C. 1864.

Dunlap, Robert M.; farmer; 6 m s e Indianapolis. Born in Ohio 1839; settled in M. C. 1858.

Daily, H.; farmer; 6 m s e Indianapolis. Born in Ind. 1855; settled in M. C. 1871.

Dilliner, John; farmer; 3½ m e Southport. Born in 1823; settled in M. C. 1836.

Duluth, Henry; farmer; 3½ m n Acton. Born in Ky. 1853; settled in M. C. 1874.

DAVIS, JOHN; farmer; 2½ m s e Southport. Born in Conn. 1851; settled in M. C. 1870.

Dregar, Wm.; farmer; 1½ m n New Bethel. Born in 1834; settled in M. C. 1850.

Eaton, W. S.; farmer; 3 m n Acton. Born in Ky. 1825; settled in M. C. 1830. Rep. Christian.

Eaton, J. M.; farmer; 3 m n Acton. Born in Ind. 1851. Rep. Christian.

Eaton, M. S.; teacher; 1 m n e New Bethel. Born in M. C. 1842.

Eaton, Bluford; farmer; 1 m n e New Bethel. Born in Ky. 1805; settled in M. C. 1823.

Eaton, Obediah; farmer; 1 m n Gallaudet. Born in M. C. 1848.

Eaton, Mrs. Sarah; 2 m n Gallaudet. Born in Ky. 1804; settled in M. C. 1840.

Eaton, Wm.; farmer; 3 m s w Julietta. Settled in M. C. 1856.

Eaton, Robert; farmer; 3 m n Gallaudet. Born in M. C. 1850.

Eaton, Wm.; retired farmer; 3 m n Gallaudet. Born in Ky. 1802; settled in M. C. 1830.

Eaton, T. S.; farmer; 1¼ m s Julietta. Born in Ky. 1827.

Engleman, C.; farmer; 3 m s e Southport. Born in 1847; settled in M. C. 1867.

EASTER, WM.; carpenter; 3½ m n e Acton. Born in Miss. 1853; settled in M. C. 1874.

Eagle, Martin; farmer; 2½ m n Acton. Born in M. C. 1853.

Fry, John; farmer; 4 m n Acton. Born in M. C. 1851.

Fry, Shepley; farmer; 4 m n Acton. Born in Pa. 1822; settled in M. C. 1848.

Fulwider, J. S.; farmer; 4 m w Acton. Born in Ind. 1840; settled in M. C. 1867. Rep. M. Baptist.

Ferguson, N. J.; farmer; 2½ m s w Gallaudet. Born in Ky 1839; settled in M. C. 1868.

Froush, Gustave; minister United Brethren Church. Born in Germany 1843; settled in M. C. 1873.

Fogarty, John; railroading; Acton. Born in Ireland 1848; settled in M. C. 1872.

Fogarty, Ed.; railroading; Acton. Born in Ireland; settled in M. C. 1872.

Fisher, Samuel; railroading; Acton. Born in Pa. 1844; settled in M. C. 1868.

Faulconer, Wm. T.; farmer; ¼ m w Acton. Born in Ky. 1819; settled in M. C. 1872.

Fitzgerland, J; dry goods clerk; Acton. Born in Ky. 1819; settled in M. C. 1874. Dem.

Floyd, Sam.; carpenter and builder; Acton. Born in W. Va. 1800; settled in M. C. 1873. Dem. Presbyterian.

Foley, John; telegraph operator; Acton. Born in Ohio 1849; settled in M. C. 1860.

FRENCH, CALVIN; farmer; 2¼ m s Julietta. Born in Ohio 1846; settled in M. C. 1847. Dem.

FREUND, HANS.; brickmason; 4½ m n w Acton. Born in Germany 1847; settled in M. C. 1873. Rep. Catholic.

Fisher, Ben; farmer; 2½ m n w Gallaudet. Born in Ind. 1824; settled in M. C. 1826.

FRANSREPE, JOHN; farmer; 6 m s e Indianapolis.   Born in
Germany 1839; settled in M. C. 1859.

Gold, George W.; merchant; Acton.   Born in Ind. 1843; settled in M. C. 1873.

Gordon, F. M.; carpenter; ¼ m s e Acton.   Born in Ind.
1840; settled in M. C. 1874.   Rep.

Graham, John; farmer; 2 m n Gallaudet.   Born in Ohio 1843.

Gray, J. M. D.; farmer; 2¾ m e Southport.   Born in Ind.
1853; settled in M. C. 1853.

Graham, Wm.; farmer; 1½ m s w Gallaudet.   Born in M. C.
1835.

HUTCHINSON, MRS. MARY; 1½ m n Acton. Born in Ohio
1813; settled in M. C. 1834.

HENSLEY, FRANK; farmer; 1½ m n Acton.   Born in Ky.;
settled in M. C. 1873.

Hart, J. W.; farmer; 3 m n Acton.   Born in Germany 1829;
settled in M. C. 1850.

Hickman, Geo.; farmer; 2¼ m s Julietta.   Born in Ohio 1815;
settled in M. C. 1834.

HANCH, C.; blacksmith; New Bethel. Born in Germany 1853, settled in M. C. 1873.

HASTINGS, F. A.; farmer; New Bethel. Born in Ohio 1842; settled in M. C. 1860.

HUTREL, T. J.; farmer; ½ m s e New Bethel. Born in Ky. 1849; settled in M. C. 1846.

Hutchinson, Frank; farmer; 2 m n Acton. Born in M. C. 1851.

Howard, George; butcher; 1 m n Gallaudet. Born in England 1833; settled in M. C. 1873.

Harris, W. M.; brick molder; Acton. Born in Va. 1847; settled in M. C. 1874.

Hamlin, Jonas; farmer; ½ m s Acton. Born in England 1835; settled in M. C. 1860.

Hutchinson, W. C.; farmer; 1 m s e Acton. Born in Ind. 1842; settled in M. C. 1868. Rep.

Hamlin, Jno.; farmer; 1 m s w Acton. Born in England 1842; settled in M. C. 1855.

Harvey, Noah; farmer; 1½ m s w Acton. Born in Ind. 1841; settled in M. C. 1865.

HENDERSON, J. W.; farmer; 2½ m w Acton. Born in Ky. 1851; settled in M. C. 1873. Dem.

HARVEY, J. G.; farmer; 3 m s w Acton. Born in Ohio 1847; settled in M. C. 1874. Dem.

Hickman, Bayard; farmer; ½ m w Acton. Born in M. C. 1847.
Dem.

Hahn, Sol.; miller; Acton. Born in Va. 1829; settled in M. C.
1857.

HENRY, JAMES; ditcher; 1½ m w Gallaudet. Born in Ireland; settled in M. C. 1870. Dem. Catholic.

Harnet, Jordan; farmer; 7 m s e Indianapolis. Born in Ohio
1853; settled in M. C. 1874.

Harrison, J. H.; farmer; 4½ m s w Acton. Born in N. J. 1838;
settled in M. C. 1861.

Hebbler, Daniel; carpenter; 8 m s e Indianapolis. Born in Ind.
1841; settled in M. C. 1870.

Henry, Mrs. Lavina; 2 m s w Gallaudet. Born in M. C. 1853.

Hill, John; farmer; 2¼ m s w Gallaudet. Born in 1829; settled
in M. C. 1856.

Hill, F.; farmer; 2¼ m s w Gallaudet. Born in Ohio 1850; settled in M. C. 1856.

Hill, L.; farmer; 2¼ m s w Gallaudet. Born in Ohio 1853; settled in M. C. 1856.

Huffington, A. C.; farmer; 7 m s e Indianapolis. Born in Del.
1819; settled in M. C. 1837.

Huffington, J. B.; farmer; 7 m s e Indianapolis. Born in M.
C. 1852.

Holman, David; farmer; 4½ m e Southport. Born in Ind.
1844; settled in M. C. 1873.

Helms, Wm. farmer; 1¼ m s e Gallaudet. Born in Va. 1795;
settled in M. C. 1836. Soldier of 1812.

Hittle, Joseph; farmer; 1½ m e Gallaudet. Born in 1819; settled in M. C. 1853.

Hittle, Isaac; farmer; 1½ m e Gallaudet. Born in Ind. 1848;
settled in M. C. 1853.

Hutsel, John; farmer; 2 m e Gallaudet. Born in Ky. 1847.
settled in M. C. 1859.

Hall, H. H.; farmer; 1 m e Gallaudet. Born in Ky. 1824; settled in M. C. 1860.

Harris, G. W.; farmer; 4 m s w Julietta. Born in M. C. 1844.

Harris, Joseph; farmer; 1¼ m s w Julietta. Born in Ohio
1828; settled in M. C. 1831.

Hill, Joseph; farmer; 1 m n New Bethel. Born in 1837; settled in M. C. 1872.

Harting, Henry; 1 m n w Gallaudet.

Hibbler, D.; carpenter; 6 m s e Indianapolis. Born in 1841;
settled in M. C. 1845.

HENDRICKS, S. M.; farmer; 2¾ m e Southport. Born in
M. C. 1850.

Henry, S. B.; farmer; 2½ m s w Acton. Born in M. C. 1850.

Hendricks, W. P.; farmer; 2¾ m e Southport. Born in M. C. 1849.

Hendricks, A.; farmer; 2¾ m e Southport. Born in 1797; settled in M. C. 1834.

HEAD, F. M.; farmer; 3½ m s e Southport. Born in 1837; settled in M. C. 1838.

Head, S. T.; farmer; 3½ m s e Southport. Born in 1834; settled in M. C. 1838.

HENRY; MOSES; brick molder; Acton. Born in Ky. 1844; settled in M. C. 1874.

JOYCE, ALEXANDER; stock raiser and farmer; 1½ m s e Acton. Born in Va. 1820; settled in M. C. 1832. Dem. Baptist.

JAMES, JAMES; farmer; 1½ m n Acton. Born in England; settled in M. C. 1874. Dem. Catholic.

Jenkins, W. H.; farmer; 1½ m n e New Bethel. Born in Ind. 1840; settled in M. C. 1874.

JINKINS, M. C.; farmer; 5¼ m s w Acton. Born in Ind. 1850; settled in M. C. 1856. Rep. Christian.

JESTER, ALLEN; farmer; 7 m s e Indianapolis. Born in Mo. 1853; settled in M. C. 1868.

Jenkins, Wm.; farmer; 1¼ m s e Gallaudet.   Born in Va. 1848; settled in M. C. 1871.

JAMASON, WM.; farmer; 3½ m e Southport.   Born in Ind. 1843; settled in M. C. 1874.

JOHNSON, H. L.; farmer; 2¾ m s e Southport.   Born in Ky. 1841; settled in M. C. 1856.

Kemper, J.; farmer; 2 m n w Acton.   Born in Ind. 1844; settled in M. C. 1845.

Kemper, H. M.; 2 m n Gallaudet.   Born in Ky. 1816; settled in M. C. 1832.   Rep.

Kemper, John; farmer; 2 m n e Gallaudet.   Born in Indianapolis 1846.   Rep.

KYLE, JOHN; farmer; 1½ m n w Gallaudet.   Born in Ind. 1832.

KEENAN, J. W.; farmer; 5½ m s w Acton.   Born in Ind. 1845; settled in M. C. 1870.   Rep.   Methodist.

KEMPER, WM. H.; farmer; 1½ m s e Gallaudet.   Born in M. C. 1856.

KEMPER, F. S.; farmer; 1½ m s e Gallaudet.   Born in M. C. 1855.

KEMPER, MISS ANNIE J.; 1½ m s e Gallaudet.   Born in M. C. 1844.

Kemper, Miss Nannie A.; 1½ m s e Gallaudet. Born in M. C. 1848.

Kemper, Sam.; carpenter; 1½ m s e Gallaudet. Born in M. C. 1850.

Kister, Peter; farmer; 2 m s w Julietta. Born in 1821; settled in M. C. 1874.

Kittley, Richard; farmer; 2 m s w Julietta. Born in Ind. 1825; settled in M. C. 1827.

Kittley, Willis; farmer; 2 m s w Julietta. Born in M. C. 1856.

Kittley, John; farmer; 2 m s w Julietta. Born in M. C. 1852.

Kemper, Peter; farmer; 3 m w Gallaudet. Settled in M. C. 1832.

Kemper, John; farmer; 6 m s e Indianapolis. Born in Ind. 1846; settled in M. C. 1847.

KEYS, JOHN; farmer; 3 m n e Southport. Born in Ohio 1840; settled in M. C. 1852.

Kelley, E.; farmer and tile manufacturer; 2 m e Southport. Born in Ohio 1843; settled in M. C. 1870.

Kelley, Harris; farmer; 2¼ m s w Southport. Born in M. C. 1853.

Lomes, M.; farmer; ½ m s e Acton. Born in Ohio 1817; settled in M. C. 1864.

LEONARD, LINDSEY; farmer; 2½ m n w Gallaudet.   Born
in N. C. 1823; settled in M. C. 1873.   Rep.   M. Baptist.

Lomes, Jas.; farmer; ½ m s w Acton.

Lancaster, Geo.; farmer; 2¼ m s Julietta.   Born in Ohio 1837;
settled in M. C. 1858.   Rep.

Leachman, G. H.; farmer; 6 m s e Indianapolis.   Born in M.
C. 1844.

LEETZ, JOHN; farmer; 6 m s e Indianapolis.   Born in Germany 1822; settled in M. C. 1855.

Lawrence, John; farmer; 3 m n e Greenwood.   Born in Ky.
1852; settled in M. C. 1864.

LAROSHA, CONRAD; farmer; 1½ m s e Gallaudet.   Born in
1851.

Lard, J. M.; farmer; 2½ m s e Gallaudet.   Born in Ind. 1849;
settled in M. C. 1870.

Leonard, George; farmer; 1¾ m e New Bethel.   Born in M. C.
1844.

Lockwood, G. W.; farmer; 9 m s e Indianapolis.   Born in Ind.
1850; settled in M. C. 1853.

Lam, John; farmer; 1¼ m n Gallaudet.   Born in M. C. 1841.

Lam, Henry; farmer; 1 m n Gallaudet.

Lither, Martin; farmer; 1½ m n w Gallaudet. Born in Germany
1838; settled in M. C. 1862.

Lee, T. R.; farmer; 6 m s e Indianapolis. Born in Ky.; settled
in M. C. 1844.

List, Cornelius; farmer; 3 m e Southport. Born in Ky. 1847;
settled in M. C. 1852.

Mitchell, Martin; farm hand; 3½ m e Southport. Born in M. C.
1846.

MARTINDALE, HARRIS; farmer; 4 m e Southport.   Born
in M. C. 1841.

McCawley, Jas.; farmer; 4 m s e Southport.   Born in 1818;
settled in M. C. 1867.

McCawley, Jesse; farmer; 4 m s e Southport.   Born in 1846;
settled in M. C. 1867.

McClain, J. P.; farmer; 4 m s e Southport.   Born in 1816; settled in M. C. 1825.

Monroe, Jas.; farmer; 4 m s e Southport.   Born in M. C. 1840;

Miles, M.; farmer; 2½ m s e Southport.   Born in 1851; settled
in M. C. 1873.

Miles, J. E.; farmer; 2½ m s e Southport.   Born in 1814; settled in M. C. 1872.

Miles, J. K. P.; farmer; 2½ m s e Southport.   Born in 1846;
settled in M. C. 1872.

Murdock, H. C.; 5 m n w Acton.   Born in Ky. 1854; settled in M. C. 1874.

Merit, W. B.; carpenter; 2½ m s w Acton.   Born in M. C. 1852.

Marriner, Dan.; farmer; 4 m s e Southport.   Born in Ky. 1848; settled in M. C. 1874.

Morgan, J. W.; farmer; 4¾ m n e Greenwood.   Born in Ind. 1832; settled in M. C. 1874.

Martin, J. H.; carpenter; 2½ m w New Bethel.   Born in Ill. 1855; settled in M. C. 1873.

Morris, James M; brickyard hand; Acton.   Born in M. C. 1849.

Mewer, James T.; retired; 3½ m s w Acton.   Born in N. Y. 1802; settled in M. C. 1873.

Millspaugh, F.; farmer; 2½ m n w Gallaudet.   Born in Ind. 1824; settled in M. C. 1864.

Millspaugh, Francis E.; farmer; 2¼ m n w Gallaudet.   Born in M . C. 1854.

MINSTER, HARRISON; farmer; 3 m n w Gallaudet.   Born in Ohio 1848; settled in M. C. 1874.

McLaughlin, Thomas; 6 m s e Indianapolis.   Born in M. C. 1836.

McLaughlin, George; farmer; 6 m s e Indianapolis.   Born in M. C. 1853.

McClain, J. W.; farmer; 3 m e Southport.   Born in M. C. 1847.

McLean, Joseph; farmer; 6 m s e Indianapolis. Born in 1821; settled in M. C. 1838.

McClain, Susana; 3 m e Southport. Born in Ky. 1811; settled in M. C. 1834.

MORAN, JOHN C.; farmer; 3 m n Acton. Born in N. C. 1841; settled in M. C. 1874.

Martin, H.; farmer; 1¼ m n New Bethel. Born in M. C. 1850.

Martin, G.; farmer; ½ m n New Bethel. Born in Germany 1814; settled in M. C. 1834.

Murphy, William B.; farmer; 3 m n e Gallaudet. Born in Ind. 1840; settled in M. C. 1841.

Murphy, J. B.; farmer; 3 m n e Gallaudet. Born in M. C. 1845.

Murphy, A. C.; farmer; 3 m n e Gallaudet. Born in M. C. 1853.

Murphy, J. T.; farmer; 3 m n e Gallaudet. Born in 1814; settled in M. C. 1841.

Market, D.; farmer; 3 m s Julietta. Born in Ind. 1847; settled in M. C. 1856.

Mason, G. W.; farmer; 2¾ m s Julietta. Born in Ky. 1844; settled in M. C. 1867.

MATTHEWS, SILAS B.; farmer; 1¼ m s w Gallaudet. Born in Ind. 1838; settled in M. C. 1844.

Matthews, Sarah; 1½ m s w Gallaudet. Born in 1803; settled in M. C. 1837.

McColum, J. W.; tile maker; 5½ m s e Indianapolis. Born in M. C. 1857.

McLean, Joseph; farmer; 3 m n Gallaudet. Born about 1824.

McClain, Joseph O.; farmer; 3½ m e Southport. Born in M. C. 1846.

McClain, John W.; farmer; 3½ m e Southport. Born in M. C. 1847.

McClain, Cornelius; farmer; 3½ m e Southport. Born in M. C. 1839.

McCawley, John W.; farmer; 4 m e Southport. Born in Ind. 1830; settled in M. C. 1844.

McMullen, John; farmer; 2 m e New Bethel. Born in Va. 1826; settled in M. C. 1838.

McMullen, P. D.; farmer; 2 m e New Bethel. Born in M. C. 1855.

Morgan, Geo. W.; farmer; ¼ m w Acton. Born in Ky. 1844; settled in M. C. 1868. Rep.

McCollum, T. J.; farmer; 1 m n Acton. Born in Ohio 1824; settled in M. C. 1826. Rep. Baptist.

McCollum, J. W. K.; carpenter; Acton. Born in M. C. 1852.

Montague, Lemuel; farmer; 1½ m n w Acton. Born in Ind. 1822; settled in M. C. 1862. Dem.

McGaughey, R. L.; farmer; ¼ m n New Bethel. Born in Ind. 1835; settled in M. C. 1854.

McGaughey, Moses; farmer; 1½ m n Gallaudet.   Born in Ind.
1832; settled in M. C. 1854.   Rep.   Presbyterian.

McGaughey, J. E.; farmer; 1½ m n Gallaudet.   Born in Ind.
1850; settled in M. C. 1854.

MILLER, FREDERICK; farmer; 1 m n Gallaudet.   Born in
Germany; settled in M. C. 1858.

McMULLEN, MEREDITH C.; painter; Poplar Grove; 2½ m
w Gallaudet.   Born in Ind. 1844.   Dem.

McELRAY, WM.; farmer; 2½ m n w Gallaudet.   Born in Ireland 1844; settled in M. C. 1872.

MORROW, JOHN; farmer; New Bethel.   Born in N. C. 1846;
settled in M. C. 1869.

Marker, J. M.; farmer 4 m s w Acton.   Born in Va. 1840; settled in M. C. 1842.   Dem.   Christian.

McMullen, T. J.; farmer; 4½ m n Acton.   Born in Ind. 1846;
settled in M. C. 1862.

Murray, Henry; farmer; 5¼ m n Acton.   Born in Tenn. 1852;
settled in M. C. 1873.

McGregor, William; farmer; ¼ m w Acton.   Born in Ind. 1828;
settled in M. C. 1858.   Dem.

Malcolm, ———; farmer; ½ m s e Acton.   Born in Ohio 1817;
settled in M. C. 1864.

Murphy, Jno.; farmer; 2½ m s Julietta.   Born in 1812.   Dem.

MORRIS, JOHN S.; farmer and teacher; 1 m s w Acton. Born in Ind. 1842.

Morris, Amos; farmer; 1 m s w Acton. Born in Pa. 1813; settled in M. C. 1839.

Maze, John A.; farmer; 1½ m s w Acton. Born in Ind. 1833; settled in M. C. 1848. Baptist.

Maze, Elijah; farmer; 2½ m s w Acton. Born in Ind. 1844.

Morris, David; 2¾ m s w Acton. Born in Ind. 1823; settled in M. C. 1824.

McGregor, J.; blacksmith; Acton. Born in Ind. 1853; settled in M. C. 1858.

MORRIS, J. J.; farmer; 1½ m n w Acton. Born in Ky. 1823; settled in M. C. 1856. Dem.

Morgan, Wm.; farmer; Acton. Born in Ind. 1852; settled in M. C. 1857.

Mason, Jas. C.; farmer; 2¼ m n Gallaudet. Born in Ky. 1831; settled in M. C. 1839. Dem. R. Baptist.

MILLS, NEWTON; general work; 5½ m w Acton. Born in Ind. 1853; settled in M. C. 1873.

McGaughey, Sam.; physician; Acton. Born in Ind. 1828; settled in M. C. 1856. Rep. Presbyterian.

Mann, Sam.; lumber dealer; Acton. Born in Ky. 1818; settled in M. C. 1836. Rep. M. Baptist.

Mare, Thos.; general purpose; Acton. Born in Ind. 1836; settled in M. C. 1856.

Murphy, Dan.; farmer; Acton. Born in Ohio 1853; settled in M. C. 1863. Dem. Catholic.

MAZE, JOSEPH; farmer; 1 m s Gallaudet. Born in M. C. 1847.

MAZE, MARGARET; 1 m s Gallaudet. Born in Ind. 1810; settled in M. C. 1847.

Morgan, J. H.; farmer; 2½ m n w Acton. Born in Ky. 1845; settled in M. C. 1863.

MYERS, ALEXANDER; farmer; 2½ m w Acton. Born in Ind. 1838; settled in M. C. 1845.

MUSE, THOMAS F.; farmer; 4 m w Acton. Born in Ky. 1847; settled in M. C. 1859.

Monroe, James; farmer; 3 m e Southport. Born in M. C. 1840.

Monroe, John; farmer; 4 m e Acton. Born in Ky. 1808.

McGREW, DANIEL; farmer; 4½ m s w Acton. Born in Ohio 1842; settled in M. C. 1867.

Mathews, John; retired farmer; 1 m s w Gallaudet. Born in 1805; settled in M. C. 1844.

NEMHART, HENRY; farmer; 1¾ m n Acton. Born in Europe; settled in M. C. 1868. Rep. Methodist.

Newman, David; farmer; 4½ m e Gallaudet. Born in Ky. 1838; settled in M. C. 1871.

Newton, J.; farmer; 2¾ m s Gallaudet. Born in Ind. 1851; settled in M. C. 1870.

Noble, Marion; farmer; 2¼ m e Southport. Born in Ind. 1856; settled in M. C. 1857.

Onerhyser, J. P.; farmer and tile manufacturer; 3½ m w Acton. Born in N. Y. 1827; settled in M. C. 1864.

Oldham, Thos.; farmer; 4 m e Southport. Born in Ohio 1822; settled in M. C. 1864.

Oldham, M. L.; farmer; 4 m e Southport. Born in Ohio 1852.

Perkins, Joseph; farmer; 1 m w Acton. Born in Ind. 1840; settled in M. C. 1840. Dem. Methodist.

Philips, J. E.; farmer; 2 m w Acton. Born in Ind. 1852; settled in M. C. 1868.

Phemister, John; farmer; 1½ m n w Acton. Born in Ky. 1809; settled in M. C. 1856.

PICK, TOM; plasterer; Acton. Born in France 1850; settled in M. C. 1859. Dem.

PARSLEY, ALEXANDER; farmer; Acton. Born in M. C. 1846.

PULLENS, MRS. AMANDA; 1½ m w Acton. Born in Ohio 1819; settled in M. C. 1864. Methodist.

PULLENS, CALVIN J.; butcher; Acton. Born in 1851; settled in M. C. 1864. Dem.

PARSLEY, JNO. W.; farmer; 1¼ m n Acton. Born in Ind. 1852; settled in M. C. 1852. Dem.

Peel, Chris.; ½ m n New Bethel. Born in Germany; settled in M. C. 1873.

Plummer, Wm.; farmer; 2 m s w Julietta. Born in Ind. 1842; settled in M. C. 1873.

PERRY, MARTHA; 1 m n w Gallaudet. Born in Va. 1792; settled in M. C. 1833.

PERRY, LOUISA; 1 m n w Gallaudet. Born in Ky. 1805; settled in M. C. 1833.

PORTER, ROBERT; farm hand; 6 m s e Indianapolis. Born in 1847; settled in M. C. 1873.

Philips, B. F.; farmer; 6 m s e Indianapolis. Born in M. C. 1851.

Philips, Polly; 6 m s e Indianapolis. Born in Ky. 1808; settled in M. C. 1834.

Parsley, Susan; 1¼ m n Acton. Born in Ky. 1821; settled in M. C. 1839. Baptist.

Philips, Volney; farmer; Acton. Settled in M. C. 1873. Dem.

Porter, Wm.; farmer; 1½ m n Acton. Born in Ky. 1851; settled in M. C. 1872. Dem. M. Baptist.

PFENILLER, SAM; farmer; 1½ m n w Acton. Born in Switzerland 1833; settled in M. C. 1847. Dem.

PENTECOST, WM. B.; farmer; 3½ m n Acton. Born in Ind. 1832; settled in M. C. 1854.

Pierce, Isaac; farmer; 2 m n Acton. Born in Ind. 1852; settled in M. C. 1869.

PRINGLE, F. M.; farmer; 2½ m w Gallaudet. Born in N. Y. 1848; settled in M. C. 1871.

PATTISON, J. D.; pork dealer and packer; also firm of Hibben, Kennedy & Co., Indianapolis.

Prine, James; farmer; 1½ m n w Gallaudet. Born in Pa. 1830; settled in M. C. 1861.

Porter, John; dentist; Acton. Born in Ohio 1833; settled in M. C. 1857. Dem. Presbyterian.

Pierson, D. W.; merchant; Acton. Born in Pa. 1843; settled in M. C. 1859. Rep.

PARSLEY, JOHN; farmer; Acton. Born in 1819; settled in M. C. 1830.

PATTON, CHAS.; general work; Acton. Born in Ind. 1847; settled in M. C. 1874.

Perry, Chas. W.; farmer; ¾ m n e Acton. Born in Ind. 1848.

Potter, Sam.; farmer; 1½ m s e Acton. Born in Ohio 1801; settled in M. C. 1869. Dem. Presbyterian.

Porter, Benton; brick molder; 6½ m s e Indianapolis. Born in 1846; settled in M. C. 1866.

PRICE, DAVID; farm hand; 5 m n Acton. Born in Ky. 1849; settled in M. C. 1874.

Pollard, Martin; farmer; 2 m s Gallaudet. Born in Ky. 1841; settled in M. C. 1869.

Pollard, Geo. T.; farmer; ½ m s Gallaudet. Born in Ky. 1844; settled in M. C. 1866.

Parr, A.; farmer; 3¾ m w Acton. Born in Ind.; settled in M. C. 1869.

POOLE, JAMES; farmer; 1½ m s Gallaudet. Born in 1811; settled in M. C. 1820.

POWERS, MRS. LUCINDA; 1½ m s Gallaudet. Born in Ky. 1814; settled in M. C. 1835.

Powers, John; farmer; 1½ m s Gallaudet. Born in M. C. 1844.

Powers, Marshal; farmer; 1½ m s Gallaudet. Born in M. C. 1849.

PARSON, SAM.; farmer; 2½ m w Gallaudet. Born in Ga. 1849; settled in M. C. 1865.

PRATT, JOSEPH; farmer; 1½ m n w Bethel. Born in Pa. 1855; settled in M. C. 1865.

Phemister, Catharine; 2 m n w Acton. Born in Ky. 1836; settled in M. C. 1860.

Ransdall, J. W.; proprietor of sawmill; Acton. Born in Ky. 1851; settled in M. C. 1872.

RUBUSH, T. R.; student at Wabash College; res 1½ m s e Acton. Born in Ind. 1853. Rep.

RABOURN, JNO.; farmer; 2 m w Acton. Born in M. C. 1853. Rep.

Rabourn, David; farmer; 2 m w Acton. Born in Ky. 1820; settled in M. C. 1837. Rep. Methodist.

Rogers, Jas. V.; postmaster, railroad agent and merchant; Gallaudet. Born in Ind. 1840; settled in M. C. 1873.

Richardson, J. T.; farmer; 1½ m n w Gallaudet. Born in Ind. 1832.

RICHARDSON, GEO.; farmer; 1 m w Gallaudet. Born in Ky. 1807; settled in M. C. 1831.

Reid, F. F.; farmer; 1 m w Gallaudet. Born in Ind. 1848; settled in M. C. 1874.

Rodgers, J. H.; farmer; 2 m n w Gallaudet. Born in Ind. 1844; settled in M. C. 1873.

RIDDLE, JOHN W.; farmer; 3 m w Acton. Born in N. C. 1832; settled in M. C. 1873.

Riddle, E. M.; farmer; 3 m w Acton. Born in Ind. 1845; settled in M. C. 1873.

Rodgers, Thomas P.; deputy post master; Gallaudet. Born in Ind. 1862; settled in M. C. 1873.

Reado, A.; farmer; 2½ m n e Gallaudet. Born in Ind. 1849; settled in M. C. 1870.

Rice, Perry; farmer; 1 m s Julietta.

Reno, George; farmer; 4 m n e Southport. Born in 1811; settled in M. C. 1865.

Ribble, J. B.; farmer; 3½ m s e Southport. Born in 1855.
Ribble, Samuel W.; farmer; 3½ m s e Southport. Born in 1819; settled in M. C. 1850.

Strain, Joseph; farmer; ½ m w Acton. Born in Ind. 1824; settled in M. C. 1834. Rep. Methodist.

Strain, Lewis M.; farmer; ½ m w Acton. Born in Ind. 1853. Rep.

Swails, J. W.; merchant; Acton. Born in Ind. 1847; settled in M. C. 1851.

STEPHENSON, GEO. W.; farmer; 2 m n Acton. Born in Va. 1850; settled in M. C. 1874. Dem. Christian.

Springer, Martin; farmer; 1 m n Acton.　Born in Ind. 1848; settled in M. C. 1868.　Rep.

SHUMAKER, J. H.; farmer; 1 m n Acton.　Born in Ky. 1852; settled in M. C. 1874.

Smock, John; retired from business; New Bethel.　Born in Ky. 1815; settled in M. C. 1825.

Springer, J. M.; farmer; 1½ m n Gallaudet.　Born in Ind. 1843.

Sloan, Wm.; farmer; 6 m s e Indianapolis.　Born in Pa. 1807; settled in M. C. 1834.

Sloan, O. B.; farmer; 6 m s e Indianapolis.　Born in Ind. 1849.

Sloan, A. J.; farmer; 6 m s e Indianapolis.　Born in Pa. 1833; settled in M. C. 1834.

SHAFER, SAM; farmer; 1 m s w Acton.　Born in Va. 1851; settled in M. C. 1874.

SMITHER, WILLIS; farmer; ¼ m s Gallaudet.　Born in Ky. 1807; settled in M. C. 1826.

STOOPS, ALEXANDER W.; farmer; 2¼ m n w Acton. Born in Ky. 1820; settled in M. C. 1833.

Smith, Thomas; farmer; 1 m s Gallaudet.　Born in M. C. 1844;

Shaefer, M. A.; farmer; 1¼ m s Acton.　Born in Ohio 1840. settled in M. C. 1872.　Dem.

Sampson, Richard; farmer; 1 m s Acton.　Born in England 1814; settled in M. C. 1858.　Rep.

STREET, ABRAHAM; farmer; 1 m s Acton. Born in Ohio 1812; settled in M. C. 1847. Dem. Christian.

Street, J. P.; farmer; 1 m s w Acton. Born in Ind. 1841; settled in M. C. 1847. Dem.

Snock, J.; farmer; 8¾ m s w Acton. Born in Ind. 1815; settled in M. C. 1837. Rep. Presbyterian.

Snock, Wm.; farmer; 2¾ m s w Acton. Born in Ind. 1840. Rep. Presbyterian.

Smith, R. C. M.; constable; Acton. Born in Va. 1844; settled in M. C. 1860. Dem.

Swails, G. W.; merchant; Acton. Born in Ind. 1841; settled in M. C. 1849.

Smith, James; farmer, 1 m s Gallaudet. Born in M. C. 1854.

SMITH, MRS. LEAH; 3 m s w Acton. Born in Ind. 1839; settled in M. C. 1851.

Strain, Lewis; farmer; 1 m w Acton. Born in Ind. 1853; settled in M. C. 1869.

Schwartz, Fred.; farmer; 1½ m n New Bethel. Born in Germany 1813; settled in M. C. 1850.

Stewart, Mary; 3 m n Gallaudet. Born in M. C. 1841.

Swayle, Henry; farmer; 3 m s Julietta. Born in Ind. 1853; settled in M. C. 1873.

Springer, David; farmer; 2½ m s Julietta. Born in M. C. 1838.

Smith, D. W.; farmer; 1 m n w Gallaudet.   Born in Pa. 1846;
   settled in M. C. 1866.

Sutherland, Ashley; farmer; 2 m e Gallaudet.   Born in M. C.
   1825.

Swails, Jno. D.; farmer; 2 m n Acton.   Born in Ind. 1844; settled in M. C. 1852.

SNYDER, JNO.; farmer; 2 m n Acton.   Born in Pa. 1855;
   settled in M. C. 1864.

SCHOOLEY, THOMAS; farmer; ⅓ m n Gallaudet.   Born in
   Md. 1830; settled in M. C. 1840.

SCHRIBACH, JOHN; farmer; 2 m n w Gallaudet.   Born in
   Germany 1841; settled in M. C. 1859.

Scott, Obediah; dairyman; 9 m s e Indianapolis.   Born in 1821;
   settled in M. C. 1874.

Scott, Wm. L.; dairyman; 9 m s e Indianapolis.   Born in 1848;
   settled in M. C. 1874.

Springer, Sarah; 2 m n Gallaudet.   Born in Ohio 1809.

Smith, Yarkin; farmer; 1½ m n Gallaudet.   Born in Germany
   1823; settled in M. C. 1854.

SHANNON, MICHAEL; railroading; Acton.   Born in M. C.
   1856.

SMITH, NATHANIEL; farmer; 2 m e Southport.   Born in
   Ind. 1842; settled in M. C. 1842.

Smith, J. W.; farmer; 3 m e Southport.   Born in Ind. 1844; settled in M. C. 1844.

Smith, Nancy; 3 m e Southport.   Born in M. C. 1851.

Shaw, Allen, farmer; 2½ m s e Southport.   Born in 1839; settled in M. C. 1874.

SWIFT, JAMES H.; farmer; 4½ m s e Southport.   Born in M. C. 1854.

Teague, John; retired; Acton.   Born in N. C. 1820; settled in M. C. 1873.   Dem.

THORMYER, GEO.; farmer; 1¼ m n Acton.   Born in Ohio 1843; settled in M. C. 1864.   Rep.   Christian.

Toon, J. M.; farmer; 3 m s Julietta.   Born in M. C. 1843.   Rep.   Christian.

Thompson, Geo. C.; farmer; 3½ m n Acton.   Born in M. C. 1842.   Rep.

THIECKE, WM. H.; farmer; 6 m s e Indianapolis.   Born in Pa. 1851; settled in M. C. 1856.

Thompson, J. L.; farmer and township trustee; 4 m w Acton. Born in Ohio 1818; settled in M. C. 1867.

Tolin, Mrs. Malissa; 1½ m s Gallaudet.   Born in 1854.

Templeton, Milton; blacksmith; 4½ m n Acton. Settled in M. C. 1874.

Tolin, Jacob; farmer; 1½ m s Acton. Born in Va. 1811; settled in M. C. 1838.

Thompson, Uriah; farmer; 4 m e Southport. Born in 1827; settled in M. C. 1850.

Toom, J. J.; farmer; 1¼ m s e Gallaudet. Born in M. C. 1844.

Terhune, Charles; farmer; 3 m s w Gallaudet. Born in M. C. 1850.

Toom, Wes. R.; farmer; 1½ m s e Gallaudet. Born in M. C. 1829.

TURNER, W. J. K. P.; carpenter; 2½ m n e Gallaudet. Born in Ga. 1847; settled in M. C. 1874.

Tarleton, Meret; farmer; ½ m n w Gallaudet. Born in Ky. 1821; settled in M. C. 1868.

Toom, Wm.; farmer; 1½ m e Gallaudet. Born in M. C. 1853.

Transom, Wm.; farmer; 1¼ m n New Bethel. Born in Ohio 1852; settled in M. C. 1866.

Truman, William; farmer; 2½ m s w Acton. Born in Ky. 1832; settled in M. C. 1872.

VAUGHN, GEORGE W.; druggist and postmaster; Acton. Born in Ind. 1843; settled in M. C. 1857. Rep. Meth.

VANDEMAN, JOHN; farmer; 3 m n w Acton. Born in Ind.
1824. Rep. M. Baptist.

fa ettc Co., J↳)

VANDEMAN, J. H.; farmer; 6 m s e Indianapolis. Born in
Ind. 1825; settled in M. C. 1826. Rep. M. Baptist.

VANARSDALL, H. C.; farmer; 4¾ m s w Acton. Born in
Va. 1844; settled in M. C. 1871. Dem. Christian.

VAWTERS, GEORGE; farmer; 2½ m s e Southport. Born
in M. C. 1848.

Vandevere, Thomas; farmer; 2¼ m e Southport. Born in Mo.
1851; settled in M. C. 1872.

Wilson, J.; merchant; New Bethel. Born in Ohio 1839; set-
tted in M. C. 1867.

WARD, A. O.; physician; New Bethel. Born in Ind. 1842;
settled in M. C. '869.

WILSEY, LEWIS B.; farmer. Born in N. Y. 1822; settled in
M. C. 1844.

WALTERS, W. H.; sawmilling; 2½ m w Gallaudet. Born in
. Vt. 1820; settled in M. C. 1855.

WHEATLEY, GEO. M.; farmer; 3 m n w Gallaudet. Born
in M. C. 1833.

Wheatley, J.; farmer; 2½ m w Gallaudet. Born in Ky. 1811;
settled in M. C. 1830.

Wheatley, Wm.; farmer; 2½ m w Gallaudet. Born in N. C. 1799; settled in M. C. 1830.

WILLIAMS, RICHARD; farmer. Born in N. C. 1847; settled in M. C. 1873. Dem. M. Baptist.

WOLFE, H. W.; farmer; 1¼ m s w Acton. Born in Ind. 1849; settled in M. C. 1850. Dem.

WOLF, JOHN W.; farmer; 1½ m s w Acton. Born in M. C. 1855.

Williams, Ben. T.; farmer; 2 m s w Acton. Born in Ohio 1845; Dem. Baptist.

Wright, Joseph; farmer; 2¼ m w Acton. Born in Ky. 1836; settled in M. C. 1864. Dem. Christian.

Wilson & Brumley; merchants; New Bethel.

WRIGHT, WM.; farmer; 2¼ m w Acton. Born in Ky. 1836; settled in M. C. 1869. Dem. Christian.

Wright, James; farmer; 2 m w Acton. Born in Ky. 1839; settled in M. C. 1862. Dem. Christian.

Willard, Milford; farmer; Acton. Born in Ind. 1848; settled in M. C. 1871.

WATKINS, BURRILL; 2 m n Acton. Born in Ky. 1840; settled in M. C. 1872.

WILSON, L. B.; farmer. Born in N. Y. 1822; settled in M. C. 1844.

Wheatley, James A.; farmer; 2 m w Gallaudet. Born in M.
C. 1840.

WILDER, J. M.; farmer; 1½ m s Poplar Grove. Born in Ind.
1847; settled in M. C. 1874.

Wilson, Harrison; carpenter; 4 m n w Acton. Born in Ind.
1841; settled in M. C. 1873.

WHITE, JAMES H.; farmer; 5½ m w Acton. Born in Ky.
1849; settled in M. C. 1874.

WARREN, JOHN Q.; farm hand; 5¼ m w Acton. Born in
Ind. 1849; settled in M. C. 1872.

WILLS, NEWTON; farm hand; 5½ m w Acton. Born in
Ind. 1853; settled in M. C. 1873.

Ward, Jennings; farmer; ¾ m n New Bethel. Born in Ky.
1851.

WHEATLEY, WM.; farmer; 2½ m w Gallaudet. Born in
Ind. 1834; settled in M. C. 1834.

WINSHIP, JAS. M.; farmer; 4¼ m s e Southport. Born in
W. Va. 1849; settled in M. C. 1874.

Woolery, J.; farmer; 2¾ m s w Gallaudet. Born in Ky. 1850;
settled in M. C. 1872.

Wells, Marion; brick mason; 4½ m s w Gallaudet. Born in
Va. 1847; settled in M. C. 1869.

28

WHITTINGTON, G.; farmer; 1¾ m e New Bethel. Born in Va. 1856; settled in M. C. 1873.

WARRENS, FRANKLIN; carpenter; 2 m n w Gallaudet. Born in Ind. 1843; settled in M. C. 1874.

WRIGHT, THEODORE; brick molder; 3½ m s e Southport. Born in 1839; settled in M. C. 1874.

Williams, George E.; farmer; 4 m s e Southport. Born in 1852; settled in M. C. 1867.

Williams, J. W.; farmer; 4 m s e Southport. Born in 1855; settled in M. C. 1867.

Williams, Wm.; farmer; 4 m s e Southport. Born in 1822; settled in M. C. 1867.

WILSON, JOHNSON; farmer; 4½ m n Acton. Born in Ind. 1856; settled in M. C. 1874.

WORRELL, JAS. M.; farmer; 3½ m s e Southport. Born in Ind. 1850; settled in M. C. 1874.

WISSTEAD, WARREN; 4¼ m e Southport. Born in 1856; settled in M. C. 1874.

WILLIAMS, JAMES M.; carpenter; Acton. Born in Ind. 1847; settled in M. C. 1873.

WARREN, J. C.; farmer; 3 m n Acton. Born in N. C. 1841; settled in M. C. 1874.

Wallcott, W. H.; farmer; 3 m e Southport. Born in Ind. 1856.

WALCOTT, MRS. LAURA A.; 3 m e Southport. Born in 1836; settled in M. C. 1855.

LAWRENCE TOWNSHIP.

LAWRENCE TOWNSHIP is located in the northeast corner of the county, and is bounded on the north by Hamilton county, on the east by Hancock, on the south by Warren township, and on the west by Washington, and contains forty-nine square miles.

The surface is generally rolling or undulating, with the exception of a few breaks on Fall Creek. It is watered by Fall Creek and other smaller streams. The soil is rich and productive, and well adapted to the growing of grain and vegetables, while the blue grass and stock water is plentiful, thereby making it an enticing locality for the stock raiser. The improvements of the township are good, and the citizens enterprising.

Some of the early settlers were Jerry Vallandingham, William Swords, Henry Newhouse, John Emry, Martha Speece, J. W. Combs and Joseph Bolander.

The population at present is near 2,500. The township vote, October, 1874, was, Dem. 260, Rep. 210, Indpt. 15; total, 485.

Post offices, Lawrence, Oakland and Castleton.

CHURCH, SCHOOL AND LODGE STATISTICS.

Universalist Church; Oakland; number members, 95; pastor, M. G. Mitchell. Sabbath school, 100; superintendent, G. W. Stanley; value of church property, $1,000.

Christian Church; Oakland; minister, J. W. Ferrell; number members, 70. Sabbath school scholars, 35; superintendent, J. W. Apple; value of church property, $2,000.

M. E. Church; Oakland; pastor, W. S. Falkensburg; membership, 60. Sabbath school scholars, 55; superintendent, Ephraim Thomas; value of church property, $1,500.

Evangelical Lutheran Church; 3 m w Lawrence; pastor, John Brown; membership, 60. Sabbath school scholars, 86; superintendent, J. A. Pressley.

Spring Valley M. E. Church; 2 m n e Lawrence; pastor, W. S. Falkenburg; membership, 55; value of church property, $1,600.

Missionary Baptist Church, Lawrence; pastor, J. S. Galispie; membership, 72; value of church property, $3,600; superintendent of Sabbath school, Dr. S. H. Mapes; average attendance, 90.

M. E. Church, Lawrence; pastor, W. S. Falkenberg; membership, 65; value of church property, $2,000; superintendent of Sabbath school, Mr. Henry Shelly; average attendance, 60.

Oakland Lodge, No. 140, F. and A. M.; membership, 65; Master, Charles Negley; Secretary, Jonathan Conkle; value of Lodge property, $1,000; organized 1852.

Millersville Lodge, No. 126, F. and A. M.; membership, 37; post office, Lawrence; Samuel Cory, representative.

Keystone Lodge, No. 251; post office, Castleton; membership, 51.

Spring Valley Grange, No. 835; Lawrence; membership, 44; Master, Abel M. Wheeler; Secretary, J. T. Bragdon; organized December, 1873.

Highland Grange, No. 1182; two miles west of Lawrence; membership, 38; Master, Samuel Cory; Secretary, W. B. Flick; organized 1873; meets at No. 10 School House.

Lawrence Grange, No. 833, meets at No. 7 School House, two and a half miles southwest of Oakland; membership, 39; master, N. C. Plummer; secretary, G. W. Bolander; organized Dec. 22, 1873.

Indian Creek Grange, No. 828, meets at Oakland; membership, 111; master, Charles Vegle; secretary, Solomon Klepfer; value of property, $1,500; organized Dec. 19, 1873.

Township Trustee, G. W. Stanley.

Number of school houses, 13; value of school property, $17,000.

Vote of township: Democratic, 270; Republican, 210; Independent, 15; Total 499; Democratic majority, 41.

DIRECTORY OF LAWRENCE TOWNSHIP.

Apple, Robert; farmer; ½ m s Oakland. Born in Ireland 1841.

Apple, Harvey; proprietor sawmill; Oakland. Born in Ind. 1849; settled in M. C. 1870.

Apple, Solomon; farmer; 2 m s w Oakland. Born in Ind. 1809; settled in M. C. 1835.

Apple, William; farmer; 2 m s w Oakland. Born in M. C. 1838.

Apple, A. J.; farmer; 2 m s w Oakland. Born in Ohio 1832; settled in M. C. 1835.

Apple, Henry; farmer; 1 m s Oakland. Born in Ohio 1822.

Apple, Marion; farmer; 1½ m s Oakland.

Apple, Joseph; farmer; 3 m s e Lawrence.

Arnold, W. M.; farmer; 1½ m n w Lawrence. Born in Ind. 1836; settled in M. C. 1871.

Avvett, James; plasterer and farmer; 1 m n w Lawrence. Born
in Ky. 1826; settled in M. C. 1854.

Brunstiter, Wm.; engineer; Oakland. Born in Ohio 1849; settled in M. C. 1867.

Barr, Charles; farmer; 1½ m n e Oakland. Born in Ohio 1850;
settled in M. C. 1863. Dem.

Bird, Jonathan; farmer; 1 m n e Lawrence.

Bragden, G. W.; farmer; 1¼ m e Lawrence. Born in Ind. 1830
settled in M. C. 1833.

Bragden, J. T.; farmer; 1½ m e Lawrence. Born in Ind. 1828;
settled in M. C. 1833.

BROWN, WM. P.; proprietor saw and planing mill; Lawrence.
Born in Pa. 1812; settled in M. C. 1837. Rep.

Bolander, Joseph; farmer; 1¾ m s w Oakland. Born in Ohio
1820; settled in M. C. 1828.

Bell, M.; farmer; 2½ m s Oakland. Born in M. C. 1839.

Bolander, G. W.; school teacher; 2½ m s w Oakland. Born in
M. C. 1850.

Bell, Robert M.; farmer; 2 m e Lawrence. Born in M. C.
1850.

Bates, Moses; farmer and school teacher; 2½ m n e Lawrence.

Bell, Henry; farmer; 2 m e Lawrence.   Born in Ky. 1820; settled in M. C. 1836.

Brown, John L.; farmer; ½ m s Lawrence.   Born in Ohio 1817; settled in M. C. 1832.

Baher, G. J.; farmer; 1½ m n w Oakland.   Born in France 1793; settled in M. C. 1834.

Bolander, Levi; farmer; 2½ m s w Oakland.   Born in Ohio 1815; settled in M. C. 1828.

Combs, J. W.; farmer and justice of the peace; Oakland.   Born in Ind. 1824; settled in M. C. 1824.   Dem.   Methodist.

Cary, Andrew F.; physician and surgeon; Oakland.

Craig, Moses; farmer; 2½ m n Oakland.   Born in N. J. 1805; settled in M. C. 1852; Dem.

Craig, Aaron; farmer; 2½ m n Oakland.   Born in Ind. 1839; settled in M. C. 1852.

Craig, M. N.; farmer; 2½ m n Oakland.   Born in Ind. 1846; settled in M. C. 1852.   Dem.

Craig, R. J.; farmer; 2½ m n Oakland.   Born in Ind. 1848; settled in M. C. 1852.   Dem.

Craig, W. W.; farmer and school teacher; 2½ m n Oakland. Born in Ind. 1852; settled in M. C. 1852.   Dem.

Cumins, W. B.; butcher; Oakland. Born in Ohio 1832; settled in M. C. 1871.

Cary, W. T; carpenter; Oakland. Born in M. C. 1846.

Crutchfield, S.; saw mill hand; Lawrence. Born in Ky. 1811; settled in M. C. 1835.

Cary, Robert; farmer; 2 m s e Lawrence. Born in M. C. 1850.

Crigler, James; 2 m w Lawrence. Born in Va. 1811; settled in M. C. 1834.

CALLON, DR. L.; veterinary surgeon; Lawrence. Born in M. C. 1839. Treats all diseases that horses and cattle are subject to.

Chapman, N.; farmer; 3 m s Oakland. Born in Ohio 1825; settled in M. C. 1832.

Church, G. W.; farmer; ¾ m n e Lawrence. Born in Pa. 1819; settled in M. C. 1846.

Church, G. W., Jr.; farmer; 1 m n Lawrence.

Cary, Samuel; farmer and County Commissioner; 2 m w of Lawrence. Born in Va. 1818; settled in M. C. 1834.

Day, J. W.; farmer; ¾ m n w Oakland. Born in Ohio 1827; settled in M. C. 1832.

Downs, F. H.; sawyer; 3½ m n Oakland. Born in Ct. 1837; settled in M. C. 1860.

Dobbins, J. W.; farmer; 3½ m n Oakland. Born in Va. 1846; settled in M. C. 1864. Rep.

Daugherty, Joseph; carpenter; 1½ m e Malott Park.

Dearmenel, T. J.; wagonmaker; Lawrence. Born in Ohio 1838; settled in M. C. 1868.

Dunn, Moses; farmer; 1½ m s e Lawrence. Born in N. C. 1809.

Day, Joseph N.; farmer; 2½ m n w Oakland. Born in Ohio 1813; settled in M. C. 1832.

Elliott, Thos.; justice of the peace and farmer; ¾ m n Lawrence. Born in Ky.; settled in M. C. 1865.

Emry, John; farmer; 1½ m w Oakland. Born in Ohio 1804; settled in M. C. 1829.

Emry, John; farmer; 2¼ m n Oakland. Born in Ohio 1830; settled in M. C. 1861.

Fawset, Charles; retired from business; Oakland. Born in Louisiana 1808; settled in M. C. 1841. Rep. U. Breth.

FREEMAN, M. E.; dealer in groceries and provisions; Lawrence. Born in Mass. 1855; settled in M. C. 1856.

Falkenburg, W. S.; minister of M. E. Church; Lawrence. Born in Ind. 1847; settled in M. C. 1874.

Fred, J. B.; farmer; 1½ m e Lawrence. Born in Ohio 1817; settled in M. C. 1833.

Fred, George; farmer; 1½ m e Lawrence. Born in M. C. 1852.

Fred, Will. W.; farmer; 1¼ m e Lawrence. Born in Ohio 1828; settled in M. C. 1833.

Fred, Jacob; farmer; 1½ m e Lawrence. Born in M. C. 1847.

Flick, W. B.; farmer and school teacher; 1¼ m w Lawrence. Born in Ohio 1840; settled in M. C. 1864.

Hunter, J. E.; farmer; 2 m n e James' Switch. Born in M. C. 1858.

Henderson, William H.; bailiff in Superior Court of Indianapolis; res 2½ m n e James' Switch. Born in Ind. 1846; settled in M. C. 1857.

Hanna, D. G.; general merchandising; Oakland. Born in Ind. 1846; settled in M. C. 1853.

Heltman, J. K.; physician; Oakland. Born in M. C. 1838.

Huff, A. M.; farmer; 1½ m n w Oakland. Born in Ohio 1843; settled in M. C. 1845.

Hanna, E. D.; farmer and trader; Oakland.

Heltman, Joseph; farmer; Oakland. Born in Ohio 1815; settled in M. C. 1837.

Hunter, G. W.; blacksmith; Lawrence. Born in Ohio 1830; settled in M. C. 1837.

Hunter, John W.; blacksmith; Lawrence. Born in Ohio 1837; settled in M. C. 1837.

Hamilton, Anderson; farmer; 3½ m s e Lawrence. Born in Ky. 1815; settled in M. C. 1830.

Haffield, W. N.; farmer; 1¼ m w Lawrence. Born in M. C. 1847.

Hensley, Wm.; farmer; 2 m n w Lawrence. Born in Va. 1822; settled in M. C. 1833.

Hensley, G. W.; college student; 2 m n w Lawrence. Born in M. C. 1850.

Herrin, J. W.; farmer; 1 m n e Lawrence. Born in M. C. 1838.

Hansafus, L.; farmer; 1½ m n w Oakland. Born in Ohio 1834; settled in M. C. 1845.

Hunter, Mrs. Hettie M.; farmer; 2½ m n e James' Switch. Born in Ind. 1826; settled in M. C. 1857.

JOHNSTON, A. A.; firm of A. A. Johnston & Bro., general merchants; Lawrence. Born in M. C. 1850.

Johnston, W. T.; of A. A. Johnston & Bro.; Lawrence. Born in M. C. 1845.

Jewett, Asa; house, sign and carriage painter; Lawrence. Born in N. Y. 1824; settled in M. C. 1870.

Johnston, J. F.; farmer; 2 m e Lawrence. Born in Ohio 1833; settled in M. C. 1835.

Johnston, James; farmer; 2¼ m n e Lawrence. Born in Ohio 1805; settled in M. C. 1834.

Jordon, Daniel; farmer; 1½ m s Oakland. Born in Ohio 1817; settled in M. C. 1861.

Karer, G. W.; blacksmith and wagon maker; Oakland. Born in Pa. 1846; settled in M. C. 1854.

Klepfer, Simon; farmer; 2½ m n w Oakland. Born in Pa. 1821; settled in M. C. 1834.

Klepfer, O. D.; carpenter and contractor; Oakland. Born in Pa. 1835; settled in M. C. 1851.

Keeler, G. W.; farmer; 3 m w Lawrence. Born in M. C. 1834.

Keller, Levi; farmer; 2 m s Oakland.

Kenny, John; farmer; 2¼ m s Oakland.

Keller, J. H.; farmer; 2½ m s w Oakland. Born in M. C. 1852.

Kimberlin, Elizabeth; farmer; 2½ m n w Oakland. Born in Ohio 1809; settled in M. C. 1834.

Kimberlin, J. W.; farmer; 2¼ m n w Oakland.

Kelpfer, George; retired from business; 2 m n w Oakland. Born in Pa. 1812; settled in M. C. 1848.

Kelpfer, S.; farmer and school teacher; 2 m n w Oakland. Born in M. C. 1850.

Kelpfer, Paul; farmer; 2 m n w Oakland. Born in Ind. 1845; settled in M. C. 1848.

KEMP, S. R.; carriage painter; res ¼ m s Millersville. Born in Ohio 1847; settled in M. C. 1871.

Leffarge, M.; farmer; 2 m n Oakland. Born in Ind. 1852; settled in M. C. 1871.

Linton, Chas.; farmer; 1 m s w Lawrence. Born in Ohio 1852; settled in M. C. 1861.

Linton, James; butcher; 1 m s w Lawrence. Born in Ohio 1829; settled in M. C. 1861.

Lindsey, H.; farmer; 2 m e Lawrence. Born in Ky. 1844; settled in M. C. 1869.

Lowden, J. D.; farmer; 1½ m w Lawrence. Born in Ky. 1818; settled in M. C. 1857.

Leatherman, David; stock raiser and farmer; ½ m n Millersville. Born in Md. 1818; settled in M. C. 1840.

Lynch, James; farmer; 4 m n Cumberland.

McCanaha, B. J.; firm of McCanaha & Co., merchants; Oakland. Born in Va. 1829; settled in M. C. 1866.

McCanaha, Samuel; firm of McCanaha & Co., merchants; Oakland. Born in Va. 1798; settled in M. C. 1849.

McCord, A.; farmer; 1 m e Oakland. Born in M. C. 1842. Universalist.

McCord, Eliza; farmer; ¾ m e Oakland. Born in Ohio 1821.

Morse, Charles A.; blacksmith; Oakland. Born in Mass. 1840; settled in M. C. 1865.

Moore, John; wagonmaker; Oakland. Born in Ind. 1849; settled in M. C. 1870.

Mock, John; farmer; ½ m n Oakland. Born in Ohio 1820; settled in M. C. 1831.

Mollenkopf, J. J.; farmer; 3 m n w Oakland. Born in Md. 1829; settled in M. C. 1834.

Mann, D. O.; farmer; 2½ m n Oakland. Born in Ky. 1822; settled in M. C. 1835. Rep.

Mock, Simeon; farmer; ¼ m s Fall Creek. Born in N. C. 1812; settled in M. C. 1831.

Miller, John; boot and shoemaker; 3¼ m n Oakland.   Born in Va. 1814; settled in M. C. 1860.

McConnel, Charles; farmer; 1½ m n e Oakland.   Born in Ohio 1809; settled in M. C. 1824.

McConnell, David; farmer; 2½ m n e Oakland.   Born in M. C. 1834.

McConnell, Hiram; farmer; 2 m n e Oakland.   Born in M. C. 1839.

McConnell, James; farmer; 1 m n Oakland.   Born in M. C. 1847.

McConnell, John; farmer; 1½ m n w Oakland.   Born in M. C. 1836.

McHaffey, James; farmer; 2¾ m w Lawrence.   Born in Ohio 1847; settled in M. C. 1858.

Miller, Daniel; farmer; 2½ m w Lawrence.   Born in Pa. 1807; settled in M. C. 1872.

MAPES, SMITH H.; physician and surgeon; Lawrence.   Born in N. Y. 1840; settled in M. C. 1867.

Mowry, George; farmer; 3 m w Lawrence.

Marshall, J. J.; farmer; ¼ m e Lawrence.   Born in Ohio 1829; settled in M. C. 1836.

Marshall, T. W.; farmer; ½ m e Lawrence.   Born in Ohio 1834; settled in M. C. 1836.

Marshall, William; farmer; Lawrence. Born in M. C.

Mock, Noah; farmer; 1¾ m e Lawrence. Born in M. C. 1842.

Mock, Michael; farmer; 1 m s w Oakland. Born in M. C. 1841.

Mock, Alexander; farmer; ¾ m s w Oakland. Born in Ohio 1815; settled in M. C. 1835.

McConnell, George; farmer; 1¾ m e Lawrence. Born in M. C. 1845.

McConnell, Christian; farmer; 2 m e Lawrence. Born in M. C. 1843.

Mollenkopf, Samuel; farmer; ¾ m s e Lawrence. Born in M. C. 1842.

Miller, Philip; farmer; 3 m n w Lawrence. Born in Va. 1817; settled in M. C. 1852.

Moore, C. G.; retired from business; 2 m n e Lawrence. Born in Vt. 1794; settled in M. C. 1854.

Newhouse, Henry; farmer; Lawrence. Born in Vt. 1807; settled in M. C. 1829. Dem. Methodist.

Newhouse, Oliver; farmer; ¾ m s w Lawrence. Born in M. C. 1832.

Newkirk, Gideon; farmer; 1 m e Lawrence.

Newhouse, George; farmer; 1½ m e Lawrence. Born in M.C.

Newhouse, John; farmer; 2 m n w Lawrence. Born in Va. 1804; settled in M. C. 1834.

Newhouse, Edmund; retired farmer; 1 m n Lawrence. Born in Va. 1798; settled in M. C. 1832.

Newhouse, Henry; ¾ m w Lawrence. Born in 1830; settled in M. C. 1832.

Newhouse, Lewis; farmer; 1 m n w Lawrence. Born in Va. 1828; settled in M. C. 1832.

Newhouse, Benjamin; farmer; 1 m w Lawrence. Born in Va. 1798; settled in M. C. 1831.

Newhouse, W. R.; farmer; 1 m w Lawrence. Born in M. C. 1843.

Newhouse, Asa S.; farmer; 1½ m w Lawrence. Born in M. C. 1845.

Newhouse, J. H.; farmer; 2½ m n w Lawrence. Born in M. C. 1849.

Negley, Charles J.; farmer; 1 m w Oakland. Born in M. C. 1836.

Paine, Frederick; miller; Germantown. Born in Germany 1848; settled in M. C. 1862.

Pressly, James H.; farmer; 2¾ m w Lawrence. Born in Ohio.

Paton, H. H. M.; boot and shoe maker; Lawrence. Born in Va. 1847; settled in M. C. 1874.

Pressly, Israel; farmer; 2 m w Lawrence. Born in Ohio 1836; settled in M. C. 1846.

Perkins, T. N.; farmer; 1½ m n w Oakland. Born in Ohio 1828.

Plummer, N. C.; farmer and carpenter; 3½ m s w Oakland. Born in Ind. 1827; settled in M. C. 1836.

Plummer, J. W.; farmer; 5 m n Cumberland. Born in Ky. 1809; settled in M. C. 1832.

Perry, William; farmer; 1½ m s e Lawrence. Born in Ohio 1810; settled in M. C. 1832.

Pace, Louis & Bro.; dairymen; 1 m n Lawrence.

Pressly, James A.; farmer; 6½ m n e Indianapolis. Born in Ind. 1840; settled in M. C. 1865.

Pressly, J. H.; farmer; 2 m w Lawrence. Born in Ohio 1835; settled in M. C. 1838.

Rinewalt, Wm.; boot and shoemaker; Oakland. Born in Ohio 1845; settled in M. C. 1872. Rep. Universalist.

Roberts, William; miller; 3 m n Oakland. Born in Ind. 1821; settled in M. C. 1868.

Riddick, J. F.; physician and surgeon; Germantown. Born in
    N. C. 1823; settled in M. C. 1868.

Robertson, Wm.; farmer; 2 m w Lawrence. Born in Ind. 1834;
    settled in M. C. 1836.

RECORDS, ISAAC; druggist; Lawrence. Born in M. C. 1841.

Razor, J. H.; minister Christian Church; Lawrence. Born in
    Ky. 1826; settled in M. C. 1857.

Ringer, Mrs. Eliza; farmer; 2½ m w Lawrence. Born in Ohio
    1837.

Ringer, Harrison; farmer; 2¼ m w Lawrence. Born in M. C.
    1828.

Russell, J. S.; farmer; 5 m n Cumberland. Born in Ind. 1821;
    settled in M. C. 1850.

Reddick, J. N.; farmer; 1 m n Lawrence. Born in M. C. 1824.

Riley, S. P.; farmer; ¾ m w Oakland. Born in M. C. 1832.

Records, Samuel; physician; Lawrence. Born in Ky. 1819;
    settled in M. C. 1834.

Ringar, John E.; farmer; 3 m n w Lawrence. Born in M. C.
    1834.

Springer, W. H. farmer; 1½ m s w Lawrence. Born in M. C.
    1842.

Sowers, Philip; boot and shoe maker; res at toll gate $\frac{1}{2}$ m n e Millersville and 7 m n e Indianapolis. Born in Va. 1826; settled in M. C. 1862.

STOOPS, POLLY ANN; farmer; 1 m n e Millersville. Born in Ky. 1820; settled in M. C. 1837.

Stoops, William; farmer; 1 m n e Millersville. Born in Ind. 1860.

Siegmund, Joseph; farmer; $\frac{1}{2}$ m s Castleton postoffice. Born in M. C. 1843.

Smith, M.; farmer; 3 m s Oakland.

Smith, William; farmer; 3 m s Oakland.

Sargent, J. L.; farmer; $2\frac{1}{4}$ m e Lawrence. Born in Ohio 1844; settled in M. C. 1852.

Smith, John; farmer; 2 m s w Oakland.

Smith, John; blacksmith; Lawrence. Born in Pa. 1844; settled in M. C. 1844.

Stoops, John; farmer; $\frac{3}{4}$ m s e Lawrence. Born in M. C. 1842.

Smart, Hezekiah, farmer; 2 m n e Lawrence. Born in M. C. 1835.

Speece, T. B. J.; farmer; $2\frac{1}{2}$ m n e Lawrence. Born in M. C. 1846.

Speece, Martha; $2\frac{1}{4}$ m n e Lawrence. Born in Va. 1809; settled in M. C. 1828.

Snyder, John J.; farmer; 1 ¼ m n w Oakland. Born in Pa. 1846.

Springer, A. N.; farmer; ¾ m w Oakland.

Spong, Thomas; proprietor tile factory; Lawrence.

Shelley, Henry; carpenter; Lawrence. Born in Va. 1839; settled in M. C. 1868.

Snyder, Anthony; merchant; Germantown; 3½ m n Oakland.

Stanley, G. W.; railroad agent; Oakland. Born in Ind. 1836; settled in M. C. 1863.

Smith, John; farmer; 1 m e Oakland. Born in N. Y. 1809; settled in M. C. 1838. Methodist.

SMITH, B. F.; stock trader and farmer; 1 m n w Oakland. Born in M. C. 1836.

Sargent, John A.; farmer; 1 ½ m e Malott Park. Born in Ky. 1818; settled in M. C. 1850.

Sargent, Jacob; farmer; 1 ½ m e Malott Park. Born in M. C. 1851.

Schlager, Philip; boot and shoemaker; Lawrence. Born in Germany 1823; settled in M. C. 1863.

Swords, Wm.; silversmith; Lawrence. Born in Ohio 1819; settled in M. C. 1829. Rep. M. Baptist.

Smock, D. J.; farmer; 2½ m s w Oakland. Born in M. C. 1840.

Swords, Geo.; silversmith; Lawrence. Born in M. C. 1849. Rep.

Stark, Christian; wagon maker; Lawrence. Born in W. Va. 1837; settled in M. C. 1856. Dem.

Springer, Geo.; blacksmith and wagon maker; Lawrence. Born in M. C. 1834.

Sargent, Alex.; farmer; ¼ m e Lawrence. Born in Pa. 1822; settled in M. C. 1852.

Sargent, John; farmer; ½ m e Lawrence. Born in Ohio; settled in M. C. 1852.

Teal, P. J.; clerk in store; Oakland. Born in M. C. 1859.

Todd, Samuel; farmer; 2 m n w Oakland. Born in Ind. 1821.

Thomas, B. E.; farmer; 2 m n e Lawrence. Born in Ohio 1831; settled in M. C. 1833.

Thomas, John; farmer; 2 m n e Lawrence. Born in Ohio 1805; settled in M. C. 1833.

Thomas William S.; farmer; 2½ m n e Lawrence. Born in Ky. 1805; settled in M. C. 1833.

Vollmer, Jacob; farmer; 1½ m e Malott Park. Born in Germany 1834; settled in M. C. 1859.

Vallandingham, Jerry; farmer; 1 m s w Oakland. Born in Ky. 1801; settled in M. C. 1827.

Voohis, O. W.; farmer; ¼ m n Lawrence. Born in Ohio 1832; settled in M. C. 1853.

Wheeler, Jason; farmer; 2½ m n e Lawrence. Born in M. C. 1842.

Wheeler, S. A.; farmer; 2½ m n e Lawrence. Born in M. C. 1839.

Wheeler, J. M.; carpenter; Lawrence. Born in M. C. 1849.

Wilmington, O. N.; carpenter and contractor; Lawrence. Born in M. C. 1845.

Wheeler, H. D.; farmer; 2½ m n e Lawrence. Born in N. Y. 1805; settled in M. C. 1834.

Wilson, Robert; farmer; 1 m w Castleton P. O. Born in N. C. 1837; settled in M. C. 1873.

Watson, Robert; farmer; ½ m s Oakland. Born in Ireland 1820; settled in M. C. 1864. Dem.

Wait, W. S.; farmer; 2¼ m n Oakland. Born in Ind. 1842; settled in M. C. 1855. Dem. Universalist.

Wait, Clark; farmer; 2¼ m n Oakland. Born in Ohio 1812; settled in M. C. 1855. Dem. Universalist.

Waddy, J. B.; farmer and school teacher; 1½ m s e Lawrence.

White, John; pump maker; Lawrence.   Born in Ohio 1824; settled in M. C. 1838.

White, J. S.; farmer; ½ m n w Lawrence.   Born in Ohio 1839; settled in M. C. 1842.

Wilson, George; farmer; toll gate keeper 1 m e Lawrence. Born in Ind. 1842; settled in M. C. 1858.

Wheeler, A. M.; farmer; 1½ m e Lawrence.   Born in N. Y. 1801; settled in M. C. 1860.

Waddy, F.; farmer; 1½ m s e Lawrence.   Born in Va. 1814; settled in M. C. 1844.

White, Robert; farmer; 2½ m n w Lawrence.   Born in Ohio 1802; settled in M. C. 1833.

White, William; farmer; 2½ m n Lawrence.   Born in M. C. 1853.

White, B. F.; farmer; 2½ m n w Lawrence.   Born in M. C. 1846.

White, G. W ; farmer; 2¼ m n w Lawrence.   Born in M. C. 1835.

White, Z.; farmer; ¼ m n Lawrence.   Born in Ohio 1815; settled in M. C. 1840.

PERRY TOWNSHIP.

PERRY TOWNSHIP is located in the south part of Marion county, and is bounded on the north by Center township, on the east by Franklin, on the south by Johnson county, and on the west by White river, and contains an area of near forty-seven square miles. It is watered by White river, Sugar creek and their tributaries. The surface is slightly rolling, and the soil rich and productive. This is rather the best township in the county for grain growing, and is also well adapted to blue grass. The timber, building material and stock water are plentiful, and the scenery is beautiful and attractive.

Some of the early settlers of this township were James M. Myers, E. McBride, Wm. P. Hankins, E. W. Coverdill, Samuel Brewer, Henry Briston, Joseph H. Alcorn, H. Hinkson, Gilbert McCoy, W. T. McLaughlin, Hezekiah Smart, Peter Smock, George Tomlinson, Samuel Woodfiil, L. D. Wright John Webb and John Myers.

Vote of the township: Democratic, 207; Republican, 276; Independent, 7; total, 490. Population, 2,600;

Post Offices: Southport and Glenn's Valley.

CHURCH; SCHOOL AND LODGE STATISTICS,

Southport Grange, No. 777; organized January, 1874; membership, 50; value of Lodge property, $75; Isaac Haverstick, Master; E. H. Barry, Secretary.

Presbyterian Church; located three miles north of Glenn's

Valley; membership, 16; value of church property, $600; H. Bushnell, pastor; average attendance Sabbath school, 15; superintendent, Edward Harness.

M. E. Center Church; located 3½ miles northwest of Southport; membership, 50; value of church property, $1,500; ——— Sparks, pastor; average attendance Sabbath school, 25; superintendent, H. Hengston.

Madison Avenue M. E. Church; located 4 miles south of Indianapolis; membership, 30; value of church property, $2,500; F. S. Turk, pastor; average attendance Sabbath school, 47; Morris Howland, superintendent.

Missionary Baptist Church; Southport; Rev. E. S. Riley, pastor; organized, 1830; membership, 200; value of church property, $2000. Sabbath School superintendent, W. R. Wicoff; average attendance at school, 100.

Presbyterian Church; Southport; Rev. H. Bushnell, pastor; organized, 1833; membership, 86; value of church property, $5000. Sabbath school superintendent, D. R. Smock; average attendance at school, 75.

Sugar Creek Sabbath School; B. F. Narvel, superintendent; average attendance at school, 40.

Sugar Creek Baptist Church; Rev. G. W. Bower, pastor; J. M. Bowman, clerk; membership, 79.

M. E. Church; Southport; J. B. Sparks, pastor; probable value church property, $9800.

Southport Lodge, No. 271, F. and A. M.; membership, 58.

Number of school houses in Perry township, 13; value of school property, $17,500.

Charles Larsh, Trustee.

DIRECTORY OF PERRY TOWNSHIP.

Alcorn, Joseph H.; farmer; res Southport. Born in M. C. 1828. Rep. Presbyterian.

ANDERSON, WILLIAM; blacksmith; firm of Golding & Anderson; res 5 m s Indianapolis. Born in Ohio 1842; settled in M. C. 1869. Dem. Protestant.

Abbett, William; farmer; 1 m n w Glenn's Valley. Born in M. C. 1840. Dem. Protestant.

Bailey, Elias; proprietor boarding house; Southport. Born in N. J. 1813; settled in M. C. 1865. Rep. Presbyterian.

Bushnell, Horace; minister Presbyterian church; res Southport. Born in Ohio 1836; settled in M. C. 1866. Rep.

Brewer, John B.; notary public; res Southport. Born in Ind. 1832; settled in M. C. 1832. Dem. Protestant.

Barnes, Riley P.; gardener; res Southport. Born in N. Y. 1809; settled in M. C. 1867. Rep. M. Baptist.

Bentley, George B.; engineer and miller; Southport. Born in Ohio 1823; settled in M. C. 1841. Dem. Methodist.

Brewer, Alfred; carpenter; res Southport. Born in M. C. 1841. Dem. M. Baptist.

Bonte, John; gardener; 4½ m s Indianapolis on Bluff road. Born in Germany 1835; settled in M. C. 1868.

Bristow, Henry; farmer and raiser of small fruit; 5 m s Indianapolis on Bluff road. Born in M. C. 1825. Dem. Prot.

Bailey, Sandford; farmer; ¾ m s Southport.

Brewer, Samuel; farmer and blacksmith; retired; Southport. Born in Ky. 1801; settled in M. C. 1823.

Bryan, G.; stock dealer; Southport. Born in Ky. 1829; settled in M. C. 1850. Rep. Methodist.

Bradley, R. H.; farmer; 2½ m s w Southport. Born in Ky. 1839, settled in M. C. 1858. Rep. M. Baptist.

Barber, William; farmer; 2 m n e Southport. Born in Va. 1817; settled in M. C. 1836.

Brackin, Solon; farmer; 2 m n Southport. Born in Ind. 1853; settled in M. C. 1865. Dem. Protestant.

Bowser, Daniel; farmer; 4 m s e Indianapolis. Born in Pa. 1812; settled in M. C. 1833.

Buser & Rou; dealers in dry goods, groceries, hardware and crockery; a general assortment of goods constantly kept in store; place of business, Glenn's Valley.

Buser, J. N.; firm of Buser & Rou; farmer and trader; res Glenn's Valley. Born in Pa. 1840; settled in M. C. 1851.

Blockinger, George; blacksmith; Glenn's Valley. Born in Europe 1834; settled in M. C. 1873. Dem. Methodist.

Bristow, Wilford; farmer; 4 m n w Southport. Born in M. C. 1838. Dem. Protestant.

Bristow, Joseph; farmer; 4½ m s Indianapolis. Born in M. C. 1840. Dem. Protestant.

Bristow, Alfred; farmer and gardener; 4½ m s Indianapolis. Born in M. C. 1847. Dem. Protestant.

Brown, Susan; farmer; 3½ m s Indianapolis. Born in Ky. 1807; settled in M. C. 1837.

Brackin, Stephen; farmer; 4½ m s e Indianapolis. Born in M. C. 1821.

Browing, Thomas; farmer; 1 m s w Southport. Born in Ind. 1840; settled in M. C. 1853. Dem. M. Baptist.

Clem, William; farmer; 1½ m s Southport. Born in Ky. 1817; settled in M. C. 1871.

Comingon; farmer; 2½ m n Greenwood postoffice. Born in Ky. 1823; settled in M. C. 1870. Rep. Protestant.

Chew, John; farmer; 2½ m s e Southport. Born in Ohio 1827; settled in M. C. 1848.

COVERDILL, E. W.; farmer; ¾ m s e Southport. Born in Ky. 1809; settled in M. C. 1824. Rep. R. Baptist.

COVERDILL, JOHN; farmer; ¾ m s e Southport. Born in M. C. 1854.

COVERDILL, ANDREW; farmer; ¾ m s e Southport. Born in M. C. 1852.

Congrow, Eli; farmer; ½ m s w Glenn's Valley.

Cave, Jonas; farmer; res Southport. Born in Ohio 1821; settled in M. C. 1871.

Canine, Abraham; keeper of toll gate; 1 m e Southport. Born in Ky. 1807; settled in M. C. 1868. Rep. Presbyterian.

CARSON, PARKER S.; farmer; 1 m n e Southport. Born in Ind. 1829; settled in M. C. 1835.

Cunningham, Levi; manufacturer of boots and shoes; Southport. Born in N. Y. 184–; settled in M. C. 1871. Rep. Protestant.

Cogill, J. H.; farmer; Southport. Born in M. C. 1830. Rep. Protestant.

Clifford, B. M.; farmer and gardener; 4½ m s Indianapolis, on Bluff Road. Born in Ind. 1845; settled in M. C. 1850. Rep. Protestant.

Copsey, Hezekiah; farmer; 5 m s Indianapolis. Born in Ohio 1822; settled in M. C. 1848. Rep. Methodist.

Christian, Edward F.; farmer; ¾ m e Glenn's Valley. Born in Ind. 1831; settled in M. C. 1833.

Christian, W. H.; farmer; 1 m n e Glenn's Valley. Born in M. C. 1843. Rep. Methodist.

Curd, William T.; farmer and justice of the peace in school district No. 6; 2 m s w Southport. Born in Ky. 1809; settled in M. C. 1836. Rep.

Curd, Brent; farmer; 2½ m s w Southport. Born in Ky. 1833. Dem. Protestant.

Carle, William H.; farmer; 2½ m n e Southport. Born in Ky. 1824; settled in M. C. 1844. Dem. M. Baptist.

Carpenter, Frederick; farmer; 5 m s Indianapolis. Born in Germany 1818; settled in M. C. 1852. Dem. German Reform.

Clary, David R.; farmer; 6 m s w Indianapolis. Born in East Tenn. 1815; settled in M. C. 1841. Dem. Protestant.

Christian, Wm.; toll-gate keeper on Madison road; Southport. Born in M. C. 1840.

Cogle, William; farmer; ½ m s e Southport.

Cohill, Dudley; gardener and farmer; 4½ m s Indianapolis. Born in Ind. 1844; settled in M. C. 1873. Dem. Prot.

Dunkin, William A.; 5 m s Indianapolis, on Bluff Road; brick-mason. Born in Md. 1824; settled in M. C. 1865. Dem. Methodist.

Davis, James; farmer; 2½ m s w Southport. Born in Ky. 1810; settled in M. C. 1836. Rep. Methodist.

Davis, Richard T.; farmer; 2½ m s w Southport. Born in M. C. 1846. Rep. Protestant.

Dunkin, H. C.; farmer and trader; 5½ m s e Indianapolis. Born in Ky. 1823; settled in M. C. 1871. Rep. Protestant.

Dophins, John; farmer; 1 m n Southport.

Epler, John; farmer; 4½ m s Indianapolis, on Madison road. Born in M. C. 1850. Rep. Protestant.

FISHER, DAVID; farmer; 7½ m s w Indianapolis and 3½ m n w Glenn's Valley. Born in Md. 1798; settled in M. C. 1837. Rep. Methodist.

FISHER, DAVID M.; farmer; 3½ m n w Glenn's Valley. Born in M. C. 1841. Rep. Methodist.

Fisher, Peter; farmer and gardener; 2½ m w Southport. Born in M. C. 1839. Rep. Methodist.

Fisher, J. L.; farmer; 1 m e Southport.

FLORANDER, N. B. S.; brick maker; firm of Florander & Lund; res Southport. Born in Denmark 1847; settled in M. C. 1868.

FLORANDER & LUND; blacksmiths and repair shop; work done to order; shop at Southport.

Ferguson, Samuel C.; farmer; 3 m s e Southport. Born in Ind. 1833; settled in M. C. 1854.

Ferguson, James T.; farmer; 3½ m s e Southport. Born in Ind. 1835; settled in M. C. 1854. Rep. Protestant.

Featherston, Robert J.; gardener; 1½ m n e Southport. Born in Ky. 1838; settled in M. C. 1830.

GOLDING & ANDREWS; blacksmith and general repair shop; work done to order at reasonable rates; shop located 5 m s Indianapolis, near Center Church, on Bluff Road.

GOLDING, JAMES E.; 4 m s e Indianapolis. Born in Ind. 1839; settled in M. C. 1858.

GLENN, ARCHIBALD; farmer and stock raiser; ½ m s Glenn's Valley. Born in Ind. 1826; settled in M. C. 1853. Rep. Methodist.

Godfordlente, John; gardener; 3½ m s Indianapolis. Born in Germany 1821; settled in M. C. 1854.

Grubs, Christopher; farmer; 4½ m s Indianapolis. Born in M. C. 1832. Dem. Methodist.

Gentle, James; farmer; 1 m w Southport. Born in Scotland 1820; settled in M. C. 1841. Rep.

Gregg, A.; farmer; ¼ m n Southport. Born in Ind. 1822; settled in M. C. 1872. Rep. Methodist.

GRIFFITH, MRS. A. H.; farmer and fruit grower; 1 m n e Southport. Born in Ky. 1820; settled in M. C. 1850.

GRIFFITH, H. C.; fruit grower and farmer; 1 m n Southport. Born in Ky. 1847; settled in M. C. 1851.

GRUBE, ISAAC; dealer in dry goods, groceries, hardware, boots, shoes, hats, caps, fancy goods and notions; Southport. Born in Ind. 1843.

GRIFFITH, J.; dealer in fancy groceries and provisions;
Southport. Born in Ohio 1830; settled in M. C. 1835.
Rep. Methodist.

Griffith, Lusford; dealer in fancy groceries and provisions.
Southport. Born in Ohio 1830, settled in M. C. 1835.
Rep. Methodist.

Graydon, R. G.; physician and surgeon, Southport. Born in
Pa. 1810; settled in M. C. 1835. Dem. Presbyterian.

Gardner, G. W. & D. M.; manufacturers of carriages, buggies,
spring and road wagons; all work done to order. Southport.

Gardner, G. W., Southport. Born in Pa. 1837; settled in M.
C. 1865. Rep. Protestant.

Gardner, D. M.; Southport. Born in Ohio 1842; settled in M.
C. 1871. Rep. Protestant.

Grube, David; carpenter and builder; Southport. Born in M.
C. 1840. Dem. Protestant.

Grube, Aaron; dealer in lumber and proprietor of Southport
Saw Mill; also carpenter and builder. Born in Pa. 1834.

HANKINS, WILLIAM P.; blacksmith shop; Southport.
Born in Ky. 1825; settled in M. C. 1827. Dem. Prot.

Hoffman, E.; wagon maker; shop and res Southport. Born in
Penn. 1821; settled in M. C. 1860. Rep.

Howard, A r n, f rmer   l   . , 6 n   l   , , . .
   Born i P n. 18 5   l   l C   7   'o for t
   nan   l t   n

Hamil on; Mr C tha   l on   N C 1   4

Hi k on, Hez r l, f r r, 5   B r   r
   Ind. 1826   t o i   l   t   l   c

HARNESS GEORGE, F   r   t   r s
   & s w li   oo   Bo   6 o   r   l C
   1841. K p   Pr   t

Harker, Pa l   , 6   l   h   y
   1825;   t d   l C 1 67

How nd, l ; f r   r, 4   6   p
   Born in N. Y. 1823;   t l d   l C   7   l p   h.th.

Haverstick, Isaac, f rmer, 1½ n   t   ort. B r   r Pa.
   1819; sett ed in M. C 1839   R p   Pr testant.

Hamilton, William Henry, 2 m w S t p rt   Born in l C.
   1843. Rep. M. Baptist.

Hamilton, Mahlon; farmer; 1 m s Southport. Born in M. C.
   1833. Dem. M. Baptist.

Harper, Edward; farmer; ½ m s G enn s Valley. Born in Ind.
   1850; settled in M. C. 1873. Dem. Protestant.

Howard, Adam; farmer; 5½ m s Indianapolis. Born in Pa 1845;
   settled in M. C. 1870.

Hendricks, Joseph; farmer; 2½ m e Southport

Huffman, Daniel; farmer; 2½ m s w Southport.   Born in Pa. 1835; settled in M. C. 1855.

Hufford, Wm.; farmer; 4 m s Indianapolis on Three Notch road; Born in Ind. 1826; settled in M. C. 1862.

Haverstick, George; farmer; 4 m s Indianapolis.

Hoss, Nelson; farmer; 4 m s Indianapolis.   Born in Ohio 1822; settled in M. C. 1846.

Hoss, William, retired farmer and minister; 4 m s Indianapolis. Born in Ohio 1817; settled in M. C. 1830.

Hoss, William H. H.; farmer; 4 m s Indianapolis.   Born in M. C. 1852.

Heiney, Eli; farmer; 4 m s Indianapolis.   Born in Pa. 1822; settled in M. C. 1847.   Dem.

HANNAH, A. M.; trader and farmer; 3 m s Indianapolis on Madison pike; Born in Ind. 1823; settled in M. C. 1856.

Hoover, J. B.; farmer; 4 m s Indianapolis on Madison pike. Born in Pa. 1824; settled in M. C. 1865.   Rep.   Prot.

Hoffman, E.; spring and road wagon maker; Southport.   Born in Penn. 1821; settled in M. C. 1860.   Rep.   Presb. .

Hunter, Margaret M.; Southport.   Born in M. C. 1836.

Hamilton, Catharine; Southport.   Born in M. C. 1834.

Irvin, J. D.; farmer and trader; Southport. Born in Ind. 1824; settled in M. C. 1844. Protestant.

Judson, William H.; farmer; ¼ m e Glenn's Valley. Born in N. Y. 1850; settled in M. C. 1873. Dem. Protestant.

Jennings, Thompson; farmer; ¾ m w Southport. Born in Ind. 1839; settled in M. C. 1873. Dem. Protestant.

Knercer, Mike; gardener; 5 m s Indianapolis on Bluff road. Born in Germany 1839; settled in M. C. 1855. Dem. Cath.

Lanphier, Wm.; farmer; 3½ m s Indianapolis. Born in Ind. 1842; settled in M. C. 1842. Rep. Protestant.

List, George; farmer; 6 m s Indianapolis. Born in Ky. 1832; settled in M. C. 1851. Rep. Protestant.

LANDERS, JOSHUA; farmer; ½ m s Glenn's Valley. Born in Ky. 1814; settled in M. C. 1863. Dem. Christian.

Lockwood, J. A.; fruit grower; 3 m n w Southport. Born in New Brunswick 1823; settled in M. C. 1844. Temperance. Protestant.

Lonergan, M.; farmer; 4 m s Indianapolis. Born in Ireland 1818; settled in M. C. 1850.

Larsh, Parker E.; farmer; 2½ m s e Southport. Born in M.
C. 1856.

Larsh, Charles; farmer; 2½ m s e Indianapolis. Born in Ky.
1818; settled in M. C. 1844.

LEWIS, CHARLES H.; blacksmith and buggy shop; work
to order and in good style; shop and res at Southport.
Born in Ky. 1849; settled in M. C. 1871. Protestant.

Lockwood, W. S.; retired carpenter; Southport. Born in New
Brunswick 1800; settled in M. C. 1867. Rep. Protestant.

LISTON, JONATHAN A.; retired lawyer; Southport. Born
in Delaware 1806; settled in M. C. 1851. Dem. Friend.

List, Garrett; farmer and elder of the Old School Presbyterian
Church; 6 m s Indianapolis on Bluff road. Born in Ky.
1809; settled in M. C. 1847. Rep.

Lenard, Henry H.; farmer; 6 m s Indianapolis. Born in Ky.
1845; settled in M. C. 1869. Dem. Protestant.

LEWIS, CHARLES H.; blacksmith and buggy work and repair shop; Southport. Born in Ky. 1849; settled in M. C.
1871. Protestant.

Miller, Daniel; farmer; 6 m s w Indianapolis. Born in Pa.
1844; settled in M. C. 1874. Dem. Lutheran.

MYERS, B. F.; farmer; ¾ m s Glenn's Valley. Born in Ind.
1850; settled in M. C. 1854. Rep. Protestant.

Myers, Benjamin; trader and farmer; ½ m s Glenn's Valley. Born in Pa. 1822; settled in M. C. 1854. Rep. Presb.

McBRIDE, E.; farmer; 2 m n e Glenn's Valley. Born in Va. 1803; settled in M. C. 1825. Joined M. E. Church, 1828.

Murry, John R.; farmer; 4 m n e Greenwood. Born in Ky. 1855; settled in M. C. 1871. Dem. Protestant.

Murry, A. H.; farmer; 4 m n e Greenwood. Born in Ky. 1852; settled in M. C. 1871. Dem. Methodist.

Murry, James M.; farmer; 4 m n e Greenwood. Born in Ky. 1812; settled in M. C. 1871. Dem. Methodist.

McClain, Solsbury; farmer; 2½ m w Southport. Born in M. C. 1836. Rep. Protestant.

Morford, J. S.; farmer; 2 m s w Southport. Born in Ohio.

McLaughlin, W. T.; farmer; east of Southport. Born in Ky. 1807; settled in M. C. 1822. Rep. Baptist.

MOORE, MRS. J. J.; dealer in millinery and fancy goods; res and shop at Southport. Born in Ind. 1847; settled in M. C. 1867. Rep. Presbyterian.

McCoy, J.; farmer and saw miller; Southport. Born in M. C. 1844. Dem.

McCoy, Gilbert; retired farmer; Southport. Born in Ohio 1805; settled in M. C. 1824. Dem.

McBride, John; farmer; 7 m s w Indianapolis.

Moody, W. M. H.; brick maker; Southport. Born in Ind. 1848; settled in M. C. 1850. Rep. Methodist.

Moody, George H.; brick maker; Southport. Born in Pa. 1809; settled in M. C. 1852. Rep. Christian.

MYERS, JOHN; farmer and justice of the peace; 6 m s Indianapolis. Born in Ky. 1796; settled in M. C. 1822. Rep. Methodist.

Myers, James M.; farmer; 6 m s Indianapolis. Born in M. C. 1822. Rep. Protestant.

Myers, Vincent; farmer; 5½ m s Indianapolis. Born in M. C. 1842. Rep. Protestant.

MILLER, TOBIAS; farmer; 6 m s w Indianapolis. Born in Pa. 1851; settled in M. C. 1869.

Marshall, James G.; farmer; 4 m s Indianapolis on Three Notch road. Born in W. Va. 1811; settled in M. C. 1852. Rep. Methodist.

Marshall, John; farmer; 4 m s Indianapolis. Born in M. C. 1854. Protestant.

Martin, R. H.; farmer; 4 m s Indianapolis. Born in M. C. 1835. Dem. Protestant.

Marquis, John; farmer; 3½ m s Indianapolis. Born in M. C. 1834. Rep. Protestant.

Miles, William D.; farmer; ½ m s w Southport. Born in M. C. 1838.

Myers, James M.; farmer; 3 m n w Glenn's Valley. Born in
M. C. 1822, and is said to be the first white person born in
Perry township.

McNuts, James; farmer; 2½ m s e Southport. Born in Ind.
1837; settled in M. C. 1872.

- Monroe, James; farmer; 2½ m s e Southport. Born in Ky.
1822; settled in M. C. 1834.

McCarty, William S.; farmer; 1½ m e Southport. Born in Ky.
1825; settled in M. C. 1829. Rep. Protestant.

McCartney, Wm. S.; farmer; 1½ m e Southport. Born in Ind.
1844; settled in M. C. 1871. Dem.

Moore, John R.; farmer; 1 m e Southport. Born in M. C. 1856.
Rep. M. Baptist.

McLaughlin, H. C.; farmer; 2 m s e Southport. Born in M.
C. 1832.

Moore, Samuel; farmer; 3 m n e Southport. Born in Ireland
1805; settled in M. C. 1834. Rep.

McCollum, John M.; tile manufacturer; 5 m s e Indianapolis.
Born in M. C. 1829. Rep. Protestant.

McFarland, Samuel; farmer; 2½ m n e Southport. Born in Ky.
1809; settled in M. C. 1836. Rep. Baptist.

NORTON, WILLIAM; dealer in fancy groceries and provisions; also, raiser of small fruit and toll gate keeper No. 2 on Bluff road; res and store at gate No. 2; Glenn's Valley. Born in Ind. 1830; settled in M. C. 1859. Methodist.

Neiman, John; farmer; Glenn's Valley. Born in M. C. 1845. Rep. Methodist.

Norwood, A. A.; farmer; 4½ m s Indianapolis. Born in Tenn. 1819; settled in M. C. 1834.

Negley, Joseph; farmer; 1 ½ m s e Southport.

NORWOOD, E. F.; farmer and township trustee; 4 m s w Indianapolis on Bluff road. Born in M. C. 1829. Rep. Protestant.

Orme, John S. M.; farmer; ¾ m n Glenn's Valley, on Bluff road. Born in Ind. 1845; settled in M. C. 1855. Dem. Christian.

Orme, Chas.; farmer; 1 ¼ m s Indianapolis. Born in Ky. 1819; settled in M. C. 1828. Dem. Protestant.

Orme, H. E.; farmer; Glenn's Valley. Born in Ky. 1822; settled in M. C. 1828. Dem. Methodist.

Orme, Eli F.; farmer; 5 m s Indianapolis. Born in M. C. 1830. Dem. Methodist.

ORME, GEORGE W.; farmer; 5 m s Indianapolis. Born in M. C. 1833. Dem. Methodist.

O'Donnell, Cornelius; farmer; 1¼ m n e Glenn's Valley. Born in Ireland 1845; settled in M. C. 1866. Dem. Catholic.

PERKINSON, G. W.; wagon and carriage shop; 4 m s Indianapolis on Bluff road. Born in Ky. 1841; settled in M. C. 1868. Dem. Christian.

Perry, Garland; farmer; 1 m n w Southport. Born in Ind. 1831; settled in M. C. 1874. Dem. Methodist.

Perry, Edward; farmer; 1¼ m w Southport. Born in Md. 1814; settled in M. C. 1854. Rep. Methodist.

PATISON, T. T. N.; farmer; 2 m n e Southport. Born in Ky. 1813; settled in M. C. 1858. Rep. Protestant.

Pratt, W. B.; fruit grower; 4 m s Indianapolis. Born in Mass. 1812; settled in M. C. 1854.

Peters, John; farmer; 4 m s e Southport.

Prince, William C.; farmer and gardener; 6 m s Indianapolis. Born in Ind. 1839; settled in M. C. 1873. Dem. Prot.

ROU, BENJAMIN; firm of Buser & Rou; Glenn's Valley. Born in Ind. 1841; settled in M. C. 1843.

Rusmisell, James A.; farmer; 5 m s e Indianapolis. Born in Va. 1846; settled in M. C. 1871. Dem.

Rudy, Samuel H.; farmer; 4½ m s Indianapolis on Madison road. Born in Penn. 1842; settled in M. C. 1864.

ROBERTSON, S. G.; farmer; 6 m s Indianapolis on Three Notch road. Born in Ind. 1839; settled in M. C. 1866. Rep. Methodist.

Smith, Daniel; farmer; 1½ m s w Southport. Born in Ky. 1835; settled in M. C. 1839. Rep. M. Baptist.

Smith, George C.; farmer; 2 m w Southport. Born in M. C. 1843. Rep. M. Baptist.

Smock, David R.; farmer; 2 m w Southport. Born in M. C. 1833. Rep. Presbyterian.

Smith, John; farmer; 2½ m w Southport. Born in M. C. 1845. Rep. M. Baptist.

Schraerbucke, John; farmer; 5½ m s Indianapolis. Born in Germany 1839; settled in M. C. 1857.

Smart, Hezekiah; farmer; southwest of Glenn's Valley. Born in Ky. 1816; settled in M. C. 1822. Rep. Methodist.

Sulgrove, John; farmer; 3½ m s Indianapolis.

Smock, T. C.; farmer; 5 m s Indianapolis. Born in Ky. 1808; settled in M. C. 1830. Rep. M. Baptist.

Smock, Peter; farmer; 1½ m n w Southport. Born in Ky. 1822; settled in M. C. 1824. Rep. Methodist.

Smock, Cornelius B.; carpenter and builder; Southport. Born in M. C. 1831.

Snider, A. J.; farmer; 2 m n e Southport. Born in M. C. 1845.

Snider, A. J.; farmer; 2½ m n e Southport. Born in M. C. 1845. Dem. Protestant.

Snider, James A. W.; farmer; 3 m n e Southport. Born in M. C. 1839.

* Smock, Isaac; farmer; 1½ m s w Southport.

Stuck, Peter; farmer; 2 m n Southport.

Stuck, William; farmer; 2¼ m n Southport.

Smock, Samuel; farmer and trader; 4½ m s e Indianapolis. Born in Va. 1819; settled in M. C. 1832. Presbyterian.

Sandlin, Adam; fruit grower; 5 m s Indianapolis. Born in Pa. 1821; settled in M. C. 1870.

SPEES, GEORGE; physician and surgeon; Glenn's Valley. Born in M. C. 1833. Dem. Methodist.

SMOCK, HENRY; blacksmith and wagon maker; Glenn's Valley. Born in M. C. 1841. All work done to order at reasonable rates.

SYLVESTER, G.; farmer; 6 m s w Indianapolis. Born in E. Tenn. 1810; settled in M. C. 1832. Methodist.

SYLVESTER, JOHN; farmer; 6 m s w Indianapolis. Born in M. C. 1846. Protestant.

SYLVESTER, MARION; farmer; 6 m s w Indianapolis. Born
in M. C. 1856. Protestant.

Smock, Abram; carpenter; Southport.

SYLVESTER, JAMES; farmer, 6 m s w Indianapolis. Born
in M. C. 1853. Protestant.

Sanders, Joseph; farmer; 2 m s e Glenn's Valley. Born in O.
1811; settled in M. C. 1828. Dem.

Smith, Robert; farmer; 1 m e Glenn's Valley. Born in Va.
1812; settled in M. C. 1862. Rep. Protestant.

Smock, Simon; farmer; 2½ m s w Southport. Born in M. C.
1836. Rep. Presbyterian.

Terhume, George; farmer; 1¾ m n w Southport. Born in Ky.
1819; settled in M. C. 1825. Rep. Methodist.

Thomas, Jessie C.; farmer; 2 m e Glenn's Valley.

Tomlinson, George; farmer; 4 m s Indianapolis on Madison
pike. Born in Va. 1807; settled in M. C. 1823. Rep.
Protestant.

Turk, F. S.; minister M. E. Church; 4½ m s Indianapolis on
Madison pike. Born in Ohio 1836; settled in M. C. 1873.
Rep.

Tomlinson, G. I.; farmer; 2 m s w Southport. Born in M. C.
1832. Rep. Christian.

Tex, John; farmer; 2½ m s e Southport.

Todd, Benjamin A.; farmer; 2½ m s w Southport. Born in Ky. 1827; settled in M. C. 1830. Rep. Protestant.

Todd, John; farmer; 3 m s e Southport. Born in M. C. 1857.

Todd, Isaac M.; farmer; 2½ m s e Southport. Born in Ind. 1828; settled in M. C. 1830. Rep. Methodist.

•Trout, William P.; carpenter and builder, Southport. Born in Mo. 1846; settled in M. C. 1867.

Tutewiler, N.; farmer; 3½ m n e Southport.

Thomas, John M.; farmer; 3½ m s Indianapolis. Born in M. C. 1833. Rep. Methodist.

Tex, John; farmer; 2 m s e Southport. Born in Germany 1834; settled in M. C. 1862. Catholic.

Vorhies, J. B.; farmer and retired carpenter; 4 m s Indianapolis. Born in 1827; settled in M. C. 1871. Dem. Methodist.

VOYLS, JOHN C.; farmer and gardener; s Indianapolis. Born in Ind. 1832; settled in M. C. 1873. Dem. Christian.

VAUTER, MRS. CATHERINE; widow of J. A. Vauter; dealer in dry goods, fancy groceries and provisions; Glenn's Valley. Born in East Tenn. 1836; settled in M. C. 1862. Goods owned by B. F. Perkins.

Wright, L. D.; farmer; 4 m s center of city. Born in Ky. 1810; settled in M. C. 1826. Dem. Methodist.

Woodfill, Samuel; farmer; 4½ m s center of city, on Bluff road. Born in Ky. 1823; settled in M. C. 1825. Dem. Prot.

WALLACE, ADAM B.; carpenter and builder; Glenn's Valley. Born in M. C. 1865. Dem. Reform Church.

Webb, Thomas; farmer and fruit raiser; 8 m s w Indianapolis; ½ m n Glenn's Valley. Born in Ky. 1828; settled in M. C. 1837. Rep. Methodist.

WHITAKER, JOHN; carpenter; 1 m s w Glenn's Valley. Born in Ind. 1835; settled in M. C. 1865.

Webb, James; farmer; 2 m e Glenn's Valley.

Webb, John S.; farmer and grist mill; 2 m s w Southport. Born in Ky, 1811; settled in M. C. 1823. Dem. Protestant.

WALLACE, WARON; farmer and minister; 2 m n w Glenn's Valley. Born in Ky. 1798; settled in M. C. 1865. Dem. Christian.

Webb, Richard; farmer; 5 m s Indianapolis. Born in Ky. 1826; settled in M. C. 1835. Rep. Methodist.

Wright, Jasper N.; farmer; 4 m s Indianapolis, on the old Madison road. Born in M. C. 1836. Rep. Methodist.

Wycoff, William; farmer; 1 m e Southport.

Woodbill, J.; farmer; ½ m n Southport.

Wycoff, John S.; farmer; 2 m n e Southport. Born in M. C. 1839. Rep. Protestant.

PIKE TOWNSHIP.

PIKE TOWNSHIP is located in the northwest corner of Marion county and is bounded on the north by Boone and Hamilton counties, on the east by Washington township, on the south by Wayne township, and on the west by Hendricks county, and contains 46 square miles. The surface is generally rolling and the soil of good quality, and is watered by Eagle Creek and spring branches. Some of the first settlers of this township were W. H. McCormick, John C. Hume, David McCurdy, S. H. Schenck, W. R. Clinton and Daniel Hartman. Mr. William H. McCormick claims to be the oldest settler now living in Marion county; he came to the county in the year 1820. Mr. John C. Hume is the oldest settler of Pike township, and perhaps the oldest man in it. He was born in the year 1790 and settled in this county in 1821. Mr. Hume distinctly remembers seeing the funeral procession that followed the remains of General George Washington to burial. Mr. Hume is near 85 years old and yet possessed of good memory, and is a clever, affable gentleman. He and McCormick and other old settlers of this township should never be forgotten, but should be held in remembrance by the people.

The present population of this township is near 2,400. The vote as taken from the report of October, 1874, for Secretary of

31

State was, for Neff, Democrat, 231; Curry, Republican, 146; Stout, Independent, 10; total, 387; Democratic majority, 75.

Postoffices, Augusta Station and Trader's Point.

SECRET SOCIETIES.

Rural Lodge, No. 416, I. O. O. F., located at Trader's Point; membership, 40; value of property, $2,000; instituted 1873; meets every Thursday night.

Hosbrook Lodge, No. 473, F. & A. M.; Augusta Station; organized June, 1873, with eleven charter members; present number of members, 40; value of Lodge property, $1,500; Lodge night on or before the full moon of each month; John W. Riley, Master; J. F. Trowbridge, S. W.; F. M. Hollingsworth, J. W.

DIRECTORY OF PIKE TOWNSHIP.

Avery, H.; farmer; 2 m n w Augusta Station. Born in M. C. 1834. Christian.

Albraugh, Henry; ½ m s e Trader's Point. Born in N. Y. 1828; settled in M. C. 1859.

Avery, Elijah W.; farmer; 1¼ m s w Augusta Station. Born 1839; settled in M. C. 1870.

Avery, George; farmer; 1½ m s w Augusta Station. Born in 1852; settled in M. C. 1870.

Avery, William; farmer; 1½ m s w Augusta Station. Born in 1854; settled in M. C. 1870.

Allen, Herman; farmer; 3 m s w Augusta Station. Born in N. Y. 1831; settled in M. C. 1853. Dem.

Brumfield, Samuel; farmer; 2 m n w Augusta Station. Born in M. C. 1833. Rep. M. Baptist.

BEAMAN, JOSIAH; farmer; ¾ m s e Trader's Point. Born in Ind. 1855; settled in M. C. 1872.

Clinton, W. R.; farmer and stock dealer; 1½ m s w Trader's Point. Born in Ky. 1826; settled in M. C. 1829. M. Bap.

Calvert, James; farmer; 1½ m n w Trader's Point. Born in Ky. 1808; settled in M. C. 1868. Rep. Christian.

Carter, Richard; farmer; 3 m s w Zionsville. Born in Ky. 1814; settled in M. C. 1862.

Crull, David; farmer and carpenter; 3½ m w Augusta Station. Born in Ohio 1812; settled in M. C. 1864. Rep. Christ.

Clift, J. M.; farmer; 1½ m n w Augusta Station. Born in Ind. 1833; settled in M. C. 1871. Rep.

Case, J.; farmer; 2½ m n w Augusta Station. Born in Ind. 1815; settled in M. C. 1844. Rep. M. Baptist.

Chass, Lewis; blacksmith; 1 m s e Trader's Point. Born in Germany 1837; settled in M. C. 1858.

Cofman, Wm.; farmer; 2½ m s w Augusta Station. Born in Va. 1847; settled in M. C. 1864.

Duncan, John; farmer; 2 m n Clermont. Born in Ohio 1840; settled in M. C. 1852. Dem. Methodist.

DUNCAN, HENRY; farmer; 1½ m s w Trader's Point. Born in Ohio 1839; settled in M. C. 1854. Christian.

Dinkle, Thomas; farmer; 2 m n Trader's Point. Born in Germany 1837; settled in M. C. 1874. Methodist.

Delong, David; farmer; 1¾ m n w Trader's Point. Born in M. C. 1837.

Delong, R. M.; farmer; Trader's Point. Born in Ind. 1847; settled in M. C. 1853. Rep. Methodist.

Davenport, J. F.; farmer; ¼ m s e Trader's Point. Born in Ohio 1836; settled in M. C. 1849. Indpt.

DINWIDDIE, WILLIAM A.; farmer; 1½ m s w Augusta Station. Born in Ky. 1837; settled in M. C. 1870. Rep. Presbyterian.

DAVIS, G. B.; farmer; 1¼ m w Augusta Station. Born in Ky. 1829; settled in M. C. 1865.

DARNELL, JAS. H.; farmer; 1½ m s e Trader's Point. Born in Ky. 1849; settled in M. C. 1874.

ENNIS, W. A.; SPECIAL GRAIN RAISER and dealer in poultry; 1½ m n e Clermont. Born in Va. 1822; settled in M. C. 1837. Rep. Methodist.

FULTS, J. W.; retired farmer; 4 m s w Zionsville.   Born in
    M. C. 1844.

FURR, JOHN; farmer; 1 m s w Trader's Point.   Born in Mo
    1848; settled in M. C. 1852.

Furr, David Franklin; farmer; 1 m s e Trader's Point.   Born in
    Ind 1853.

Gardner, Benjamin; farmer; 4 m s w Zionsville.   Born in N.
    Y. 1815; settled in M. C. 1872.   Granger.   Christian.

Gossett, J. B.; merchant; Trader's Point.   Born in Ind. 1843;
    settled in M. C. 1871.   Rep.   Methodist.

Gossett, T. A.; merchant; Trader's Point.   Born in Md. 1841;
    settled in M. C. 1873.   Rep.   Methodist.

Glidewell, Thomas; farmer and proprietor saw mill; 2 m n w
    Trader's Point.   Born in Ind. 1830; settled in M. C. 1863.
    Rep.

Hickey, J. F.; physician and surgeon; Trader's Point.   Born in
    Ohio 1844; settled in M. C. 1872.   Rep.   Methodist.

Hufman, J.; farmer; 3 m s w Zionsville.   Born in Ohio 1831;
    settled in M. C. 1867.

Hartman, Daniel; farmer; 1 m n e Trader's Point.　Born in N. C. 1828; settled in M. C. 1831.　Dem.　Methodist.

Heavenridge, J. B.; farmer; 2 m w Augusta.　Born in Ind. 1827; settled in M. C. 1858.　Rep.

Heather, Henry; farmer; 2½ m s Zionsville.　Born in Germany 1822; settled in M. C. 1864.　Dem.

HULS, ALFRED D.; carpenter and builder; Trader's Point. Born in Ky. 1834; settled in M. C. 1837.　Rep.　Chris.

Hanster, C.; wagon maker; 1 m s e Trader's Point.　Born in Germany 1822; settled in M. C. 1871.

HUME, JOHN C.; retired farmer; s e Trader's Point.　Born in Pa. 1790; settled in M. C. 1821; one of the oldest settlers of the county.　(See history.)

Hamilton, Aaron; farmer and timber dealer; 2½ m s w Augusta.　Born in Ind. 1836; settled in M. C. 1871.

HOLLINGSWORTH, F. M.; justice of peace, farmer, trader, stock dealer, etc.; 2½ m s e Trader's Point.　Born in M. C. 1837.　Rep.

Hollingsworth, W. H. H.; farmer; 2½ m s e Trader's Point. Born in M. C. 1840.　Rep.

Hollingsworth, S.; farmer; 2½ m s e Trader's Point.　Born in M. C. 1846.　Rep.

Hollingsworth, Deborah; 2½ m s e Trader's Point.　Born in N. C. 1808; settled in M. C. 1836.

Harmon, John; farmer; 2 m n Trader's Point. Born in M. C.
1851.

Irick, David; miller; Trader's Point. Born in Ind. 1850; settled
in M. C. 1871.

Irick, John R.; farmer; 1 m n w Trader's Point. Born in Va.
1808; settled in M. C. 1871.

Jessup, Ellis; farmer; 2 m n e Trader's Point. Born in Ind.
1824; settled in M. C. 1869.

JENNINGS, PRESLEY; blacksmith and carriage maker; Trader's Point. Born in M. C. 1834. Rep. Christian.

John, M. T.; horticulturist; 2½ m w Augusta Station. Born
in Md. 1834; settled in M. C. 1863. Rep. Christian.

JENNINGS, JOHN; FARMER; ¼ m s Trader's Point. Born in
Ind. 1837; settled in M. C. 1837. Rep.

Jones, William P.; farmer; 1 m s Trader's Point. Born in Ind.
1836; settled in M. C. 1836.

LONG, WILLIAM P.; farmer; ½ m n Clermont. Born in
Ohio 1825; settled in M. C. 1848. Rep. Christian.

Long, J. B.; farmer and school teacher; Clermont P. O. Born
in M. C. 1854.

Leonard, J. R.; 2 m w Augusta Station. Born in Ohio 1844; settled in M. C. 1873. Rep.

Long, D. S.; farmer; 2 m s Trader's Point. Born in Ind. 1856; settled in M. C. 1856.

McCORMICK, W. H.; farmer; 2½ m n Clermont. Born in Ohio 1813; settled in M. C. 1820. One of the oldest settlers in Marion county; the oldest settler now living in Pike township.

McCormick, N. A.; farmer; 2½ m n Clermont. Born in Ind. 1849; settled in M. C. 1870.

Miller, Jacob; farmer and butcher; 1 m s Trader's Point. Born in Ind. 1850; settled in M. C. 1853. Rep.

McCurdy, Wm.; farmer; 2½ m n e Clermont. Born in M. C. 1835. Dem. Protestant.

MAINES, JOSEPH; farmer and stock dealer; 1½ m s Trader's Point. Born in Ohio 1826; settled in M. C. 1859.

McCurdy, Daniel; farmer; 2 m s w Trader's Point. Born in N. Y. 1818; settled in M. C. 1823. Dem. Methodist.

McCurdy, Samuel; farmer; 4 m s w Trader's Point.

McCurdy, Asa; farmer; 2½ m n e Clermont. Born in M. C. 1842. Dem. Methodist.

Moor, John; farmer; 1½ m n e Clermont. Born in Ohio 1816; settled in M. C. 1830. Rep. Presbyterian.

Meyers, John; farmer; 2 m n w Augusta Station. Born in Pa. 1837; settled in M. C. 1856. Christian.

Madison, Rewlen; toll gate keeper; 1 m s e Trader's Point. Born in 1810; settled in M. C. 1856.

Parker, A.; manufacturer of barrels; Trader's Point. Born in Canada 1842; settled in M. C. 1866. Rep. Christian.

Pollard, Henry A.; farmer; 1 m w Augusta Station. Born in Ohio 1820; settled in M. C. 1838.

Pollard, J. N.; farmer; 1 m w Augusta Station. Born in M. C. 1845.

POLLARD, MRS. RACHEL; 1¼ m w Augusta Station. Born in 1826; settled in M. C. 1838. Christian.

Reval, James; farmer and fine hog raiser; 2 m n e Clermont. Born in Pa. 1813; settled in M. C. 1836. Dem. Pres.

Reval, W. O.; farmer; 2 m n e Clermont. Born in M. C. 1847.

Ray, C.; merchandising; Trader's Point. Born in M. C. 1845. Rep. Christian.

REYNOLDS, H. C.; farmer; 2½ m s e Trader's Point. Born in M. C. 1843. Rep.

READE, JOHN H.; farmer; 1 m s e Trader's Point.   Born in
Ind. 1847; settled in M. C. 1847.

Reade, Enoch; farmer; 1 m s e Trader's Point.   Born in Ohio
1814; settled in M. C. 1831.

STARKEY, NELSON; stock raiser, carpenter and farmer; 2 m
s w Trader's Point.   Born in M. C. 1847.   Protestant.

STARKEY, SILAS; farmer; 2½ m s w Trader's Point.   Born
in M. C. 1849.

STARKEY, ALBERT; farmer; 2½ m s w Trader's Point.
Born in M. C. 1852.   Protestant.

STARKEY, SHAMBERS; FARMER and trader; 2½ m s
w Trader's Point.   Born in M. C. 1839.

Senioe, Joshua; farmer; 3 m w Augusta Station.   Born in Ky.
1810; settled in M. C. 1839.   Dem.

Schenck, S. H.; school teacher and farmer; 2½ m s Zionsville.
Born in Ohio 1827; settled in M. C. 1828.

SAULSBERRY, LUCINDA; 2½ m s w Augusta Station.
Born in Ind. 1842; settled in M. C. 1871.

SAULSBERRY, DAVID; Franklin farmer; 2½ m s w Augusta Station.   Born in Ind. 1860; settled in M. C. 1871.

Vorhis, Allen; farmer, blacksmith and carpenter; Trader's Point. Born in Ind. 1853; settled in M. C. 1855.

Vorhis, Columbus; works at will; Trader's Point. Born in Ind. 1851.

VORHIS, MANNING; farmer; Trader's Point. Born in Ind. 1825; settled in M. C. 1840. Rep. Christian.

Vortis, Oliver; farmer; Trader's Point. Born in Ind. 1845; settled in M. C. 1845. Rep.

Wilson, James; farmer; ½ m n Clermont. Born in M. C. 1830. Methodist.

WILEY, JOHN H.; farmer and stock raiser; 2 m n w Trader's Point. Born in Ky. 1821; settled in M. C. 1850. Reform. Temperance Christian.

Walker, John; farmer; 2¼ m n w Trader's Point. Born in N. C. 1804; settled in M. C. 1852. Temperance.

White, Frank; farmer; 1¼ m n e Trader's Point. Born in M. C. 1858. Methodist.

White, Silas B.; farmer; 1½ m n e Trader's Point. Born in M. C. 1858. Methodist.

WHITE, SILAS; farmer; 1½ m n e Trader's Point. Born in Ky. 1807. Methodist.

Welchans, Milton; carriage painter, Trader's Point. Born in Ind. 1853; settled in M. C. 1873. Rep. Methodist.

WALLROITZ, F. G.; blacksmith; ½ m s e Trader's Point. Born in Germany 1836; settled in M. C. 1857.

WARREN TOWNSHIP.

WARREN TOWNSHIP is located on east side of Marion county, and is bounded by Lawrence township on the north, Hancock county on the east, Franklin township on the south, and Center township on the west, and contains an area of forty-nine square miles.

The surface of the township is slightly rolling, and might be classed as level land with the exception of a few small breaks or hills. The soil is rich and productive, and is watered by Buck Creek and spring branches.

The improvements speak well for the enterprise of the citizens. The public roads are in fine condition, while her churches and school houses, as well as dwellings, look neat and tidy.

The timber, building materials and gravel are of sufficient quantity for present demands, and the farmer, stock raiser and mechanic all seem to be doing a thriving business.

The present population of the township is near 2,500. The vote, as taken from the official report of October election, 1874, for Secretary of State, was, Dem., 335; Rep., 173; Indpt., 21; total, 529; Dem. majority, 141.

The post offices are Cumberland, Irvington and Julietta.

Some of the early settlers were Henry Brady, T. H. Lancaster, F. Kitley, A. B. Harlan, H. Grooves, J. C. Furguson, E. D. Cotton, John Buchanan, John Wallace, J. L. White, G.

White, Peter Wagner, C. F. Hartman, S. Deboy, Joseph Clinton and W. T. Buchanan.

CHURCH STATISTICS.

St. John's Church; 1 mile west of Cumberland; membership, 54; value of church property, $11,500; Rev. E. F. Beller, pastor.

Mt. Zion M. E. Church, 5 miles east of Indianapolis; membership, 20; value of church property, $2,500.

Cumberland Union Sabbath School; John Buchanan, superintendent; average attendance of scholars, 50.

DIRECTORY OF WARREN TOWNSHIP.

Ayers, J.; farmer; Cumberland.   Born in Va. 1815; settled in
    M. C. 1871.   Methodist.

Apple, D. M.; farmer; 5½ m e Indianapolis.   Born in Ind. 1848;
    settled in M. C. 1866.   Dem.

ANDERSON, E. H.; farmer; 5 m e Indianapolis.   Born in
    Ohio 1807; settled in M. C. 1846.   Rep.   Methodist.

Askren, William D.; farmer; 3 m s Lawrence.   Born in Ohio
    1821; settled in M. C. 1830.   Rep.

Askren, G. W.; farmer; 3 m s Lawrence.   Born in Ind. 1830;
    settled in M. C. 1830.   Rep.

Apple, A.; farmer; 2½ m s w Lawrence.   Born in Ohio 1817;
    settled in M. C. 1830.   Rep.   Methodist.

Apple, J. M.; farmer; 2½ m s w Lawrence.   Born in Ind. 1838;
    settled in M. C. 1838.   Rep.   Methodist.

Apple, Valentine; farmer; 3 m s w Lawrence. Born in M. C. 1840. Rep. Methodist.

Bouge, Albert; farmer; Cumberland. Born in M. C. 1832.

Buchanan, W. T.; carpenter; Cumberland. Born in M. C. 1827.

Bouge, Edward; merchant; Cumberland. Born in M. C. 1848. Baptist.

Bouge, Charles; farmer and postmaster; Cumberland. Born in Germany 1798; settled in M. C. 1835. Lutheran.

Ball, James; farmer; Cumberland. Born in Ind.; settled in M. C. 1872.

BALL, J.; plasterer; Cumberland. Born in Ind. 1849; settled in M. C. 1854.

Bade, C.; farmer; ½ m s Julietta. Born in Germany 1834; settled in M. C. 1860. Christian.

Beller, Rev. E. F.; 1 m w Cumberland. Born in Germany 1827; settled in M. C. 1845.

Beller, A. H.; teacher; 1 m w Cumberland. Born in Ky. 1850; settled in M. C. 1870.

BUCHANAN, JOHN; farmer; 1 m w Cumberland. Born in M. C. 1829. R. Baptist.

Bolen, P.; farmer; 3¾ m w Cumberland. Born in Tenn. 1840; settled in M. C. 1871. Methodist.

Ball, J. P.; farmer; 1½ m e Irvington. Born in Wis. 1849; settled in M. C. 1866. Rep. Methodist.

Ball, S.; farmer; ½ m e Irvington. Born in Ohio 1813; settled in M. C. 1865.

Bartholomew, C. G.; real estate agent; Irvington. Born in Ohio 1831; settled in M. C. 1872. Christian.

Boman, W.; farmer; 1 m n e Irvington. Born in Ky. 1814; settled in M. C. 1863. Dem. Baptist.

Boman, W. H.; dairyman; 1 m n w Irvington. Born in Ind. 1844; settled in M. C. 1863. Dem.

Bookshort, Wm.; farmer; 2½ m s w Cumberland. Born in Germany 1797; settled in M. C. 1839.

Bookshort, F.; farmer; 2½ m s w Cumberland. Born in Germany 1834; settled in M. C. 1839

Baker, W. H.; painter; 2 m w Julietta. Born in Ind. 1849; settled in M. C. 1873.

Beeler, Joel; farmer; 2¼ m w Julietta. Born in Ohio 1821; settled in M. C. 1874. Methodist.

Birth, John J.; toll gate keeper; 2¾ m w Julietta. Born in Pa. 1802; settled in M. C. 1854. Independent.

Beelman, Wm.; farmer; 3 m s w Cumberland. Born in Germanp 1851; settled in M. C. 1854. Dem.

Butcher, John; general worker; 6 m s w Cumberland. Born in Hanover 1846; settled in M. C. 1866.

Brady, Henry; 6 m s e Indianapolis. Born in Pa. 1794; settled in M. C. 1829. Dem. Baptist.

Bezer, George; farmer; 6 m n e Indianapolis. Born in Germany 1812; settled in M. C. 1870. Christian.

Burnford, S S.; county commissioner; 2½ m s Lawrence. Born in N. J. 1824; settled in M. C. 1850. Rep.

Bogemire, F.; farmer; 2 m n Cumberland. Born in Germany 1819; settled in M. C. 1849.

Colman, H.; butcher; Cumberland. Born in Germany 1824; settled in M. C. 1870.

Cox, L.; farmer; Cumberland. Born in Ind. 1825; settled in M. C. 1837. Rep.

Cook, J.; engineer; Cumberland. Born in Germany 1824. Presbyterian.

Collins, W. F.; physician; Cumberland. Born in S. C. 1830; settled in M. C. 1855. Dem.

Calley, Louisa; farmer; 3½ m s w Lawrence. Born in Ind. 1837; settled in M. C. 1861. Methodist.

Calley, C.; farmer; 3½ m s w Lawrence. Born in M. C. 1854. Methodist.

Cotton, E. D.; farmer; 2½ m w Cumberland. Born in Va. 1811; settled in M. C. 1820. Baptist.

Carr, A.; farmer; 1 m w Julietta. Born in Ohio 1808; settled in M. C. 1830. Rep. Methodist.

Cotton, John; farmer; 5 m s w Cumberland. Born in M. C. 1849. Rep. Baptist.

Clinton, Wm. P.; farmer; 6 m s e Indianapolis. Born in Ind. 1849; settled in M. C. 1849. Rep.

Clinton, Joseph; farmer; 6 m s e Indianapolis. Born in Ky. 1796; settled in M. C. 1829. Dem.

Darrach, G. H.; physician; Cumberland. Born in Pa. 1827; settled in M. C. 1853.

Deboy, S.; farmer; 3 m n Cumberland. Born in M. C. 1828.

Ebaugh, J. R.; grocery; Cumberland. Born in Md. 1841; settled in M. C. 1863.

Foley, J. E.; telegraph operator and agent; Cumberland. Born in Ireland 1853; settled in M. C. 1869. Dem.

Foley, Dennis; railroading; Cumberland. Born in Ireland 1817; settled in M. C. 1869. Dem.

Foley, D.; retired; Cumberland P. O. Born in Ireland; settled in M. C. 1869. Dem.

Furry, William; dealer in family and fancy groceries; Irvington. Born in Ind. 1854; settled in M. C. 1874. Rep.

FURGUSON, J. C. farmer; 1½ m e Irvington. Born in Ohio 1808; settled in M. C. 1825. Rep. Baptist.

Furguson, J. A.; merchant; Indianapolis. Born in Ind. 1830; settled in M. C. 1833. Rep. Baptist.

Furguson, F. M.; Born in Ind. 1833. Rep. Baptist.

Furguson, A. C.; farmer; 2 m w Cumberland. Born in M. C. 1838. Rep. Baptist.

Furguson, J. M.; farmer; 1½ m e Irvington. Born in M. C. 1840. Rep. Baptist.

Furguson, C. W.; farmer; 1½ m e Irvington. Born in M. C. 1851. Rep. Baptist.

Felton, J.; farmer; 1 m n e Irvington. Born in Ohio 1834; settled in M. C. 1872. Rep.

Foster, A.; farmer; 1 m n e Indianapolis. Born in Va. 1799; settled in M. C. 1829. Dem.

Fouts, G.; farmer; Cumberland. Born in Va. 1819; settled in M. C. 1872.

Franke, C.; shoemaker; 2 m n Cumberland.   Born in Germany
    1835; settled in M. C. 1848.

Gales, C.; miller; Cumberland.   Born in Germany 1835; set-
    tled in M. C. 1860.   Lutheran.

Gowin, J.; 1 m n w Irvington.   Born in Ky. 1833; settled in
    M. C. 1863.   Rep.

Greenleaf, C. A.; machinist; 5 m n e Indianapolis.   Born in
    Tenn. 1838; settled in M. C. 1854.   Rep.   Presbyterian.

Grooves, H.; farmer; 4 m s w Lawrence.   Born in Ohio 1818;
    settled in M. C. 1828.   Dem.   Baptist.

Gray, William H.; farmer; 1½ m n w Cumberland.   Born in
    Ohio 1821; settled in M. C. 1849.   Rep.   Methodist.

Green, J. N.; physician and surgeon; Irvington.

Heinrichs, Charles E.; merchant; Cumberland.   Born in Ger-
    many 1819; settled in M. C. 1852.   Dem.   Lutheran.

Heinrichs, Charles E.; merchant; Cumberland.   Born in Ohio
    1851; settled in M. C. 1853.   Dem.

Huntington, J. N.; farmer; ½ m s Cumberland.   Born in N.
    Y. 1808; settled in M. C. 1855.   Universalist.

Huntington, E.; farmer; ½ m s Cumberland. Born in M. C. 1855.

Hanlien, J.; blacksmith; Cumberland. Born in Germany 1836; settled in M. C. 1865. Dem.

HOUSTON, J. M.; Irvington. Born in Ohio 1826; settled in M. C. 1873. Christian.

Hobolt, William; toll-gate keeper; 5 m n Irvington. Born in Pa. 1819; settled in M. C. 1836. Dem. Lutheran.

Hardesty, L. A.; farmer; 3½ m s w Lawrence. Born in Ohio 1811; settled in M. C. 1835. Rep. Methodist.

Huntington, S.; farmer; ¼ m s Cumberland. Born in Ky. 1814; settled in M. C. 1836. Rep. Universalist.

Hobbs, John; farmer; 1½ m n w Julietta. Born in Va. 1804; settled in M. C. 1838. Rep.

Hobbs, Oliver P.; carpenter; Palestine. Born in Ind. 1846; settled in M. C. 1846. Rep.

Hobbs, Wm.; farmer; 1½ m n w Julietta. Born in Ind. 1844; settled in M. C. 1844. Rep.

Hobbs, P. F.; carpenter; Palestine. Born in Ind. 1849; settled in M. C. 1849. Rep. Methodist.

Harlan, A. B.; farmer; 1½ m w Julietta. Born in Ind. 1825; settled in M. C. 1825. Dem.

Hoffman, C.; carpenter; 1½ m w Julietta.   Born in Md. 1835; settled in M. C. 1854.   Rep.

Hartman, Frederick; 3½ m s w Cumberland.

Hunter, William; farmer; 5 m s e Indianapolis.   Born in Ohio 1817; settled in M. C. 1835.   Dem.

Hunter, J. B.; trader; Indianapolis.   Born in Ind. 1839.   Dem. Protestant.

Hunter, J. L.; farmer; 5 m e Indianapolis.   Born in M. C. 1851. Dem.

Hunter, Wm. B.; farmer; 5 m e Indianapolis.   Born in M. C. 1848.   Dem.   Protestant.

Hunter, E. C.; farmer; 5 m e Indianapolis.   Born in Ind. 1854. settled in M. C. 1854.   Rep.

Hartman, C. F.; farmer; ½ m s Irvington.   Born in Germany 1826; settled in M. C. 1830.   Dem.

Irwin, J.; farmer; 3½ m s w Lawrence.   Born in Ohio 1839; settled in M. C. 1862.   Rep.   Methodist.

Jones, I. S.; farmer; Cumberland.   Born in Ind. 1832; settled in M. C. 1871.   Rep.   Methodist.

JOHNSON, C.; farmer; 5½ m n e Indianapolis.   Born in Ind. 1838; settled in M. C. 1840.   Dem.

Julian, George W ; lawyer; Irvington. Born in Ind. 1817; settled in M. C. 1873.

Johnson, Sylvester; real estate broker; Irvington.

Kitley, F.; farmer; ½ m s Cumberland. Born in Ohio 1824; settled in M. C. 1827. Granger.

Kern, N.; farmer; 1½ m w Cumberland. Born in Va. 1811; settled in M. C. 1854. Dem.

Kuhn, C.; butcher; Irvington. Born in Ind. 1848; settled in M. C. 1851.

Krumrine, J. A.; physician; Irvington. Born in Pa. 1842; settled in M. C. 1872.

Kinder, W. M.; farmer; 1 m n w Irvington. Born in Ind. 1848; settled in M. C. 1863.

Kuhn, O.; farmer; 3 m s Lawrence. Born in Ind. 1845; settled in M. C. 1851. Rep. Baptist.

Kissel, P.; farmer; 5½ m s w Cumberland. Born in Prussia 1850; settled in M. C. 1852. Dem.

Lynch, J. J.; wagon maker; Cumberland. Born in M. C. 1848. Dem.

Lancaster, T. H.; blacksmith; Cumberland. Born in Ky. 1821; settled in M. C. 1826.

Lynch, W.; teamster; Cumberland. Born in Ky. 1819; settled in M. C. 1834.

Londragon, J.; dairyman; ¼ m w Cumberland. Born in M. C. 1850. Catholic.

Loutt, C.; farmer; 2½ m s w Lawrence. Born in Germany 1826; settled in M. C. 1844. Dem.

Lout, C.; farmer; 2¼ m s w Lawrence. Born in Prussia 1827; settled in M. C. 1844. Dem.

Long, S. D.; miller; 1½ m w Julietta. Born in Pa. 1799; settled in M. C. 1844. Dem.

Licturburg, Henry; farmer; 4 m n w Julietta. Born in Germany 1830; settled in M. C. 1850. Dem.

McConnell, J.; merchant; Cumberland. Born in Pa. 1812; settled in M. C. 1832.

McConnell, W.; retired farmer; Cumberland. Born in Pa. 1810; settled in M. C. 1831.

McConnell, C.; mechanic; Cumberland. Born in M. C. 1853.

McConnell, J. S.; merchant; Cumberland. Born in Ind. 1851; settled in M. C. 1851.

Miller, C.; farmer; 2 m s Cumberland. Born in Germany 1825; settled in M. C. 1866.

Mix, J. S.; farmer; 1 m s w Cumberland. Born in Conn. 1799; settled in M. C. 1833. Rep.

McVey, J. M.; farmer; 2 m e Irvington. Born in Ind. 1818; settled in M. C. 1832. Rep. Methodist.

McVey, J. F.; farmer; 2 m s e Irvington. Born in Ind. 1822; settled in M. C. 1832. Rep.

McVey, B. F.; farmer; 2 m s e Irvington. Born in Ind. 1829; settled in M. C. 1832.

Mulis, J.; farmer; 4½ m n e Irvington. Born in Ind. 1837; settled in M. C. 1872. Rep.

Mahan, W. T.; farmer; 5 m n e Indianapolis. Born in Pa. 1841; settled in M. C. 1855. Dem.

Maryman, J. A.; farmer; 1¼ m n w Lawrence. Born in Va. 1810; settled in M. C. 1836. Dem. Old School Baptist.

McVey, E. W.; farmer; 3½ m s Lawrence. Born in Ind. 1826; settled in M. C. 1832. Rep. Methodist.

Mithopir, H.; farmer; 2 m s Lawrence. Born in Germany 1825; settled in M. C. 1852. Dem.

Maxwell, E. F.; carpenter; Irvington. Born in Ind. 1848. Rep. Protestant.

Moorhouse, H.; farmer; 3 m w Julietta. Born in Ind. 1834. Rep. Protestant.

Moorhouse, Hiram; farmer; 5 m e Indianapolis.

Newhouse, A. J.; farmer; 1¼ m s w Lawrence. Born in M. C. 1831. Dem. Methodist.

Newhouse, Calvin; farmer; 2¼ m s w Lawrence. Born in Ind. 1834; settled in M. C. 1834. Dem.

Ofsswald, F. C.; retired farmer; Cumberland. Born in Germany 1798; settled in M. C. 1844. Lutheran.

Osborn, B. F.; farmer; 3 m n w Julietta. Born in Ind. 1838; settled in M. C. 1838. Dem.

Pyle, W.; carpenter and joiner; Cumberland. Born in N. C. 1835; settled in M. C. 1859.

Price, W.; laborer; Cumberland. Born in Ohio 1829; settled in M. C. 1864.

Pritchard, W. H.; contractor; Irvington. Born in Ind. 1849; settled in M. C. 1874.

Parker, H. C.; blacksmith; ½ m w Irvington. Born in M. C. 1845. Dem.

PLUMMER, J.; farmer; 4 m n̂ Cumberland. Born in M. C. 1840. Rep.

Peale, C.; farmer; 3 m n w Julietta. Born in Germany 1819; settled in M. C. 1843. Dem.

Rogers, R. D.; saloon keeper; Cumberland. Born in Ala. 1839; settled in M. C. 1872. Dem.

Riley, T.; railroader; Cumberland. Born in Ireland 1819; settled in M. C. 1852. Dem. Catholic.

Redmire, C.; saw mill; Cumberland. Born in Germany 1837; settled in M. C. 1844.

Right, J.; carpenter; Cumberland. Born in Va. 1840; settled in M. C. 1866.

REDMIRE, W.; carpenter and joiner; Cumberland. Born in 1849; settled in M. C. 1873. Dem. Lutheran.

Russell, T.; farmer; Cumberland. Born in Ky. 1839; settled in M. C. 1865.

Redmire, C.; carpenter and joiner; Cumberland. Born in Ind. 1845; settled in M. C. 1870. Lutheran.

Rice, M. T.; carpenter; 5 m n e Indianapolis. Born in Md. 1838; settled in M. C. 1871. Lutheran.

RICE, W. D.; farmer; 5 m e Indianapolis. Born in Md. 1839; settled in M. C. 1859. Rep. Lutheran.

Simcocks, J. G.; saddler; Cumberland. Born in Ohio 1825; settled in M. C. 1832. Dem.

Snyder, W.; teamster; Cumberland.

Shierl, E. M.; farmer; Cumberland. Born in Tenn. 1824; settled in M. C. 1862. Methodist.

Strubber, H. H.; farmer; Cumberland. Born in Germany 1820; settled in M. C. 1852. Baptist.

Senur, C.; farmer; ¼ m s Julietta. Born in Ky. 1812; settled in M. C. 1833. Christian.

Smith, W. G.; blacksmith; Julietta. Born in N. J. 1814; settled in M. C. 1865. Methodist.

Senur, R.; farmer; ¼ m n w Julietta. Born in M. C. 1837.

Staley, Isaac; toll gate keeper; 1 m w Cumberland. Born in Va. 1812; settled in M. C. 1833. Granger.

Shepherd, A. R.; blacksmith; Cumberland. Born in Ind. 1851; settled in M. C. 1860. Rep. Methodist.

Steele, H.; farmer; 3 m w Cumberland. Born in Ind. 1820; settled in M. C. 1857. Baptist.

Stofer, J.; toll gate keeper; 1½ m e Irvington. Born in Pa. 1817; settled in M. C. 1852.

Shank, W. H. H.; butcher; Irvington. Born in Ind. 1840; settled in M. C. 1854. Rep.

SUNDERLAND, G. E.; farmer; 5 m n Irvington. Born in Ohio 1839; settled in M. C. 1873. Dem. Presbyterian.

Stoops, P.; farmer; 3 m s w Lawrence. Born in Ky. 1815; settled in M. C. 1833. Rep.

SWARMS, JOSEPH; farmer; 5 m e Indianapolis. Born in Pa. 1804; settled in M. C. 1839. Rep. Lutheran.

Swarms, T. J.; farmer; 5 m e Indianapolis. Born in M. C. 1852. Rep. Lutheran.

Sweney, J. O.; farmer; 5 m e Indianapolis. Born in N. C. 1845; settled in M. C. 1848. Rep.

Shereer, Charles; farmer; 5 m e Indianapolis. Born in M. C. 1850. Rep. Methodist.

Springer, John; farmer; 2 m s Lawrence. Born in Ohio 1827; settled in M. C. 1830.

Springer, B.; farmer; 4 m s w Lawrence. Born in M. C. 1839. Dem. Baptist.

Springer, D.; farmer; 4 m s e Lawrence. Born in Ohio 1821; settled in M. C. 1839. Dem.

Springer, J.; farmer; 4 m s Lawrence. Born in Ohio 1823; settled in M. C. 1839. Dem.

Sherrer, W.; day laborer; 4 m n w Cumberland. Born in Pa. 1819; settled in M. C. 1872. Baptist.

Smith, G. M.; farmer; 1 m s e Irvington. Born in Germany 1836; settled in M. C. 1869. Independent.

Steinmyer, C. F.; farmer; ⅓ m s Irvington.   Born in Germany
    1823; settled in M. C. 1837.

Shimer, C. R.; farmer; ½ m s Irvington.   Born in M. C. 1838.
    Democrat.

Shimer, A. N.; farmer; 1 m s Irvington.   Born in M. C. 1832.
    Democrat.

Settle, Wm.; millright; 1 m n Irvington.   Born in Va. 1846;
    settled in M. C. 1870.   Dem.

Shue, J.; farmer; 4 m s w Cumberland.   Born in Md. 1808;
    settled in M. C. 1844.   Rep.

Sweeney, B. F. N.; laborer; 4 m n w Cumberland.   Born in
    Ind. 1849; settled in M. C. 1871.   Dem.

Toon, H. J.; farmer; 3¼ m s w Julietta.   Born in Ky. 1820;
    settled in M. C. 1834.   Christian.

Turner, J. P.; farmer; 1½ m e Irvington.   Born in Ind. 1859;
    settled in M. C. 1859.   Rep.   Baptist.

Tillinghast, J. B.; grape nurseryman; 5 m n e Indianapolis.
    Born in Ireland 1799; settled in M. C. 1865.   Rep.   Meth.

TILLINGHAST, WILLIAM; fruit grower; 5 m n e Indiana-
    polis.   Born in Ohio 1829; settled in M. C. 1865.   Rep.

Tyner, S.; farmer; 3 m s w Lawrence.   Born in Ind. 1811; set-
    tled in M. C. 1846.   Dem.

Tyner, J. W.; farmer; 3 m s w Lawrence. Born in M. C. 1850. Dem.

Tuttle, Thos.; farmer; 5½ m s w Cumberland. Born in Ky. 1837; settled in M. C. 1870. Dem.

VEACH, H.; carpenter; Cumberland. Born in Ind. 1822; settled in M. C. 1867. Dem. Methodist.

Veach, L. C.; farmer; Cumberland. Born in Ind. 1849; settled in M. C. 1867. Dem.

Vansickle, A. J.; farmer; 2¼ m s Lawrence. Born in M. C. 1830. Dem.

Vansickle, William; farmer; 3 m s w Lawrence. Born in M. C. 1813. Rep. Methodist.

Vansickle, L.; farmer; 3 m n w Cumberland. Born in M. C. 1839. Rep.

Vansickle, W. M.; farmer; 3 m w Cumberland. Born in Ohio 1820; settled in M. C. 1830. Dem. Granger. R. Baptist.

Vansickle, J. M.; farmer; 2½ m w Julietta. Born in Ind. 1847. Baptist.

WALLACE, JOHN; hotel keeper. Born in Ind. 1833; settled in M. C. 1833. Protestant.

Wolf, F.; butcher; Cumberland. Born in Germany 1838; settled in M. C. 1865.

Wallace, John; shoemaker; Cumberland. Born in Del. 1806; settled in M. C. 1827. Dem.

Wolf, W.; wagonmaker; Cumberland. Born in Prussia 1845; settled in M. C. 1865.

White, T.; railroad hand; Cumberland. Born in Ireland 1838; settled in M. C. 1873. Dem. Catholic.

Wilson, J.; farmer; Cumberland. Born in Ind. 1826; settled in M. C. 1871. Rep.

Walter, C.; carpenter; Cumberland. Born in Germany 1846; settled in M. C. 1874. Lutheran.

West, G.; farmer; Cumberland. Born in Ind. 1846.

Welling, J. S.; merchant; Cumberland. Born in Ohio 1845; settled in M. C. 1871.

West, S.; farmer; Cumberland. Born in N. J. 1820; settled in M. C. 1854. Baptist.

Whistler, A.; farmer; 1 m s w Cumberland. Born in M. C. 1848. Dem.

Wesling, H. F.; farmer; Cumberland. Born in Prussia 1841; settled in M. C. 1843.

Wilson, J.; farmer; Cumberland. Born in Ind. 1826; settled in M. C. 1872. Dem.

White, O. B.; farmer; 1½ m w Cumberland.   Born in M. C. 1846. Rep.

Wagner, Peter; farmer; 1½ m n e Irvington. Born in Germany 1810; settled in M. C. 1828.

Wilson, W. W.; merchant; Irvington. Born in M. C. 1837. Rep. Methodist.

Wells, E. T.; shoemaker; 3¼ m s w Lawrence.   Born in Ky. 1832; settled in M. C. 1834. Rep.

White, T. J.; farmer; 2 m e Irvington.   Born in Ohio 1833; settled in M. C. 1840. Dem.

White, G.; farmer; 3 m e Irvington.   Born in Ohio 1801; settled in M. C. 1829. Dem. Baptist.

White, J. L.; farmer; 3 m e Irvington.   Born in M. C. 1829. Dem. Baptist.

White, W. T.; farmer; 3 m e Irvington.   Born in M. C. 1853. Democrat.

White, S. A.; farmer; 3 m e Irvington.   Born in M. C. 1849. Democrat.

Woodard, J.; farmer; 3½ m w Cumberland.   Born in Ohio 1835; settled in M. C. 1847. Dem. Methodist.

Wattson, P.; farmer; 1½ m w Cumberland.   Born in Ohio 1845; settled in M. C. 1860. Methodist.

Wiese, Andrew; farmer; Cumberland. Born in Germany 1829; settled in M. C. 1850. Dem.

White, L.; farmer; 8 m n w Cumberland. Born in Ohio 1829; settled in M. C. 1837. Baptist.

Whitesides, B. L.; farmer; 4 m n Cumberland. Born in Ky. 1811; settled in M. C. 1849. Dem. Baptist.

Whitesides, O.; farmer; 4 m n Cumberland. Born in M. C. 1847. Dem.

Whitesides, A.; farmer; 4 m n Cumberland. Born in M. C. 1851. Dem.

Whitesides, J.; farmer; 4 m n e Cumberland. Born in M. C. 1844. Dem.

Witt, Wm.; farmer; 2 m n w Cumberland. Born in Germany 1833; settled in M. C. 1844.

WHISTLER, J. E.; farmer; 1 m w Cumberland. Born in Pa. 1821; settled in M. C. 1847. Rep. Granger. Baptist.

Wilgus, I. E.; farmer; 2½ m w Julietta. Born in Ohio 1853; settled in M. C. 1853.

York, J. W.; farmer; ½ m s Irvington. Born in Ky. 1821; settled in M. C. 1872. Rep.

WASHINGTON TOWNSHIP.

WASHINGTON TOWNSHIP is located in the center of the north tier of townships of Marion county, and is bounded as follows: On the north by Hamilton county; on the east by Lawrence township; on the south by Center township; and on the west by Pike township. It contains an area of about forty-nine square miles.

The surface is slightly rolling or level, except a few breaks on White river and Fall creek. The soil is rich and productive, and well adapted to blue grass. Its good supply of stock water, its rolling fields, and rich blue grass pastures, make this one of the best stock raising townships in the county.

Some of the early settlers of this township were Daniel Smith, Jacob J. Ringer, Oliver Johnson, Nora Parr, Michael Pattison, Moses McClarin, Rany Fox, Jacob Robards, S. W. Watte, David Trester, John Essary, Charles Davidson, J. C. Coil and John Ballinger.

The present population of the township is near 2,600. The vote for Secretary of State, October, 1874, was for Neff, Democrat, 126; for Curry, Republican, 162; Stout, Independent, 136; total vote, 424.

The post offices are: Broad Ripple, James' Switch, and Woodbank.

CHURCH, SCHOOL AND LODGE STATISTICS.

Allisonville M. E. Church; membership, 50; value of church property, $20,000; ——— Holliday, presiding elder; ——— Neville, minister; average attendance Sabbath school, 45 ; superintendent, Moses McClain.

Number of school houses in Washington township, 15 ; value of school property, $7,500.

William H. Sharp, Trustee.

Millersville Lodge, No. —, F. and A. M.; organized, 1851; membership, 43; value of property, $500; Joseph Boswell, Secretary; Mr. Horniday, Master.

Nora Grange, No. 375; organized Sept. 3d, 1873; membership, 140; value of fixtures, $100; located at Broad Ripple; A. Culbertson, Secretary; Samuel Farley, Master.

Lutheran Church, organized in 1845; membership, 118; value of church property, $10,000; located four miles north east of Indianapolis; O. Brown, pastor; Samuel Harper, elder; Luther Johnson and John Sargent, deacons; regular attendance at Sabbath school, 115; Samuel Harper, superintendent.

Millersville M. E. Church; organized in 1859; membership, 24; value of property, $300; Mr. Neville, pastor; regular Sabbath school attendance, 40; Mr. Carpenter, superintendent.

Wellington Union Church, located at Broad Ripple; value of church property, $200.

Malott Park M. E. Church, organized in 1874; membership, 20; value of church property, $4,000; Rev. Holoway, presiding elder.

DIRECTORY OF WASHINGTON TOWNSHIP.

Allen, David; farmer; ½ m n w Woodbank.　Born in Pa. 1801; settled in M. C. 1851.　Dem.　Baptist.

Allen, Jacob; farmer; ¾ m n w Woodbank.　Born in Ohio 1834; settled in M. C. 1851.

Andrews, Wm.; wagon maker; Allisonville.　Born in Pa. 1852; settled in M. C. 1872.

Adams, Isaac; farmer; 6½ m n e Indianapolis. Born in Ind. 1851; settled in M. C. 1864.

Bailey, A. J.; farmer and dairyman; 3 m n Indianapolis. Born in Ind. 1851; settled in M. C. 1861.

Blue, George W.; farmer; 3 m n Indianapolis, on Indianapolis and Westfield pike. Born in Ind. 1832; settled in M. C. 1835.

BLUE, PETER; farmer; 5 m n Indianapolis, on Indianapolis and Westfield gravel road. Born in Ind. 1818; settled in M. C. 1837.

Blue, Garrett; farmer; 5 m n Indianapolis, on Indianapolis and Westfield gravel road. Born in M. C. 1843.

BLUE, BENJAMIN; farmer; 5 m n Indianapolis, ½ m w Indianapolis and Westfield gravel road. Born in Ind. 1813; settled in M. C. 1835.

Blue, G. W.; farmer and fruit grower; 5 m n Indianapolis, ½ m w Indianapolis and Westfield gravel road. Born in M. C. 1842.

Baliff, D. W.; farmer; 4 m n Indianapolis, on Central avenue gravel road. Born in Ohio 1826; settled in M. C. 1869.

Ballinger, John; farmer; ¼ m n Millersville. Born in Ohio 1804; settled in M. C. 1818.

BECKEM, ABRAM; farmer; 6 m n Indianapolis, on Central avenue gravel road, ¾ m s Broad Ripple. Born in Ky. 1832; settled in M. C. 1865. Rep.

Ballinger, James; farmer; ¼ m n Millersville. Born in M. C. 1832.

Byers, George; carpenter and builder; Malott Park. Born in Pa. 1834; settled in M. C. 1858.

Brunson, L.; farmer; 2 m s w Castleton. Born in M. C. 1837.

Baer, John; farmer; 1½ m s w Castleton. Born in M. C. 1844.

Brunson, E.; farmer; 2½ m s w Castleton. Born in M. C. 1830.

Brunson, Mrs. E.; keeper of toll gate; Alisonville. Born in Md. 1824; settled in M. C. 1873.

Brunson, James M.; farmer; Alisonville. Born in M. C. 1851.

Bash, J. E.; physician; Allisonville. Born in Ind. 1850; settled in M. C. 1856.

Blue, William G.; farmer; 1 m n w Woodbank. Born in M. C. 1837.

Bowers, J. W.; manufacturer of shingles. 5 m n e Indianapolis. Born in Ind. 1839; settled in M. C. 1844.

Butt, L.; carpenter and farmer; res ¼ m w Woodbank.

Ballinger, William R.; farmer; 4 m n e Indianapolis. Born in M. C. 1837.

Brown, Henry; farmer; 6 m n e Indianapolis. Born in M. C.
1847.

Brown, Ellison; painter and farmer; 6½ m n Indianapolis.
Born in Ohio 1823; settled in M. C. 1849. Dem. Meth.

Bruce, J. M.; farmer; 6 m n Indianapolis. Born in Ind. 1833.
Rep. Protestant.

Butterfield, S. G.; minister and farmer; 2 m n e Broad Ripple.
Born in N. Y. 1817; settled in M. C. 1864. Christian..

Bowers, F. M.; farmer; 2½ m e Augusta Station. Born in O.
1842; settled in M. C. 1873. Dem.

Boardman, A. Q.; farmer; 2 m e Augusta Station. Born in
1816; settled in M. C. 1832. Rep. Methodist..

Bridgford, Mary C.; farmer; 5 m n Indianapolis. Born in Md.
1827. Baptist.

BRIDGFORD, ANDY. S.; trader and farmer; 6 m n Indianapolis. Born in M. C. 1853. Rep. Granger. Baptist.

Blackwell, David F.; farmer; 6 m n Indianapolis. Born in Ind.
1846. Rep. U. Brethren.

Cones, Sarah; farmer; 2½ m s e Augusta Station. Born in Ky.
1806.

Cokley, Isaac; farmer; 6 m n Indianapolis. Born in Va. 1812;
settled in M. C. 1845. Rep. Baptist.

CONNIAR, G. W.; farmer; 6 m n Indianapolis. Born in N.
Y. 1816; settled in M. C. 1874. Rep. Protestant.

Cline, Barney; farmer; 3 m n e Augusta Station. Born in Pa.
1815; settled in M. C. 1857.

CORDUA, EDWARD; proprietor wagon shop; Allisonville,
1½ m w Castleton P. O., also proprietor paint shop.
Born in Germany 1839; settled in M. C. 1865.

CRAIG, ISAAC N.; physician and surgeon; Allisonville, ½ m
w Castleton P. O. Born in Ind. 1851; settled in M. C.
1849.

CALKINS, A. M.; farmer and retired sailor; 5 m n Indianapolis, on the Indianapolis and Westfield Gravel Road. Born
in N. Y. 1831; settled in M. C. 1870.

CLARK, SAMUEL; farmer and gardener; 4½ m n Indianapolis, on the Indianapolis and Westfield Gravel Road. Born
in Ky. 1842; settled in M. C. 1848.

Coil, Jacob C.; farmer; Broad Ripple. Born in Ohio 1820; settled in M. C. 1822.

Culburson, William, 1 m n w James' Switch.

Culberson, A.; farmer and Justice of Peace, 2 m e Broad Ripple.
Born in M. C. 1833.

Cale, Robert; farmer; Broad Ripple. Born in Va. 1828; settled
in M. C. 1838.

Colwell & Negley; blacksmiths; Millersville.

CHANCE, JACKSON; blacksmith and repair shop; all work done to order at reasonable rates; Allisonville. Born in Ind. 1836; settled in M. C. 1874.

Colwell, John. Born in Ind. 1843; settled in M. C. 1872.

Coon, Perry; farmer; Allisonville. Born in Ohio 1832; settled in M. C. 1852.

DeHaven, A. J.; farmer and gardener; 4 m n Indianapolis. Born in Pa. 1837; settled in M. C. 1864.

Dawson, Wm. M.; farmer; 5 m n Indianapolis. Born in M. C. 1836.

Dawson, Chas.; farmer; 1 m e Broad Ripple. Born in M. C. 1824.

Deford, Francis A.; farmer; 3 m s w Castleton P. O. Born in M. C. 1848.

Deford; G. W.; farmer and carpenter; 3 m s w Castleton P. O. Born in Ind. 1808; settled in M. C. 1832.

Dronberger, Lewis; farmer; 1½ m w Castleton P. O. Born in Pa. 1817; settled in M. C. 1849.

Dawson, M. H.; farmer; ½ m s e Broad Ripple. Born in M. C. 1852.

Day, Ezra; blacksmith; Broad Ripple. Born in Ohio 1820; settled in M. C. 1830.

Deford, Perry; farmer; 3 m s w Castleton P. O. Born in M. C. 1852.

Dawson, M.; farmer; 5 m n Indianapolis on Central avenue. Born in Ind. 1808; settled in M. C. 1833.

Darius, Baker; farmer; 5 m n Indianapolis. Born in N. C. 1851.

Dawson, Jackson; farmer; Broad Ripple. Born in 1828. Granger. Protestant.

Day, Uriah; farmer; 1½ m n w Broad Ripple. Born in Ohio 1823; settled in M. C. 1854. Methodist.

Draper, James M.; farmer; 6 m n Indianapolis. Born in Ind. 1832. Dem. Christian.

Eaton, Charles H.; farmer and gardener; 4 m n e Indianapolis. Born in M. C. 1838.

Easterday, Thomas C.; farmer; 6 m n e Indianapolis. Born in Md. 1828; settled in M. C. 1836.

Easterday; L. R.; farmer and gardener; 5 m n Indianapolis. Born in Md. 1829; settled in M. C. 1836.

Essary, John; dealer in butter and eggs; Allisonville. Born in N. C. 1801; settled in M. C. 1821.

Evans, Wm.; farmer and stock broker; 1½ m n James' Switch. Born in M. C. 1843.

Ellis, Alfred; farmer; ¾ m e James' Switch. Born in M. C. 1830.

Ferris, H.; farmer; 5 m n Indianapolis. Born in Ohio 1822; settled in M. C. 1852. Baptist.

Fetrow, Alex.; mechanic; n Indianapolis. Born in Pa. 1830; settled in M. C. 1857. Rep.

Fisher, Henry; farmer and gravel road contractor; 2 m n w Broad Ripple. Born in Ind. 1821; settled in M. C. 1833.

Fatout, Harvey; farmer; 5 m n Indianapolis. Born in Ohio 1828. Rep. Protestant.

Fox, Rany; farmer; 6 m n Indianapolis. Born in Ohio 1816; settled in M. C. 1822. Dem.

Farlew, W.; 2 m n e Nora. Born in Ind 1845; settled in M. C. 1863.

Green, Henry C.; school teacher; 5 m n Indianapolis. Born in Ind. 1842. Rep. Baptist.

Gresh, Levi; farmer; 2 m s e Augusta Station. Born in Tenn. 1817; settled in M. C. 1846. Rep. Methodist. Grange

Grestley, Henry; farmer; ½ m s e Malott Park.   Born in Pa.
1849; settled in M. C. 1858.

GRESTLEY, JOHN; dealer in dry goods, fancy groceries and
provisions; Allisonville, on Allisonville and Fall Creek
Pike, 10 m n Indianapolis.   Born in Pa. 1840; settled in
M. C. 1857.

HENESLEY, THOMAS J.; model farmer; 5 m n Indianapolis.
and ¼ m w Indianapolis and Westfield Gravel road.   Born
in M. C. 1835.

Hildebrand, Uriah; farmer; 4 m n Indianapolis.   Born in Ohio
1813; settled in M. C. 1839.

HAMMOND, R. R.; farmer and stock broker; 3½ m n Indianapolis on Central avenue.   Born in Ind. 1828; settled in
M. C. 1848.

Huff, Amos; farmer; 2 m n e Broad Ripple. Born in Ohio 1827;
settled in M. C. 1848.

Huffman, James; farmer; ¼ m e Broad Ripple.   Born in M. C.
1836.

Horniday, W. H.; physician and surgeon; James' Switch. Born
in Ind. 1837; settled in M. C. 1845.

Herrion, John; farmer; 2 m n e Broad Ripple.   Born in Ky.
1828; settled in M. C. 1834.

HUFF, DAVID; farmer and postmaster; ½ m e James' Switch.
Born in Pa. 1808; settled in M. C. 1843.

HUFF, W. H.; farmer; ½ m e James' Switch. Born in M. C. 1847.

Hicks, A. M.; carpenter and builder; 1½ m w Castleton P. O. Born in Va. 1806; settled in M. C. 1834.

Howard, S. A.; toll gate keeper; 5 m n Indianapolis. Born in Ind. 1836.

Hilton, J. W.; farmer; 5 m n Indianapolis. Born in Ky. 1817; settled in M. C. 1831. Rep. Baptist.

Hessong, Martin S.; farmer; 6 m n Indianapolis. Born in Ind. 184–. Rep. Granger. Lutheran.

Hessong, Geo. W.; farmer; 6 m n Indianapolis. Born in Ind. 1842. Rep.

Herm, George W.; farmer; 2 m s e Augusta Station. Born in 1846. Rep. Protestant.

Hessong, John J.; farmer; 6 m n Indianapolis. Born in Md. 1832; settled in M. C. 1836. Rep.

HESSONG, DAVID; farmer; 6 m n Indianapolis. Born in Md. 1811; settled in M. C. 1839. Rep. Granger. Lutheran.

Hessong, Sarah; farmer; 1¼ m w Broad Ripple. Born in Va. 1819. Lutheran.

Hessong, Henry M.; farmer; 1¼ m w Broad Ripple. Born in Ind. 1850. Rep. Granger. Lutheran.

Hushan, Jasper; farmer and teamster; 1½ m n w Broad Ripple.
Born in 1840. Rep. Protestant.

House, G. W.; firm of Ryan & House; Woodbank. Born in
Md. 1818; settled in M. C. 1837.

Harrison, T. W.; farmer; ¼ m w Woodbank. Born in Ind.
1848; settled in M. C. 1872.

HAMMOND UPTON J.; farmer and stock broker; 5 m
n e Indianapolis, on Fall Creek and Millersville Gravel
Road.

HAMMOND, THOMAS C.; farmer and stock broker; 5 m n
e Indianapolis, on Fall Creek and Millersville Gravel Road.
Born in Ind. 1826; settled in M. C. 1866.

IRVIN, PERRY; 3 m n Indianapolis. Born in Mo. 1851; settled in M. C. 1870.

JOHNSON, OLIVER; model farmer; 4 m n Indianapolis, on
Central avenue Gravel Road. Born in Ind. 1821; settled
in M. C. 1822.

Jones, A. P.; farmer; 4 m n Indianapolis, on Indianapolis and
Westfield Gravel Road. Born in Ohio 1832; settled in M.
C. 1858.

JUSTICE, GILBERT; proprietor of blacksmith shop; all work
done to order at reasonable rates; Broad Ripple. Born in
Ind. 1837; settled in M. C. 1874.

Johnson, John V.; farmer; 1 m s e Broad Ripple. Born in M. C. 1839.

Johnson, Luther; farmer; ½ m n Woodbank. Born in M. C. 1824.

Johnson, S. H.; farmer; 4 m n Indianapolis. Born in M. C. 1848.

Jones, Lewis H.; teacher; Woodbank. Born in Ind. 1844; settled in M. C. 1874.

Johnston, Thomas; farmer; 5 m n e Indianapolis. Born in Ireland 1813; settled in M. C. 1870.

KERN, LEWIS; dealer in fancy dry goods and groceries; Millersville. Born in Germany 1835; settled in M. C. 1857.

Karer, Charles; carpenter and builder; Millersville. Born in Pa. 1850; settled in M. C. 1854.

Karer, Henry A.; brick maker; Millersville. Born in Pa. 1832; settled in M. C. 1854.

Kelley, William; farmer; 1½ m w Malott Park. Born in M. C. 1852.

Kelley, John; farmer; 1½ m w Malott Park. Born in M. C. 1846.

Kemps, Benjamin J.; farmer; 7 m n Indianapolis. Born in Md. 1831; settled in M. C. 1854. Dem.

Rail, Robard; farmer; Broad Ripple.   Born in Va.; settled in
M. C. 1839.   Protestant.

Karer, Fred.; carpenter and builder; Millersville.

Leonard, Jesse; farmer; 6½ m n Indianapolis.   Born in 1838;
settled in M. C. 1857.   Protestant.

Loyd, I. S.; farmer; 4⅓ m n Indianapolis.   Born in N. C. 1819.
Rep.   Protestant.

Loyd, Wm. R.; farmer; 4½ m n Indianapolis.   Born in N. C.
1852.

Lankford, Thomas; farmer; 5 m n e Indianapolis.   Born in Ky.
1800.

Lankford, T. W.; farmer; 5 m n e Indianapolis.   Born in M.
C. 1845.

Lock, John G.; farmer; ¼ m e Broad Ripple.   Born in Ky.
1843; settled in M. C. 1864.

Lleuellyn, Lafayette; farmer; ½ m s Woodbank.   Born in N.
C. 1850; settled in M .C. 1869.

LOUHON, LOUIS N.; farmer; 2 m n e Broad Ripple.   Born in
W. Va. 1839; settled in M. C. 1861.

Leever, P. A.; farmer; ½ m n Woodbank.   Born in Ohio
1815; settled in M. C. 1873.

Llyod, John T.; toll gate keeper; ½ m n Woodbank. Settled
in M. C. 1873.

Lleuellyn, Richard; farmer; 1½ m n e Malott Park. Born in N.
C. 1817; settled in M. C. 1869.

Lleuellyn, J. M.; farmer; 1¼ m n e Malott Park. Born in N.
C. 1846; settled in M. C. 1869.

LANCASTER, G. W.; farmer and dairyman; 3 m n Indianapolis. Born in Ind. 1843; settled in M. C. 1867.

Letherman, Joseph; farmer; 2 m n Malott Park. Born in Md.
1827; settled in M. C. 1832.

Magsam, Henry; farmer; 2½ m s w Castleton. Born in Germany
1836; settled in M. C. 1856.

Morris, Isaac; farmer; 2 m n e Broad Ripple. Born in Ind.
1835; settled in M. C. 1848.

McManama, Edward; wagon maker; Allisonville. Born in Mo.
1844; settled in M. C. 1862.

Mann, A.; farmer; 3 m n e Broad Ripple.

McHaffey, John; toll gate keeper; 5 m n e Indianapolis, on Fall
Creek and Millersville gravel road. Born in Ohio 1851;
settled in M. C. 1862.

34

Mowary, John; farmer; 6 m n e Indianapolis. Born in Pa. 1814; settled in M. C. 1864.

Miller, Joseph; farmer; 5½ m n e Indianapolis. Born in Va.; settled in M. C. 1871.

Miller, Jacob; farmer; 7 m n e Indianapolis.

McIlvain, Calvin; farmer; 4 m n Indianapolis. Born in M. C. 1852.

MUSTARD, JACOB S.; farmer; 2 m s Broad Ripple, on Central avenue pike. Born in Pa. 1821; settled in M. C. 1834.

Mustard, James; farmer; ¾ m s Broad Ripple.

Morris, James; farmer; 1 m s Broad Ripple. Born in Ind. 1830; settled in M. C. 1848.

Meelsker, Mrs. Nancy A.; farmer; ¾ m s e Broad Ripple. Born in M. C. 1833.

MILLARD, B. W.; carpenter and millwright; ½ m e Malott Park. Born in N. Y. 1837; settled in M. C. 1849.

MILLARD, WILLIAM; retired millwright; ½ m e Malott Park. Born in N. Y. 1796; settled in M. C. 1849.

Morgan, A.; physician; Millersville. Born in Ohio 1835; settled in M. C. 1871.

Mowery, Elijah; farmer; Millersville. Born in Ind. 1847; settled in M. C. 1847.

McDade, Fred; farmer; ½ m n e Millersville. Born in Ky. 1819; settled in M. C. 1865.

McClarin, Moses; farmer; 1 m w Castleton. Born in Ohio 1811; settled in M. C. 1824.

Mier, William; farmer; ½ m w Allisonville.

MARTIN, ABRAHAM J.; farmer; 6 m n Indianapolis. Born in O. 1832; settled in M. C. 1841. Rep. Baptist minister.

Martin, Thos.; farmer, 4½ m s e of Augusta Station. Born in 1805; settled in M. C. 1831. Dem. Baptist.

McKainey; farmer; 1½ m s w of Broad Ripple. Born in Ind. 1834; settled in M. C. 1866.

Mustard, James; farmer; 1 m n w of Broad Ripple. Born in Tenn. 1834; settled in M. C. 1834.

Morgan, A. W.; farmer; 5 m n Indianapolis. Born in Mo. 1844.

Michel, Pattison; farmer; 6 m n Indianapolis. Born in Ind. 1822.

NOBLE, JOHN F.; farmer; ¾ m s Broad Ripple, on Central avenue gravel road. Born in Ohio 1846; settled in M. C. 1854.

NOBLE, LEWIS; farmer; ¼ m e Malott Park, 6 m n e Indianapolis. Born in N. J. 1817; settled in M. C. 1854.

Negley, W. H. Born in M. C. 1850.

Negley, David D.; farmer; ½ m s e Nora P. O. Born in M. C. 1835.

Nesbit, Joseph; physician; Allisonville. Born in Ky. 1821; settled in M. C. 1830.

Negley, John; farmer; Millersville. Born in Ky. 1804; settled in M. C. 1822.

Nelson, W. H.; gardener; Woodbank; 5½ m n e Indianapolis. Born in Illinois, 1845; settled in M. C. 1868.

Newman, Benjamin; farmer; Augusta Station. Born in 1843. Rep. Baptist.

Neiman, Benjamin; farmer; Augusta Station. Born in 1843. Rep. Baptist.

Parr, Nora; retired farmer; Broad Ripple. Born in Va. 1803; settled in M. C. 1823.

Parr, C. D.; farmer; Broad Ripple. Born in M. C. 1853.

Privett, Willis; farmer; 1 m n Malott Park. Born in N. C. 1824; settled in M. C. 1862.

Previt, J. C.; farmer; 1½ m n Malott Park. Born in Ark. 1856; settled in M. C. 1869.

Pattison, Michael; farmer; 6 m n Indianapolis. Born in Ind. 1822.

Pugh, Wm.; farmer; 7 m n Indianapolis. Born in Ind. 1831. Rep.

Runnels, James; farmer; 2½ m s e Malott Park. Born in Ind. 1847; settled in M. C. 1871.

Ringer, George; farmer and retired miller; ½ m s Malott Park.

Roe, Robert; farmer; ½ m e Malott Park. Born in Ireland 1816; settled in M. C. 1838.

RINGER, JACOB J.; farmer and miller; Millersville, 1½ m e Malott Park. Born in Md. 1823; settled in M. C. 1827.

Ringer, George; farmer and teamster; Millersville. Born in M. C. 1852.

Rowe, George M.; farmer; 1 m n e Malott Park. Born in Pa. 1837; settled in M. C. 1857.

Rowney, Wm. W.; farmer; 1½ m n Malott Park. Born in N. J. 1842; settled in M. C. 1858.

RICE, A. J.; farmer and gardener; 1 m n Woodbank Born in Md. 1831; settled in M. C. 1862.

Ryan & House; proprietors of Fall Creek mill; Woodbank, 5 m n e Indianapolis.

Ryan, G. W. Born in N. Y. 1843; settled in M. C. 1845.

Ryan, John; miller, with Ryan & House.   Born in Ind. 1851; settled in M. C. 1851.

Rhoads, P. T. B.; farmer and proprietor grist mill; 5 m n e Indianapolis.   Born in Md. 1839; settled in M. C. 1853.

Robards, Jacob; farmer; 1½ m w Broad Ripple.   Born in Md. 1802; settled in M. C. 1824.   Dem.   Lutheran.

SILVEY, H. L.; farmer: 1½ m n e Malott Park.   Born in Va. 1818; settled in M. C. 1833.

SILVEY, WILLIAM A.; farmer; 2 m s w Castleton P. O.   Born in Ind. 1831; settled in M. C. 1833.

Smith, Jeremiah; farmer; 2 m n e Malott Park.   Born in Ky. 1820; settled in M. C. 1871.

Simson, John; farmer; 2 m n e Malott Park.   Born in England, 1844; settled in M. C. 1869.

SHARP, WILLIAM H.; farmer and Township Trustee; 2 m n w Broad Ripple.   Born in M. C. 1841.

SHOCK, DANIEL; carpenter and wagon maker; Allisonville, 1¼ m w Castleton P. O.   Born in Ohio 1826; settled in M. C. 1852.

SHAWCROSS, THOMAS T.; blacksmith and repair shop; all work done to order; Allisonville, 1½ m w Castleton P. O.   Born in Connecticut in 1832.

Sanders, William; farmer; ¾ m n James' Switch.

Speece, W. H.; carpenter and builder; 1½ m w Castleton P. O. Born in M. C. 1831.

Sammons, William; farmer; 1½ m n James' Switch. Born in Arkansas, 1856; settled in M. C. 1862.

Sapp, John; farmer and miller; Woodbank. Born in N. C. 1839; settled in M. C. 1865.

Sharts, Harmon; farmer; ¾ m s Broad Ripple. Born in M. C. 1832.

Snowden, Richard; farmer; 4½ m n Indianapolis. Born in Ind. 1840; settled in M. C. 1864.

Smith, James S.; painter; Malott Park. Born in Ohio 1837; settled in M. C. 1863.

Seltzer, Jos. G.; miller; Millersville. Born in Pa. 1851; settled in M. C. 1874.

Staley, M. F.; carpenter and builder; Millersville. Born in Md. 1830; settled in M. C. 1861.

SPAHR, WILLIAM H.; farmer and breeder of Golddust and Mambrino horses and Poland and China hogs. ½ m n Millersville., and 7 m n e Indianapolis. Born in Va. 1842; settled in M. C. 1845.

SMITH, JOHN H.; farmer; 1¼ m n e Malott Park. Born in M. C. 1836.

SMITH, DANIEL R.; attorney and counsellor at law; 7 m n e Indianapolis. Born in Ky. 1801; settled in M. C. 1821.

Stilz, Jacob; gardener; 1 m n e Malott Park. Born in Germany 1845; settled in M. C. 1871.

Stilz, Daniel; gardener; 1 m n e Malott Park. Born in Germany 1817; settled in M. C. 1854.

See, W. C.; farmer; 5 m n Indianapolis. Born in Ind. 1829. Protestant.

SANDERS, BUTLER S.; farmer; 6 m n Indianapolis. Born in Ind. 1848. Dem. F. M. Christian.

Sutton, J. B.; farmer; 6½ m n Indianapolis. Born in Ind. 1858. Rep. Baptist.

Savage, Thos. J.; farmer; 1¼ m w Broad Ripple. Born in East Tenn. 1846; settled in M. C. 1871.

Sheets, Samuel; dry goods merchant; Broad Ripple. Born in Va. 1835; settled in M. C. 1862.

Sharpe, Wm. H.; 1½ m n w Broad Ripple. Born in Ind. 1842. Rep. Protestant.

Swift, Elias B.; farmer; 6 m n Indianapolis. Born in 1833. Dem. Granger. Baptist.

Schofield, Mrs. Nancy; one of the proprietors of the Woodbank mill. Born in Ind. 1822; settled in M. C. 1853.

Smith, Edward; farmer; 6 m n e Indianapolis. Born in Ind. 1845; settled in M. C. 1873.

Schofield, Wm. A.; farmer and stock broker and dealer in real estate; 5 m n e Indianapolis. Born in D. C. 1812; settled in M. C. 1832.

Trester, David; farmer; 6 m n Indianapolis. Born in Ky. 1798; settled in M. C. 1830. Rep.

Tyner, Benjamin; farmer; 6 m n e Indianapolis. Born in Ky. 1800.

Tyner, Silas; farmer; 6 m n e Indianapolis. Born in M. C. 1849.

Wright, J. J.; farmer; 3 miles s Broad Ripple P. O. Born in Ohio, 1832; settled in M. C. 1871.

Whitsell, John; farmer; ¾ miles n w Nora P. O. Born in M. C. 1853.

White, Jeremiah; farmer; 5 m n Indianapolis. Born in Ky. 1822; settled in M. C. 1834.

Wood, James; farmer; 2½ m n e Broad Ripple. Born in N. C. 1840.

Winkle, Henry; farmer; 1¼ m s e Broad Ripple. Born in M. C. 1844.

Wright, T. J.; carpenter; ¾ m n Woodbank P. O. Born in Ohio 1830; settled in M. C. 1850.

Williams, Jacob; farmer and retired printer and paper hanger; 1 m s Broad Ripple P. O. Born in Penn. 1812; settled in M. C. 1859.

WINENOW, FREDERICK; stone mason and bricklayer; Millersville. Born in Penn. 1820; settled in M. C. 1853. Dem. Protestant.

Wakeland, John J.; farmer; 6 m n Indianapolis. Born in Ohio 1833; settled in M. C. 1834. Rep.

Wright, Emily, farmer; 1½ m e Augusta Station. Born in Ind. 1820. Dem. Protestant.

Wright, John; farmer; 1½ m e Augusta Station. Born in 1851. Dem. Protestant.

WHEALER & WHEALER; butchers; Millersville, 1 m e James' Switch.

WHEALER, HILLIS. Born in Iowa 1850; settled in M. C. 1874.

WHEALER, WILSON. Born in Iowa 1853; settled in M. C. 1874.

Winpenny, G. W.; farmer; Millersville.

Whealer, William H.; butcher; ½ m n Millersville. Born in M. C. 1851.

Whitsel, Arthur E.; farmer; 1 m w Castleton. Born in M. C. 1851.

WHITESELL, WILLIAM & SON; farmers and stock brokers; 1½ m w Castleton; ½ m n Allisonville.

WHITESELL, WILLIAM. Born in Pa. 1818; settled in M. C. 1840.

WHITESELL, WM. H. Born in Ind. 1840; settled in M. C. 1840.

White, W. G.; teacher; bds at P. T. Rhoad's, 5 m n e Indianapolis. Born in Ind. 1850; settled in M. C. 1866.

Watts, G. W.; carpenter and builder; 6 m n e Indianapolis. Born in Me. 1832; settled in M. C. 1873.

Yancey, John G.; farmer; 4½ m n Indianapolis. Born in Ky. 1839. Rep. Protestant.

Yancey, Joseph A.; farmer and constable; Broad Ripple. Born in Ind. 1828. Rep. Protestant.

WAYNE TOWNSHIP.

THIS TOWNSHIP is located on the west side of Marion county, and is bounded by Pike and Washington townships on the north, Center township on the east, Decatur on the south, and Hendricks county on the west, and contains an area of forty-nine square miles.

The surface of the greater part of the township is level or un-dulating. The soil is generally of a medium quality, and is well adapted to blue grass and small grain. The yield of Indian corn is a fair average of the county, and the horticulturist re-ceives rich returns for his labor.

The State Insane Asylum is located in this township, four miles west of Indianapolis, also the County Asylum for the Poor. By the way, the corps of officers of the institution ap-pears to be composed of the right men in the right place; they are clever, affable gentlemen.

Some of the first settlers of the township were, Obediah Har-ris, Wm. Gladden, Andrew Willson, J. D. McClelland, James Johnson, W. M. Johnson, Hiram Rhoads, John Martindale, G. G. Menefee, Jesse Johnson, Laban Harding, George Hoover, Daniel Hoover, W. C. Holmes, Isaac Furnace, Wm. Cassell, Fielding Beeler and Lot Reagan.

The present population of the township is near 4000. The vote at the October election, 1874, for Secretary of State, was, Curry, Rep., 326; Neff, Dem., 269; total, 595; Rep. majority, 57.

The postoffices are. Bridgeport, Clermont, Maywood, Sabine and Sunnyside.

L. R. Harding, Township Trustee.

Number of school houses, 18; value of school property, $14,400.

CHURCH, SCHOOL AND LODGE STATISTICS

Bridgeport Lodge, No. 162, F. and A. M; membership, 40; value of Lodge property, $4,000.

Bridgeport M. E. Church; Rev. J. Whorton, pastor; membership, 35; value of church property, $500; average attendance Sabbath school, 35; superintendent, G. W. Sullivan.

Bridgeport Friends' Meeting House; ½ m n w Bridgeport; membership, 225, value of church property, $1,500; average attendance Sabbath school, 68; superintendent, Eli Spray; overseers, Isaac Morgan and James Mills.

Pleasant View M. E. Church; 1 mile east of Sabine P. O., on Rockville pike; Rev. T. C. Webster, pastor; membership, 30; value of church property, $1,000; average attendance Sabbath school, 30; superintendent, James T. Hardin.

Christian Church, Clermont; Elder John C. Barnhill, minister; membership, 80; value of church property, $3,500; average attendance Sabbath school, 50; Wm. Brown and Wm. Long, superintendents.

Foster Lodge, No. 372, I. O. O. F., Clermont; membership, 70; value of church property, $4,000; organized June, 1871.

West Union Missionary Baptist Church (burnt); 4½ miles west of Indianapolis, near Lafayette pike.

Clermont Presbyterian Church; Rev. N. F. Tuck, pastor; membership, 22; average attendance at Sabbath school, 35; John Moore, superintendent; value of church property, $3,000.

M. E. Church, Clermont; Rev. T. C. Webster, pastor; membership, 48; average attendance at Sabbath school, 40; David Farmer, superintendent; value of church property, including parsonage, $1,500.

Zion Chapel, United Brethren in Christ; 1½ miles west of Sunnyside, on National Road; membership, 30; average attendance at Sabbath school, 20; James Mullen, superintendant; value of church property, $1,500.

Mt. Olive M. E. Church; 1½ miles west of Sunnyside, just south of the National Road; Rev. J. Wharton, pastor; membership, 50; average attendance at Sabbath school, 45; I. Dunn, superintendent; value of church property, $2,000; built 1870.

Old Union Christian Church; six miles west of Indianapolis, on the I. B. & W. R. R.; membership disbanded; value of church property, $400.

The hospital for the poor of Marion county is located about four miles northwest of Indianapolis, between the Crawfordsville and Lafayette pikes, Wayne township. The farm of 160 acres is in a very desirable location, and the buildings are very fine, put up at a cost of $100,000. The present officers are Samuel Royster, superintendent, and Wm. B. Fulton, steward, with Mrs. Royster and Mrs. Fulton as matrons.

DIRECTORY OF WAYNE TOWNSHIP.

Abraght, August; gardener; 2½ m n w Indianapolis. Born in Germany, 1834; settled in M. C. 1865.

Amus, Christ.; retired; 3 m n w Indianapolis. Born in Germany, 1798; settled in M. C. 1853.

Adams, Robert; farmer; 3½ m n w Indianapolis. Born in M. C. 1847.

AVERY, LEONARD; justice of the peace and postmaster; Sunnyside, 4½ m w Indianapolis. Born in Ohio 1818; settled in M. C. 1859.

Anderson, Wm. W.; proprietor saw mill; ½ m n Bridgeport. Born in Ky. 1815; settled in M. C. 1857.

Anderson, Benjamin; works at saw mill; Bridgeport. Born in Ky. 1842; settled in M. C. 1857.

Athon, J. S.; apothecary Insane Hospital.

Arnold, Samuel; farmer; ¾ m e Sabine P. O. Born in Ky. 1820; settled in M. C. 1832.

Arnold, C.; farmer; ¾ m s e Sabine P. O. Born in Ind. 1850; settled in M. C. 1852.

BEELER, FIELDING; farmer, stock raiser and dairyman, * (Hazel Dell), 3 m s w Indianapolis. Born in M. C. 1823.

Brown, Jacob; farmer; 1 m n Maywood. Born in Ohio 1840; settled in M. C. 1870.

Barker, George; gardener; ¼ m s Sunnyside. Born in Ohio 1838; settled in M. C. 1859.

Burgelin, George; blacksmith; 3 m n w Indianapolis. Born in Germany 1831; settled in M. C. 1874.

Brown, Peter D.; farmer; Sabine. Born in Ohio 1809; settled in M. C. 1834.

Beenson, Wm.; miller; Bridgeport. Born in N. C. 1841; settled in M. C. 1873. Rep. Methodist.

Burdge, Jonathan; farmer; 2½ m s e Bridgeport. Born in Ohio 1830; settled in M. C. 1852. Dem. Methodist.

Burk, John; section boss I. C. & L. R. R.; ½ m e Spry. Born in Ireland 1845; settled in M. C. 1873.

Blank, Peter; farmer; ½ m w Sabine. Born in Germany 1844; settled in M. C. 1850.

Blank, George; ½ m w Sabine. Born in Germany 1800; settled in M. C. 1850.

Ballard, George; carpenter; Clermont. Born in Ky. 1822; settled in M. C. 1834.

Buck, Pressley; farmer; 1 m n Sabine. Born in Ohio 1828; settled in M. C. 1872.

Baker, James G.; foreman at the car repairing shops I. & St. L. R. R. Co.; 2 m w Union Depot. Born in England, 1835; settled in M. C. 1870.

Bailey, Wm. H.; farmer and carpenter; 2 m e Bridgeport. Born in Ohio, 1825; settled in M. C. 1829.

Bidwell, Abraham; farmer; ½ m s Bridgeport. Born in Ohio, 1847; settled in M. C. 1870. Dem. Methodist.

Blank, Ignatz; farmer; 1½ m n e Bridgeport. Born in Germany 1826; settled in M. C. 1854.

Barton, J. R.; blacksmith; Bridgeport. Born in N. C. 1842; settled in M. C. 1873. Rep.

Beachly, N. J.; physician; Bridgeport. Born in Pa. 1831; settled in M. C. 1865. Rep.

Busch, Christian; shoe and boot maker; 2½ m w Indianapolis. Born in Germany 1832; settled in M. C. 1854.

BAKER, W. H.; general stock broker; 3 m w Indianapolis. Born in Ind. 1819.

BAKER, A. E.; firm of Baker's Sons; distillery; 3 m w Indianapolis. Born in Ind. 1843; settled in M. C. 1874.

BAKER, D. J.; firm of Baker's Sons; distillery; 3 m w Indianapolis. Born in Ind. 1815; settled in M C. 1878.

BAKER, Z. T.; firm of Baker's Sons; distillery; 3 m w Indianapolis. Born in Ind. 1848; settled in M. C. 1874.

BECKER, JOHN; gardener; 2½ m s w Indianapolis. Born in Germany 1821; settled in M. C. 1851.

Bond Riley; flouring mills; Maywood. Born in Ind. 1819; settled in M. C. 1852.

Combs, William F.; farmer; 1½ m w Sunnyside. Born in Va. 1820; settled in M. C. 1862.

CHILTON, THOMAS; gardener; 3¼ m n w Indianapolis. Born in England 1818; settled in M. C. 1874.

CHILTON, BEN., JR.; gardener; 3¼ m n w Indianapolis. Born in England 1848; settled in M. C. 1873.

Cossel, Abijah; farmer and miller; 4 m w Indianapolis. Born in M. C. 1837.

Cossell, Wm.; farmer and miller; 4 m w Indianapolis. Born in Ohio 1811; settled in M. C. 1823.

Cossel, John; farmer; 4½ m w Indianapolis.

Cossel, Daniel; farmer; 1 m w Sunnyside.

Cumberworth, G.; tile maker; ½ m w Sunnyside. Born in England 1842; settled in M. C. 1868.

Clark, Alfred; farmer; 2 m n e Bridgeport. Born in Ohio 1819; settled in M. C. 1853. Methodist.

CARPENTER, HENRY W.; farmer; 2½ m w Indianapolis, on National road. Born in Ky. 1840; settled in M. C. 1863. Rep. Christian.

Cox, Columbus; postmaster and grocer; Maywood Station.

Crowe, Geo. W.; blacksmith; Maywood. Born in Ind. 1840; settled in M. C. 1870.

Cline, George W.; farmer; 1½ m s e Sunnyside. Born in Tenn. 1823; settled in M. C. 1851.

Copland, David; farmer; 1½ m n Bridgeport.

Carter, L. L.; cooper; 1¾ m s w Sunnyside. Born in Ohio 1819; settled in M. C. 1861.

Cochler, George; farmer; 1 m e Bridgeport. Born in Ind. 1841; settled in M. C. 1850.

Charles, Jacob; farmer; 1 m n w Maywood. Born in Pa. 1824; settled in M. C. 1849.

Charles, John; farmer; 1 m n w Maywood. Born in Pa. 1827; settled in M. C. 1849.

Clements, Chas. W.; farmer; ½ m s Sunnyside. Born in M. C. 1847.

Coffman, Barton; farmer; 3 m s e Bridgeport. Born in East Tenn. 1805; settled in M. C. 1836. Dem.

Carter, John V., Sr.; farmer; 1½ m s Clermont. Born in Ohio 1819; settled in M. C. 1852.

Campbell, John; stock trader; Clermont. Born in Ky. 1819; settled in M. C. 1847.

Clements, Leo; farmer; ½ m e Sabine. Born in Ky. 1816; settled in M. C. 1834.

Carter, John V., Jr.; farmer and stock raiser; 5½ m w Indianapolis. Born in M. C. 1850. Rep. Protestant.

Carter, James W.; farmer and stock trader; 5½ m w Indianapolis. Born in Ohio 1817; settled in M. C. 1846.

Carter, Wm. D.; farmer; 5½ m w Indianapolis. Born in M. C. 1852.

CHAMBERS, JOSEPH M.; farmer; 4 m w Indianapolis, near Cassel's Mill. Born in Ind. 1847; settled in M. C. 1852.

Denk, Andrew; gardener; 3 m n w Indianapolis. Born in Germany 1824; settled in M. C. 1853.

Dunn, Edward; supt. Holmes, Pettit & Bradshaw's Pork House at foot Kentucky avenue, Indianapolis; res 2½ m n w Indianapolis. Born in Pa. 1828.

Dawson, A. H.; retired farmer; 2½ m w Indianapolis. Born in Ky. 1804; settled in M. C. 1832. Rep. Christian. Mrs. Jamima Dawson, formerly Harding, is still living; was one of the third family that built in the Donation, March, 1820. Born in Ky. 1797.

Dotey, John; gardener; 1½ m e Sunnyside. Born in M. C. 1835.

DELL, JOHN; farmer; 2 m s e Sunnyside. Born in Prussia 1819; settled in M. C. 1838. Lutheran.

DELL, WM. H.; farmer; 2 m s e Sunnyside. Born in Indianapolis 1844.

Darnell, Lewis; farmer; 3½ m s w Indianapolis. Born in N. C. 1805; settled in M. C. 1824. Methodist.

Darnell, David H.; gardener; 3½ m s w Indianapolis. Born in M. C. 1836.

Dunn, I. N.; wagon maker; ¼ m s Sunnyside. Born in Pa. 1838; settled in M. C. 1864.

Davidson, W. A.; wagon maker; Clermont. Born in Pa. 1844; settled in M. C. 1871.

Davis, B. F.; engineer and sawyer; Clermont. Born in N. C. 1829; settled in M. C. 1847.

Dickerson, Charles E.; farmer; 3 m e Clermont. Born in M. C. 1855.

Duncan, Hardin; farmer; 1½ m e Clermont. Born in Ky. 1814; settled in M. C. 1851.

Dunn, Albert; carpenter and builder; 1½ m w Sunnyside. Born in Pa. 1834; settled in M. C. 1853. Methodist.

Dunn, Geo. W.; blacksmith and farmer; 1 m w Sunnyside. Born in Pa. 1850; settled in M. C. 1863.

Emrich, Frank; gardener and farmer; 3 m n w Indianapolis. Born in Bavaria, Germany, 1835; settled in M. C. 1854.

Emrich, Jacob A.; blacksmith and wagonmaker; 3 m n w Indianapolis. Born in Bavaria, Germany, 1838; settled in M. C. 1854.

Eaglefield, Margaret; farmer; 2 m w Sunnyside.

Engling, Thomas W.; dealer in dry goods and notions; Bridgeport. Born in N. Y. 1819; settled in M. C. 1854.

Engling, J. H.; telegraph operator; Bridgeport. Born in Ohio 1852; settled in M. C. 1854.

EVERTS, ORPHEUS, M. D.; Superintendent Insane Hospital; 3 m w Indianapolis. Born in Ind. 1826; settled in M. C. 1868.

Elstun, W. J., M. D.; second assistant physician Insane Hospital. Born in Ind. 1838; settled in M. C. 1866.

Everts, Mrs. Mary; matron Insane Hospital.

Eck, Teterick; farmer and gardener; 4½ m n w Indianapolis. Born in Germany 1839; settled in M. C. 1854.

Evans, John; grocer and toll gate keeper; 3 m e Bridgeport. Born in Va. 1827; settled in M. C. 1872.

Engle, Chris.; farmer; 4½ m n w Indianapolis.

Faucett, Joseph T.; farmer and stock raiser; Spray. Born in M. C. 1830. Rep. Methodist.

Freeland, James; farmer; 2½ m n Bridgeport.

Fellenzer, Elizabeth; 6 m n w Indianapolis. Born in Germany 1802; settled in M. C. 18—.

Fellenzer, P. J.; farmer; 6 m n w Indianapolis.

Fellenzer, John and Francis; farmers; 6 m n w Indianapolis. Born in M. C. 1846.

Fellenzer, Joseph; farmer; 6 m n w Indianapolis.

FOREMAN, JOHN M.; blacksmith; carriage, buggy, horse-shoeing and plow work a specialty; Clermont. Born in O. 1829; settled in M. C. 1835. Methodist.

Foltz, David; farmer; 1¾ m w Sunnyside. Born in M. C. 1851.

Foltz, Jesse; carpenter and plasterer; 1½ m w Sunnyside. Born in M. C. 1849.

Foltz, Jacob; cooper; 1½ m s w Sunnyside. Born in M. C. 1853.

Fling, Henry; farmer; 2 m s e Bridgeport. Born in Ohio 1850; settled in M. C. 1850.

Furnas, Isaac; physician and farmer; ½ m s Bridgeport. Born in S. C. 1798; settled in Ohio 1804; in M. C. 1826. Rep. Friend.

Furnas, Isaac H.; farmer; ½ m s Bridgeport. Born in M. C. 1840. Rep. Friend.

Foltz, Jacob; farmer; 2½ m s w Sunnyside. Born in Pa. 1818; settled in M. C. 1838. Rep. Christian.

Foltz, J.; farmer and blacksmith; 2½ m s w Sunnyside. Born in M. C. 1848. Rep.

Fulton, Wm. B.; steward Marion County Hospital for the Poor; 4 m n w Indianapolis. Born in Ohio 1839; settled in M. C. 1862.

Fulton, Mrs. Arminta; assistant matron Marion County Hospital for the Poor; 4 m n w Indianapolis.

FLACK, JOSEPH F.; brick manufacturer and farmer; 4 m n w Indianapolis, on Lafayette pike. Born in Ohio 1843; settled in M. C. 1845. Dem.

Fatout, David B.; farmer; 3 m w Indianapolis.

Foltz, Jonathan; farmer; 1½ m s Sunnyside. Born in Pa. 1825; settled in M. C. 1838.

Foltz, Simon; farmer; 2 m s Sunnyside. Born in Pa. 1827; settled in M. C. 1838.

Forsha, H.; shoe and boot maker; Bridgeport. Born in Ohio 1841; settled in M. C. 1845.

Foltz, Joseph; farmer; 1 m e Bridgeport. Born in M. C. 1850. Rep. Methodist.

Foltz, Enos; farmer; 2½ m s e Bridgeport. Born in M. C. 1852.

Foltz, Fred; farmer, 2 m s e Sunnyside. Born in Pa. 1829; settled in M. C. 1836. Rep. Protestant.

Groff, A. F.; gardener; 3 m w Indianapolis. Born in Pa. 1831; settled in M. C. 1864.

Goodwin, James M.; farmer; 5 m n w Indianapolis. Born in Ind. 1836; settled in M. C. 1860.

Groff, F. W.; farmer and gardener; 3 m n w Indianapolis. Born
in Pa. 1846; settled in M. C. 1873.

GALE, HENRY; gardener; 3¼ m n w Indianapolis. Born in
England 1840; settled in M. C. 1870.

Grant, James; blacksmith; 3 m n e Bridgeport. Born in Mich.
1830; settled in M. C. 1865.

Granger, Harry; farmer; 2½ m w Indianapolis. Born in Va.
1842; settled in M. C. 1866.

Gregg, A. W.; dealer in walnut lumber; Maywood. Born in
Pa. 1826; settled in M. C. 1872. Rep. Meth. Minister.

Gossett, A. M.; general store; Bridgeport. Born in Ind. 1849;
settled in M. C. 1864. Rep. Methodist.

Gossett, Wm.; farmer; 2 m n Bridgeport. Born in N. C. 1825;
settled in M. C. 1862.

Guthrie, A. P.; farmer; 5½ m n w Indianapolis. Born in Ky.
1814; settled in M. C. 1831.

Graham, James P.; farmer and trader; Clermont. Born in Ind.
1828; settled in M. C. 1851.

Goldsborough, John J.; blacksmith; Clermont. Born in Ind.
1832; settled in M. C. 1860.

GLADDEN, GEO.; farmer; 2½ m s Clermont. Born in M.
C. 1841. Rep. Methodist.

GLADDEN, WM.; farmer; 1½ m n e Spray. Born in Pa.
1796; settled in M. C. 1823. Has lived on the same farm
fifty-one years, and was one of the first trustees of the
county.

GLADDEN, D. F.; farmer; 2 m n w Spray. Born in M. C.
1848. Protestant.

Gladden, Frank; attorney; 6 and 8 Hubbard Block, Indianapolis; res ½ m e Spray. Born in M. C. 1851.

Goepper, Jacob; farmer; 5 m w Indianapolis. Born in Germany 1834; settled in M. C. 1847.

Griswold, Samuel; farmer; 1¾ m w Sunnyside. Born in M.
C. 1826.

Harding, Israel P.; farmer; 3 m w Indianapolis. Born in M. C.
1842.

Hamilton, J. Miller; toll gate keeper; National road; 2 m w
Indianapolis. Born in Ohio 1836; settled in M. C. 1863.

Hester, Wm. W., M. D.; first assistant physician Insane Hospital.

Hoover, Cary; farmer; 1 m n Maywood. Born in M. C. 1832.

Hoover, Perry; farmer; ½ m n Maywood. Born in M. C. 1832.

Harsin, Wm.; carpenter and builder; Maywood. Born in Ky.
1840; settled in M. C. 1865.

Hart, Thos. H.; gardener; 1½ m n w Maywood.   Born in England 1803; settled in M. C. 1859.

Haugh, Jacob; farmer; ½ m s Sunnyside.   Born in Md. 1829; settled in M. C. 1842.

Harding, Noah; farmer; 2 m e Sunnyside.   Born in Ind. 1817; settled in M. C. 1820; one of the first.

Harding, C. A.; farmer; 3 m e Sunnyside.   Born in M. C. 1848.

Hoffman, J. W.; farmer; 1½ m s e Bridgeport.   Born in Ohio 1823; settled in M. C. 1829.   Rep.   Methodist.

Hoffman; Peter; farmer; 1½ m s e Bridgeport.   Born in M. C. 1830.   Rep.   Protestant.

Hoffman, Mrs. Mary; farmer; 1½ m s e Bridgeport.   Born in Pa. 1806; settled in M. C. 1829.   Methodist.

HOLMES, W. C.; pork packer; foot of Kentucky avenue, 6 m n w Indianapolis, on I., B. & W. Railway.   Born in M. C. 1825.

Holmes, N. P.; farmer and stock trader; 4 m w Indianapolis. Born in M. C. 1839.'

Hosbrook, Percy; surveyor and farmer; 3½ m n w Indianapolis. Born in Ohio 1811; settled in M. C. 1839.

Heckman, Joseph; farmer; 4 m n w Indianapolis.   Born in Pa. 1827; settled in M. C. 1856.

Harding, Mordecai; farmer; ½ m w Sunnyside.   The first white man born in Indianapolis, 1820.

Harris, Obediah; farmer; 2½ m w Indianapolis. Born in N. C. 1789; settled in M. C. 1824. Until late days his house has been a home for weary drovers.

HARDING, LAZARUS R.; township trustee and farmer; 3½ m n w Indianapolis, on Lafayette pike. Born in M. C. 1826. Rep. M. Baptist.

Holloway, Wm.; tile maker; ½ m w Sunnyside. Born in England 1851; settled in M. C. 1873.

Harding, T. M.; farmer; 2 m w Sunnyside. Born in M. C. 1853.

Hanch, G. B. N.; farmer and stock trader; 6½ m w Indianapolis. Born in Pa. 1835; settled in M. C. 1839.

Hole, Benjamin; carpenter and builder; Bridgeport. Born in 1820; settled in M. C. 1864. Rep. Friend.

Hall, Richard; farmer; 1 m n Bridgeport. Born in Ind. 1823; settled in M. C. 1866. Rep. Friend.

Hoffman, Peter N.; farmer; ½ m e Bridgeport. Born in Ohio 1820; settled in M. C. 1829. Rep. Methodist.

Hardin, James T.; farmer; 1½ m n Sunnyside. Born in M. C. 1828. Methodist.

Hightshue, Caleb; farmer; 2½ m n e Clermont. Born in Ohio 1827; settled in M. C. 1856.

Hockensmith, Benjamin; farmer; 2½ m e Clermont. Born in Ind. 1839; settled in M. C. 1846.

Holliday, Thomas; farmer; 5½ m n w Indianapolis. Born in
Pa. 1810; settled in M. C. 1835.

Holliday, Marion; farmer; 5 m n w Indianapolis. Born in M.
C. 1839.

Harding, Laban; farmer; 6 m n w Indianapolis. Born in Ind.
1817; settled in M. C. 1823.

Hoover, Daniel; farmer; 2 m e Clermont. Born in Ohio 1816;
settled in M. C. 1822.

Hornaday, S. W.; farmer; 1 m e Clermont. Born in Ind. 1847.

Hadley, Wm.; farmer; ¾ m s Clermont. Born in Ind. 1851.

Hoover, Erastus; farmer; 6 m w Indianapolis. Born in Iowa
1852; settled in M. C. 1854. Dem.

Hoover, George; farmer; 6 m w Indianapolis. Born in Ohio
1812. settled in M. C. 1821. Rep.

Hardin, Isaac; farmer; 1¼ m n Spray.

Hardin, C.; farmer; 1¼ m n Spray. Born in M. C. 1844. Dem.
Methodist.

Hack, John V.; gardener; ¾ m w Sunnyside. Born in Germany 1809; settled in M. C. 1867.

Harding, I. S.; firm of I. S. & L. N. Harding; farmer and dairyman; 4 m w Indianapolis. Born in M. C. 1843.

HATTON, MARTILLES; grocer and toll gate keeper; 5 m w
Indianapolis, on Crawfordsville pike. Born in Ky. 1840;
settled in M. C. 1863.

Harding, L. N.; 4 m w Indianapolis. Born in M. C. 1844.

Harding, R. N.; deputy sheriff Marion county; 4 m w Indianapolis. Born in M. C. 1827.

Jameson, Alex.; county commissioner and farmer; 5 m s w Indianapolis. Born in Ind. 1814; settled in M. C. 1842.
Rep. Christian.

Jordan, John; farmer; 3 m n w Indianapolis. Born in Va.
1823; settled in M. C. 1850.

Johnson, John; farmer and dairyman; 3 m n w Indianapolis.
Born in M. C. 1830. Dem.

Johnson, W. S.; farmer and teamster; $2\frac{1}{2}$ m w Indianapolis.

Johnson, Isaac; farmer; $2\frac{1}{2}$ m s w Indianapolis. Born in M. C.
1842.

Johnson, Wm. M.; retired farmer; 3 m s w Indianapolis. Born
in N. J. 1802; settled in M. C. 1822.

Johnson, John J.; farmer and contractor public works; $2\frac{1}{2}$ m w
Indianapolis.

Johnson, Theodore; farmer; 4 m s w Indianapolis.

Julian, John B. & Sons; Harvest City Flouring Mills; 4 m w Indianapolis.

Julian, John W.; Harvest City Mills. Born in Ohio 1834; settled in M. C. 1868.

Julian, Isaac; miller; Harvest City Mills; Born in Ohio 1846; settled in M. C. 1868.

Julian, James B.; Harvest City Mills. Born in Ohio 1849; settled in M. C. 1868.

Johnson, Henry A.; farmer; 4 m s w Indianapolis. Born in M. C. 1827.

JOHNSON, WILLIS; farmer and sewing machine agent; ½ m e Spray. Born in M. C. 1849.

JOHNSON, MRS. S.; ½ m e Spray. Born in M. C. 1845.

Jones, Marcus; farmer; 1 m e Sabine P. O. Born in Ohio 1833; settled in M. C. 1836.

Johnson, James, Jr.; farmer; 5½ m n w Indianapolis. Born in M. C. 1832.

Johnson, John; farmer and carpenter; 4½ m n w Indianapolis.

Jones, Mrs. Julia A.; farmer; 3 m e Clermont. Born in Ohio 1829; settled in M. C. 1850.

Johnson, Thomas; farmer; 1¾ m e Clermont Born in M. C. 1849.

Johnson, Nelson; general store; Clermont. Born in M. C. 1847.

Jones, Van S.; retired; Clermont. Born in Ky. 1799; settled in M. C. 1840.

JOHNSON, E. V.; firm of Johnson & Stout; keep general assortment of dry goods and groceries; Odd Fellows' Block, Clermont. Born in M. C. 1852.

Johnson, Samuel; farmer; ¾ m s Clermont. Born in Va. 1808; settled in M. C. 1826.

Johnson, S. W.; farmer and photographer; ¼ m s Clermont. Born in M. C. 1837.

Johnson, R. M.; farmer; ½ m s Clermont. Born in M. C. 1845.

Johnson, Jesse; farmer; 3 m s e Clermont. Born in Va. 1787; settled in M. C. 1826. Dem. Christian. It is said he is the oldest man in the township.

Johnson, James, Sr.; farmer; 5 m w Indianapolis. Born in Va. 1801; settled in M. C. 1822.

Johnson; Isaac B.; farmer; 5 m w Indianapolis. Born in M. C. 1843.

KRAFT, JOHN F.; farmer; 3 m s w Indianapolis. Born in Bavaria, Germany, 1820; settled in M. C. 1853.

KRAFT, JOHN; farmer; 3 m s w Indianapolis. Born in M. C. 1853.

Kunkel, Henry; teamster; 3 m n w Indianapolis.

Ketrow, Calvin; farmer and carpenter; 4½ m w Indianapolis. Born in Ohio 1829; settled in M. C. 1830.

Ketrow, Charles; farmer; 5 m w Indianapolis. Born in Ohio 1822; settled in M. C. 1830.

Knower, Geo.; gardener; 2¼ m w Indianapolis.

Kirland, P.; farmer; 4 m w Indianapolis. Born in Ireland 1822; settled in M. C. 1835.

Kyser, Nicholas; wagon woodworker; Clermont. Born in Germany 1845; settled in M. C. 1870.

Kesler, A. J.; farmer; 4½ m n w Indianapolis. Born in M. C. 1834.

Kunkle, J. F.; miller; 5 m n w Indianapolis. Born in M. C. 1836.

KINDER, VALENTINE; plasterer and contractor; 1½ m n e Spray. Born in Ky. 1829; settled in M. C. 1874.

Kelley, Joseph; farmer; 1 m n Sabine.

Long, John; farmer; 4½ m n w Indianapolis.

Lendar, John; gardener; 3½ m w Indianapolis.

Lawson, Jacob; 1½ m w Sunnyside.

Landrey, Jacob; gardener and farmer; 4½ m n w Indianapolis. Born in Ohio 1828; settled in M. C. 1840.

Laws, George; farmer; 6 m w Indianapolis. Born in M. C. 1844. Dem.

MANKER, LEWIS; physician and surgeon; Bridgeport. Born in Ohio 1826; settled in M. C. 1850. Rep. Methodist.

Milhouse, David; farmer; ½ m s Bridgeport. Born in M. C. 1846. Rep. Friend.

MARTIN, AMBROSE S.; farmer and gardener; 3 m n w Indianapolis. Born in Ohio 1823; settled in M. C. 1837.

Martin, Joseph; farmer; 3 m n w Indianapolis. Born in Ohio 1818; settled in M. C. 1850.

Martin, Ezra G.; teacher; 3 m n w Indianapolis. Born in Ohio 18—.

McCaw, Melville; farmer; 4 m n w Indianapolis. Born in M. C. 1845.

MEYERS, JOHN H.; farmer; 4 m n w Indianapolis. Born in Pa. 1808; settled in M. C. 1850.

MEYERS, JOHN W.; eagle dairyman No. 1; 4 m n w Indianapolis. Born in Pa. 1846.

MEYERS, FLAVIUS J.; eagle dairyman No. 1; 4 m w Indianapolis. Born in M. C. 1854.

Mills, Wm.; farmer; 1½ m n e Bridgeport. Born in S. C. 1803; settled in M. C. 1860. Rep. Friend.

Muston, Wm.; general labor; Bridgeport. Born in Ind. 1822; settled in M. C. 1841.

McCoy, Wm.; farmer; 4 m n Indianapolis.

McMillian, David J.; farmer and fruit grower; ½ m e Bridgeport. Born in Ohio 1825; settled in M. C. 1860. Friend.

McMillian; Josiah; farmer; ½ m e Bridgeport. Born in Ohio 1854; settled in M. C. 1860. Rep. Friend.

McCray, Aaron; farmer; 4¼ m n w Indianapolis. Born in Ind. 1820; settled in M. C. 1833.

McCRAY, FARMER, 4¼ m n w Indianapolis. Born in M. C. 1851.

McCRAY SAMUEL; farmer; 4¼ m n w Indianapolis. Born in M. C. 1853.

McCray, Lucas; farmer; 4¼ m n w Indianapolis. Born in M. C. 1849.

Martindale, M. L.; farmer; 6 m n w Indianapolis. Born in M. C. 1847.

Meyers, John W.; farmer; 5 m n w Indianapolis. Born in M. C. 1840.

Meyers, Isaac; farmer; 4½ m n w Indianapolis. Born in Pa. 1811; settled in M. C. 1839.

Meyers, Isaac; farmer; 4 m n w Indianapolis. Born in M. C.
1838.

Miller, H. W.; farmer and brick manufacturer; 4¼ m n w Indianapolis. Born in M. C. 1845.

Miller, Samuel; farmer; 4½ m n w Indianapolis. Born in Md.
1819; settled in M. C. 1825.

Meyer, Isaac; farmer; 6½ m n w Indianapolis. Born in Pa.
1816; settled in M. C. 1856.

Meyers, Emanuel; farmer; 6½ m n w Indianapolis. Born in
Pa. 1850; settled in M. C. 1856.

Meyer, Levi; farmer; 6½ m n w Indianapolis. Born in Pa.
1852; settled in M. C. 1856.

Manley, John H.; farmer and huckster; 2 m e Clermont. Born
in Ohio 1819; settled in M. C. 1869.

MONTGOMERY, CHAS.; farmer; ¾ m e Clermont. Born in
Pa. 1840; settled in M. C. 1865.

Martindale, John P.; farmer and carpenter; Clermont. Born in
Ind. 1822; settled in M. C. 1823. Rep. Christian.

Merrill, J. M.; physician; firm of Merrill & Shewee, druggists;
Clermont. Born in W. Va. 1850; settled in M. C. 1874.

Menefee, G. G.; firm of G. G. Menefee & Co., merchants;
Clermont. Born in Ky. 1813; settled in M. C. 1826.

Miller, Vincent; farmer; 7 m w Indianapolis. Born in M. C.
1845.

Miller, A. N.; farmer; 7 m w Indianapolis.   Born in M. C. 1843.

Marley, Uriah B.; farmer; 1 m n w Sabine.   Born in Ind. 1842; settled in M. C. 1873.

McCaslin, Geo.; farmer; 6 m w Indianapolis.   Born in M. C.

McCLEALAND, J. D.; farmer; 2 m n e Spray.   Born in Ind. 1816; settled in M. C. 1822, before Indiana was a State.

Mullin, James M.; farmer; 1 ¼ m w Sunnyside.   Born in Ind. 1835; settled in M. C. 1853.   United Brethren.

Mann, A. C.; gardener and farmer; 1 m w Sunnyside.   Born in Ky. 1821; settled in M. C. 1861.

Melling, Charles; farmer; 1 m w Sunnyside.   Born in Va. 1814; settled in M. C. 1840.

MICKLEY, J. A.; practical boot and shoe manufacturer; all work warranted and promptly done to order; ¾ m w Sunnyside, on National road.   Born in Pa. 1840; settled in M. C. 1868.

MITCHELL, JAMES M.; farmer; 1½ m s e Clermont.   Born in Ky. 1826; settled in M. C. 1867.

McClelland, B. F.; farmer; 2 m s e Clermont.

McClelland, John; farmer; 2 m s e Clermont.

McCray, Moses; farmer; 4 m w Indianapolis. Born in Ohio 1795; settled in M. C. 1866.

Miller, Vincent; farmer; 6½ m w Indianapolis, on I. B. & W. R. R., 2 m e Clermont.

Minnemeyer, Charles H.; sawyer; 1¾ m w Sunnyside. Born in Pa. 1839; settled in M. C. 1865.

Newland, Jehu; farmer; 1 m n e Bridgeport.

Nicholson, John H.; farmer; Bridgeport. Born in N. Y. 1820; settled in M. C. 1860. Friend.

Norris, Martin V.; farmer; ¼ m w Sabine.

Nelson, Whitson; farmer; 1½ m e Clermont. Born in Ky. 1802; settled in M. C. 1858.

Off, George Philip; farmer and gardener; 2½ m w Indianapolis. Born in Germany 1822; settled in M. C. 1852.

Orner, Samuel O.; carpenter; 2½ m w Indianapolis. Born in N. J. 1840.

O'Connor, Michael; farmer and gardener; 3 m s w Indianapolis.

Oakley, Henry D.; saw miller; Maywood Station.

PIERSON, JOHN; farmer and cooper; 1¾ m s w Sunnyside. Born in Ohio 1832; settled in M. C. 1848. Methodist.

Pierson, Ch.; farmer; 1¾ m s w Sunnyside. Born in M. C. 1856.

Poland, Geo.; farmer; 1¾ m w Sunnyside. Born in M. C. 1847.

Poland, Nicholas, Sen.; farmer; 1¾ m w Sunnyside. Born in Ohio 1817; settled in M. C. 1828.

Poland, Nicholas, Jr.; farmer; 2 m s e Bridgeport. Born in M. C. 1846.

Poland, Henry; tollgate keeper and grocer; 4 m w Indianapolis. Born in M. C. 1831.

Poland, Nathaniel; farmer; 1 m s Sabine. Born in Ohio 1822; settled in M. C. 1829.

Pedigo, Edward; carpenter; Bridgeport.

Porter, C. N.; physician; 2½ m w Indianapolis.

Patterson, Geo.; steward Insane Hospital.

Peachee, H.; physician and surgeon; Maywood. Born in Ind. 1842; settled in M. C. 1873.

PORTER, JAMES H.; farmer, gardener and dairyman; 4½ m s w Indianapolis. Born in Indianapolis, 1837.

Pence, Henry; farmer; 4 m s w Indianapolis. Born in M. C. 1834.

Pence, Joel; farmer and gardener; ½ m e Sunnyside.

PUGH, JESSE; farmer and stock broker; 6 m w Indianapolis, on I. B. & W. R. R. Born in N. C. 1818; settled in M. C. May 1824.

Pugh, Marshal; farmer and stock broker; 6 m w Indianapolis. Born in M. C. 1845.

Pugh, Enoch; farmer and stock broker; 6 m w Indianapolis. Born in M. C. 1851.

Pugh, Joel; farmer; 3½ m s e Clermont. Born in M. C. 1853.

Pratt, Phillip; farmer; 1½ m e Bridgeport.

Rhoads, Hiram; farmer; 6 m s e Indianapolis. Born in N. J. 1805; settled in M. C. 1824. Rep. Lutheran.

Rhoads, W. F.; farmer; 6 m s w Indianapolis. Born in M. C. 1839.

Rhoades, Chas. S.; retired farmer; Bridgeport. Born in N. J. 1800; settled in M. C. 1832. Rep. Methodist.

Robey, Geo.; farmer; 1½ m s Sunnyside. Born in M. C. 1842.

Robey, F. M.; teacher; 1 m s Sunnyside. Born in M. C. 1847.

Rude, Wm.; farmer; ½ m Sunnyside. Born in Conn. 1804; settled in M. C. 1836.

Rybolt, Wm. L.; farmer and teacher; ½ m s Sunnyside. Born in Ohio 1850; settled in M. C. 1863.

Rhoads, Wallace; farmer; 6 m s w Indianapolis. Born in M. C. 1841. Rep. Methodist.

Robey, Hezekiah; farmer; 2 m s Sunnyside. Born in M. C. 1837.

Royster, Samuel; superintendent Marion Co. Hospital for the Poor; 4 m n w Indianapolis. Born in M. C. 1836.

Royster, Mrs. Mary E.; matron Marion Co. Hospital for the Poor.

Redmond, John; farmer; ¼ m e Spray. Born in M. C. 1847.

Reagan, Lot; physician; Bridgeport. Born in Ohio 1816; settled in M. C. 1827. Rep.

Redmond, John; farmer; 1½ m e Bridgeport. Born in Va. 1794; settled in M. C. 1835.

Redmond, Israel; farmer; 1½ m e Bridgeport. Born in Ohio 1822; settled in M. C. 1835.

Roberson, David J.; farmer and dairyman; 3½ m s w Indianapolis. Born in M. C. 1836.

Roberson, Charles, Jr.; farmer; 3½ m s w Indianapolis. Born in M. C. 1851.

Roberson, Charles; farmer; 3½ m s w Indianapolis. Born in Tenn. 1808; settled in M. C. 1832.

Royster, Wm.; farmer; 6 m n w Indianapolis.

Rader, W. J.; farmer; Maywood. Born in Ind. 1835; settled in M. C. 1873.

Ray, Eli; cooper; Clermont. Born in M. C. 1833.

Ross, S. A.; farmer; 1½ m e Clermont. Born in Ky. 1832; settled in M. C. 1844.

Royster, Oliver; farmer; 6 m n w Indianapolis. Born in Ind. 1834; settled in M. C. 1835.

Royster, Peter; farmer; 5 m n w Indianapolis. Born in Ky. 1807; settled in M. C. 1835.

Rushton, Alford; dairyman; 4½ m n w Indianapolis. Born in Ind. 1832; settled in M. C. 1856.

Rushton, Elias; farmer; 4½ m n w Indianapolis.

Renard, John; farmer; 4½ m n w Indianapolis. Born in France 1834; settled in M. C. 1854.

Reagan, Noah; stock broker; 2 m w Sunnyside. Born in Ohio; settled in M. C. 1827.

Rybolt, Michael; farmer; 2 m s w Sunnyside. Born in Ohio 1824; settled in M. C. 1852.

Rybolt, M. W.; farmer; Ben Davis Station, 1 m w Sunnyside. Born in Ohio 1848; settled in M. C. 1863.

Rybolt, W. D.; farmer; Ben Davis Station and National road, 1 m w Sunnyside. Born in Ohio 1819; settled in M. C. 1863.

Roberson, W. N.; farmer; ¼ m e Sunnyside. Born in East Tenn. 1816; settled in M. C. 1832.

Sutherland, James W.; farmer and mechanic; 2 m s Sunnyside. Born in Ky. 1830; settled in M. C. 1860.

SELKING, WM., JR.; restaurant and saloon, 33 North Pennsylvania street, Indianapolis; farmer; 5 m w Indianapolis. Born in Germany 1833; settled in M. C. 1852.

SELKING, WM., SEN.; farmer; 5 m w Indianapolis. Born in Germany 1791; settled in M. C. 1844.

Speer, W. H.; farmer; 3 m w Indianapolis. Born in M. C. 1845.

Smith, Wm. J.; farmer; 4 m n w Indianapolis. Born in Va. 1843; settled in M. C. 1869. Rep.

Slimmer, Thos. B.; gardener; Bridgeport. Born in Pa. 1829; settled in M. C. 1853.

Sullivan, Gazaway; Justice of the Peace, shoe and boot maker; Bridgeport. Born in Ohio 1832; settled in M. C. 1854. Rep. Methodist.

Speer, John F.; farmer and dairyman; ½ m n w Bridgeport. Born in Ohio 1837; settled in M. C. 1863. Rep. Friend.

Sims, John; small fruit grower; Bridgeport.

Stout, Richard; carpenter; 2½ m w Indianapolis.

Strothman, William; grocer; Mt. Jackson, 2¾ m w Indianapolis. Born in 1843; settled in M. C. 1861.

STORZ, JOHN; gardener and farmer; 3½ m w Indianapolis. Born in Wurtemberg, Germany, 1812; settled in M. C. May, 1853.

Smith, Adolph; painter and gardener; Maywood. Born in Germany 1833; settled in M. C. 1858.

Spray, Eli; farmer; 1 m n Bridgeport. Born in M. C. 1838. Friend.

Stout, George; farmer; ¾ m e Sabine. Born in Ill. 1828; settled in M. C. 1835.

Stout, David; farmer; 4 m n w Indianapolis. Born in M. C. 1840.

Smith, Canaday; minister and author; 5 m n w Indianapolis. Born in S. C. 1807. Christian.

STANDIFORD, W. F.; physician and surgeon; Clermont. Born in Ind. 1850; settled in M. C. 1874.

STOUT, THEODORE; firm of Johnson & Stout; keep a general assortment of dry goods and groceries; Clermont. Born in Ill. 1833; settled in M. C. 1837.

Stout, John S.; farmer; 1¼ m n e Sabine. Born in M. C. 1851.

Stout, James; farmer; 1 m n Sabine. Born in M. C. 1839. Protestant.

Steback, Fred.; farmer; 6 m w Indianapolis. Born in Germany 1832; settled in M. C. 1867.

Stamm, Philip; mechanic; 1 m w Sunnyside. Born in Ind. 1837; settled in M. C. 1850.

Stamm, John H. G.; farmer; 1½ m w Sunnyside. Born in Md. 1800; settled in M. C. 1850.

Tomlinson, F. M.; gardener; 4½ m s w Indianapolis. Born in Ohio 1842.

Frost, John; farmer, gardener and manufacturer of cider; 3½ m w Indianapolis. Born in Germany 1832; settled in M. C. 1851.

Thompson, James; teamster; 2½ m s w Indianapolis.

Tinsman, Samuel; proprietor of Brighton House; Mt. Jackson, 2¾ m w Indianapolis. Born in Pa. 1821; settled in M. C. 1870.

Thornbrough, Henry; carpenter; Bridgeport. Born in Ind. 1834; settled in M. C. 1868.

TEMPLIN, ALFORD M.; postmaster, dealer in family groceries and notions; Bridgeport. Born in Ind. 1836; settled in M. C. 1859. Rep. Methodist.

Thompson, R. W.; notary public; Bridgeport. Born in Ind. 1834. Settled in M. C. 1849. Rep. Methodist.

Thompson, E. M.; farmer and stock raiser; 1 m w Sunnyside. Born in Ky. 1816; settled in M. C. 1865.

Thompson, Woodford; farmer; 1 m w Sunnyside. Born in Ky. 1851; settled in M. C. 1865.

Tomlin, John J.; farmer; 5½ m w Indianapolis. Born in Ohio 1840; settled in M. C. 1843.

Turner, Wm. H.; farmer; Brooklyn Hights Station I. C. & L. R. R. 4 m n Indianapolis. Born in N. Y. 1823; settled in M. C. 1852.

Tansel, George F.; farmer; 1½ m s Clermont. Born in M. C. 1838.

Tansel, Payton; farmer; 1 m s Clermont. Born in Ky. 1821; settled in M. C. 1829.

Turpin, J. T.; Justice of the Peace and Postmaster; firm of G. G. Menefee & Co., general store; Clermont. Born in Ind. 1829; settled in M. C. 1849.

Tomlinson, J. H.; farmer; Clermont. Born in Md. 1823; settled in M. C. 1836.

Todd, Henry P.; farmer; 5½ m n w Indianapolis. Born in Ind. 1814.

THORNEY, GEO. W.; runs Western Omnibus Line from corner Meridian and Washington streets, Indianapolis, to Mt. Jackson, Insane Hospital and Sunnyside, with U. S. mail; 4 m w Indianapolis. Born in Denmark 1834; settled in M. C. 1863.

WININGS, JAMES; farmer; 2½ m e Bridgeport. Born in Pa. 1817; settled in M. C. 1844.

WININGS, VISON; farmer; 2½ m e Bridgeport. Born in M. C. 1853.

WOENER, PHILIP; gardener; 3 m n w Indianapolis. Born in Hesse, Germany, 1817; settled in M. C. 1839.

WOENER, C.; gardener; 3 m n w Indianapolis. Born in Indianapolis 1853.

Watt, Chas. B.; farmer and stock raiser; 3 m s e Clermont. Born in Ky. 1820; settled in M. C. 1832.

Watt, Wm. H.; farmer and stock raiser; 3 m n w Indianapolis. Born in Ky. 1825; settled in M. C. 1832.

WARMAN, JASPER; farmer; 2¼ m w Indianapolis, on National road. Born in M. C. 1848.

Wishmier, Christian F.; farmer; 1¼ m e Bridgeport. Born in Prussia 1822; settled in M. C. 1843.

WEBB, WM. W.; firm of Wm. W. Webb & Son, carriage and wagon makers; repairing and smith work of all kinds promptly done; 2½ m w Indianapolis. Born in Ind. 1851; settled in M. C. 1854.

WEBB, LEONIDAS; firm of Wm. W. Webb & Son; 2½ m w Indianapolis, opposite Insane Asylum. Born in Ind. 1849; settled in M. C. 1854.

WRIGHT, JEHU V.; farmer; ¾ m s e Bridgeport.   Born in
Ind. 1820; settled in M. C. 1853.   Rep.   Friend.

Wright, Hiram; retired farmer; ½ m n Maywood.   Born in Ind.
1819; settled in M. C. 1831.

Wright, W. T.; farmer; ½ m n Maywood.   Born in M. C.
1847.

Wright, Jesse; farmer; ¾ m s e Sunnyside.   Born in M. C.
1830.

Wilson, Andrew; farmer; 4½ m s w Indianapolis.   Born in Pa.
1798; settled in M. C. 1821.

Welborn, J. M. T.; farm hand; ½ m s Bridgeport.   Born in N.
C. 1852; settled in M. C. 1873.   Rep.

Waker, August; gardener; 3½ m n w Indianapolis.   Born in
Germany 1848; settled in M. C. 1869.

Wilson, Chas.; farmer; 1½ m n Bridgeport.   Born in O. 1813;
settled in M. C. 1838.   Friend.

Winings, Samuel; farmer; ¾ m w Sabine.   Born in Pa. 1814;
settled in M. C. 1854.   Rep.   Methodist.

Williams, Joseph; farmer and postmaster; Sabine.   Born in Ohio
1820; settled in M. C. 1861.

Williams, Aaron; farmer; Sabine.   Born in Ind. 1846; settled
in M. C. 1861.

Wells, Giles; farmer; ¼ m w Sabine. Born in N. Y. 1832; settled in M. C. 1873.

Williams, C. S.; stock broker; Clermont. Born in Ind. 1840; settled in M. C. 1860.

Webster, T. C.; minister M. E. Church; Clermont. Born in Ind. 1851; settled in M. C. 1874.

Wall, David; physician and surgeon; Clermont. Born in Pa. 1836; settled in M. C. 1864.

Wilson, Samuel; farmer; ¼ m w Sabine.

Wilson, James; farmer; ½ m e Spray.

Wilson, James; farmer; 1½ m n e Spray.

Whieker, Frederick; farmer; 1¾ m w Sunnyside.

Weekerly, George; farmer and cooper; 1¾ m s w Sunnyside. Born in Ind. 1820; settled in M. C. 1866.

Weekerley, Conrad; farmer and cooper; 1¾ m s w Sunnyside. Born in Ind. 1832; settled in M. C. 1866.

Weekerley, Jackson; farmer and cooper; 1¾ m w Sunnyside. Born in Ohio 1812; settled in M. C. 1866.

WILSON, HENRY; farmer and cooper; 2 m s w Sunnyside. Born in Ohio 1824; settled in M. C. 1854.

Wimer, Jacob; farmer; 4½ m w Indianapolis.   Born in Ohio
   1842; settled in M. C. 1867.

Youngerman, George; farmer; 4½ m w Indianapolis.   Born in
   Germany 1820; settled in M. C. 1837.

APPENDIX.

ARTICLES OF CONFEDERATION

AND

PERPETUAL UNION BETWEEN THE STATES.

The Articles of Confederation reported July 12, 1776, and debated from day to day, and time to time, for two years, were ratified July 9, 1778, by ten States, by New Jersey, on the 28th of November of the same year; and by Delaware, on the 23d of February following. Maryland, alone, held off two years more, acceding to them March 1st, 1781, and thus closing the obligation. The following are the Articles:

To all whom these presents shall come. We, the undersigned, Delegates of the States affixed to our names, send greeting:

WHEREAS, The Delegates of the United States of America, in Congress assembled, did, on the 15th day of November, in the year of our Lord 1777, and in the Second Year of the Independence of America, agree to certain Articles of Confederation and Perpetual Union between the States of New Hampshire, Massachusetts Bay, Rhode Island and Providence Plantations, Connecticut, New York, New Jersey, Pennsylvania, Delaware, Maryland, Virginia, North Carolina, South Carolina and Georgia, in the words following, viz.:

Articles of Confederation and Perpetual Union between the States of New Hampshire, Massachusetts Bay, Rhode Island and Providence Plantations, Connecticut, New York, New Jersey, Pennsylvania, Delaware, Maryland, Virginia, North Carolina, South Carolina and Georgia.

ARTICLE 1. The style of this Confederacy shall be "The United States of America."

Art. 2. Each State retains its sovereignty, freedom and independence, and every power, jurisdiction and right, which is not by this confederation expressly delegated to the United States in Congress assembled.

Art. 3. The said States hereby severally enter into a firm league of friendship with each other, for their common defense, the security of their liberties, and their mutual and general welfare, binding themselves to assist each other against all force offered to, or attacks made upon them, or any of them, on account of religion, sovereignty, trade, or any other pretense whatever.

Art. 4. The better to secure and perpetuate mutual friendship and intercourse among the people of the different States in this Union, the free inhabitants of each of these States—paupers, vagabonds and fugitives from justice excepted—shall be entitled to all privileges and immunities of free citizens in the several States; and the people of each State shall have free ingress and regress to and from any other State, and shall enjoy therein all the privileges of trade and commerce, subject to the same duties, impositions and restrictions as the inhabitants thereof respectively, provided that such restriction shall not extend so far as to prevent the removal of property, imported into any State, to any other State of which the owner is an inhabitant; provided, also, that no imposition, duties or restriction shall be laid by any State on the property of the United States or either of them.

If any person guilty of or charged with treason, felony or other high misdemeanor in any State, shall flee from justice, and be found in any of the United States, he shall, upon demand of the Governor, or executive power of the State from which he fled, be delivered up and removed to the State having jurisdiction of his offense.

Full faith and credit shall be given in each of these States to the records, acts and judicial proceedings of the courts and magistrates of every other State.

Art. 5. For the more convenient management of the general interest of the United States, Delegates shall be annually appointed, in such manner as the Legislature of each State shall direct, to meet in Congress on the first Monday in November in every year, with a power reserved to each State to call its Delegates, or any of them, at any time within the year, and to send others in their stead for the remainder of the year.

No State shall be represented in Congress by less than two, nor by more than seven members; and no person shall be capable of being a Delegate for more than three years in any term of six years; nor shall any person, being a delegate, be capable of holding any office under the United States, for which he, or another for his benefit, receives any salary, fees or emolument of any kind.

Each State shall maintain its own Delegates in any meeting of the States, and while they act as members of the Committee of the States.

In determining questions in the United States, in Congress assembled, each State shall have one vote.

Freedom of speech and debate in Congress shall not be impeached or questioned in any court or place, out of Congress, and the members of Congress shall be protected in their persons from arrests and imprisonments, during the time of their going to and from, and attendance on Congress, except for treason, felony, or breach of the peace.

Art. 6. No State, without the consent of the United States in Congress assembled; shall send an embassy to, or receive an embassy from, or enter into any conference, agreement, alliance or treaty with any King, Prince, or State; nor shall any person holding any office of profit or trust under the United States, or any of them, accept of any present, emolument, office or title of any kind whatever from any King, Prince, or Foreign State; nor shall the United States in Congress assembled, or any of them, grant any title of nobility.

No two or more States shall enter into any treaty, confederation or alliance whatever between them, without the consent of the United States in Congress assembled; specifying accurately the purposes for which the same is to be entered into, and how long it shall continue.

No State shall lay any imposts or duties which may interfere with any stipulations in treaties, entered into by the United States in Congress assembled, with any King, Prince or State, in pursuance of any treaties already proposed by Congress, to the Courts of France and Spain.

No vessels of war shall be kept up in time of peace by any State, except such number only as shall be deemed necessary by the United States in Congress assembled for the defense of such State or its trade; nor shall any body of forces be kept up by any State, in time of peace, except such number only as, in the judgment of the United States in Congress assembled, shall be deemed requisite to garrison the forts necessary for the defense of such State; but every State shall always keep up a well regulated and disciplined militia; sufficiently armed and accoutred, and shall provide and have constantly ready for use, in public stores, a due number of field-pieces and tents, and a proper quantity of arms, ammunition and camp equipage.

No State shall engage in any war without the consent of the United States in Congress assembled, unless such State be actually invaded by enemies, or shall have received certain advice of a resolution being formed by some nation of Indians to invade such a State, and the danger is so imminent as not to admit of a delay, till the United States in Congress assembled can be consulted; nor shall any State grant commissions to any ships or vessels of war, nor letters of marque or reprisal, except it be after a declaration of war by the United States in Congress assembled, and then only against the Kingdom or State, and the subjects thereof, against which war has been so declared, and under such regulations as shall be established by the United States in Congress assembled, unless such State be infested by pirates, in which case vessels of war may be fitted out for that occasion, and kept so long as the danger shall continue, or until the United States in Congress assembled shall determine otherwise.

Art. 7. When land forces are raised by any State for the common defense, all officers of or under the rank of colonel shall be appointed by the legislature of each State respectively, by whom such forces shall be raised, or in such manner as such State shall direct, and all vacancies shall be filled up by the State which first made the appointment.

Art. 8. All charges of war, and all other expenses that shall be incurred for the common defense or general welfare, and allowed by the United States in Congress assembled, shall be defrayed out of the common treasury, which shall be supplied by the several States, in proportion to the value of all land within each State, granted to or surveyed for any person, as such land and the buildings and improvements thereon shall be estimated according to such mode as the United States in Congress assembled shall from time to time direct and appoint. The taxes for paying that proportion shall be laid and levied by the authority and direction of the legislatures of the several States within the time agreed upon by the United States in Congress assembled.

Art. 9. The United States in Congress assembled shall have the sole and exclusive right and power of determining on peace and war, except in the cases mentioned in the 6th article—of sending and receiving embassadors—entering into treaties and alliances, provided that no treaty of commerce shall be made whereby the legislative power of the respective States shall be restrained from imposing such imposts and duties on foreigners as their own people are subjected to, or from prohibiting the exportation or importation of any species of goods or commodities whatsoever—of establishing rules for deciding in all cases what captures on land or water shall be legal, and in what manner prizes taken by land or naval forces in the service of the United States shall be divided or appropriated—of granting letters of marque and reprisal in times of peace—appointing courts for the trial of piracies and felonies committed on the high seas, and establishing courts for receiving and determining finally appeals in all cases of capture, provided that no member of Congress shall be appointed a judge of any of the said courts.

The United States in Congress assembled shall also be the last resort or appeal in all disputes and differences now subsisting, or that hereafter may arise between two or more States concerning boundary, jurisdiction, or any other cause whatever; which authority shall always be exercised in the manner following:—Whenever the legislative or executive authority or lawful agent of any State in controversy with another shall present a petition to Congress, stating the matter in question, and praying for a hearing, notice thereof shall be given by order of Congress to the legislative or executive authority of the other State in controversy, and a day assigned for the appearance of the parties by their lawful agents, who shall then be directed to appoint, by joint consent, commissioners or judges to constitute a court for hearing and determining the matter in question; but if they can not agree, Congress shall name three persons out of each of the United States, and from the list of such persons each party shall alternately strike out one, the petitioners beginning, until the number shall be reduced to thirteen; and from that number no less than seven, nor more than nine names, as Congress shall direct, shall in the presence of Congress be drawn out by lot, and the persons whose names shall be so drawn, or any five of them, shall be commissioners or judges, to hear and finally determine the controversy, so always as a major part of the judges who shall hear the cause shall agree in the determination; and if either party shall neglect to attend at the day appointed, without showing reasons which Congress shall judge sufficient, or being present shall refuse to strike, the Congress shall proceed to nominate three persons out of each State, and the Secretary of Congress shall strike in behalf of such party absent or refusing; and the judgment and sentence of the court, to be appointed in the manner above prescribed, shall be final and conclusive; and if any of the parties shall refuse to submit to the authority of such court, or to appear or defend their claim or cause, the court shall, nevertheless, proceed to pronounce sentence or judgment, which shall in like manner be final and decisive, the judgment or sentence and other proceedings being in either case transmitted to Congress and lodged among the acts of Congress for the security of the parties concerned; provided that every commissioner, before he sits in judgment, shall take an oath, to be administered by one of the judge of the Supreme or Superior Court of the State where the cause shall be tried, "well and truly to hear and determine the matter in question according to the best of his judgment, without favor, affection, or hope of reward;" provided also that no State shall be deprived of territory for the benefit of the United States.

All controversies concerning the private right of soil claimed under different grants of two or more States, whose jurisdictions as they may respect such lands, and the States which passed such grants, are adjusted, the said grants or either of them being at the same time claimed to have originated antecedent to such settlement of jurisdiction, shall, on the petition of either party to the Congress of the United States, be finally determined as near as may be in the same manner as is before prescribed for deciding disputes respecting territorial jurisdiction between different States.

The United States in Congress assembled shall also have the sole exclusive right and power of regulating the alloy and value of coin struck by their own authority, or by that of the respective States—fixing the standard of weights and measures throughout the United States—regulating the trade and managing all affairs with the Indians, not members of any of the States; provided that the legislative right of any State within its own limits be not infringed or violated—establishing or regulating post-offices from one State to another, throughout all the United States, and exacting such postage on the papers passing through the same as may be requisite to defray the expenses of the said office—appointing all officers of the land forces, in the service of the United States, excepting regimental officers—appointing all the officers of the naval forces, and commissioning all officers whatever in the service of the United States—making rules for the government and regulation of the said land and naval forces, and directing their operations.

The United States in Congress assembled shall have authority to appoint a committee, to sit in the recess of Congress, to be denominated "A Committee of the States," and to consist of one delegate from each State; and to appoint such other committees and civil officers as may be necessary for managing the general affairs of the United States, under their direction—to appoint one of their number to preside; provided that no person be allowed to serve in the office of president more than one year in any term of three years—to ascertain the necessary sums of money to be raised for the service of the United States, and to appropriate and apply the same for defraying the public expenses—to borrow money, or emit bills on the credit of the United States, transmitting every half year to the respective States an account of the sums of money so borrowed or emitted —to build and equip a navy—to agree upon the number of land forces, and to make requisitions from each State for its quota, in proportion to the number of white inhabitants in such State, which requisition shall be binding; and thereupon the legislatures of each State shall appoint the regimental officers, raise the men, and clothe, arm, and equip them in a soldier-like manner, at the expense of the United States; and the officers and men so clothed, armed, and equipped, shall march to the place appointed, and within the time agreed on by the United States in Congress assembled; but if the United States in Congress assembled shall, on consideration of circumstances, judge proper that any State should not raise men, or should raise a smaller number than its quota, and that any other State should raise a greater number of men than the quota thereof, such extra number shall be raised, officered, clothed, armed, and equipped in the same manner as the quota of such State, unless the legislature of such State shall judge that such extra number can not be safely spared out of the same; in which case they shall raise, officer, clothe, arm, and equip as many of such extra number as they judge can be safely spared. And the officers and men so clothed, armed and equipped, shall march to the place appointed, and within the time agreed on by the United States in Congress assembled.

The United States in Congress assembled shall never engage in a war, nor grant letters of marque and reprisal in time of peace, nor enter into any treaties or alliances, nor coin money, nor regulate the value thereof, nor ascertain the sums and expenses necessary for the defense and welfare of the United States, nor any of them, nor emit bills, nor borrow money on the credit of the United States, nor appropriate money, nor agree upon the number of vessels of war to be built or purchased, or the number of land or sea forces to be raised, nor appoint a commander-in-chief of the army or navy, unless nine States assent to the same ; nor shall a question on any other point, except for adjourning from day to day, be determined, unless by the votes of a majority of the United States in Congress assembled.

The Congress of the United States shall have power to adjourn to any time within the year, and to any place within the United States, so that no period of adjournment be for a longer duration than for the space of six months, and shall publish the journal of their proceedings monthly, except such parts thereof relating to treaties, alliances, or military operations, as in their judgment require secrecy ; and the yeas and nays of the delegates of each State on any question shall be entered on the journal when it is desired by any delegate ; and the delegates of a State, or any of them, at his or their request, shall be furnished with a transcript of the said journal, except such parts as are above excepted, to lay before the legislatures of the several States.

Art. 10. The Committee of the States, or any nine of them, shall be authorized to execute, in the recess of Congress, such of the powers of Congress as the United States in Congress assembled, by the consent of nine States, shall, from time to time, think expedient to vest them with ; provided that no power be delegated to the said committee, for the exercise of which, by the Articles of Confederation, the voice of nine States in the Congress of the United States assembled is requisite.

Art. 11. Canada, acceding to this confederation and joining in the measures of the United States, shall be admitted into, and entitled to all the advantages of this union ; but no other colony shall be admitted into the same unless such admission be agreed to by nine States.

Art. 12. All bills of credit emitted, moneys borrowed, and debts contracted by, or under the authority of Congress, before the assembling of the United States, in pursuance of the present confederation, shall be deemed and considered as a charge against the United States—for payment and satisfaction whereof the said United States and the public faith are hereby solemnly pledged.

Art. 13. Every State shall abide by the determinations of the United States in Congress assembled on all questions which, by this confederation, are submitted to them. And the articles of this confederation shall be inviolably observed by every State, and the Union shall be perpetual; nor shall any alteration at any time hereafter be made in any of them, unless such alteration be agreed to in a Congress of the United States, and be afterward confirmed by the legislatures of every State.

And Whereas, It hath pleased the Great Governor of the World to incline the hearts of the legislatures we respectively represent in Congress, to approve of and to authorise us to ratify the said Articles of Confederation and perpetual Union,

Know Ye, That we, the undersigned delegates, by virtue of the power and authority to us given for that purpose, do, by these presents, in the name and in behalf of our respective constituents, fully and entirely ratify and confirm each and every of the said Articles of Confederation and perpetual Union, and all and singular the matters therein contained. And we do further solemnly plight and engage the faith of our respective constituents, that they shall abide by the determination of the United States in Congress assembled, on all questions which, by the said Confederation, are submitted to them. And that the articles thereof shall be inviolably observed by the States we respectively represent, and that the Union shall be perpetual. In witness whereof, we have hereunto set our hands in Congress.

Done at Philadelphia, in the State of Pennsylvania, the 9th day of July, in the year of our Lord 1778, and in the third year of the Independence of America.

38

CONSTITUTIONAL AMENDMENTS.

The Amendment proposed to the Constitution, June 8, 1866.

ARTICLE XIV.

SECTION 1. All persons born or naturalized in the United States, and subject to the jurisdiction thereof, are citizens of the United States, and of the State wherein they reside. No State shall make or enforce any law which shall abridge the privileges or immunities of citizens of the United States; nor shall any State deprive any person of life, liberty or property, without due process of law, nor deny to any person within its jurisdiction the equal protection of the laws.

SEC. 2. Representatives shall be apportioned among the several States according to their respective numbers, counting the whole number of persons in each State, excluding Indians not taxed. But when the right to vote at any election for the choice of electors for President and Vice President of the United States, Representatives in Congress, the executive and judicial officers of a State, or the members of the legislature thereof, is denied to any of the male inhabitants of such State, being twenty-one years of age, and citizens of the United States, or in any way abridged, except for participation in rebellion or other crime, the basis of representation therein shall be reduced in the proportion which the number of such male citizens shall bear to the whole number of male citizens twenty-one years of age in such State.

SEC. 3. No person shall be a Senator or Representative in Congress, ot Elector or President and Vice President, or hold any office, civil or military, under the United States, or under any State, who, having previously taken an oath, as a member of Congress, or as an officer of the United States, or as a member of any State Legislature, or as an executive or judicial officer of any State, to support the Constitution of the United States, shall have engaged in insurrection or rebellion against the same, or given aid or comfort to the enemies thereof. But Congress may, by a vote of two-thirds of each house, remove such disability.

SEC. 4. The validity of the public debt of the United States, authorized by law, including debts incurred for payment of pensions and bounties for services in suppressing insurrection or rebellion, shall not be questioned. But neither the United States nor any State shall assume or pay any debt or obligation incurred in aid of insurrection or rebellion against the United States, or any claim for the loss or emancipation of any slave; but all such debts, obligations and claims shall be held illegal and void.

SEC. 5. The Congress shall have power to enforce, by appropriate legislation, the provisions of this article.

The amendment passed the Senate by a vote of 33 yeas to 11 nays, and the House by a vote 138 yeas to 36 nays.

ARTICLE XV.

SEC. 1. The right of citizens of the United States to vote

shall not be denied or abridged by the United States, or by any State on account of race, color, or previous condition of servitude.

SEC. 2. The Congress shall have power to enforce this article by appropriate legislation.

HOMESTEAD LAW.,

By act of Congress May 20, 1862, any person who is the head of a family, or who has arrived at the age of twenty-one years, or has performed service in the army or navy, and is a citizen of the United States, or shall have filed his declaration of intention to become such, and has never borne arms against the Government of the United States, or given aid and comfort to its enemies, shall, from and after the 1st of January, 1863, be entitled to enter a quarter section (160 acres) of unappropriated public land, upon which he or she may have already filed a pre-emption claim, or which is subject to pre-emption, at $1.25 per acre; or 80 acres of unappropriated lands, at $2.50 per acre.

In order to make his or her title good to such lands, however' such person must make affidavit that such application is made for his or her exclusive use or benefit, and that said entry is made for the purpose of actual settlement and cultivation, and not, either directly or indirectly, for the use or benefit of any other person or persons whomsoever; and upon filing the affidavit, and paying the sum of ten dollars to the register or receiver, such person shall be allowed to enter the land specified; but no certificate or patent is issued for the land until five years from the date of such entry, and the land must, during that time, be improved and not alienated (it can not be taken for debt).

At any time within two years after the expiration of said five years, the person making the entry, or, in case of his or her death, his widow or heirs, may, on proof by two witnesses that he or she has cultivated or improved said land, has not alienated any part of it, and has borne true allegiance to the United States, be entitled to a patent, if at that time a citizen of the United States. In case of the abandonment of the lands by the person making the entry, for a period of more than six months at one time, they revert to the United States.

INDEX.